Complete Solutions Manual

Topics in Contemporary Mathematics

TENTH EDITION

Ignacio Bello
University of South Florida

Anton Kaul
Cal Poly, San Luis Obispo

Jack R. Britton
University of South Florida

Prepared by

Ann K. Ostberg
AIB College of Business/Grace University

CENGAGE
Learning·

Australia · Brazil · Mexico · Singapore · United Kingdom · United States

Table of Contents

Chapter 1   Problem Solving

1.1 Inductive Reasoning and Deductive Reasoning   1
1.2 Estimation: A Problem-Solving Tool   4
1.3 Graph Interpretation: A Problem-Solving Tool   7
    Chapter 1 Practice Test   12

Chapter 2   Sets

2.1 Sets: A Problem-Solving Tool   14
2.2 Set Operations   17
2.3 Venn Diagrams   22
2.4 The Number of Elements in a Set: A Problem-Solving Tool   28
2.5 Infinite Sets   35
    Chapter 2 Practice Test   37

Chapter 3   Logic

3.1 Statements   40
3.2 Truth Tables: A Problem-Solving Tool   42
3.3 The Conditional and the Biconditional   48
3.4 Variations of the Conditional and Implications   53
3.5 Euler Diagrams: A Problem-Solving Tool   56
3.6 Truth Tables and Validity of Arguments   64
    Chapter 3 Practice Test   71

Chapter 4   Numeration System

4.1 Egyptian, Babylonian, and Roman Numeration Systems   74
4.2 The Hindu-Arabic (Decimal) System   77
4.3 Number Systems with Bases Other Than 10   80
4.4 Binary, Octal, and Hexadecimal Arithmetic   83
    Chapter 4 Practice Test   85

Chapter 5   Number Theory and the Real Numbers

5.1 Number Theory: Primes and Composites	88
5.2 Whole Numbers, Integers, and Order of Operations	92
5.3 Operations with Rational Numbers, Expanded and Scientific Notation	96
5.4 Rationals and Irrationals as Decimals: Percents	103
5.5 Radicals and Real Numbers	107
5.6 Number Sequences	111
Chapter 5 Practice Test	117

Chapter 6   Equations, Inequalities, and Problem Solving

6.1 Solutions of First Degree (Linear) Sentences	120
6.2 Graphs of Algebraic Sentences	129
6.3 Sentences involving Absolute Values	133
6.4 Quadratic Equations	137
6.5 Modeling and Problem Solving	145
6.6 Ratio Proportion, and Variation	152
Chapter 6 Practice Test	157

Chapter 7   Functions and Graphs

7.1 Graphing Relations and Functions	161
7.2 Linear Functions, Relations, and Applications	167
7.3 Slopes and Equations of a Line	172
7.4 Quadratic Functions and Their Graphs	180
7.5 Exponential and Logarithmic Functions	191
7.6 Two Linear Equations in Two Variables	200
7.7 Linear Inequalities	208
7.8 Linear Programming	216
Chapter 7 Practice Test	227

Chapter 8   Geometry

8.1 Points, Lines, Planes, and Angles	233
8.2 Triangles and Other Polygons	236
8.3 Perimeter and Circumference	240
8.4 Area Measure and the Pythagorean Theorem	243
8.5 Volume and Surface Area	247
8.6 Networks, Non-Euclidean Geometry, and Topology	251
8.7 Right Triangle Trigonometry	254
8.8 Chaos and Fractals	258
Chapter 8 Practice Test	260

Chapter 9   Mathematical Systems

9.1 Clock and Modular Arithmetic   264
9.2 Abstract Mathematical Systems: Groups and Fields   270
9.3 Game Theory   275
    Chapter 9 Practice Test   279

Chapter 10   Counting Techniques

10.1 The sequential Counting Principle (SCP): A Problem-Solving Tool   282
10.2 Permutations   284
10.3 Combinations   287
10.4 Miscellaneous Counting Methods   290
    Chapter 10 Practice Test   294

Chapter 11   Probability

11.1 Sample Spaces and Probability   296
11.2 Counting Techniques and Probability   300
11.3 Computation of Probabilities   305
11.4 Conditional Probability   309
11.5 Independent Events   313
11.6 Odds and Mathematical Expectation   319
    Chapter 11 Practice Test   322

Chapter 12   Statistics

12.1 Sampling, Frequency Distributions, and Graphs   325
12.2 Measures of Central Tendency: The Mean, Median, and Mode   333
12.3 Measures of Dispersion: The Range and Standard Deviation   337
12.4 The Normal Distribution: A Problem-Solving Tool   343
12.5 Statistical Graphs: A Problem-Solving Tool   350
12.6 Making Predictions: Linear Regression   358
12.7 Scattergrams and Correlation   367
    Chapter 12 Practice Test   371

Chapter 13   Your Money and Your Math

13.1 Interest, Taxes, and Discounts   374
13.2 Credit Cards and Consumer Credit   378
13.3 Annual Percentage Rate (APR) and the Rule of 78   381
13.4 Buying a House   384
13.5 Invest in Stocks, Bonds, and Mutual Funds   388
      Chapter 13 Practice Test   392

Chapter 14   Voting and Appointment

14.1 Voting Systems   394
14.2 Voting Objections   399
14.3 Apportionment Methods   403
14.4 Apportionment Objections   410
      Chapter 14 Practice Test   413

Chapter 15   Graph Theory

15.1 Introduction to Graph Theory   418
15.2 Euler Paths and Euler Circuits   419
15.3 Hamilton Paths and Hamilton Circuits   421
15.4 Trees   422
      Chapter 15 Practice Test   424

Appendix   The Metric System

A.1 Metric Units of Measurement   426
A.2 Convert If You Must   427

Chapter 1 Problem Solving

Section 1.1 Inductive Reasoning and Deductive Reasoning

1. **Step 1.** Understand the problem.
   Step 2. Devise a plan.
   Step 3. Carry out the plan.
   Step 4. Look back.

2. 1. Read the problem.
   2. Select the unknown.
   3. Think of a plan.
   4. Use the techniques you are studying to carry out the plan.
   5. Verify your answer.

3. What does the problem ask for? (What is the unknown? After all, if you don't know the question, how can you find the answer?)

4. Compare the number of messages for the lowest monthly fee. Sprint costs $5.00 for 300 messages and AT&T costs $5.00 for 200 messages. Sprint is the most economical.

5. Look under the "Monthly Fee" column and look for a fee of $15.00. AT&T has the $15.00 per month plan.

6. If you send about 1400 text messages a month, the most economical plan would be AT&T (1500 messages). This plan would cost $15.00 per month.

7. If you send 900 text messages a month, the most economical plan would be Sprint (1000 messages). This plan would cost $10.00 per month.

8. For children aged 9 – 12 sending 1146 messages per month, the best choice would be AT&T at $15.00, which allows 1500 messages.

9. For the average teenager sending 3339 messages per month, the best choice would be to have an unlimited plan. AT&T and Sprint both charge $20.00 per month, so either company would be the most economical.

10. Due to the large number of text messages sent per month for males and females, the best choice would be to have an unlimited plan. The cost for males or females is $20.00 per month.

11. To get the 2nd term (2), you added 1 to the 1st term.
    To get the 3rd term (4), you added 2 to the 2nd term.
    To get the 4th term (7), you added 3 to the 3rd term.
    To get the 5th term (11), you might add 4 to the 4th term.
    In general, the pattern to get the $(n + 1)^{st}$ term is: Add n to the nth term
    The 6th and 7th terms would be $11 + 5 = 16$ and $16 + 6 = 22$.

12. To get the 2nd term (5), you added 3, or $2(1)+1$, to the 1st term.
    To get the 3rd term (10), you added 5, or $2(2)+1$, to the 2nd term.
    To get the 4th term (17), you added 7, or $2(3)+1$, to the 3rd term.
    To get the 5th term (26), you might add 9, or $2(4)+1$, to the 4th term.
    In general, the pattern to get the $(n + 1)^{st}$ term is: Add the next odd number, or $2n+1$, to the nth term. The 6th and 7th terms are $26 + 11 = 37$ and $37 + 13 = 50$.

13. Note that the odd numbered terms are always 1's and the even numbered terms are multiples of 5. Thus, the 7th and 9th terms are 1's and the eighth term is the next multiple of 5 after 15, that is 20. Hence, the next three terms are 1, 20 and 1.

14. Note that the exponent of each subsequent term is double the previous terms exponent. The next three terms would be 3^{16}, 3^{32}, 3^{64}.

15. Going clockwise, the shaded region is moved 1 place, 2 places, 3 places and so on. The next three moves will move the shaded region 4, 5 and 6 places. The answer is shown.

16. Answers may vary. Going clockwise move the shaded region 2, 3, and 3 places, then repeat.

(Another possibility would be to use the integers 2, 3, 4, 5, 6, 7, etc. interspersing them with 3s: 2, *3*, *3*, *3*, 4, *3*, 5, *3*, 6, *3*, 7, *3*, etc.)

17. The numbers in the denominator are obtained by doubling. Thus, each term is half the preceding term. The next three terms are $\dfrac{1}{16}, \dfrac{1}{32}$, and $\dfrac{1}{64}$.

18. $\dfrac{1}{5}, \dfrac{1}{8}, \dfrac{1}{3}$ Decrease the denominator of the odd terms by 2; decrease the denominator of the even terms by 2.

19. The odd numbered terms are 1, 2, 3 and we hypothesize 4, 5, 6, ... and the even numbered terms are 5, 6 and we hypothesize 7, 8, 9, ... The next three terms are 7, 4, 8 as shown.
    1, 5, 2, 6, 3, <u>7</u>, <u>4</u>, <u>8</u>

20. The difference between the odd terms is 3 and the difference between the even terms is 4. To find the next three terms add 3 to the odd terms and 4 to the even terms: 13, 18, 17.

21. a.

15

   b. The rows are constructed by adding one more dot than on the preceding row. The next triangular numbers after 10 are $10 + \mathbf{5} = \underline{15}$
      $15 + \mathbf{6} = \underline{21}$ and $21 + \mathbf{7} = \underline{28}$.
   c. Following the pattern after the 7th triangular number which is 28, the 10th triangular number is:
      $28 + 8 + 9 + \mathbf{10} = \underline{55}$.
      (Problem 23 develops the formula for triangular numbers. You might want to give it a try.)

22. a. The differences between adjacent triangular numbers are 2, 3, 4, 5, 6, 7, 8, 9, 10.
   b. The sums between adjacent triangular numbers are 4, 9, 16, 25, 36, 49, 64, 81, 100.
   c. The sum of the ninth and tenth triangular numbers is 100.
   d. The sums of adjacent triangular numbers are perfect squares. The sum of the fourteenth and fifteenth triangular number is $15^2 = 225$.
      (Problem 23 develops the formula for triangular numbers.)

23. a. The eighth triangular number is 36.
      $(1 + 2 + 3 + 4 + 5 + 6 + 7 + \mathbf{8} = \underline{36})$
   b. $1 + 2 + 3 + 4 + 5 + 6 + 7 + 8 = 36$
   c. The twelfth triangular number is 78.
      $(1 + 2 + 3 + ... + \mathbf{12} = \underline{78})$
   d. $1 + 2 + 3 + ... + 12 = 78$
   e. $1 + 2 + 3 + ... + (n - 1) + n = \dfrac{n(n+1)}{2}$
   f. $\dfrac{100 \cdot 101}{2} = 50 \cdot 101 = 5050$

24. a.

25

   b. The nth square number is n^2; 25, 36, 49
   c. The twelfth square number is $12^2 = 144$.

25. a.

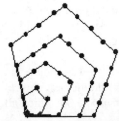

35

   b. At each step, increase the length of the bottom and left lower side of the pentagon by one unit. The number of dots on each side is increased by one unit. (This is adding recursively: if $p(n)$ = the number of the nth pentagonal number, then $p(n+1) = p(n) + 3n + 1$.)
   c. The 6th pentagonal number is 51.

26. a. For 6 noncollinear points, $5 + 4 + 3 + 2 + 1 = 15$ line segments can be drawn.

    b. For 9 noncollinear points, $8 + 7 + 6 + 5 + 4 + 3 + 2 + 1 = 36$ line segments can be drawn.

27. Here is a summary of the information shown in the figure:

    Sides   4 5 6 7
    Diagonals   1 2 3 4

    The number of diagonals is three less than the number of sides. Thus, $10 - 3 = 7$ diagonals can be drawn from one vertex of a decagon. (Geometrically , you connect the originating vertex with each of the others (yielding $n - 1$ connections) of which two are sides; leaving $n - 3$, which are diagonals.)

28. a.

Start	5	10	20	100
	12	17	27	107
	36	51	81	321
	30	45	75	315
	10	15	25	105
End	5	10	20	100

    The final result and the original number are the same.

    b.

Start	n
	$n + 7$
	$3(n + 7) = 3n + 21$
	$3n + 21 - 6 = 3n + 15$
	$\dfrac{3n + 15}{3} = n + 5$
End	$n + 5 - 5 = n$

29. a.

Start	5	10	20	100
	12	17	27	107
	36	51	81	321
	30	45	75	315
	10	15	25	105
End	5	5	5	5

    The final result is always 5.

    b.

Start	n
	$n + 7$
	$3(n + 7) = 3n + 21$
	$3n + 21 - 6 = 3n + 15$
	$\dfrac{3n + 15}{3} = n + 5$
End	$n + 5 - n = 5$

30. a.

Start	5	10	20	100
	10	15	25	105
	40	60	100	420
	20	30	50	210
End	10	20	40	200

    The final result is twice the original number.

    b.

Start	n
	$n + 5$
	$4(n + 5) = 4n + 20$
	$\dfrac{4n + 20}{2} = 2n + 10$
End	$2n + 10 - 10 = 2n$

31. a.

Start	5	10	20	100
	10	15	25	105
	40	60	100	420
	20	30	50	210
End	10	10	10	10

    The final result is always 10.

    b.

Start	n
	$n + 5$
	$4(n + 5) = 4n + 20$
	$\dfrac{4n + 20}{2} = 2n + 10$
End	$2n + 10 - 2n = 10$

32. a. 22, 11, 34, 17, 52, 26, 13, 40, 20, 10, 5, 16, 8, 4, 2, 1

    b. 15, 46, 23, 70, 35, 106, 53, 160, 80, 40, 20, 10, 5, 16, 8, 4, 2, 1

    c. The last three numbers in each pattern is 4, 2, 1.

    d. No

33. a. It is always 4.

    b. If you pick any number and follow the instructions you eventually get to a number less than or equal to 10. For any of these numbers the pattern leads to the number 4.

34. a. $1 + 3 + 5 + 7 + 9 = 5^2$

    $1 + 3 + 5 + 7 + 9 + 11 = 6^2$

    $1 + 3 + 5 + 7 + 9 + 11 + 13 = 7^2$

    b. 10^2

35. a. $(1 + 2 + 3 + 4)^2 = 1^3 + 2^3 + 3^3 + 4^3$

$(1 + 2 + 3 + 4 + 5)^2$
$= 1^3 + 2^3 + 3^3 + 4^3 + 5^3$

$(1 + 2 + 3 + 4 + 5 + 6)^2$
$= 1^3 + 2^3 + 3^3 + 4^3 + 5^3 + 6^3$

b. The square of the sum of the first n counting numbers equals the sum of the cubes of these numbers.

36. a. $3^4 + 4^4 + 5^4 + 6^4 = 7^4$
b. No

37. The number of units of length of the pendulum is always the square of the number of seconds in the time of the swing.

38. a. For each inch increase in foot length, the shoe size increases by 3: 14, 17, 20
b. His shoe size would be 32.

39. a. For each inch increase in foot length, the shoe size increases by 3: 12, 15, 18
b. We can see from the table that each unit increase in size corresponds to a $\frac{1}{3}$ of an inch increase in length. Thus, a 2 unit increase in size (from 6 to 8) corresponds to a $\frac{2}{3}$ in. increase in length, from 9 to $9\frac{2}{3}$ in.

40. a. For each five year increase, the daily cost increases by $85: $382, $467, $552, $637
b. $85 increase each period
c. Probably not. (Answers will vary.)

41. Answers may vary.

42. Answers will vary.

43. Answers may vary.

44. The reasoning is going from general (small drip from a tap) to specific (small drip from your tap), so this is deductive reasoning.

45. The reasoning is going from general (average toilet uses 3 gallons per flush) to specific (your toilet uses 3 gallons per flush), so this is deductive reasoning.

46. The reasoning is going from specific (homeowners in Los Angeles) to general (homeowners in California), so this is inductive reasoning.

47. The reasoning is going from general (save when computer is in "sleep mode") to specific (your computer is in "sleep mode"), so this is deductive reasoning.

Collaborative Learning

1. Many topics (including bees) about the Fibonacci sequence can be found at: **http://www.maths.surrey.ac.uk/hosted-sites/R.Knott/Fibonacci/fibnat.html**

2. Answers will vary.

3. The results correspond to the terms in the Fibonacci sequence.

4. a. Yes. Every fourth Fibonacci number (3, 21, 144) is a multiple of 3.
   b. Every fifth Fibonacci number (5, 55, 610) is a multiple of 5.
   c. Every sixth Fibonacci number (8, 144) is a multiple of 8.
   d. Every k^{th} Fibonacci number is a multiple of $F(k)$, where $F(k)$ denotes the kth Fibonacci number. Note: $F(1) = 1$, $F(2) = 1$, $F(3) = 2$, $F(4) = 3$ and so on.

Section 1.2 Estimation: A Problem-Solving Tool

1. 416.38 rounded to the nearest 100 is 400. $30.28 rounded to the nearest dollar is $30. Thus, a reasonable estimate of the value of the investor's stock is $400 \cdot \$30 = \$12,000$.

2. $1.88 rounded to the nearest dollar is $2. 50.439 rounded to the nearest unit is 50. Thus, a reasonable estimate of the bill is $100.

3. $7.80 → $8.00
   $2.29 → $2.00
   $3.75 → $4.00
   $1.85 → $2.00
   $2.90 → $3.00
   Estimate: $19.00

4. $8.99 $\rightarrow$ $9.00
    $2.39 $\rightarrow$ $2.00
    $3.79 $\rightarrow$ $4.00
    $1.79 $\rightarrow$ $2.00
    $8.79 $\rightarrow$ $9.00
    $9.99 $\rightarrow$ $\underline{$10.00}$
    Estimate: $36.00

5. $6 \cdot 150 = 900$ gallons is a good estimate.

6. $2 \cdot 150 = 300$ acres is a reasonable estimate.

7. a. $\dfrac{4256}{14,053} \approx 0.303$ (to 3 decimal places)

    b. $\dfrac{4300}{14,100} \approx 0.305$ (to 3 decimal places)

8. a. $\dfrac{236}{539} \approx 0.438$ (to 3 decimal places)

    b. $\dfrac{240}{540} \approx 0.444$ (to 3 decimal places)

9. ERA $= \dfrac{9 \cdot 14}{140} = \dfrac{9}{10} = 0.900$

10. ERA $= \dfrac{9 \cdot 25}{222\frac{2}{3}} \approx 1.010$; No, Leonard's

    ERA is not lower than Schupp's.

11. It takes 4 to 8 hors d'oeuvres per person, so for 100 persons it takes 100 times as much, that is, 400 to 800 hors d'oeuvres.

12. It takes 1 cup soup per person, so for 100 persons it takes 100 times as much, that is, 100 cups. One gallon is 16 cups, so $100 \div 16 = 6.25$ gal, since more than 6, you would need 7 gallons of soup.

13. It takes $\frac{1}{3}$ lb of boneless meat or fish per person, so for 100 persons it takes 100 times as much or $100 \cdot \dfrac{1}{3} = 33\dfrac{1}{3}$ lb. To the nearest pound, 33 lb are needed.

14. It takes $\frac{1}{3}$ lb of rice, beans, etc. per person, so for 100 persons it takes 100 times as much or $100 \cdot \dfrac{1}{3} = 33\dfrac{1}{3}$ lb. To the nearest pound, 33 lb are needed.

15. It takes $\frac{1}{4}$ lb of raw pasta per person, so for 100 persons it takes 100 times as much or $100 \cdot \dfrac{1}{4} = 25$ lb of pasta.

16. It takes $\frac{1}{4}$ cup of gravy per person, so for 100 persons it takes 100 times as much or $100 \cdot \dfrac{1}{4} = 25$ cups. One gallon is 16 cups, so you would need $25 \div 16 = 1.5625$ gal of gravy, round to 2 gal of gravy.

17. a. The reading is: 5 1 8 2
    b. $5182 - 5102 = 80\,\text{KWH}$
    c. $\$0.08 \cdot 80 = \$6.40$
    d. $30 \cdot \$6.40 = \$192.00$

18. a. The reading is: 5 5 4 0
    b. $5540 - 5501 = 39\,\text{KWH}$
    c. $\$0.08 \cdot 39 = \$3.12$
    d. $30 \cdot \$3.12 = \$93.60$

19. a. The reading is: 7 0 0 1
    b. $7001 - 6951 = 50\,\text{KWH}$
    c. $\$0.08 \cdot 50 = \$4.00$
    d. $30 \cdot \$4 = \$120.00$

20. a. The reading is: 6 1 4 5
    b. $6145 - 6100 = 45\,\text{KWH}$
    c. $\$0.08 \cdot 45 = \$3.60$
    d. $30 \cdot \$3.60 = \$108.00$

21. $\$4681.25 + 0.25\big(\$60,000 - \$34,000\big)$
    $= \$4681.25 + 0.25\big(\$26,000\big)$
    $= \$4681.25 + \$6500.00$
    $= \$11,181.25$

22. $\$4681.25 + 0.25\big(\$50,000 - \$34,000\big)$
    $= \$4681.25 + 0.25\big(\$16,000\big)$
    $= \$4681.25 + \$4000.00$
    $= \$8681.25$

23. a. $H = 2.89 \cdot 15 + 27.81$
$= 43.35 + 27.81$
$= 71.16$ in.

b. Rounded to the nearest whole number,
$H = 3h + 28$
When $h = 15$, $H = 3 \cdot 15 + 28 = 73$
The difference is
$73 - 71.16 = 1.84$ in.

24. a. $H = 2.75 \cdot 15 + 28.14$
$= 41.25 + 28.14$
$= 69.39$ in.

b. Rounded to the nearest whole number, $H = 3h + 28$
When $h = 15$, $H = 3 \cdot 15 + 28 = 73$
The difference is $(73 - 69.39)$ in. = 3.61 in.

25. $\text{BMI} = \dfrac{705W}{H^2} = \dfrac{705 \cdot 150}{68^2} \approx 22.87$ (to the nearest hundredth). Since 22.87 is greater than 18 and less than 24, the person's BMI is normal.

26. $\text{BMI} = \dfrac{705W}{H^2} = \dfrac{705 \cdot 170}{70^2} \approx 24.46$. To be overweight, the BMI has to be 25–29, so technically, 24.46 is normal but very close to overweight!

27. $W = \dfrac{G^2 \cdot L}{330} = \dfrac{70^2 \cdot 66}{330} = 980$ pounds
Measured in 100 pound units, this is 9.8 or about 10 to make it safe. The horse needs 0.6 gal of water, 1 lb of hay and $\frac{1}{2}$ lb of grain for each 100 lb of body weight. Thus, the horse needs:
$0.6 \cdot 10 = 6$ gal of water
$1 \cdot 10 = 10$ lb of hay
$\frac{1}{2} \cdot 10 = 5$ lb of grain

28. $W = \dfrac{G^2 \cdot L}{330} = \dfrac{70^2 \cdot 70}{330} = 1039$ pounds
Measured in 100 pound units, this is 10.39 or about 10 to make it safe. The horse needs 0.6 gal of water, 1 lb of hay and $\frac{1}{2}$ lb of grain for each 100 lb of body weight. Thus, the horse needs:
$0.6 \cdot 10 = 6$ gal of water

$1 \cdot 10 = 10$ lb of hay
$\frac{1}{2} \cdot 10 = 5$ lb of grain

29. $C = 596 + 0.0019V + 21.7A$
$= 596 + 0.0019 \cdot 500,300 + 21.7 \cdot 5$
$= 596 + 950.57 + 108.50$
$\approx \$1655$

30. $C = 596 + 0.0019V + 21.7A$
$= 596 + 0.0019 \cdot 500,000 + 21.7 \cdot 10$
$= 596 + 950 + 217$
$= \$1763$

31. a. For the first 2 years, we have 24 human years. For the next 3 years, we have $3 \cdot 4 = 12$ human years. Thus, for $2 + 3 = 5$ years, we have $24 + 12 = 36$ human years.

b. For the first 2 years, we have 24 human years. For the next 8 years, we have $8 \cdot 4 = 32$ human years. Thus, for $2 + 3 = 5$ years, we have $24 + 32 = 56$ human years.

32. a. For the first 3 years, we have 29 human years. For the next 2 years, we have $2 \cdot 4 = 8$ human years. Thus, for $3 + 2 = 5$ years, we have $29 + 18 = 37$ human years.

b. For the first 3 years, we have 29 human years. For the next 7 years, we have $7 \cdot 4 = 28$ human years. Thus, for $3 + 7 = 10$ years, we have $29 + 28 = 57$ human years.

33. The distance between the intersection of 90 and 128 to the intersection of 90 and 495 is about one inch on the map or about 15 actual miles.

34. The distance between the intersection of 90 and 495 to the intersection of 90 and 290 is about one and one-half inches on the map or about $1.5 \cdot 15 = 22.5$ miles.

35. The distance between the intersection of 90 and 290 to the intersection of 90 and 86 is about one inch on the map or about 15 actual miles.

36. The distance between the intersection of 90 and 86 to the intersection of 90 and 32 is about one and one-fourth inches on the map or about $1.25 \cdot 15 = 18.75$ miles.

37. The distance between the intersection of 90 and 32 to the intersection of 90 and 91 is about 1.5 in on the map or $1.5 \cdot 15 = 22.5$ miles.

38. The distance in problem 33 is 15 miles. If the car makes 20 miles per gallon, it would need $\dfrac{15}{20}$ gallons that would cost

$$\$4.00 \cdot \dfrac{15}{20} = \$3.00.$$

39. The distance in problem 34 is 22.5 miles. If the car makes 20 miles per gallon, it would need $\dfrac{22.5}{20}$ gallons that would cost

$$\$4.00 \cdot \dfrac{22.5}{20} = \$4.50.$$

40. The distance in problem 35 is 15 miles. If the car makes 20 miles per gallon, it would need $\dfrac{15}{20}$ gallons that would cost

$$\$4.00 \cdot \dfrac{15}{20} = \$3.00.$$

41. The distance in problem 36 is $1\frac{1}{4}$ in. on the map or 18.75 miles. If the car makes 20 miles per gallon, it would need $\dfrac{18.75}{20}$ gallons that would cost

$$\$4.00 \cdot \dfrac{18.75}{20} = \$3.75.$$

42. The distance in problem 37 is 22.5 miles. If the car makes 20 miles per gallon, it would need $\dfrac{22.5}{20}$ gallons that would cost

$$\$4.00 \cdot \dfrac{22.5}{20} = \$4.50.$$

43. A gray whale consumes $\dfrac{268,000}{30} \approx$ 8933.33 lb of amphipods per day.

44. Refer to problem 43, a gray whale eats approximately 8933.33 lb of amphipods per day, which is $8933.33 \cdot 16 \approx 142933.33$ oz . Each amphipod is 0.004 oz so $142933.33 \div 0.004 \approx 35,733,333$ amphipods.

45. A killer whale eats $\dfrac{14,000}{30} \approx 466.67$ pounds of herring per day.

46. Refer to problem 45, a killer whale eats approximately 466.67 lb of herring per day, which is $466.67 \cdot 16 \approx 7466.67$ oz . Each herring is 3.2 oz so $7466.67 \div 3.2 \approx 2333$ herring.

47. For a 150 lb male: Multiply the body weight 150 by 10 which is 1500; Add twice the body weight or 300; The BMR is $1500 + 300 = 1800$.

48. For a 120 lb female: Multiply the body weight 120 by 10 which is 1200; Add the body weight or 120; The BMR is $1200 + 120 = 1320$.

49. Answers may vary.

50. Answers may vary. The last digit is almost at the maximum, so the dial for the 10s place is about to, but hasn't yet, changed to a higher number.

51. $23\,\text{ft} \cdot 5.5\ \text{mi} \cdot \dfrac{5280\,\text{ft}}{1\ \text{mi}} \cdot 2 = 1,335,840\,\text{ft}^2$

52. From problem 51, $1,335,840\ \text{ft}^2$ is available. Each spectator occupies $2\ \text{ft}^2$, so $1,335,840 \div 2 = 667,920$ spectators.

Section 1.3 Graph Interpretation: A Problem-Solving Tool

1. a. The largest category of materials is the one that covers the *most area*, that is, Paper. You can reach the same conclusion by noting that Paper is the category with the highest percent (41%).
   b. The smallest category of materials is the one that covers the *least area,* that is, Plastic (7%).
   c. Since 1000 tons of materials are sent to the landfill each day, the percent of each category times 1000 will be the number of tons of that category going to the landfill each day. Paper (41%) will have $0.41 \cdot 1000 = 410$ tons. Plastic (7%) will have $0.07 \cdot 1000 = 70$ tons.

2. a. The percent of glass going to the landfill is 8%.
    b. Since 1000 tons of materials are sent to the landfill each day, 8% times 1000 will be the number of tons of glass going to the landfill each day: $0.08 \cdot 1000 = 80$ tons.
    c. The percent difference in the amount of paper and glass going to the landfill daily is $41\% - 8\% = 33\%$, which yields $0.33 \cdot 1000 = 330$ tons.

3. a. The cheese produced the most is Cheddar (36%).
    b. The cheese produced the least is Swiss (2.8%).
    c. The second most popular cheese is Mozzarella (30.6%).

4. a. The highest percent of food a stellar sea lion eats is fish, so stock fish the most.
    b. 7% of the food is squid. If 100 lb of food is bought, $0.07 \cdot 100 = 7$ lb should be squid.
    c. 7% of the food is squid. If 200 lb of food is bought, $0.07 \cdot 200 = 14$ lb should be squid.
    d. 30% of the food is other invertebrates. If 300 lb of food is bought, $0.3 \cdot 300 = 90$ lb should be other invertebrates. One-third of other invertebrates is crab, so purchase $90 \cdot \frac{1}{3} = 30$ lb. (Assume that equal amounts of and only octopuses, shrimp, and crabs are in "Other invertebrates.")
    e. 63% of the food eaten per day is fish. If 50 lb of food is eaten, $0.63 \cdot 50 = 31.5$ lb of fish is eaten.
    f. 7% of the food eaten per day is squid. If 15 lb of food is eaten, $0.07 \cdot 15 = 1.05$ lb of squid is eaten.
    g. Shrimp comprises $\frac{1}{3}$ of "Other invertebrates," therefore $\frac{1}{3}$ of the 30% of the total is 10%. If 15 lb of food is eaten, then $0.10 \cdot 15 = 1.5$ lb of shrimp is eaten.

5. a. Water is used the most for bathing (30%).
    b. 30% of 500 = $0.30 \cdot 500 = 150$ gal used for bathing.

    c. The dishwasher uses 3% of the water and the toilet leak uses 5%, thus the toilet leak uses more water.
    d. The dishwasher uses 3% of the water, which represents 5 gallons. The faucet uses 12% of the water, which is 4 times as much, that is, the faucet uses $4 \cdot 5 = 20$ gal of water.

6. a. The fraction of pizza that is crust is $\frac{1}{2}$.
    b. The fraction of pizza that is cheese is $\frac{1}{4}$.
    c. Mushrooms (0.05) make the smallest part of the pizza by weight.
    d. One-half of the weight of pizza is crust: $\frac{1}{2} \cdot 4 = 2$ lb crust; one-fourth of the weight of pizza is cheese: $\frac{1}{4} \cdot 4 = 1$ lb cheese.
    e. Each pizza requires 1 lb of cheese. To make 100 pizzas, $100 \cdot 1 = 100$ lb of cheese would be needed.

7. a. Paper (40%) is the most prevalent item in average trash.
    b. Yard trimmings (18%) is the second most prevalent.
    c. It would contain 40% of 50 = $0.40 \cdot 50$ or 20 lb of paper; it would also contain 18% of 50 = $0.18 \cdot 50$ or 9 lb of yard trimmings

8. a. An employed person sleeps 7.6 hr and a college student sleeps 8.3 hr for a difference of $8.3 - 7.6 = 0.7$ hr.
    b. An employed person spends 2.6 hr in leisure and sports, while a college student spends 3.7 hr. This is a difference of $3.7 - 2.6 = 1.1$ hr.
    c. The amount of time spent eating and drinking is the same (1.0 hr).

9. a. Oil (33%) produces the most energy.
    b. Nuclear (5%) produces the least energy.
    c. Natural gas (18%) produces the least energy.

10. a. Most of the money went to military and defense, 30%.
    b. 20.3% of the money went to health.
    c. Of the $10,000 you paid in federal income taxes, 20.3% went to health, which is $0.203 \cdot 10,000 = \$2030$.
    d. The category with the smallest percent is Job training, 0.4%, so this category received the least money.

e.   Of the $10,000 you paid in federal income taxes, 3.7% went to education, which is $0.037 \cdot 10,000 = \$370$.

f.   Of the $10,000 you paid in federal income taxes, 30% went to military and defense, or $0.3 \cdot 10,000 = \$3000$. $370 of your federal income taxes went to education for a difference of $3000 - 370 = \$2630$.

11. a.   "No drinks per day" means "None" and the bar representing "None" is about 114 units long (actually, it is 114.4).   Thus, the systolic blood pressure for young adults consuming no drinks per day is 114.4.

b.   The bar representing < 1/day is a little less than the bar of part (a), so the approximate answer is 114.

c.   The bar corresponding to 1–< 2/day is about 111.2 long. (Answers may vary.)

d.   The lowest blood pressure corresponds to the category 2–< 3/day (110 systolic blood pressure).

e.   The longest bar (highest blood pressure) corresponds to > 3/day (almost 120 systolic blood pressure).

12. a.   The risk of stroke for current drinking men is 1.0.

b.   The risk of stroke for men who abstain is 2.7.

c.   The risk of stroke for abstaining men is
$$\frac{\text{risk for abstaining men}}{\text{risk for drinking men}} = \frac{2.7}{1} = 2.7$$
times more than the risk for drinking men.

d.   The risk of stroke for current drinking women is 1.0.

e.   The risk of stroke for women who abstain is 3.1.

f.   The risk of stroke for abstaining women is
$$\frac{\text{risk for abstaining women}}{\text{risk for drinking women}} = \frac{3.1}{1} = 3.1$$
time more than the risk for drinking women.

g.   Abstaining women have the highest risk of stroke.

13. a.   The number of fatalities with a negative blood alcohol level was 39.

b.   Blood alcohol levels (BAL) .10–.19, .20–.29, and .30+ define a legally drunk person. There are $13 + 14 + 2 = 29$ people who were legally drunk.

c.   The most prevalent BAL for those legally drunk was .20– .29. Fourteen (14) people had that BAL.

14. a.   The number of fatalities between 12:01 and 3:00 A.M. was 23.

b.   The number of fatalities between 3:01 and 6:00 A.M. was 8.

c.   The period most likely for a fatal traffic accident to occur is 6:01 P.M.–9:00 P.M. with 36 fatal accidents.

d.   The period least likely for a fatal traffic accident to occur is 3:01 A.M.–6:00 A.M. with 8 fatal accidents.

15. a.   The longest bar represents the age group with most of the fatalities. This is the 20–29 age group with 40 fatalities.

b.   The shortest bar represents the age group with the least fatalities. This is the 13–15 age group with 1 fatality.

c.   The number of fatalities involving people who are less than 50 years old is $5 + 1 + 31 + 40 + 22 + 27 = 126$. For more than 50 years old: $28 + 9 + 19 + 17 + 2 = 75$. More fatalities involve people less than 50 years old.

d.   The age group 90+ had only two fatalities. Answers may vary. The number in that age group is small compared to the other groups.

16. a.   Of the 3000 people surveyed, 85% owned a cell phone.

b.   Forty-seven percent (47%) owned an mp3 player.

c.   The percent that owned a desktop computer was 59% and for a laptop, 52%. The difference is $59\% - 52\% = 7\%$.

17. a.   85% of the 3000 adults owned a cell phone, which is $0.85 \cdot 3000 = 2550$ adults.

b.   59% of the 3000 adults owned a desktop computer, which is $0.59 \cdot 3000 = 1770$ adults.

c.   52% of the 3000 adults owned a cell phone, which is $0.52 \cdot 3000 = 1560$ adults.

d.   The difference between the number of people that owned a laptop and those that owned a desktop computer is $1770 - 1560 = 210$ people.

18. a. There are 240 calories in the Cherry Garcia ice cream.
    b. There are 200 calories in the Cherry Garcia yogurt.
    c. There are 260 calories in the Chocolate Fudge ice cream.
    d. There are 180 calories in the Chocolate Fudge yogurt.
    e. The product with the least calories is Chocolate Fudge yogurt (180 cal).
    f. The product with the most calories is Chocolate Fudge ice cream (260 cal).

19. a. The Chocolate Fudge ice cream is about 260 calories ($\frac{1}{2}$ cup) or 520 per cup.
    The Chocolate Fudge yogurt is about 180 calories ($\frac{1}{2}$ cup) or 360 per cup.
    The difference (per cup) is $520 - 360 = 160$ calories.
    b. 2 cups of the Chocolate Fudge ice cream has $2 \cdot 520 = 1040$ calories.
    2 cups of the Chocolate Fudge yogurt has $2 \cdot 360 = 720$ calories.
    The difference is $1040 - 720 = 320$ calories. (Or simply double the answer in part a.)

20. a. The second most popular sport is a tie between Marathon; HS baseball, and *Ekiden*. About 30% preferred high school baseball.
    b. The least popular spectator sport is Martial arts. About 10% of the peopled preferred this sport.
    c. The three sports that enjoyed about the same popularity in the survey was Marathon, HS baseball, and *Ekiden.*
    d. About 50% preferred Japanese professional baseball while about 15% preferred major league baseball. The difference is $50\% - 15\% = 35\%$ of 3000 or 1050.

21. a. The longest bar represents the most popular item sold, Cuban toast.
    b. The second longest bar represents the second most popular item, Cheese toast.
    c. $60 + 20 + 10 + 15 = 105$ breakfasts. Since each breakfast uses $\frac{1}{4}$ of a loaf of bread, we need $\frac{1}{4} \cdot 105 = 26\frac{1}{4}$ loaves, or 27 loaves, of Cuban bread.

22. a. The longest bar represents the most popular sandwich sold, Cuban.
    b. The shortest bar represents the least popular sandwich sold, Cuban Special.
    c. $80 + 10 + 20 + 40 = 150$ sandwiches. Since each sandwich uses $\frac{1}{4}$ loaf of Cuban bread, we need $\frac{1}{4} \cdot 150 = 37\frac{1}{2}$ loaves, or 38 loaves, of Cuban bread.

23. a. The horizontal bar corresponding to the password **123456** represents approximately 3100 persons (go down to the horizontal axis to estimate).
    b. The horizontal bar corresponding to the password **consumer** represents approximately 250 persons.
    c. The horizontal bar corresponding to the password **lifehack** represents approximately 700 persons.

24. a. To the nearest one-tenth percent, the orange vertical bar (indicating Yahoo) corresponding to the password **iloveyou** represents 0.20% of the people.
    b. Problem 23 stated that there were 188,279 leaked passwords. On Yahoo 0.20% passwords are **iloveyou**, which would represent about $0.20\% \cdot 188,279 \approx 377$ people.
    c. To the nearest one-tenth percent, the blue vertical bar (indicating Google) corresponding to the password **blahblah** represents 0.10% of the people.
    d. There were 188,279 leaked passwords with 0.10% being **blahblah** on Google. This represents about $0.10\% \cdot 188,279 \approx 188$ people.

25. a. From 1960, move up to the Total population line (red), from that point move to the left to estimate about 175,000,000.
    b. From 1970, move up to the Total population line (red), from that point move to the left to estimate about 200,000,000.
    c. From 1990, move up to the Total population line (red), from that point move to the left to estimate about 250,000,000.
    d. From 2010, move up to the Total population line (red), from that point move to the left to estimate about 300,000,000.

e.   From 2020, move up to the Total population line (red), from that point move to the left to estimate about 325,000,000.

26. a.   From 1960, move up to the 65 years of age or older line (blue), from that point move to the left to estimate about 12,500,000.
    b.   From 1980, move up to the 65 years of age or older line (blue), from that point move to the left to estimate about 25,000,000.
    c.   From 2020, move up to the 65 years of age or older line (blue), from that point move to the left to estimate about 50,000,000.
    d.   From 2040, move up to the 65 years of age or older line (blue), from that point move to the left to estimate about 75,000,000.
    e.   From 2050, move up to the 65 years of age or older line (blue), from that point move to the left to estimate about 80,000,000.

27. a.   From 1°C , move to the right to the line (red), from that point move down to read the year 2040.
    b.   From 2.5°C , move to the right to the line (red), from that point move down to read the year 2100.

28. a. $I = 0.025x$, where I is the total temperature increase and x is the number of years after 2000.
    b.   Replace x with 40 in the formula $I = 0.025x.$ $I = 0.025(40) = 1$°C
    c.   Yes, both are 1°C.

29. a.   Go to 9 in human years, move up to the line (red), then to the left to 60 dog years.
    b.   Go to 65 in dog years, move to the right to the line (red), then down to about 10 human years.
    c.   Go to 21 in dog years, move to the right to the line (red), then down to about 2 human years.

30. a.   Go to 6 in human years, move up to the dot, then to the left to 40 cat years.

b.   Go to 65 in cat years, move to the right to the dot, then down to about 12 human years.
c.   Go to 21 in cat years, move to the right to the dot, then down to about 2 human years.
d.   As found in problem 29 a dog retires at about 10 human years. A cat retires in about 12 human years. The dog would retire first.

31. a.   Go to 4 months badger age, move up to the line, then to the left to about 3 kg.
    b.   Go to 8 months badger age, move up to the line, then to the left to about 8 kg.
    c.   When the line becomes nearly horizontal, it represents when badgers stop growing. This is at about 9 months.

32. Go to 6 on the horizontal axis and up until you meet the top curve (blue), from that point move to the left to the vertical axis to estimate the balance to be $950.

33. Go to 6 on the horizontal axis and up until you meet the lower curve (red), from that point move to the left to the vertical axis to estimate the balance to be $570.

34. Go to 18 on the horizontal axis and up until you meet the top curve (blue) , from that point move to the left to the vertical axis to estimate the balance to be $800.

35. Go to 48 on the horizontal axis and up until you meet the top curve (blue) , from that point move to the left to the vertical axis to estimate the balance to be $300.

36. Go to 60 on the horizontal axis and up until you meet the top curve (blue). The intersection, which represents the balance, occurs at about $0.

37. Answers will vary.

38. Answers will vary.

39. Answers will vary.

40. a.   Refer to the bar graph where the red bar represents women who took the estrogen-plus-progestin medicine. About 38 had heart attacks, 29 strokes, 38 breast cancer, and 34 blood clots for a total of $38 + 29 + 38 + 34 = 139.$

b. Refer to the bar graph where the blue bar represents women who took the placebo. About 30 had heart attacks, 22 strokes, 30 breast cancer, and 17 blood clots for a total of 30 + 22 + 30 + 17 = 99.

c. The difference in the number of women having heart attacks, strokes, breast cancer, and blood clots between that that took the medicine and those that took the placebo is 139 − 99 = 40 women (per 10,000).

d. The benefits were less colorectal cancer and hip fractures when taking the medicine. Refer to the bar graph and estimate the number of women in each category. Then take the difference of incidences between colorectal cancer and hip fractures.

e. The neutral areas were endometrial cancer and deaths.

41. a. Look for the years where the blue line (placebo group) is below the red line (medicine group) on the graph titled Heart Attack. This occurs during years 1–7.

b. Look for the years where the blue line (placebo group) is below the red line (medicine group) on the graph titled Stroke. This occurs during years 2–7.

c. Look for the years where the blue line (placebo group) is below the red line (medicine group) on the graph titled Blood Clots. This occurs during years 1–7.

d. Look for the years where the blue line (placebo group) is below the red line (medicine group) on the graph titled Breast Cancer. This occurs during years 4–7.

e. Look for the graph which has the greatest distance vertically between the blue line (placebo group) and the red line (medicine group). This occurs at year 7 of either the breast cancer or the stroke group. The numerical difference is about 0.005.

f. Look for the graph where the red line (medicine group) is above the blue line (placebo group) for the most years. The condition where the medicine group fared better than the placebo group was breast cancer. This occurred during years 0–4.

Chapter 1 Practice Test

1. **R**ead the problem
    Select the unknown
       Think of a plan
          Use the techniques you are
             studying to carry out the plan
                Verify the answer

2. Inductive reasoning is the process of arriving at a general conclusion on the basis of repeated observations of specific examples.

3. Look at the difference between successive terms as shown

	1		2		7		19		41		76
Diff		1		5		12		22		35	
Diff			4		7		10		13		
Diff				3		3		3			

The third differences are constant (3), so the next number can be constructed by addition. Add the last diagonal from bottom to top. We obtain the next number in the pattern, 3 + 13 + 35 + 76 = 127.

	1		2		7		19		41		76		127
Diff	1		5			12		22		35		51	
Diff		4		7			10		13		16		
Diff		3		3			3		3				

Now, we can use the 127 to continue the last three rows as shown. The next term now is 3 + 16 + 51 + 127 = 197. If you do this one more time, you will find the next term to be 289. Once you get four terms you can show that all the following terms can be obtained from the formula:

$$a_{n+1} = 3 + 3a_n - 3a_{n-1} + a_{n-2}$$

Thus, the next three terms after 76 are 127, 197, 289.

4. a.
Select a number: n
Multiply by 4: $4n$
Add 6 to the product: $4n + 6$

Divide the sum by 2: $\dfrac{4n+6}{2} = 2n + 3$

Subtract 3 from the quotient:
        $2n + 3 - 3 = 2n$

b. Using 1, the final result is 2.
Using 10, the final result is 20.
Using 100, the final result is 200.

c. The conjecture is that the final result is twice the original number.

5. a.   319.$\underline{2}$6 → 319.3
        Since the 6 after the 2 is greater than 5,
        add one to the 2.
    b. $\underline{3}$19.26 → 300
        Since the 1 after the 3 is less than 5, leave
        the 3 alone; add 0's.

6. a.   6064 KWH
    b.   6064 – 6002 = 62 KWH
    c. $0.10 · 62 = $6.20
    d.   30 · $6.20 = $186.00

7. a.   Female: $H = 28.6 + 2.5(15) \approx 66$ in.
        (rounded from 66.1)
    b.   Male: $H = 32.2 + 2.4(15) \approx 68$ in.
        (rounded from 68.2)

8. a.   Public Safety
    b.   1/2
    c.   Sales tax

9. a.   About $50 million
    b.   About $52 million
    c.   About $116 million
    d.   About $75 million
    e.   About ($75 – $50) million = $25 million

10. a.   About 6.91%
    b.   About 6.76%
    c.   About 6.91 – 6.76 = 0.15%
    d.   They seem to be decreasing.

Chapter 2 Sets

Section 2.1 Sets: A Problem-Solving Tool

1. People do not agree on the meaning of "grouchy," so this description does not define a set.

2. People do not agree on what is "good," so this description does not define a set.

3. A set   4. A set

5. A set   6. A set

7. People do not agree on what is "good," so this description does not define a set.

8. People do not agree on what is "bad," so this description does not define a set.

9. a. *Incorrect.* The letter D is not an element of A.
   b. *Correct.* Desi is an element of A.
   c. *Incorrect.* Jane is an element of A, not the other way around.
   d. *Correct.* The letter D is not an element of A.
   e. *Incorrect.* Jane is an element of A

10. a is an element of the set X. Fill the blank with $\in$.

11. x is an element of the set X. Fill the blank with $\in$.

12. X is not an element of the set X. Fill the blank with $\notin$.

13. A is not an element of the set X. Fill the blank with $\notin$.

14. $\{bay\}$ is not an element of the set X. Fill the blank with $\notin$.

15. 2 is an element of the set $\{2, 4, 6, 8\}$. The statement is True.

16. 6 is not an element of the set $\{1, 3, 5, 11\}$. The statement is False.

17. 0 is not an element of the set **N** (the set of counting numbers). The statement is False.

18. 0 is an element of the set **W** (the set of whole numbers). The statement is True.

19. 5 is an element of the set **N** (the set of counting numbers) and is odd. The statement is True.

20. 10 is an element of the set **N** (the set of counting numbers) but is not less than 10. The statement is False.

21. The set consisting of the first and last letters of the English alphabet.

22. The set consisting of the letters in the word "man."

23. The set consisting of the names of the first biblical man and woman.

24. The set consisting of the name of the man who is accredited with the discovery of America.

25. The set of counting numbers from 1 to 7. Note that the numbers do not have to be in any specific order.

26. The set of products of the pairs of consecutive counting numbers from $1 \cdot 2$ to $5 \cdot 6$.

27. The set of odd counting numbers from 1 to 51.

28. The set of hours slept per day by 15- to 19-year-old men.

29. The set of hours slept per day by 15- to 19-year-old women.

30. The set of hours slept per day by 20- to 24-year-old men and women.

31. {Dioxin, Xylene} is the set of compounds that were found in everybody's tissue.

32. {Chloroform, Heptachlor} is the set of compounds that were found in less than 90% of the people.

33. {1, 2, 3, 4, 5, 6, 7}   34. {1}

35. {0, 1, 2, 3, 4, 5, 6, 7}

36. {0, 1, 2, 3, 4, 5, 6, 7, 8}

37. The word "between" is to be taken literally. The 3 and the 8 are not elements of this set. The answer is {4, 5, 6, 7}.

38. The word "between" is to be taken literally. The 2 and the 7 are not elements of this set. The answer is {3, 4, 5, 6}.

39. Identify the set of generations that greater than 50% go online wirelessly. These generations are Millennial, Gen X, and Younger Boomers. The set is {M, X, Y}.

40. Identify the set of generations that less than 50% go online wirelessly. These generations are Older Boomers, Silent Generation, and G.I. Generation. The set is {O, S, $G.I.$}.

41. Identify the set of generations where the members are younger than 65. These generations are Millennial, Gen X, Younger Boomers, and Older Boomers. The set is {M, X, Y, O}.

42. Identify the set of generations where the members are older than 64. These generations are Silent Generation and G.I. Generation. The set is {S, $G.I.$}.

43. The ranking numbers of the cars made by Volkswagen corresponds to {4, 6}.

44. The ranking numbers of the cars with automatic transmissions corresponds to {1, 2, 3, 5, 7, 8}.

45. The ranking numbers of the cars with manual transmissions corresponds to {4, 6, 9, 10}.

46. The ranking number of the car that seats at most two passengers corresponds to {2}.

47. The ranking number of the car that has the highest 150 MPG corresponds to {1}.

48. The ranking numbers of the cars that have the lowest 150 MPG corresponds to {6, 7}.

49. The ranking number of the car that makes more than 50 highway MPG corresponds to {1}.

50. The set A = {3, 5, 7, …} and the set B = {1, 3, 5, …}. The smallest number in set A is 3 and in set B it is 1, so these sets are not equal ($A \neq B$).

51. The set A = {4, 8, 12, 16, …} and the set B = {2, 4, 6, 8, …}, so these sets are not equal ($A \neq B$).

52. The set A = {1, 1, 2, 2, 3} and the set B = {1, 2, 3}. Since the repetitions in A do not affect the equality these set are equal ($A = B$).

53. The set A is the empty set and the set B is the empty set. Both A and B are empty, so these sets are equal ($A = B$).

54. a. The set containing five elements is set D, which is the set of letters in the word *repeat*. In roster notation set D = {r, e, p, a, t}.
    b. Set B has elements f, i, v, and e. Set C has elements e, f, v, and i. Since order of elements does not affect equality, Set C is equal to set B. (It is also true that set B is equal to set B due to the reflexive property.)
    c. Set B or set C both are sets of letters in the word *five*.

55. a. Every element of A is an element of B, and every element of B is an element of A. Thus, $A = B$.
    b. Because 0 is an element of C but not of A, $A \neq C$ is correct.
    c. Because 0 is an element of C but not of B, $B \neq C$ is correct.

56. a. Set A is a set with no elements and set B is also a set with no elements. Thus, $A = B$.
    b. Set A is a set with no elements and set C is a set with one element. Thus, $A \neq B$.
    c. Set B is a set with no elements and set C is a set with one element. Thus, $B \neq C$.

57. $\varnothing$, {a}, {b}, {a, b}; the first three of these are proper subsets of the given set.

58. $\varnothing$, {1}, {2}, {3}, {1, 2}, {1, 3}, {2, 3}, {1, 2, 3}; all but the last one are proper subsets.

59. $\varnothing$, {1}, {2}, {3}, {4}, {1, 2}, {1, 3}, {1, 4}, {2, 3}, {2, 4}, {3, 4}, {1, 2, 3}, {1, 2, 4}, {1, 3, 4}, {2, 3, 4}, {1, 2, 3, 4};

all but {1, 2, 3, 4} are proper subsets of
the given set.

60. $\varnothing, \{\varnothing\}$; only $\varnothing$ is a proper subset.

61. $\varnothing$, {1}, {2}, {1, 2}; the first three of these
are proper subsets of the given set.

62. $\varnothing$, {x}, {y}, {z}, {x, y}, {x, z}, {y, z},
{x, y, z}; the first seven are proper subsets.

63. Since there are 4 elements in this set, there
are 2^4 or 16 subsets.

64. Since there are 4 elements in this set, there
are 2^4 or 16 subsets. All but the subset
{1, 2, 3, 4} are proper, so there are
$2^4 - 1 = 16 - 1 = 15$ proper subsets.

65. There are 10 elements in A, so A has 2^{10} or
1024 subsets.

66. Since there are 10 elements in this set, there
are 2^{10} or 1024 subsets. All but the subset
$\left\{ \dfrac{1}{1}, \dfrac{1}{2}, \dfrac{1}{3}, ..., \dfrac{1}{10} \right\}$ are proper, so there are
$2^2 - 1 = 1024 - 1 = 1023$ proper subsets.

67. Note that $32 = 2^5$, so there are 5 elements.

68. A set with 31 proper subsets has 32 subsets.
Since $32 = 2^5$, there are 5 elements.

69. Since $64 = 2^6$, there are 6 elements.

70. A set with 63 proper subsets has 64 subsets.
Since $64 = 2^6$, there are 6 elements.

71. Yes. Since $\varnothing$ has no elements, there is no
element of $\varnothing$ that is not in $\varnothing$. Furthermore,
every set is a subset of itself.

72. No. $\varnothing$ contains no elements that are not
elements of $\varnothing$.

73. $B \subseteq A$ because every counting number that
is divisible by 4 is also divisible by 2. (A is
not a subset of B because a number can be
divisible by 2 and not by 4. For instance, 6 is
divisible by 2, but not by 4.)

74. $P = \{a, b\}, Q = \{a, b, \{a, b\}\}$. (Answers
will vary.)

75. a. There are 5 toppings, so you have 5
choices.

    b. There are 10 subsets with 2 elements in
each. So you have 10 choices. (Assume
no double toppings. Try writing these
out.)

    c. You can choose which two toppings
you don't want. So the answer is 10 as
in (b). (Assume that a topping cannot be
used more than once on a single pizza.)

76. There are 32 subsets for a set with 5
elements. There are 5 toppings, and the
pizza must have at least one topping, so the
subset $\varnothing$ is not included. You can order 31
different kinds of pizza with at least one
topping. (Assume that a topping cannot be
used more than once on a single pizza.)

77. Since $256 = 2^8$, you would need 8 different
condiments.

78. Since $512 = 2^9$, you would need at least 9
different toppings.

79. Answers will vary.

80. Answers may vary. The set of all good
students is not well defined because the
meaning of the word "good" is not agreed
upon by everyone. (Answers to the second
question vary.) One example is: the set of
students who scored above 80 on the test.

81. Answers may vary.
    a. The empty set $\varnothing$ does not contain any
elements, so it is true that $\varnothing \notin \varnothing$.
    b. The set $\{\varnothing\}$ contains the element $\varnothing$, so
it is true that $\varnothing \in \{\varnothing\}$.
    c. The set {0} contains the element 0, so it
is true that $\varnothing \neq \{0\}$.
    d. { } is another way to express the empty
set $\varnothing$.

82. a. Every set is a subset of itself.
    b. No set is a proper subset of itself.
    c. The empty set is a proper subset of
every non-empty set.
    d. The empty set is a subset of every set.

e. Every set is a subset of the corresponding universal set.

83. a. If $g \in S$, then Gepetto shaves himself, which contradicts the statement that Gepetto shaves all those men and only those men of the village who do not shave themselves. Hence, $g \notin S$.

    b. If $g \in D$, then Gepetto does not shave himself, and so by the same statement, he does shave himself. Thus, there is again a contradiction and $g \notin D$.

84. a. No, if $N \in M$, then $N \in N$, which contradicts the definition of N.

    b. No, if $N \in N$, it contradicts the definition of N.

    (The consequences are that the sets N and M are complements of each other and therefore any set must belong to one and only one of them, but N cannot belong to either.)

85. The word "*non-self-descriptive*" cannot be classified in either way without having a contradiction. If it is an element of S, then it is a self-descriptive word, which contradicts the definition, "*non-self-descriptive is a non-self-descriptive word.*" On the other hand if non-self-descriptive is a non-self-descriptive word, then it is an element of S, which is again a contradiction.

86. If Paradox.html has a link to itself by definition it does not link to itself. But if it does not link to itself, then it has to have a link to itself. In either case, it is a paradox.

Collaborative Learning

1. For set $\{1, 2\}$ the subsets are $\varnothing, \{1\}, \{2\}, \{1,2\}$.

    For set $\{+, -\}$ the subsets are $\varnothing, \{+\}, \{-\}, \{+,-\}$.

    For set $\{a, b\}$ the subsets are $\varnothing, \{a\}, \{b\}, \{a,b\}$.

2. – 4. If you do get to select the subsets, then the answers would be two as one would always choose the empty set. However, if the sets are, for instance, placed in a bag and you had to draw them out, the answer for #2 would be 3. Worst case example: $\{a\}$, $\{b\}$ are the two-set that does not work; any

three-set contains either { } or (a, b). *For these answers, use the second scenario of drawing out of a bag.*

2. three   3. five   4. nine

5.

Number of Elements in the Set	Number of Subsets	Number of Subsets That Have to Be Selected …
1	2	2
2	4	3
3	8	5
4	16	9

Section 2.2 Set Operations

1. a. $A \cap B$, the set of all elements in both A and B, is $\{1, 3, 4\}$.

    b. $A \cap C$, the set of all elements in both A and C, is $\{1\}$.

    c. $B \cap C$, the set of all elements in both B and C, is $\{1, 6\}$.

2. a. $A \cup B$, the set of all elements either in A or in B, is $\{1, 2, 3, 4, 5, 6\}$.

    b. $A \cup C$, the set of all elements either in A or in C, is $\{1, 2, 3, 4, 5, 6, 7\}$.

    c. $B \cup C$, the set of all elements either in B or in C, is $\{1, 3, 4, 6, 7\}$.

3. a. $A \cap (B \cup C)$, the set of all elements in both A and $B \cup C$, is $\{1, 3, 4\}$.

    b. $A \cup (B \cap C)$, the set of all elements in A or in $B \cap C$, is $\{1, 2, 3, 4, 5, 6\}$.

4. a. $(A \cap B) \cup C$, the set of all elements either in C or in $A \cap B$, is $\{1, 3, 4, 6, 7\}$.

    b. $(A \cap B) \cup (A \cap C)$, the set of all elements either in $A \cap B$ or in $A \cap C$, is $\{1, 3, 4\}$.

5. $A \cup (B \cup C)$, the set of all elements in A or in $B \cup C$, is $\{1, 2, 3, 4, 5, 6, 7\}$.

6. $(A \cup B) \cap (A \cup C)$, the set of all elements in both $A \cup B$ and $A \cup C$, is $\{1, 2, 3, 4, 5, 6\}$.

7. $A \cap (B \cap C)$, the set of all elements in A and in $B \cap C$, is {1}.

8. $(A \cup B) \cap C$, the set of all elements in $A \cup B$ and in C, is {1, 6}.

9. a. $A \cap B$, the set of all elements in both A and B, is {c}.
    b. $A \cap C$, the set of all elements in both A and C, is $\varnothing$. Note: the set $\{a, b\}$ is an element of A, but a and b, separately, are not elements of A.

10. a. $A \cup B$, the set of all elements in either A or in B, is $\{\{a, b\}, a, b, c\}$.
    b. $A \cup C$, the set of all elements in either A or in C, is $\{\{a, b\}, a, b, c\}$.

11. a. *Correct*. The set {b} is a subset of the set $A \cap B$.
    b. *Incorrect*. The set {b} is not an element of the set $A \cap B$.

12. a. *Correct*. The set {a, b} is a subset of the set $A \cap B$.
    b. *Correct*. The set {a, b} is an element of both the sets A and B, so it is an element of the set $A \cap B$.

13. a. *Correct*. The set {a, b, c} is a subset of the set $A \cup B$.
    b. *Correct*. The set {a, b, c} is an element of the set A, so it is an element of the set $A \cup B$.

14. a. *Incorrect*. The element c is not a subset of the set $A \cap B$.
    b. *Incorrect*. The element c is not an element of the set $A \cap B$.

15. a. A', the set of elements in U but not in A, is {b, d, f}.
    b. B', the set of elements in U but not in B, is {a, c}.

16. a. $A' \cap B'$, the set of elements in both A' and B' is $\varnothing$.
    b. $(A \cap B)'$, the set of elements in U but not in both A and B is {a, b, c, d, f}.

17. a. $(A \cup B)'$, the set of elements in U but not in $A \cup B$, is $\varnothing$. Note that $A \cup B$ includes all the elements in U.
    b. $A' \cup B'$, the set of elements in A' or in B' is {a, b, c, d, f}.

18. a. $(A \cup B) \cap C'$, the set of elements in both $A \cup B$ and C' is {c, e}. Note that $A \cup B$ is U.
    b. $(A \cup B)' \cap C$, the set of elements in both $(A \cup B)'$ and C is $\varnothing$. Note that $(A \cup B)'$ is $\varnothing$.

19. a. $(A \cap B) \cup C'$, the set of elements in $A \cap B$ or in C', is {c, e}. Note that $A \cap B$ is {e}.
    b. $C \cup (A \cap B)'$, the set of elements in C or not in $A \cap B$ is {a, b, c, d, f}.

20. a. $A' \cup B$, the set of elements in A' or in B, is {b, d, e, f}. Note that A' is {b, d, f}.
    b. $A \cup B'$, the set of elements in A or in B', is {a, c, e}. Note that B' is {a, c}.

21. a. $A' \cap B$, the set of elements not in A but in B, is {b, d, f}. Note that A' is {b, d, f}.
    b. $A \cap B'$, the set of elements in A but not in B, is {a, c}. Note that B' is {a, c}.

22. a. $A' \cap (A \cup B')$, the set of elements in both A' and $A \cup B'$ is $\varnothing$. Note that $A \cup B'$ is A.
    b. $A \cup (A \cap B')$, the set of elements in A or in $A \cap B'$ is {a, c, e}.

23. a. The elements in C' are c and e and those in $(A \cap B)'$ are a, b, c, d, and f. Thus, $C' \cup (A \cap B)' = \{a, b, c, d, e, f\}$.
    b. $C' = \{c, e\}$, $A \cup B = U$, so $(A \cup B)' = \varnothing$. Thus, $C' \cup (A \cup B)' = \{c, e\}$.

24. a. The elements in A are a, c and e and those in $(C \cup B)'$ are c. Thus, $(C \cup B)' \cap A = \{c\}$.

b. The elements in A' are b, d, and f and those in $C \cup B$ are a, b, d, e, and f. Thus, $(C \cup B) \cap A' = \{b, d, f\}$.

25. a. This is the set U with the elements in A taken out, that is, $\{b, d, f\}$.
    b. This is the set U with the elements in B taken out, that is, $\{a, c\}$.

26. a. This is the set A with any element of B taken out, that is $\{a, c\}$.
    b. This is the set B with any element of A taken out, that is $\{b, d, f\}$.

27. a. This is the set of elements not in B. The answer is $\{2, 3\}$.
    b. This is the set U with the elements in B taken out. The answer is the same as in part a, $\{2, 3\}$.

28. a. This is the set A with any element of B taken out, that is $\{2, 3\}$.
    b. This is the set B with any element of A taken out, that is $\{1, 5\}$.

29. $\varnothing'$, the set of all elements in U that are not in the empty set, is U.

30. U', the set of all elements that are not in U, is $\varnothing$.

31. The set of all elements that are in both A and the empty set is $\varnothing$.

32. The set of all elements that are in both A and A is A.

33. This is the set of all elements that are in both A and U, that is, A.

34. The set of all elements that are either in A or in $\varnothing$ is A.

35. This is the set of elements that are both in A and not in A, that is, $\varnothing$.

36. The set of all elements that are either in A or in A' is U.

37. This is a double negative; the elements that are not in "not A" are, of course, in A. Thus, the answer is A.

38. The set of all elements that are either in A or in A is A.

39. To include A, you must have the elements 1, 2, 3. Then, to include B, you must have the element 4, and to include C, you must have the element 5. Thus, the smallest set that can be used for U is $\{1, 2, 3, 4, 5\}$.

40. To include M_w, you must have the elements Beauty, Intelligence, Cheerfulness, and Congeniality. Then to include W_m, you must have the elements Consideration and Kindliness. To include M_m, you must include Friendliness, and finally, to include W_w, you must include Helpfulness and Loyalty. Thus the smallest set that can be used for U is {Beauty, Intelligence, Cheerfulness, Congeniality, Consideration, Kindliness, Friendliness, Helpfulness, Loyalty}.

41. The set of traits that are only mentioned once are {Beauty, Consideration, Kindliness, Friendliness, Helpfulness, Loyalty}.

42. The traits that are in both M_w and W_w are {Intelligence, Cheerfulness}.

43. This is the set of traits that are in both M_w and M_m, so the answer is {Intelligence, Cheerfulness, Congeniality}.

44. The set of traits common to M_w and M_m are {Intelligence, Cheerfulness, Congeniality}.

45. This is the set of traits that are in all four of the sets, that is, {Intelligence, Cheerfulness}.

46. The traits that are in both S_1 and S_2 are {Encourages suggestions, Sets goals with me, Gets me to have high goals, Listens carefully, Is self-aware}.

47. The traits only mentioned once are {Is aware of others, Follows up on action}.

48. To include S_1, you must have elements Encourages suggestions, Sets goals with me, Gets me to have high goals, Listens carefully, Is self-aware, and Is aware of others. Then, to include S_2, you must have element Follows up on action. Thus, the smallest set that will serve as a universal set for S_1 and S_2 is {Encourages suggestions, Sets goals with me, Gets me to have high goals, Listens carefully, Is self-aware, Is

aware of others, Follows up on action}.

49. S_1' would be all elements in the universal set that are not in set S_1. The set S_1' is {Follows up on action}.

50. S_2' would be all elements in the universal set that are not in set S_2. The set S_2' is {Is aware of others}.

51. Refer to the diagram. The set of all five categories is {p, n, a, t, l}.

52. The set of categories C that actually use the word "credit" in the description is {n, t, l}.

53. C' is a set of all elements in the set of all five categories {p, n, a, t, l} that are not in set C {n, t, l}. Thus, C' is {p, a}.

54. The set of categories M that account for more than 30% of your score would be payment history (35%). Set $M = \{p\}$.

55. The set of categories H that account for the highest portion of your score would be payment history (35%). Set $H = \{p\}$.

56. The set of categories that account for less than 15% of your score would be new credit (10%) and types of credit (10%), that is, {n, t}.

57. H' is the set of elements in {p, n, a, t, l} that are not in H. Thus, H' is {n, a, t, l}.

58. $H \cup C$, the set of all elements in either H or in C, is {p, n, t, l}.

59. $(H \cup C)'$, the set of elements not in either H or in C, is {a}.

60. $H \cap C$, the set of all elements in both H and C, is $\varnothing$.

61. $(H \cap C)'$ is the set of elements in {p, n, a, t, l} that are not in $H \cap C$. Thus, $(H \cap C)'$ is {p, n, a, t, l}.

62. $H' \cup C'$, the set of elements in either H' and in C', is {p, n, a, t, l}.

63. Compare both lists to find that the set of names that appear only once is {Blogspot.com, Baidu.com, Qq.com, MSN.com, MySpace.com, Blogger.com}.

64. Compare both lists; Wikepedia.org has the same ranking on both lists. The set of all names that have the same ranking on both lists is {Wikepedia.org}.

65. M', the set of all names on the second list that are not on the first list, is {MSN.com, MySpace.com, Blogger.com}.

66. L', the set of all names on the first list that are not on the second list, is {Blogspot.com, Baidu.com, Qq.com}.

67. Look for 2.4 as the first number in the second column, Eng Size/Cylinders. The set with a 2.4-liter engine is {Toyota}.

68. Look for 41 as the first number in the third column, MPG/City/Hwy. The set with a 41-mpg fuel economy in the city is {Ford, Mercury, Lincoln}.

69. Look for the highest mpg as the first number in the third column, MPG/City/Hwy. The set with the highest fuel economy in the city is {Toyota (Prius)}.

70. Look for the lowest mpg as the first number in the third column, MPG/City/Hwy. The set with the lowest fuel economy in the city is {BMW}.

71. Look for the highest mpg as the second number in the third column, MPG/City/Hwy. The set with the highest fuel economy in the city is {Toyota (Prius)}.

72. Look for the highest first number in the second column, Eng Size/Cylinders. The set with the largest engine is {Lexus}.

73. Look for the smallest first number in the second column, Eng Size/Cylinders. The set with the smallest engine is {Toyota (Prius)}.

74. Look for the lowest number in the fourth column, Annual Fuel Cost. The set with the lowest annual fuel cost is {Toyota (Prius)}.

75. Look for the highest number in the fourth column, Annual Fuel Cost. The set with the highest annual fuel cost is {BMW, Lexus}.

76. Look for 2.5 as the first number in the second column, Eng Size/Cylinders. Then, find the smallest number in the corresponding fourth column, Annual Fuel Cost. The set with the 2.5 engine with the lowest annual fuel cost is {Ford, Lincoln, Mercury}.

77. Answers will vary. A and B have no elements in common. (Set examples may vary: A may be a set of cats and B a set of dogs.)

78. Answers will vary. All the elements of A are elements of B. A could be the set of all bloodhounds and B the set of all dogs. (Set examples may vary.)

79. Answers may vary. All the elements of A are elements of B, and all the elements of B are elements of A ($A = B$). (Set examples may vary: the same set defined two different ways.)

80. Answers may vary. A and B have some elements in common. A could be the set of bulldogs and B the set of dogs who will bite people. (Set examples may vary.)

81. a.   This is the set of characteristics that are in both columns of the table: {Long tongue, Skin-covered horns, Native to Africa}
    b.   The same answer as in part a.
    c.   This is the set of characteristics that occur in either column of the table: {Tall, Short, Long neck, Short Neck, Long tongue, Skin-covered horns, Native to Africa}
    d. $G' = $ {Short, Short neck}
    e. $O' = $ {Tall, Long neck}

82. $M \cap D$, the set of males who are 35 years or older, is the first item in the 35 and older row: 3,293,000 elements.

83. $F \cap D$, the set of females who are 35 years

or older, is the second item in the 35 and older row: 685,000 elements.

84. $(F \cup M) \cap D$, the set of all the males and females who are 35 years or older, is the sum of the first and second items in the 35 and older row:
$3{,}293{,}000 + 685{,}000 = 3{,}978{,}000$

85. Look for the smallest number in either the second or third columns. This is the set of 12-17 year old females: $F \cap A$

86. This is the Universal set of both males and females ages 12-17, 18-25, 26-34, and 35 and over.

87. There are no persons that are both male and female. This set is empty.

88. $M \cap B$, the set of males with a bachelor's degree, is the first item in the Bachelor's degree row: $94,206

89. $F \cap B$, the set of females with a bachelor's degree, is the second item in the Bachelor's degree row: $60,293

90. $A \cap M$, the set of males with an associate degree, is the first item in the Associate degree row: $54,830

91. $A \cap F$, the set of females with an associate degree, is the second item in the Associate degree row: $39,935

92. Look for the smallest earnings. This occurs for females with a high school degree:
$F \cap H$

93. Average earnings of males with a High School degree; $43,493

94. The set of people (male and female) who have a High School, Associate or Bachelor's degree.

Collaborative Learning

Comets only: Made of frozen ice, gas or dust; Halley is one; Have a long gas tail; Have a long dust tail; Have a long ion tail; Highly elliptical orbit; Surrounded by hydrogen cloud; Sungrazers are ones that crash into the Sun.

Asteroids only: Made of rock and/or metal; Ceres is the biggest; Have no tail; Most orbit between Jupiter and Mars; Also known as planetoids; Have no atmosphere.

Intergalactics: Orbit the sun; Some come close to the Earth; Part of our Solar System; Some have hit the Earth.

Section 2.3 Venn Diagrams

1. **Step 1**: Draw a diagram with two circles and label the regions *w*, *x*, *y*, *z*, as shown.

    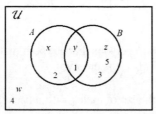

    Step 2: Select the element that is in both *A* and *B*, the number 1. Write 1 in region *y*.
    Step 3: Select the element that is in *A* but not in *B*, the number 2. Write 2 in region *x*.
    Step 4: Select the elements that are in *B* but not in *A*, the numbers 3 and 5. Write 3 and 5 in region *z*.
    Step 5: Select the element that is not in *A* or *B*, the number 4, and write 4 in region *w*. This completes the diagram.

2. **Step 1**: Note that Set *A* and Set *B* do not have any points in common. Draw a diagram with two circles and label them *A* and *B*, as shown.

    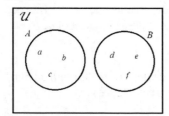

    Step 2: Select the elements that are in *A*. Write them in the circle labeled *A*.
    Step 3: Select the elements that are in *B*. Write them in the circle labeled *B*.
    Step 4: Note that all elements of the universal set have been placed in the diagram. Your diagram is complete.

3. Draw a Venn diagram labeled as in the figure. Then look at the regions corresponding to the various sets. *A*: regions 1, 3; *B'* (regions outside of *B*) regions 1, 4; $A \cap B'$ (regions in both *A* and *B'*): region 1. Shade region 1 for the desired diagram.

    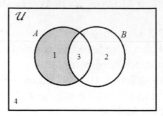

4. Draw a Venn diagram labeled as in the figure. Then look at the regions corresponding to the various sets. *A'* : regions 2, 4; *B'* (regions outside of *B*) regions 1, 4; $A' \cup B'$ (regions in both *A'* and *B'*): regions 1, 2, 4. Shade regions 1, 2, 4 for the desired diagram.

    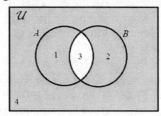

5. Draw a Venn diagram labeled as in the figure. Then find the regions corresponding to the various sets. $A \cup B$ (regions in *A* or *B*): regions 1, 2, 3; $A \cap B$ (regions in both *A* and *B*): region 3; $(A \cup B) - (A \cap B)$: Take the region in $A \cap B$ away from the regions in $A \cup B$, leaving regions 1, 2. Shade regions 1, 2 for the desired diagram.

    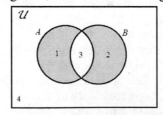

6. Draw a Venn diagram labeled as in the figure. Then look at the regions corresponding to the various sets. *A* : regions 1, 3; *B'* (regions outside of *B*) regions 1, 4; $A \cup B'$ (regions either in *A'* or in *B'*): regions 1, 3, 4. Shade regions 1, 3, 4 for the desired diagram.

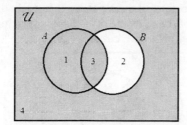

7. Draw a Venn diagram labeled as in the figure. The region corresponding to A' is the entire area outside of circle A, regions 2, 4. The region corresponding to B' is the entire area outside of circle B, regions 1, 4. Thus, the region corresponding to $A' \cap B'$ is the region outside both circles, region 4.

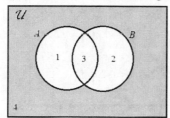

8. Draw a Venn diagram labeled as in the figure. Then find the regions corresponding to the various sets. $A \cup B$ (regions in A or B): regions 1, 2, 3; A: regions 1, 3;
$(A \cup B) - A$: Take the region in A away from the regions in $A \cup B$, leaving region 2. Shade region 2 for the desired diagram.

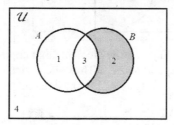

Refer to the following diagram for solutions to exercsises 9 – 16.

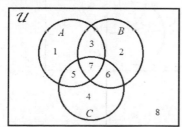

9. A: regions 1, 3, 5, 7; $B \cup C$ (regions in B or C): regions 2, 3, 4, 5, 6, 7; $A - (B \cup C)$:

Take the regions common to A and $B \cup C$ away from the regions in A, leaving the answer: region 1.

10. C: regions 4, 5, 6, 7; $A \cup B$ (regions in A or B): regions 1, 2, 3, 5, 6, 7; $C \cap (A \cup B)$ (regions in both C and $A \cup B$): regions 5, 6, 7.

11. $A \cap B \cap C$ (regions common to A, B, C): region 7; $A \cap B$ (regions in both A and B): regions 3, 7; $(A \cap B \cap C) - (A \cap B)$: Take the regions common to $A \cap B \cap C$ and $A \cap B$ away from those in $A \cap B \cap C$. This leaves no regions, so we get the empty set, $\varnothing$.

12. $A \cap B'$ (regions in both A and B'): regions 1, 5; $A \cap C'$ (regions in both A and C'): regions 1, 3; $(A \cap B') \cup (A \cup C')$ (regions in either $A \cap B'$ or in $A \cap C'$): regions 1, 3, 5.

13. $A \cup B'$ (regions in A or outside of B): regions 1, 3, 4, 5, 7, 8; C: regions 4, 5, 6, 7; $(A \cup B') \cap C$ (regions in both $A \cup B'$ and C): regions 4, 5, 7.

14. $A \cup B$: regions 1, 2, 3, 5, 6, 7; C: regions 4, 5, 6, 7; $(A \cup B) - C$: Take the regions common to $A \cup B$ and C away from the regions in $A \cup B$, leaving the answer: regions 1, 2, 3.

15. $A \cap B'$ (regions in A and not in B): regions 1, 5. $(A \cap B') \cup C$ (regions in either $A \cap B'$ or C): regions 1, 4, 5, 6, and 7.

16. B: regions 2, 3, 6, 7; C': regions 1, 2, 3, 8; and A: regions 1, 3, 5, 7. $B \cap C' \cap A$ (regions in B and C' and A): region 3.

17. This consists of the region that is outside all three of A, B, C: region 8.

18. This includes all the elements that are inside of *A* or inside of *B*. Thus, shade all of *A* and *B*.

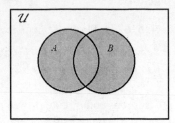

19. This includes all the elements that are outside of *A* or outside of *B*. Thus, everything except the region common to the two circles is shaded.

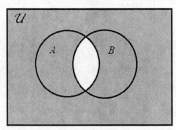

20. This includes all the elements that are inside of *A* and outside of *B*. Thus, everything common to inside of *A* and outside of *B* is shaded.

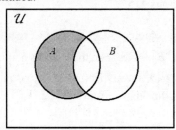

21. This includes all the elements that are in *A* and also in *B*, but not in *C*. Thus, the region that is common to *A* and *B* but is outside of *C* is shaded.

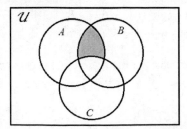

22. This includes all the elements that are both inside of *A* and inside of *B*. Thus, everything common to the two circles is shaded.

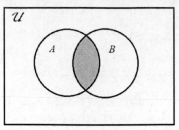

23. This includes all the elements of *B* that are not elements of *A*. Thus, the region in *B* that is outside of *A* is shaded.

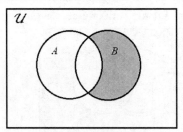

24. This includes all the elements that are inside of *A* or inside of *B* or inside of *C*. Thus, shade all three circles.

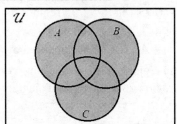

25. This includes all the elements that are in both *B* and *C*, but not in *A*. Thus, the region common to *B* and *C*, but outside of *A* is shaded.

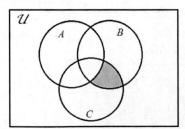

26. Because the intersection of *A* and *B* is given equal to the empty set, *A* and *B* are non-overlapping circles.

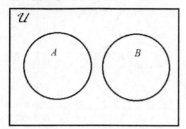

27. Because the intersection of *A* and *B* is given equal to *B*, all of *B* is contained in *A*, as shown in the diagram.

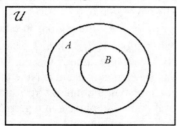

28. Because the intersection of the union *A* or *B* and *C* is given equal to the empty set, *A* and *B* are overlapping circles yet not overlapping with *C*.

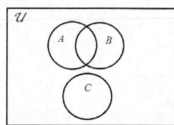

29. Note that $A \cap B$ contains all the elements common to *A* and *B*, so that $A \cap (A \cap B)$ is the same as $A \cap B$. Because $A \cap (A \cap B) = A$, all the elements of *A* must be in *B*. Thus, the circle *A* was drawn inside the circle *B*.

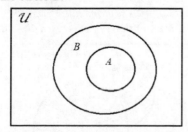

30. a. $A \cup B$ (regions in *A* or *B*): regions 1, 2, 3, 5, 6, 7. Similarly, we have the following correspondences. $B \cup A$ (regions in *B* or *A*): regions 1, 2, 3, 5, 6, 7. Both sets correspond to regions 1, 2, 3, 5, 6, 7. This verifies the given equality.

   b. $A \cap B$ (regions in both *A* and *B*): regions 3, 7. Similarly, we have the following correspondences. $B \cap A$ (regions in both *A* and *B*): regions 3, 7. Both sets correspond to regions 3, 7. This verifies the given equality.

31. a. *A*: regions 1, 3, 5, 7; $B \cup C$: regions 2, 3, 4, 5, 6, 7. Thus, for $A \cup (B \cup C)$, we have regions 1, 2, 3, 4, 5, 6, 7. Similarly, we have the following correspondences. $A \cup B$: regions 1, 2, 3, 5, 6, 7; *C*: regions 4, 5, 6, 7. So for $(A \cup B) \cup C$, we have regions 1, 2, 3, 4, 5, 6, 7. This verifies the given equality.

   b. *A*: regions 1, 3, 5, 7; $B \cap C$: regions 6, 7. Thus, for $A \cap (B \cap C)$, we have region 7. Also, $A \cap B$: regions 3, 7; *C*: regions 4, 5, 6, 7. Thus, for $(A \cap B) \cap C$, we have region 7. This verifies the given equality.

32. *A*: regions 1, 3, 5, 7; $B \cap C$: regions 6, 7. Thus, for $A \cup (B \cap C)$, we have regions 1, 3, 5, 6, 7. Similarly, we have the following correspondences. $A \cup B$ (regions in *A* or *B*): regions 1, 2, 3, 5, 6, 7; $A \cup C$: regions 1, 3, 4, 5, 6, 7. Thus, for $(A \cup B) \cap (A \cup C)$, we have regions 1, 3, 5, 6, 7. Both sets correspond to regions 1, 3, 5, 6, 7. This verifies the given equality.

33. a. *A*: regions 1, 3, 5, 7; *A'*: regions 2, 4, 6, 8. Thus, for $A \cup A'$, we have regions 1, 2, 3, 4, 5, 6, 7, 8, the same set of regions that represents *U*. This verifies the given equality.

   b. From part a, we see that *A* and *A'* have no elements in common. Therefore, $A \cap A' = \varnothing$.

   c. $A - B$: regions 1, 5; $A \cap B'$: regions 1, 5. This verifies the equality.

34. a $(A \cup B)'$ (regions not in A or B): regions 4, 8. Similarly, we have the following correspondences. A' (regions not in A): regions 2, 4, 6, 8; B' (regions not in B): regions 1, 4, 5, 8. Thus for $A' \cap B'$ (regions common to both A' and B'): regions 4, 8. Both sets correspond to regions 4, 8. This verifies the given equality.

   b. $(A \cap B)'$ (regions not in both A and B): regions 1, 2, 4, 5, 6, 8. Similarly, we have the following correspondences. A' (regions not in A): regions 2, 4, 6, 8; B' (regions not in B): regions 1, 4, 5, 8. Thus for $A' \cup B'$ (regions in A' or B'): regions 1, 2, 4, 5, 6, 8. Both sets correspond to regions 1, 2, 4, 5, 6, 8. This verifies the given equality.

35. $A \cap B$ (The regions that are in both A and B): regions 3, 7.

36.   The set of regions {1, 2, 3} represents $(A \cup B) \cap C'$ or (b).

37.   Draw a Venn diagram with the regions numbered as shown.

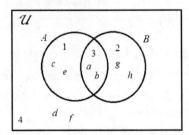

   $A \cap B$: the region common to A and B is region 3, so write a, b in region 3.
   $A \cap B'$: the region in A and not in B is region 1, so write c, e in region 1.
   $A' \cap B$: the region in B but not in A is region 2, so write g, h in region 2.
   $(A \cup B)'$: the region that is outside the union of A and B is region 4. Write d, f in region 4. Now, you can read off each of the required sets:
   a. $A = \{a, b, c, e\}$, $B = \{a, b, g, h\}$, $U = \{a, b, c, d, e, f, g, h\}$
   b. $A \cup B = \{a, b, c, e, g, h\}$
   c. $(A \cap B)' = \{c, d, e, f, g, h\}$

38.   Draw a Venn diagram with the regions numbered as shown.

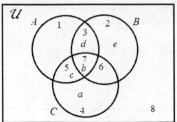

   $A \cap B = \{b, d\}$: the regions common to A and B are regions 3 and 7. To determine placement of the elements b and d, note that element b is in all of the unions and intersections listed. Write b in region 7, then d would be in region 3.
   $A \cup B = \{b, c, d, e\}$: the regions in either A or in B are regions 1, 2, 3, 4, 6, 7. Since elements b and d are already placed, we only need to place elements c and e. Note that element c is also in the intersection and union of A and C, so place c in region 5, then e would be in region 2.
   For $A \cap C = \{b, c\}$ and $A \cup C = \{a, b, c, d\}$, these elements have already been placed. Now, you can read off each of the required sets:
   a. $A = \{b, c, d\}$, $B = \{b, d, e\}$, $C = \{a, b, c\}$
   b. $A \cap B \cap C = \{b\}$
   c. $A \cup B \cup C = \{a, b, c, d, e\}$

39.

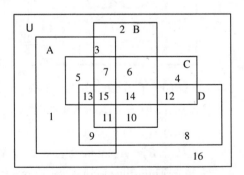

Refer to the following diagram from Example 6, with regions numbered for clarity, for solutions to exercises 40 – 43.

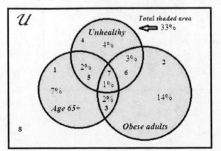

40. a. Unhealthy, but not obese would be regions 4 and 5: 4% + 2% = 6%
    b. Unhealthy, not obese, and over 65+ would be region 5: 2%

41. a. Obese but not unhealthy would be regions 2 and 3: 14% + 2% = 16%
    b. Obese, not unhealthy, and under 65 would be region 2: 14%

42. a. Not in the shaded area would be region 8: 67%
    b. In one shaded set only would be regions 1, 2, and 4: 7% + 14% + 4% = 25%

43. a. In two shaded sets only would be regions 3, 5, and 6: 2% + 2% + 3% = 7%
    b. In all shaded sets would be region 7: 1%

44. Let H' = Unhealthy, E = Age 65+, and O = Obese adults. The set notation for the shaded area is $E \cup O \cup H'$.

45. Let H' = Unhealthy, E = Age 65+, and O = Obese adults. The set notation for the area not shaded is $(E \cup O \cup H')'$.

46. $E \cap R$ includes all sites in both E and R: {Facebook, MySpace}.

47. The number one Web site in set E and in set R is Facebook.

48. Facebook. They rank number one on both lists. (Answers may vary.)

49. Answers will vary. 50. Answers will vary.

51. Answers will vary. 52. Answers will vary.

53. Answers may vary. The set of elements common to A and B.

54. Answers may vary. The set of elements in B but not in A.

55. Answers may vary. The set of elements in U and not in either A or C.

56. Answers may vary. The set of elements common to B and C, but not in A.

57. Answers may vary. Look at the third column for numbers greater than 83. The corresponding countries with females life expectancy greater than 83 would be Switzerland (S) and France (F). Set $A = \{S, F\}$. To determine set B, look at the fourth column for numbers greater than 78. The corresponding countries with males life expectancy greater than 78 would be Switzerland (S) and Canada (C). Set $B = \{S, C\}$.

58. Answers may vary. Set $A = \{S, F\}$ and set $B = \{S, C\}$. $A \cap B$, the countries in both A and B, is Switzerland. Find Switzerland in the first column, then the corresponding number in the second column, Annual per capita health expenditures, is 4417.

59. Answers may vary. Look at the third column for numbers less than 83. The corresponding countries with females life expectancy less than 83 would be USA (U) and Malta (M). Set $A = \{U, M\}$. To determine set B, look at the fourth column for numbers less than 78. The corresponding countries with males life expectancy less than 78 would be USA (U) and Luxenbourg (L). Set $B = \{U, L\}$.

60. Set $A = \{U, M\}$ and set $B = \{U, L\}$. $A \cap B$, the countries in both A and B, is United States. Find United States in the first column, then the corresponding number in the second column, Annual per capita health expenditures, is $7285.

61. An AB$^+$ person has all three antigens and thus may receive blood from any donor.

62. An O$^-$ person has no antigens and thus may donate blood to any recipient.

63. No, because the B$^-$ person does not have the A antigen, which the AB$^-$ does have.

64. Yes, because the B$^-$ person has only the B antigen which the AB$^-$ person also has. Note that a donor does not need to have all of the antigens present in the recipient, but what is donated must be in the recipient.

65. No, because the O$^-$ person does not have the Rh antigen, which the O$^+$ does have.

66. Yes, because the O$^-$ person has no antigens and so can donate to anyone.

67. Add all the percents of people with the A antigen: $34 + 6 + 3 + 1 = 44\%$

68. Add all the percents of people with the B antigen: $9 + 2 + 3 + 1 = 15\%$

69. Add all the percents of people without A or B antigens (that is, O type blood): $38 + 7 = 45\%$

70. O is most common with 45% of the U.S. population.

71. Note the pattern that is developed in the text before the problem. We see that with one set, we have $2^1 = 2$ regions; with two sets, we have $2^2 = 4$ regions; and with three sets, $2^3 = 8$ regions. So, for n sets, we will have 2^n regions. Thus, four sets will have $2^4 = 16$ regions in the Venn diagram.

72. The maximum number of regions into which n sets will divide the universe is 2^n.

73. a. This requires everything common to A, B, and D, that is not in C. Thus, the answer is region 11.
    b. This requires everything that is outside of the union of A, B, and C. Thus, the answer is regions 8 and 16.

Collaborative Learning

1. The color of the intersection of the three additive primary colors is white.

2. The color of the intersection of the three subtractive secondary colors is black.

3. None; there is no other intersection of three colors that produce white.

4. None; there is no other intersection of three colors that produce black.

5. When you mix red and green, you will get yellow.

6. When you mix red and blue, you will get magenta.

7. When you mix green and blue, you will get cyan.

Section 2.4 The Number of Elements in a Set: A Problem-Solving Tool

1. Use Equation (1):
$$n(A \cup B) = n(A) + n(B) - n(A \cap B).$$
Then, since $n(A) = 15$, $n(B) = 20$, and $n(A \cap B) = 5$, it follows that
$$n(A \cup B) = 15 + 20 - 5 = 30.$$

2. Use Equation (1), solving for $n(A \cap B)$:
$$n(A \cap B) = n(A) + n(B) - n(A \cup B).$$
Then, since $n(A) = 12$, $n(B) = 6$, and $n(A \cup B) = 14$, it follows that
$$n(A \cap B) = 12 + 6 - 14 = 4.$$

3. Use the same equation as in problem 1. Thus, $n(A) = 15$, $n(A \cap B) = 5$, and $n(A \cup B) = 30$, which we substitute into Equation (1) to get
$$30 = 15 + n(B) - 5$$
$$30 = 10 + n(B)$$
$$n(B) = 20$$

4. a. $n(A)$, the number of students in an algebra class, is 50.
   b. $n(C)$, the number of students in a chemistry class, is 30.
   c. Since none are taking both classes, we have $n(A) + n(C) = 50 + 30 = 80$ students.
   d. Since 10 students are taking both classes, we use equation 1,
$$n(A \cup B) = n(A) + n(B) - n(A \cap B)$$
$$= 50 + 30 - 10$$
$$= 70 \text{ students}$$

5. Let T be the set of families who subscribe to *Time* and N be the set who subscribe to *Newsweek*. Since 100 families were surveyed and 10 subscribe to neither magazine, 90 subscribe to one or both. Hence, we can use Equation (1) in the form:
$$n(T \cup N) = n(T) + n(N) - n(T \cap N)$$
With $n(T \cup N) = 90, n(T) = 75,$ and $n(N) = 55$, we get the equation

$$90 = 75 + 55 - n(T \cap N)$$

$$90 = 130 - n(T \cap N)$$

$$n(T \cap N) = 40$$

which says that 40 families subscribe to both.

6. Let T be the set of families who subscribe to Time and N be the set who subscribe to Newsweek. Since 100 families were surveyed and 83 subscribe to Time, 40 to Newsweek, and 30 to both. Hence, we can use Equation (1) in the form:

$$n(T \cup N) = n(T) + n(N) - n(T \cap N)$$

With $n(T) = 83$, $n(N) = 40$, $n(T \cap N) = 30$ we get the equation

$$n(T \cup N) = 83 + 40 - 30$$

$$= 93$$

which says that 93 families subscribe to either Times or Newsweek. So, $100 - 93 = 7$ families who subscribe to neither.

7. To do this problem, first draw a Venn diagram. Let C be the set of students taking Chemistry, E be the set taking English, and M the set taking Mathematics. Draw the diagram with three circles as shown.

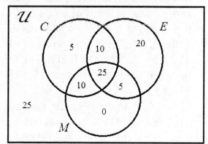

Start at the end of the given listing to fill in the proper numbers in the various regions. Because 25 are taking all three courses, write 25 in the region common to all three circles. Since 35 are taking Math and Chem, and we have accounted for 25 of these, write 10 in the remainder of the region common to M and C. Likewise, 35 are taking English and Chem, and we have accounted for 25 of these, write 10 in the remainder of the region common to E and C. Similarly, because 30 are taking English and Math, and we have accounted for 25 of these, write 5 in the remainder of the region common to E and M. Then, because 50 are taking Chem, and we have accounted for $10 + 25 + 10 =$

45 of these, write 5 in the region of C that is outside of E and M. There are 40 in Math, and we have accounted for $5 + 10 + 25 = 40$, so write 0 in the region of M that is outside of E and C. Since there are 60 taking English, and we have accounted for $5 + 10 + 25 = 40$ of these, write 20 in the region of E that is outside of C and M. Up to this point, we have accounted for $20 + 5 + 5 + 10 + 10 + 25 = 75$ students. Because 100 students were surveyed, write 25 in the region outside of the three circles. This completes the diagram and we can now read off the answers.

a. No students were taking Math and neither Chem nor English. (See the region of M that is outside of C and E.)

b. There were 10 students taking both Math and Chem, but not English. (See the region that is inside both M and C, but is outside of E.)

c. There were 10 students taking both English and Chem but not Math. (See the region inside both E and C, but outside of M.)

8. To do this problem, first draw a Venn diagram. Let N be the set of 9 A.M. classes, T be the set of 10 A.M. classes, and E the set of 11 A.M. classes. Draw the diagram with three circles as shown.

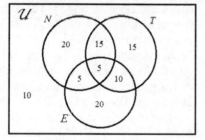

Start at the bottom of the given listing to fill in the proper numbers in the various regions. Because 5% are taking all three class, write 5 in the region common to all three circles. Since 15% have both 10 A.M. and 11 A.M. classes, and we have accounted for 5% of these, write 10 in the remainder of the region common to T and E. Ten percent have both 9 A.M. and 11 A.M. classes, and we have accounted for 5% of these, write 5 in the remainder of the region common to N and E. Similarly, because 20% have both 9 A.M. and 10 A.M. classes, and we have accounted for 5% of these, write 15 in the remainder of the region common to N and T. Then, because 40% have an 11 A.M. class, and we have accounted for $5 + 5 + 10 = 20\%$ of these, write 20 in the region of *E* that is outside of *N* and *T*. There are 45% with a 10 A.M. class, and we have accounted for 15 + 5 + 10 = 30, so write 15 in the region of *T* that is outside of *N* and *E*. Since 45% have a 9 A.M. class, and we have accounted for 5 + 5 + 15 = 25 of these, write 20 in the region of *N* that is outside of *T* and *E*. Up to this point, we have accounted for 20 + 15 + 5 + 5 + 15 + 10 + 20 = 90% of the students. Therefore 100 – 90 = 10% of the students have classes at other times. Write 10 in the region outside of the three circles. This completes the diagram and we can now read off the answers.

   a. 20% of the students have only a 9 A.M. class. (See the region of *N* that is outside of *T* and *E*.)

   b. 10% of the students have no classes at these times. (See the region that is outside all three circles.)

9. a. From the public 2-year college row, find the largest number, and then identify the corresponding column. The largest expense is Room and Board at $7259. The total cost is the sum of all the expenses: 2713 + 7259 + 1135 + 1491 + 2041 = $14,637

   b. From the public 4-year college (in-state) row, find the largest number, and then identify the corresponding column. The largest expense is Room and Board at $8535. The total cost is the sum of all the expenses: 7605 + 8535 + 1137 + 1073 + 1959 = $20,339

   c. From the public 4-year college (out-state) row, find the largest number, and then identify the corresponding column. The largest expense is Tuition and Fees at $19,595. The total cost is the sum of all the expenses: 19,595 + 8535 + 1137 + 1073 + 1959 = $32,329

10. Refer to problem 9 solutions for annual costs.

   a. The difference in annual costs between a public 2-year college (annual cost $14,637) and a public 4-year in-state college (annual cost $20,339) is 20,339 – 14,637 = $5702.

   b. The difference in annual costs between a public 2-year college (annual cost $14,637) and a public 4-year out-of-state college (annual cost $32,329) is 32,329 – 14,637 = $17,692.

   c. The difference in annual costs between a public 4-year in-state college (annual cost $20,339) and a public 4-year out-of-state college (annual cost $32,329) is 32,329 – 20,339 = $11,990.

11. a. From the horizontal bar representing a public 2-year college, find the smallest number, and then identify the corresponding color with the legend. The least expense is Books and Supplies at $1133.

   b. From the horizontal bar representing a public 4-year college (in-state), find the smallest number, and then identify the corresponding color with the legend. The least expense is Transportation at $1073.

   c. From the horizontal bar representing a public 4-year college (out-state), find the smallest number, and then identify the corresponding color with the legend. The least expense is Transportation at $1073.

12. Look at the legend to find the color representing Tuition and Fees.

   a. Identify that color on the horizontal bar representing a public 2-year college, note the corresponding number: $2713. Identify the same color on the horizontal bar representing a public 4-year in-state college, note the corresponding number: $7605 Subtract to find the difference between the two colleges: 7605 – 2713 = $4892

   b. Using the same color as in part a, identify that color on the horizontal bar representing a public 2-year college, note the corresponding number: $2713. Identify the same color on the horizontal bar representing a public 4-year out-of-state college, note the corresponding number: $19,595. Subtract to find the difference between the two colleges: 19,595 – 2713 = $16,882

   c. Using the same color as in part a, identify that color on the horizontal bar representing a public 4-year in-state college, note the corresponding number: $7605. Identify the same color on the horizontal bar representing a public 4-year out-of-state college, note the corresponding number: $19,595. Subtract to find the difference between the two colleges: 19,595 – 7605= $11,990

13. a. $C \cap M$, the set of cell phone (*C*) users who are Millennials (*M*), is the first item in the cell phone row: 95%

   b. $D \cap X$, the set of desktop computer (*D*) users who are Gen X (*X*), is the second item in the desktop computer row: 69%

   c. $L \cap Y$, the set of laptop computer (*L*)

users who are Younger Baby Boomers (*Y*), is the third item in the laptop computer row: 49%

d. $X \cap I$, the set of Gen X (*X*) who are iPod/MP3 player (*I*) users, is the fourth item in the Gen X column: 56%

e. $Y \cap G$, the set of Younger Baby Boomers (*Y*) who are game console (*G*) users, is the fifth item in the Younger Baby Boomers column: 38%

14. a. The set that corresponds to 69% of Gen X (*X*) owning desktop computers (*D*) is $D \cap X$.

b. The set that corresponds to 65% of Younger Baby Boomers (*Y*) owning desktop computers (*D*) is $D \cap Y$.

c. The set that corresponds to 74% of Millennials (*M*), owning MP3 players (*I*) is $M \cap I$.

d. The set that corresponds to 56% of Gen X (*X*) owning MP3 players (*I*) is $X \cap I$.

15. Let *O* stand for onions, *M* for mustard, and *C* for catsup. Draw a Venn diagram as shown.

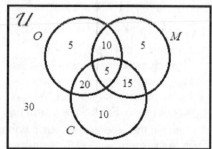

The numbers are obtained as follows: Start at the end of the list. Since 5 had all three condiments, write 5 in the region common to the three circles. Because 25 had onions and catsup, the region common to *O* and *C* must have a total of 25. We have already put 5 into this region, so 20 goes into the remainder of the region. Next, we see that 20 had mustard and catsup, so the region common to *M* and *C* must have a total of 20. Since 5 have already been put in this region, 15 must be put in the remainder of the region. Since 15 had onion and mustard, the region common to *O* and *M* must have a total of 15. Because 5 have already been put in this region, 10 must be in the remainder of the region. Now we see that 50 had catsup, so circle *C* must contain a total of

50. The diagram shows that we already have put 5 + 15 + 20 = 40 in *C*, so 10 must be put in the remainder of the region. Next, we see that 35 had mustard. Thus, circle *M* must have a total of 35. Since we have entered 5 + 15 + 10 = 30 in this circle, 5 must go into the remainder of this circle. Since 40 had onions, and the diagram shows that 5 + 10 + 20 = 35 have already been put in circle *O*, an additional 5 must go in this circle. Now, the diagram shows that 70 persons have been put into the three circles. Since 100 were surveyed, we must put 30 into the rectangle outside of the three circles. This completes the diagram and we can read off the answers to the questions.

a. 5 (See the region inside *O* and outside *M* and *C*.)

b. 30 (See the region in the rectangle outside of the three circles.)

c. 5 + 5 + 10 = 20 (See the non overlapping regions of the three circles.)

16. Let *H* stand for owning a house, *C* for owing a car, and *B* for owning a boat. Draw a Venn diagram as shown.

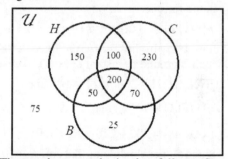

The numbers are obtained as follows: Start at the end of the list. Since 200 had owned all three, write 200 in the region common to the three circles. Because 270 owned cars and boats, the region common to *C* and *B* must have a total of 270. We have already put 200 into this region, so 70 goes into the remainder of the region. Next, we see that 250 owned houses and boats, so the region common to *H* and *B* must have a total of 250. Since 200 have already been put in this region, 50 must be put in the remainder of the region. Since 300 owned cars and houses, the region common to *C* and *H* must have a total of 300. Because 200 have already been put in this region, 100 must be in the remainder of the region. Now we see that 345 owned boats, so circle *B* must contain a total of 345. The diagram shows that we already have put 50 + 200 + 70 =

320 in B, so 25 must be put in the remainder of the region. Next, we see that 600 owned cars. Thus, circle C must have a total of 600. Since we have entered $100 + 200 + 70 = 370$ in this circle, 230 must go into the remainder of this circle. Since 500 owned houses, and the diagram shows that $100 + 200 + 50 = 350$ have already been put in circle H, an additional 150 must go in this circle. Now, the diagram shows that 825 persons have been put into the three circles. Since 900 were surveyed, we must put 75 into the rectangle outside of the three circles. This completes the diagram and we can read off the answers to the questions.

a. There are 75 workers who do not own any houses (look outside of the three circles).

b. Look at where two circles overlap, excluding where all three overlap: $100 + 50 + 70 = 220$ workers owned only two of the items.

17. Let G be the set of people who liked ground coffee, and I be the set of people who liked instant coffee. Then we can use Equation (1) in the form

$n(G \cup I) = n(G) + n(I) - n(G \cap I)$ to find how many of those surveyed liked coffee (either ground or instant or both). We were given $n(G) = 200, n(I) = 270$, and

$n(G \cap I) = 70$, so that

$n(G \cup I) = 200 + 270 - 70 = 400$.

Since 50 people did not like coffee, 450 people were surveyed, and the company had to pay out $450.

18. Draw a Venn diagram as shown here, and then add the numbers in each region.

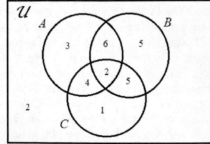

His data account for only $2 + 1 + 2 + 4 + 5 + 3 + 6 + 5 = 28$ persons; hence his figures are unreliable.

19. The Venn diagram for the data reported in problem 18 is shown below.

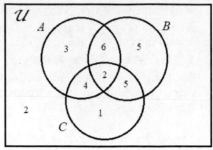

The sum of the numbers in the diagram is 28, which is the correct number of persons interviewed to give this data.

20. a. $M \cap X$, the set of substances that are of type x (X) with characteristic m (M), is the sum of the items in the second and fourth columns in the x row:
$6 + 10 = 16$

b. $(X \cup Y) \cap (M \cup N)$ is the set of substances that are of type x (X) or type y (Y) and characteristic m (M) or n (N). Sum all the samples except those that contained neither m nor n.
$6 + 7 + 9 + 11 + 10 + 15 = 58$

c. $(Y \cap M) - (Y \cap N')$ is the set of substances of type y (Y) with characteristic m (M) minus the set of substances of type y (Y) with characteristic that is not n (N) (not n would be m). For $Y \cap M$, sum the items in the second and fourth columns in the y row: $7 + 15 = 22$ samples; for $Y \cap N'$, this is the item in the second column in the y row: 7 samples. The difference is $22 - 7 = 15$ samples.

d. $(X \cup Y) \cap (M \cup N')$ is the set of substances that are of type x (X) or type y (Y) and characteristic m (M) or not n (N). Sum all the samples in columns 'm Only' and 'Neither m nor n':
$6 + 7 + 20 + 9 = 42$

21. a. $n(A)$ is the sum of the numbers in A, $70 + 50 = 120$.

b. $n(C)$ is the sum of the numbers in C, $30 + 50 = 80$.

c. $n(A \cap C)$ is the number in the overlapping portion of the two circles, 50.

22. Use this equation and solutions from problem 21:

$$n(A \cup B) = n(A) + n(B) - n(A \cap B) \, n(A)$$
$$= 120 + 80 - 50 = 150$$

Alternate method: $n(A \cup C)$ is the sum of the three regions: $70 + 50 + 30 = 150$.

23. a. $n(A')$ is the number of students in U and not in A, which is $200 - (70 + 50) = 80$.

b. $n(C')$ is the number of students in U and not in C, which is $200 - (50 + 30) = 120$.

c. $n(A' \cap C')$ is the number of students outside of both A and C, that is, $200 - (70 + 50 + 30) = 50$.

24. From problem 23, 200 students were surveyed. Problem 22 found that $n(A \cup C)$ is 150, therefore 50 of the 200 students were not taking either algebra or chemistry. Refer to the Venn diagram as show here.

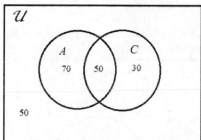

a. $n(A' \cup C)$ is the number of students either not taking algebra or taking chemistry.

$$n(A' \cup C) = n(A') + n(C) - n(A' \cap C)$$
$$= 80 + 80 - 30$$
$$= 130$$

b. $n(A \cup C')$ is the number of students either taking algebra or not taking chemistry.

$$n(A \cup C') = n(A) + n(C') - n(A \cap C')$$
$$= 120 + 120 - 70$$
$$= 170$$

25. a. This is the sum of the numbers in E and T that are not in the region common to these two circles,
$35 + 20 + 12 + 6 = 73$.

b. This is the sum of the numbers in E and

T that are not in M, $35 + 8 + 12 = 55$.

c. This is the sum of all the numbers in the diagram except the number in the region common to all three circles. Thus, we get
$35 + 8 + 12 + 20 + 6 + 10 = 91$.

d. This is the sum of the numbers in all the regions common to at least two of the circles, $8 + 6 + 20 + 4 = 38$.

e. Since the sum of all the numbers in the diagram is 95 and 100 persons were interviewed, 5 persons must have had none of these three types of investment.

26. a. This is the sum of the numbers in the diagram in the regions in A:
$5 + 3 + 2 + 7 = 17$

b. This is the sum of the numbers in the diagram in the regions in A that are not in B: $5 + 7 = 12$

c. This is the sum of the numbers in the diagram in the regions in B and C that are not in A: $15 + 10 + 23 = 48$

d. This is the sum of the numbers in the diagram in all regions except those in C:
$5 + 3 + 23 + 20 = 51$

e. This is the sum of the numbers in the diagram in all regions:
$5 + 3 + 2 + 7 + 23 + 10 + 15 + 20 = 85$

27. Draw a diagram with two circles labeled C for cake and F for frosting.

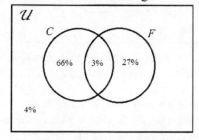

Since 3% eat them together, place 3% on the region common to C and F. The circle labeled C must contain 69% of the people, so enter 66% (69% – 3%) in the other region of C. The set F has 30% of the people, so we enter 27% (30% – 3%) on the other region of F. We now have accounted for 66% + 3% + 27% = 96% of the people, so 4% must be outside both circles and 27% + 4% = 31% are outside C. Thus, 31% do not eat cake.

28. Draw a diagram with two circles labeled L for left corner of envelope and B for back flap.

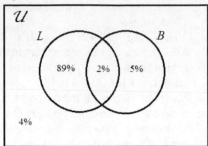

Since 2% write the return address either way, place 2% on the region common to L and B. The circle labeled L must contain 91%, so enter 89% (91% – 2%) in the other region of L. The set B has 7% of the people, so we enter 5% (7% – 2%) on the other region of B. We now have accounted for 89% + 2% + 5% = 96% of the people, so 4% must be outside both circles. Thus, 4% do not write a return address on their envelopes.

29. Draw a diagram with two circles labeled O for optimist and P for pessimist.

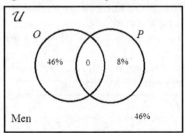

The intersection of O and P is empty, so we enter a 0. According to the data, 46% of the men are optimists (enter 46%) and 8% are pessimists (enter 8%). We now have accounted for 46% + 8% = 54% of the men, so there must be 46% of the men that are neither optimists nor pessimists, that is, outside both circles.

30. Draw a diagram with two circles labeled O for optimist and P for pessimist.

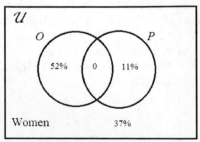

The intersection of O and P is empty, so we enter a 0. According to the data, 52% of the women are optimists (enter 52%) and 11% are pessimists (enter 11%). We now have accounted for 52% + 11% = 63% of the women, so there must be 37% of the women that are neither optimists nor pessimists, that is, outside both circles.

31. Answers may vary. False. A counterexample is $A = \{1, 2\}$ and $B = \{m, n\}$.

32. Answers may vary. True. If $A = B$, then the number of elements in A must be equal to the number of elements in B since A and B are identical.

33. Answers may vary. False. A counterexample is $A = \{1, 2\}$ and $B = \{1, 2, 3\}$.

34. Answers may vary. False. Let $A = \{1, 2\}$ and $B = \{a, b\}$. Then $n(A) = 2 = n(B)$, but $A - B = A$ since no elements of B are in A.

35. The Venn diagram shows that with the added information, the statistics in the cartoon are possible.

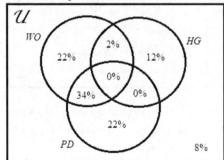

36. Include:

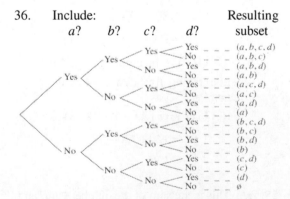

37. If there are 4 elements and each element can be either included or not included (two choices for each element), then there is a total of $2 \cdot 2 \cdot 2 \cdot 2 = 2^4 = 16$ different

subsets.

38. If there are n elements and each element can be either included or not included (2 choices for each element), then there is a total of $2 \cdot 2 \cdot 2 \cdot \ldots \cdot 2 = 2^n$ different subsets. (A recursive relationship argument would be thus: a three-element set has 8 subsets; a fourth element can either not be in those 8 (leaving 8 subsets of the 4-element set) or be "added to" those subsets – no duplication – resulting in an additional 8, doubling the number of subsets. Thus, 0-element sets have 1 subset; double for each additional element: 2^n .)

Section 2.5 Infinite Sets

1. $n(A) = 26$ 2. $n(B) = 10$ 3. $n(C) = 50$

4. The set D can be put into one-to-one correspondence with the set N of counting numbers: $n \leftrightarrow \dfrac{1}{2n}$. So, $n(D) = \aleph_0$.

5. The set E can be put into one-to-one correspondence with the set N of counting numbers: $n \leftrightarrow \dfrac{1}{n^2}$. So, $n(E) = \aleph_0$.

6. 1   2   3   4   5
    ↕   ↕   ↕   ↕   ↕
    a b c d e
   This shows that $A \sim B$.

7. We can set up the correspondence
    2   4   8   12
    ↕   ↕   ↕   ↕
    6   12   24   36
   Thus, the sets P and Q are equivalent.

8. 0   1   2   3   ... n ...
    ↕   ↕   ↕   ↕   ↕
    1   2   3   4   ... $n+1$ ...
   This shows that $W \sim N$.

9. The correspondence
    -1 -2 -3 ... $-n$ ...
    ↕   ↕   ↕   ↕
    1   2   3   ... n ...
   shows that I^- and N are equivalent.

10. 1   2   3   ... n ...
    ↕   ↕   ↕   ↕
    $\dfrac{1}{1}$ $\dfrac{1}{2}$ $\dfrac{1}{3}$ ... $\dfrac{1}{n}$ ...
   This shows that $N \sim F$.

11. One such correspondence is
    1   2   3   ... n
    ↕   ↕   ↕   ↕
    1   3   5   ... $2n-1$ ...
   Thus, the two sets N and O are equivalent.

12. 1   2   3   ... n ...
    ↕   ↕   ↕   ↕
    5   10   15   ... $5n$ ...
   This shows that $N \sim F$.

13. One such correspondence is
    2   4   6   ... $2n$ ...
    ↕   ↕   ↕   ↕
    102   104   106   ... $100+2n$ ...
   Thus, the two sets E and G are equivalent.

14. 1   3   5   ... $2n-1$ ...
    ↕   ↕   ↕   ↕
    2   4   6   ... $2n$ ...
   This shows that $O \sim E$.

15. One such correspondence is
    202   204   206   ... $200+2n$ ...
    ↕   ↕   ↕   ↕
    302   304   306   ... $300+2n$ ...
   Thus, the two sets G and T are equivalent.

16. The set $\{1, 2, 3, \ldots, 999,999\}$ can be counted so it is finite. That is, the cardinality of the set is equal to a counting number.

17. The set $\{100, 200, 300, \ldots\}$ can be put into one-to-one correspondence with a subset of itself, $\{200, 300, 400, \ldots\}$.

$$
\begin{array}{ccccc}
100 & 200 & 300 & \ldots & 100n & \ldots \\
\updownarrow & \updownarrow & \updownarrow & & \updownarrow \\
200 & 300 & 400 & \ldots & 100(n+1) & \ldots
\end{array}
$$

This shows that the set is infinite.

18. The set $\{5, 10, 15, \ldots\}$ can be put into one-to-one correspondence with a subset of itself, $\{10, 15, 20, \ldots\}$.

$$
\begin{array}{ccccc}
5 & 10 & 15 & \ldots & 5n & \ldots \\
\updownarrow & \updownarrow & \updownarrow & & \updownarrow \\
10 & 15 & 20 & \ldots & 5(n+1) & \ldots
\end{array}
$$

This shows that the set is infinite.

19. The set $\left\{\dfrac{1}{3}, \dfrac{2}{3}, \dfrac{3}{3}, \ldots\right\}$ can be put into one-to-one correspondence with a subset of itself, $\left\{\dfrac{2}{3}, \dfrac{3}{3}, \dfrac{4}{3}, \ldots\right\}$.

$$
\begin{array}{ccccc}
\dfrac{1}{3} & \dfrac{2}{3} & \dfrac{3}{3} & \ldots & \dfrac{n}{3} & \ldots \\
\updownarrow & \updownarrow & \updownarrow & & \updownarrow \\
\dfrac{2}{3} & \dfrac{3}{3} & \dfrac{4}{3} & \ldots & \dfrac{n+1}{3} & \ldots
\end{array}
$$

Thus, the set is infinite.

20. The set $\{2^{64}, 2^{32}, 2^{16}, \ldots, 2\}$ can be counted so it is finite. That is, the cardinality of the set is equal to a counting number.

21. Sets B and D are equal and equivalent.

22. Sets B and C and sets C and D are equivalent but not equal. (Sets B and D are equal and equivalent.)

23. Set A is neither equivalent nor equal to any of the other sets.

24. Answers may vary. Fill in the blank with $\aleph_0$. The set $\{0, 1, 2, 3, \ldots\}$ can be put into one-to-one correspondence with the set $\{1, 2, 3, \ldots\}$.

25. Answers may vary. Fill in the blank with $\aleph_0$. This is justified by considering the combination of two sets such as $\{1, 3, 5, \ldots\}$ and $\{2, 4, 6, \ldots\}$ into the set $N = \{1, 2, 3, 4, 5, 6, \ldots\}$. Since all three of these sets have $\aleph_0$ as their cardinality, it follows that $\aleph_0 + \aleph_0 = \aleph_0$.

26. Answers may vary. Fill in the blank with $\aleph_0$. The sets $\{1, 3, 5, \ldots\}$ and $\{2, 4, 6, \ldots\}$ can be combined to form the set $\{1, 2, 3, 4, 5, 6, \ldots\}$. All three of these sets have the same cardinal numbers which shows that $2 \times \aleph_0 = \aleph_0$.

27. Answers may vary. Fill in the blank with $\aleph_0$. This is justified by considering the multiplication table for the set N of counting numbers. The set of products in this table can be put into one-to-one correspondence with the set N itself. This shows that $\aleph_0 \cdot \aleph_0 = \aleph_0$.

28. Answers may vary.
$n\{1, 2, 3, 4, 5, 6, \ldots\} =$
$n\{1, 3, 5, \ldots\} + n\{2, 4, 6, \ldots\}$
The cardinal number of the set of all counting numbers is the sum of the cardinal numbers of the set of all odd counting numbers and the set of all even counting numbers, showing a result as in problem 25.

29. Answers may vary.

 a. The next two points are $\dfrac{7}{9}$ and $\dfrac{8}{9}$. (For the next cut, the points would be $\dfrac{1}{27}$ and $\dfrac{2}{27}$.)

 b. $\dfrac{1}{3} + \dfrac{2}{9} + \dfrac{4}{27} + \dfrac{8}{81} + \ldots$; the sum gets closer and closer to 1.

30. Yes. It can be shown that there are as many points in the Cantor set as there are points in the unit interval. (You will find Cantor set on the Internet.)

31. To room 223.   32. Into Room 1.

33. Rooms 1, 3, 5, …, $2n + 1, \ldots$
 (Let $n = 0, 1, 2, \ldots$)

34. Into Room 2.

35. They would move to room 666.

36. a. Set *A* is the set of all cities with a 14%
score, thus *A* = {London, Paris}. Set *B* is
the set of all cities with a 38% score, thus
B = {San Francisco, Toronto}.
   b. Yes. *A* and *B* can be placed into a one-to-
one correspondence.
   c. No. The elements in *A* and *B* are not the
same.
   d. Both sets are finite.

37. The points in *CD* can be put into one-to-one
correspondence with the points in *AB* by
using the construction in the Figure. For any
point *X* on *CD* draw a line through *O* and *X*.
This line cuts *AB* at some point *Y*, so *X* and
Y are corresponding points. Thus, there are
as many points in *CD* as in *AB*.

Chapter 2 Practice Test

1. b, c, and d define sets. Brilliant students (a)
does not define a set.

2. The counting numbers between 2 and 10 are
3, 4, 5, 6, 7, 8, and 9, so the set is
{3, 4, 5, 6, 7, 8, 9}.

3. a. This is the set of vowels in the English
alphabet. In set-builder notation, it is
$\{x \mid x$ is a vowel in the English
alphabet$\}$.
   b. This is the set of even counting numbers
less than 10. In set builder notation, it is
$\{x \mid x$ is an even counting number less
than 10$\}$.

4. The proper subsets are:
$\varnothing, \{\$\}, \{\cent\}, \{\%\}, \{\$, \cent\}, \{\$, \%\}, \{\cent, \%\}$

5. a. Both blanks take the symbol $\in$,
because $A \cup B$ is the set of all elements
that are in *A* or *B*.
   b. The first blank takes the symbol $\in$. The
second blank takes the symbol $\notin$,
because $A \cap B'$ is the set of elements
that are in *A* and not in *B*.
   c. *A'* is the complement of *A*, that is, the
set of elements in *U*, but not in *A*. Thus,
the first blank takes the symbol $\in$, and
the second blank takes the symbol $\notin$.
   d. Recall that *A* – *B* is the set of elements
in *A* with the elements that are also in *B*
removed, that is, it is the set of elements
that are in *A* and not in *B*. Thus, both

blanks take the symbol $\in$.

6. a. *A'*, the complement of *A*, = {King}.
   b. In this problem, $A \cup B = U$, so the
complement of $A \cup B$ is the empty set,
$\varnothing$.
   c. $A \cap B$ is the set of elements that are in
both *A* and *B*, so the answer is {Queen}.
   d. The complement of $A \cap B$ is {Ace,
King, Jack}. Taking this set away from
U gives $U - (A \cap B)' = \{Queen\}$.

7. a. In problem 6c, we found that
$A \cap B = \{Queen\}$. The union of this set
with the set *C* gives
$(A \cap B) \cup C = \{Ace, Queen, Jack\}$.
   b. In problem 6a, we found that
A' = {King}, so that $A' \cup C = \{Ace,$
King, Jack}, which has only the element
King in common with *B*. Thus,
$(A' \cup C) \cap B = \{King\}$.

8. The two diagrams for this problem are
shown:

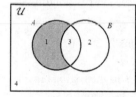 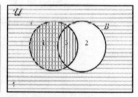

Refer to the diagram on the left. Since
A – *B* is the set *A* with the elements common
to *A* and *B* removed, this corresponds to
region 1, that is, circle *A* with region 3
removed. Shade region 1. Now, refer to the
diagram on the right. $A \cap B'$ is the set of
elements common to *A* and the complement
of *B*. To show this, shade circle *A* one way
and the region outside of *B* another way.
The cross-hatched region corresponds to
$A \cap B'$. The diagrams show that
$A - B = A \cap B'$.

9. In the diagram below, first shade the region outside the circle C. This region corresponds to C'. Then shade darker that portion of the shaded region that lies inside both A and B. The darkly-shaded region corresponds to the set $A \cap B \cap C'$.

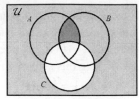

10. a. $A \cup B$ is the set of elements in A or in B, so the corresponding regions are 1, 2, 4, 5, 6, 7. C' is the set of elements in U but not in C, so the corresponding regions are 1, 2, 5, 8. The regions common to $A \cup B$ and C' are 1, 2, 5.

    b. A' is the complement of A, so the corresponding regions are those in U that are not in A; regions 2, 3, 6, 8. Similarly, the regions corresponding to B' are those in U that are not in B; regions 1, 3, 4, 8. The regions common to B' and C; regions 3, 4, correspond to $B' \cap C$. Thus, the regions corres-ponding to $A' \cup (B' \cap C)$ are those in A' or in $B' \cap C$; regions 2, 3, 4, 6, 8.

11. $A \cap B$ corresponds to the regions inside both circles A and B; regions 5, 7. $(A \cap B) \cup C$ corresponds to the regions in $A \cap B$ or in C; regions 3, 4, 5, 6, 7. Similarly, $A \cup C$ corresponds to the regions in A or C; regions 1, 3, 4, 5, 6, 7. $B \cup C$ corresponds to the regions in B or C; regions 2, 3, 4, 5, 6, 7. $(A \cup C) \cap (B \cup C)$ corresponds to the regions common to $A \cup C$ and $B \cup C$; regions 3, 4, 5, 6, 7. This verifies the equation $(A \cap B) \cup C = (A \cup C) \cap (B \cup C)$.

12. $(A \cap B)'$ is the complement of $A \cap B$, so the corresponding regions are those in U and not in $A \cap B$. This gives us regions 1, 2, 3, 4, 6, 8 (all except 5 and 7). A' is the complement of A, so it corresponds to regions 2, 3, 6, 8; B' is the complement of B, so it corresponds to regions 1, 3, 4, 8.

Since $A' \cup B'$ must correspond to the regions in A' or in B', we get regions 1, 2, 3, 4, 6, 8, as before. This verifies that $(A \cap B)' = A' \cup B'$.

13. Part (b) is correct: $(A \cup C) \cap B$

14. None of these. $B \cap C$ is represented by regions 6, 7.

15. a. $A \cup C = \{1, 3, 4, 5, 7, 8\}$, so $n(A \cup C) = 6$.

    b. $B \cap C = \{4, 8\}$, so $n(B \cap C) = 2 \neq 3$.

16. You can use the equation $n(A \cup B) = n(A) + n(B) - n(A \cap B)$ for both parts of this problem.

    a. $n(A) = 25, n(B) = 35, n(A \cap B) = 0$
        Therefore, $n(A \cup B) = 25 + 35 - 0 = 60$

    b. $n(A) = 25, n(B) = 35, n(A \cap B) = 5$
        Therefore,
        $n(A \cup B) = 25 + 35 - 5 = 55$.

17. a. You can use the same equation as in problem 16, but with $n(A) = 15, n(B) = 25, n(A \cup B) = 35$. With these values, you get $35 = 15 + 25 - n(A \cap B)$, or $n(A \cap B) = 15 + 25 - 35 = 5$.

    b. $n(A' \cap B') = 8$ means there are 8 elements outside of both A and B. Since $n(A \cup B) = 35$, $n(U) = 35 + 8 = 43$.

18. The shaded region is the region inside of B and outside of A, so it may be described as $B - A$ or as $B \cap A'$. ($A' \cap B$ is also correct.)

19. First make a Venn diagram showing the various sets. Then start at the end of the list and work back through it.

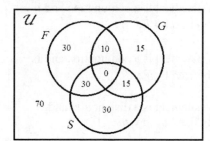

Since no students are taking all three of the courses, put a 0 in the region common to the circles F, G, and S. Because 70 are taking no language, write 70 in the rectangle outside of the three circles. As 15 are taking German and Spanish, write 15 in the region common to G and S, but outside of F. 30 are taking French and Spanish, so write 30 in the region common to F and S, but outside of G. 10 are taking French and German, so write 10 in the region common to F and G but outside of S. 75 are taking Spanish and of these, you have accounted for $0 + 30 + 15 = 45$. (See the diagram.) Hence, you must write 30 in the region inside S but outside both F and G. 40 are taking German, and you have accounted for $0 + 10 + 15 = 25$ of these, so write 15 in the region inside G, but outside F and S. 70 are taking French, and you have accounted for $0 + 10 + 30 = 40$ of these, so write 30 in the region inside F, but outside G and S. This completes the diagram and you can get the answers from it.

a. To get the number of students taking two languages, add the numbers common to two of the circles:
$10 + 15 + 30 = 55$.

b. You can read this directly as the number 30, which is inside S and outside the other two circles.

c. This number is the sum of all the numbers inside S, but outside F:
$15 + 30 = 45$.

20. a. This is the sum of all the numbers in the diagram:
$10 + 5 + 15 + 2 + 4 + 3 + 8 = 47$

b. This is the sum of the numbers that are in A, but not in B: $10 + 2 = 12$

c. This is the sum of the numbers that are in B or C, but not in A: $15 + 3 + 8 = 26$.

d. This is the number that is in both B and C, but not in A, so the answer is 3.

e. This is the sum of all the numbers in the diagram that are not in either B or C, so the answer is 10.

21. The one-to-one correspondence

1	3	5	...	$2n-1$	...
$\updownarrow$	$\updownarrow$	$\updownarrow$		$\downarrow$	
2	4	6	...	$2n$	...

shows that the two sets have the same cardinal number.

22. The one-to-one correspondence

1	2	3	...	n	...
$\updownarrow$	$\updownarrow$	$\updownarrow$		$\updownarrow$	
4	16	36	...	$(2n)^2$	...

shows that the two sets are equivalent.

23. $n\{1, 4, \ldots, n^2, \ldots, 144\} = 12$

24. Since you can set up a one-to-one correspondence between the given set and the set $\{1, 2, \ldots, n, \ldots\}$, the cardinality of the given set is the same as that of the set of counting numbers, $\aleph_0$.

25. The one-to-one correspondence

$\frac{1}{2}$	$\frac{1}{3}$	$\frac{1}{4}$	...	$\frac{1}{n}$	...
$\updownarrow$	$\updownarrow$	$\updownarrow$		$\updownarrow$	
$\frac{1}{2}$	$\frac{1}{4}$	$\frac{1}{6}$	...	$\frac{1}{2n-1}$	...

between the given set and a subset of itself shows that the given set is infinite.

Chapter 3 Logic

Section 3.1 Statements

1. This sentence cannot be classified as either true or false. It is not a statement.

2. This sentence is either true or false, so it is a statement. It is a compound statement with two components: *Lemons are citrus fruits. Oranges are citrus fruits.*

3. This sentence is either true or false, so it is a statement. It is a compound statement with two components: *Jane is taking an English course. She has four themes to write.*

4. This sentence is either true or false, so it is a statement. It has only one component, so it is a simple statement.

5. This sentence is a question and so is not a statement.

6. This sentence is a command and so is not a statement.

7. This sentence is either true or false, so it is a statement. It is a compound statement with the two components: *Students at Ohio State University are required to take a course in history. Students at Ohio State University are required to take a course in economics.*

8. This sentence is either true or false, so it is a statement. It is a compound statement with the two components: *Today is Sunday. Tomorrow is Monday.*

9. This statement is a conjunction and is symbolized by $a \wedge f$.

10. This statement is a conjunction and is symbolized by $r \wedge \sim e$.

11. This statement is a disjunction and is symbolized by $d \vee f$.

12. This statement is a disjunction and is symbolized by $\sim a \vee p$.

13. This statement is a conjunction and is symbolized by $b \wedge p$.

14. This statement is a conjunction and is symbolized by $u \wedge d$.

15. This statement is a disjunction and is symbolized by $a \vee m$.

16. This statement is a conjunction and is symbolized by $\sim d \wedge (t \vee p)$.

17. The conjunction of p and q: $p \wedge q$

18. The conjunction of p and q: $q \wedge \sim p$

19. The negation of the disjunction of p and q: $\sim (p \vee q)$

20. The negation of the conjunction of q and p: $\sim (q \wedge p)$

21. Ricky loves Lucy, or Lucy does not love Ricky.

22. It is not the case that Ricky loves Lucy or Lucy loves Ricky.

23. Ricky loves Lucy but Lucy does not love Ricky.

24. Ricky does not love Lucy and Lucy does not love Ricky.

25. It is not the case that Ricky and Lucy love each other.

26. It is not a long time before the end of the term.

27. Bill's store is not making a good profit.

28. The number ten is not a round number.

29. My dog is not a spaniel.

30. Your cat is a Siamese.

31. I like to work overtime.

32. These are not negations of each other.

33. These two are negations of each other because if either is true, the other is false.

34. These are negations of each other.

35. This statement is negated by replacing the "All" by "Some… not": *Some men are not mortal.*

36. This statement is negated by replacing the "Some" by "No": *No women are engineers.*

37. This statement is negated by replacing the "Some … not" by "All": *All basketball players are 6 feet tall.*

38. This statement is negated by replacing the "Some … are not" by "All": *All things are what they appear to be.*

39. Since this statement is a disjunction, you must negate both components: *It is not the case that he is bald or that he has a 10-in. forehead,* alternatively, *He is not bald, and he does not have a 10-inch forehead.*

40. This statement is negated by replacing the "Nobody" by "Somebody": *Somebody does not like Sara Lee.*

41. This statement is negated by replacing the "Some" by "No": *No circles are round.*

42. Since this statement is a conjunction, you must negate both components: *No men earn less than $8.00 an hour or no men earn more than $50.00 an hour.*

43. This statement is negated by replacing the "Somebody" by "Nobody": *Nobody up there loves me.*

44. This statement is negated by replacing the "Nothing…. and" by "Something other…. or": *Something other than death or taxes is certain.*

45. This statement is negated by replacing the "Everybody" by "Somebody does not": *Somebody does not like to go on a trip.*

46. This statement is negated by replacing the "No one" by "Someone": *Someone can sue us under this coverage.*

47. This statement is negated by replacing the "All…" by "Some…. not": *Some persons occupying your covered auto are not insured.*

48. This statement is negated by replacing the "None" by "Some": *Some of your contributions are deductible.*

49. This statement is negated by replacing the "Some… not" by "All": *All expenses are subject to the 2% limit.*

50. Statement c. "Not all are p" means the same as "Some are not p."

51. Statement d. Conditions a, b, and c do not make the chairperson mistaken; only statement d does that.

52. $(m \lor d) \land e$

53. $(d \land p) \lor r$

54. $(c \lor n) \land e$

55. $r \land (t \lor g)$

56. Answers may vary.
    a. Today is not Friday or tomorrow is not Saturday.
    b. Today is not Friday or tomorrow is Saturday.
    c. Today is not Friday and tomorrow is not Saturday.

57. Answers may vary.
    a. The diagram is neither a square nor a rectangle. (The diagram is not a square and is not a rectangle.)
    b. The diagram is a square or not a rectangle.
    c. The diagram is a square and a rectangle.

58. Answers may vary. If Sentence (1) is true, then sentence (2) is true. But if sentence (2) is true, then sentence (1) has to be false, a contradiction!

59. Answers may vary. Sentence (1) is true, sentence (2) is false. If we assume that sentence (3) is true, there will be two sentences, sentence (1) and sentence (3), that are true, and thus, sentence (3) is false! (Consider if sentence (3) is false as we have just determined, then there IS only one statement that is true (sentence (1)), thus

making sentence (3) true. Paradox!)

60. Answers may vary. No. A statement is a declarative sentence that can be classified as true or false but not both simultaneously. (This sentence is simply the negation of "This sentence is false." From the discussion in the text, we see that if we assume the sentence "This sentence is false" is true, then it is false, and if we assume that it is false, then it is true. This is an example of a paradox.)

61. False   62. False   63. False

64. False   65. True   66. True

67. False   68. True

69. a. (Hispanics and females and not high school graduates) or (white and females and not high school graduates): $16,500
    b. Males and Hispanics and not high school graduates: $22,200

70. a. Females and Asian and Advanced Degrees: $67,200
    b. Asian

Section 3.2 Truth Tables: A Problem-Solving Tool

1. To write the disjunction, use the word "or": *Today is Friday or Monday.*

2. To write the conjunction, use the word "and": *Today is Friday and Monday.*

3. Here, you only have to insert the word "not": *Today is not Friday.*

4. The statement in problem 2 is always false because today cannot both be Friday and Monday.

5. To write the disjunction, use the word "or": *He is a gentleman or a scholar.*

6. Here, you only have to insert the word "not": *He is not a gentleman.*

7. To write the conjunction, use the word "and": *He is a gentleman and a*

scholar.

8. This statement is the negation of the disjunction of the given statements: $\sim (g \vee s)$

9. This statement is the conjunction of the given statements: $g \wedge s$

10. This statement is the conjunction of the negation of the given statements: $\sim g \wedge \sim s$

11. a. $p \wedge q$ b. $p \vee q$
    c. The statement in (a) is false, the one in (b) is true.

12. This statement is the conjunction of the statement p and the negation of statement q: $p \wedge \sim q$

13. This is the conjunction of the negation of statement q and the statement p: $\sim q \wedge p$, or equivalently $\sim (q \vee \sim p)$

14. This is the negation of the conjunction of the negation of statement p and the statement q: $\sim (\sim p \wedge q)$

15. This is the disjunction of the two given statements: $p \vee q$

16. With the given assumptions, the statements in problems 14 and 15 are both true.

17. $p \vee q$. This is the disjunction of p and q. Since p is true, the disjunction is true.

18. $p \vee \sim q$. This is the disjunction of p and not q. Since p and $\sim q$ are true, the disjunction is true.

19. $\sim p \wedge \sim q$. This is the conjunction of (not p) and (not q). Since (not p) is false, the conjunction is false.

20. $(p \vee q) \wedge \sim (p \wedge q)$. This is the conjunction of p or q and the negation of p and q. Since $p \vee q$ is true and the negation of $p \wedge q$ is true, the conjunction is true.

21. $\sim q \wedge \sim p$. This is the conjunction of (not q) and (not p). Since (not p) is false, the conjunction is false.

22. $g \vee j$. This is the disjunction of g and j. Since j is true, the disjunction is true.

23. $g \vee \sim j$. This is the disjunction of g and $\sim j$. Since g and $\sim j$ are both false, the disjunction is false.

24. $\sim g \wedge \sim j$. This is the conjunction of (not g) and (not j). Since (not j) is false, the conjunction is false.

25. $(g \vee j) \wedge \sim (g \wedge j)$. This is the conjunction of $g \vee j$ and $\sim (g \wedge j)$. Since j is true, the disjunction $g \vee j$ is true. Since g is false, the conjunction $g \wedge j$ is false, so that $\sim (g \wedge j)$ is true. Thus, the statement $(g \vee j) \wedge \sim (g \wedge j)$ is true.

26. $\sim g \wedge \sim j$. This is the conjunction of (not g) and (not j). Since (not j) is false, the conjunction is false.

27.

1	2	3	4
p	q	$\sim q$	$p \vee \sim q$
T	T	F	T
T	F	T	T
F	T	F	F
F	F	T	T

To construct the table, first fill in Columns 1 and 2: under p, 2 T's, 2 F's and under q, $T\,F\,T\,F$. This gives all the combinations of truth values for p and q. Next fill in Column 3, the negation of q: $F\,T\,F\,T$. Then fill in Column 4, the disjunction of p and $\sim q$. This combines Columns 1 and 3. Since the disjunction is false only when both components are false, write F in the third line and T's in the other lines. This completes the table and shows that $T\,T\,F\,T$ are the truth values for $p \vee \sim q$.

28.

1	2	3	4
p	q	$p \vee q$	$\sim (p \vee q)$
T	T	T	F
T	F	T	F
F	T	T	F
F	F	F	T

To construct the table, first fill in Columns 1 and 2: under p, 2 T's, 2 F's and under q, $T\,F\,T\,F$. This gives all the combinations of truth values for p and q. Next fill in Column 3, $p \vee q$: $T\,T\,T\,F$. Then fill in Column 4, the negation of $p \vee q$. This completes the table and shows that $F\,F\,F\,T$ are the truth values for $\sim (p \vee q)$.

29.

1	2	3	4
p	q	$\sim p$	$\sim p \wedge q$
T	T	F	F
T	F	F	F
F	T	T	T
F	F	T	F

First fill in Columns 1 and 2 just as in problem 27. Then fill in Column 3, the negation of p, $F\,F\,T\,T$. Then do Column 4, the conjunction of $\sim p$ and q. This combines Columns 3 and 2. Since the conjunction is true only when both components are true, write T in the third line and F's in the other lines. This completes the table and shows that $F\,F\,T\,F$ are the truth values for $\sim p \wedge q$.

30.

1	2	3	4	5
p	q	$\sim p$	$\sim q$	$\sim p \vee \sim q$
T	T	F	F	F
T	F	F	T	T
F	T	T	F	T
F	F	T	T	T

First fill in Columns 1 and 2 just as in problem 28. Then fill in Column 3, the negation of p, $F\,F\,T\,T$. Then do Column 4, the negation of q, $F\,T\,F\,T$. Then do Column 5, the disjunction of $\sim p$ and $\sim q$. This combines Columns 3 and 4. Since the disjunction is false only when both components are false, write F in the first line and T's in the other lines. This completes the table and shows that $F\,T\,T\,T$ are the truth values for $\sim p \vee \sim q$.

31.

1	2	3	4	5
p	q	$\sim q$	$p \vee \sim q$	$\sim(p \vee \sim q)$
T	T	F	T	F
T	F	T	T	F
F	T	F	F	T
F	F	T	T	F

First fill in Columns 1 and 2 just as in problem 27. Then do Column 3, the negation of q: $F\,T\,F\,T$. Next, do Column 4, the disjunction of p and $\sim q$ (Columns 1 and 3). Since the disjunction is false only when both components are false, write F in the third row, where p and q are both F's and write T's in the remaining rows. Column 5 is the negation of Column 4: $F\,F\,T\,F$ are the truth values for

$$\sim(p \vee \sim q).$$

32.

1	2	3	4	5	6
p	q	$\sim p$	$\sim q$	$\sim p \vee \sim q$	$\sim(5)$
T	T	F	F	F	T
T	F	F	T	T	F
F	T	T	F	T	F
F	F	T	T	T	F

First fill in Columns 1 and 2 just as in problem 28. Then fill in Column 3, the negation of p, $F\,F\,T\,T$. Then do Column 4, the negation of q, $F\,T\,F\,T$. Then do Column 5, the disjunction of ~p and ~q. This combines Columns 3 and 4. Since the disjunction is false only when both components are false, write F in the first line and T's in the other lines. Finally, fill in Column 6, which is the negation of Column 5. This completes the table and shows that $T\,F\,F\,F$ are the truth values for

$$\sim(\sim p \vee \sim q).$$

33.

1	2	3	4	5	6
p	q	$\sim p$	$\sim q$	$\sim p \wedge \sim q$	$\sim(\sim p \wedge \sim q)$
T	T	F	F	F	T
T	F	F	T	F	T
F	T	T	F	F	T
F	F	T	T	T	F

First fill in Columns 1 and 2 as in problem 27. Then do Column 3, the negation of p: $F\,F\,T\,T$; and Column 4, the negation of q: $F\,T\,F\,T$. Next, do Column 5, the conjunction of ~p and ~q. Since the conjunction is true only when both components are true, write T in the bottom row, where ~p and ~q are both T's, and write F's in the remaining rows. Column 6 calls for the negation of Column 5, so write T where Column 5 has F, and F where Column 5 has T. The final result gives $T\,T\,T\,F$ for the truth values of $\sim(\sim p \wedge \sim q)$.

34.

1	2	3	4	5	6
p	q	$p \vee q$	$p \wedge q$	~ 4	$3 \wedge 5$
T	T	T	T	F	F
T	F	T	F	T	T
F	T	T	F	T	T
F	F	F	F	T	F

First fill in Columns 1 and 2 just as in problem 28. Next fill in Column 3, $p \vee q : T\,T\,T\,F$. Then fill in Column 4, $p \wedge q : T\,T\,T\,F$. For This completes the table and shows that $F\,F\,F\,T$ are the truth values for $\sim(p \vee q)$.

Then fill in Column 5, the negation of $p \wedge q$, $F\,T\,T\,T$. Then do Column 6, the conjuction of $p \vee q$ and $p \wedge q$. This combines Columns 3 and 5. Since the conjunction is true only when both components are true, write T in the second and third line and F's in the first and last lines. This completes the table and shows that $F\,T\,T\,F$ are the truth values for

$$(p \vee q) \wedge \sim(p \wedge q).$$

35.

1	2	3	4	5	6
p	q	$p \wedge q$	$\sim p$	$\sim p \wedge q$	$3 \vee 5$
T	T	T	F	F	T
T	F	F	F	F	F
F	T	F	T	T	T
F	F	F	T	F	F

Fill in Columns 1 and 2 as in problem 27. Then do Column 3, the conjunction of p and q. The conjunction is true only when both components are true, so write T in the first row and F in the other rows. Next, do Column 4, which calls for the negation of p: $F\,F\,T\,T$; and then do Column 5, the conjunction of $\sim p$ and q. This takes a T in the third row, where both Columns 4 and 2 have Ts, and takes Fs in the other rows. Finally, Column 6, the disjunction of Columns 3 and 5, takes T in the rows where Column 3 or 5 is T, and F where both Columns 3 and 5 are Fs. The required truth values are $T\,F\,T\,F$.

36.

1	2	3	4	5	6	7
p	q	$\sim p$	$\sim q$	$p \wedge 4$	$3 \wedge q$	$5 \wedge 6$
T	T	F	F	F	F	F
T	F	F	T	T	F	F
F	T	T	F	F	T	F
F	F	T	T	F	F	F

First fill in Columns 1 and 2 just as in problem 28. Then fill in Column 3, the negation of p, $F\,F\,T\,T$. Then do Column 4, the negation of q, $F\,T\,F\,T$. Then do Column 5, the conjunction of p and ~q. This combines Columns 1 and 4. Since the conjunction is true only when both components are true, write T in the second line and Fs in the other lines. Then do Column 5, the conjunction of p and ~q. This combines Columns 5 and 6. Since the conjunction is true only when both components are true, write Fs in all the lines. This completes the table and shows that $F\,F\,F\,F$ are the truth values for $(p \wedge \sim q) \wedge (\sim p \wedge q)$.

37.

1	2	3	4	5
p	q	r	$q \vee r$	$p \wedge (q \vee r)$
T	T	T	T	T
T	T	F	T	T
T	F	T	T	T
T	F	F	F	F
F	T	T	T	F
F	T	F	T	F
F	F	T	T	F
F	F	F	F	F

First, write four Ts and then four Fs in Column 1; then two Ts, two Fs, two Ts, two Fs in Column 2; in Column 3, write alternately T and F. This gives all the possible combinations of Ts and Fs for p, q, and r. Next, do Column 4, the disjunction of Columns 2 and 3. The disjunction is false only when both components are false, so write F in the 4th and 8th rows, where Columns 2 and 3 are both Fs, and write T in the other rows. Column 5 calls for the conjunction of Columns 1 and 4, so write T in the first three rows, where Columns 1 and 4 are both Ts, and write F in the remaining rows. This completes the table.

38.

1	2	3	4	5
p	q	r	$q \wedge r$	$p \vee (q \wedge r)$
T	T	T	T	T
T	T	F	F	T
T	F	T	F	T
T	F	F	F	T
F	T	T	T	T
F	T	F	F	F
F	F	T	F	F
F	F	F	F	F

First, write four Ts and then four Fs in Column 1; then two Ts, two Fs, two Ts, two Fs in Column 2; in Column 3, write alternately T and F. This gives all the possible combinations of Ts and Fs for p, q, and r. Next, do Column 4, the conjunction of Columns 2 and 3. The conjunction is true only when both components are true, so write T in the 1st and 5th rows, where Columns 2 and 3 are both Ts, and write F in the other rows. Column 5 calls for the disjunction of Columns 1 and 4, so write F in the last three rows, where

Columns 1 and 4 are both *F*'s, and write *T* in the remaining rows. This completes the table.

First write four *T*'s and then four *F*'s in Column 1; then, two *T*'s, two *F*'s, two *T*'s, two *F*'s in Column 2; in Column 3, write *T* and *F* alternately. This gives all the possible combinations of *T*'s and *F*'s for *p*, *q*, and *r*. Next, do Column 4, by combining Columns 1 and 2 to form the disjunction of *p* and *q*. Thus, write *F* in the last two rows, where *p* and *q* are both *F*'s, and write *T*'s in the remaining rows. Then do Column 5, the negation of *q*: *F F T T F F T T*. Column 6 is the conjunction of *r* and ~*q*, Columns 3 and 5, so write *T* in the third and seventh rows, where *r* and ~*q* are both *T*, and write *F* in the other rows. Finally, Column 7 is the disjunction of Columns 4 and 6, so write *F* in the last row, where Columns 4 and 6 are both *F*, and write *T* in the remaining rows. This completes the table.

39.

1	2	3	4	5	6	7
p	*q*	*r*	$p \vee q$	~*q*	$r \wedge \sim q$	$4 \vee 6$
T	*T*	*T*	*T*	*F*	*F*	*T*
T	*T*	*F*	*T*	*F*	*F*	*T*
T	*F*	*T*	*T*	*T*	*T*	*T*
T	*F*	*F*	*T*	*T*	*F*	*T*
F	*T*	*T*	*T*	*F*	*F*	*T*
F	*T*	*F*	*T*	*F*	*F*	*T*
F	*F*	*T*	*F*	*T*	*T*	*T*
F	*F*	*F*	*F*	*T*	*F*	*F*

40.

1	2	3	4	5	6	7	8	9	10	11
p	*q*	*r*	*s*	~*r*	~*s*	$p \wedge q$	$q \wedge 5$	$r \wedge 6$	$7 \vee 8$	$10 \vee 9$
T	*T*	*T*	*T*	*F*	*F*	*T*	*F*	*F*	*T*	*T*
T	*T*	*T*	*F*	*F*	*T*	*T*	*F*	*T*	*T*	*T*
T	*T*	*F*	*T*	*T*	*F*	*T*	*T*	*F*	*T*	*T*
T	*T*	*F*	*F*	*T*	*T*	*T*	*T*	*F*	*T*	*T*
T	*F*	*T*	*T*	*F*	*F*	*F*	*F*	*F*	*F*	*F*
T	*F*	*T*	*F*	*F*	*T*	*F*	*F*	*T*	*F*	*T*
T	*F*	*F*	*T*	*T*	*F*	*F*	*F*	*F*	*F*	*F*
T	*F*	*F*	*F*	*T*	*T*	*F*	*F*	*F*	*F*	*F*
F	*T*	*T*	*T*	*F*	*F*	*F*	*F*	*F*	*F*	*F*
F	*T*	*T*	*F*	*F*	*T*	*F*	*F*	*T*	*F*	*T*
F	*T*	*F*	*T*	*T*	*F*	*F*	*T*	*F*	*T*	*T*
F	*T*	*F*	*F*	*T*	*T*	*F*	*T*	*F*	*T*	*T*
F	*F*	*T*	*T*	*F*	*F*	*F*	*F*	*F*	*F*	*F*
F	*F*	*T*	*F*	*F*	*T*	*F*	*F*	*T*	*F*	*T*
F	*F*	*F*	*T*	*T*	*F*	*F*	*F*	*F*	*F*	*F*
F	*F*	*F*	*F*	*T*	*T*	*F*	*F*	*F*	*F*	*F*

First, write eight *T*'s and then eight *F*'s in Column 1; then four *T*'s, four *F*'s, four *T*'s, four *F*'s in Column 2; then two *T*'s, two *F*'s, two *T*'s, two *F*'s in Column 3; in Column 4, write alternately *T* and *F*. This gives all the possible combinations of *T*'s and *F*'s for *p*, *q*, *r*, and *s*. Next, do Column 5, the negation of *r*, *F F T T F F T T F F T T F F T T*. Next, do Column 6, the negation of *s*, *F T F T F T F T F T F T F T F T*. Column 7 is the conjunction of Columns 1 and 2. The conjunction is true only when both components are true, so write *T* in the first four rows, where Columns 1 and 2 are both *T*'s, and write *F* in the other rows. Column 8 is the conjunction of Columns 2 and 5. The conjunction is true only when both components are true, so write *T* in the 3rd, 4th, 11th, and 12th rows, where Columns 2 and 5 are both *T*'s, and write *F* in the other rows. Column 9 is the conjunction of Columns 3 and 6. The conjunction is true only when both components are true, so write *T* in the 2nd, 6th, 10th, and 14th rows, where Columns 3 and 6 are both *T*'s, and write *F* in the other rows. Column 10 is the disjunction of Columns 7 and 8. The disjunction is false only when both components are false, so write F in the 5th through 10th and 13th through 14th rows, where Columns 7 and 6 are both F's, and write T in the other rows. Column 11 is the disjunction of Columns 10 and 9. The disjunction is false only when both components are false, so write F in the 5th, 7th through 9th, 13th, 15th through 16th rows, where Columns 10 and 9 are both F's, and write T in the other rows. This completes the table.

41. Let j be "I have a job." and let h be "I hate it."
   a. Since this is the conjunction of the two statements, it will be true when j and h are both true.
   b. This will be false if either j or h is false.
   c. This is the disjunction of the two statements, so it will be true if either j or h is true.
   d. This will be false only if both j and h are false.

42. a. Answers will vary.
   b. Since this is the conjunction of the negation of the two statements, it will be true when u and p are both false.
   c. This is the disjunction of the two statements, so it will be true if either u or p is true.
   d. This is the disjunction of the two statements, so it will be false when both u and p are false.

43.

1	2	3	4	5	6	7	8
p	q	r	$q \wedge r$	$1 \vee 4$	$p \vee q$	$p \vee r$	$6 \wedge 7$
T	T	T	T	T	T	T	T
T	T	F	F	T	T	T	T
T	F	T	F	T	T	T	T
T	F	F	F	T	T	T	T
F	T	T	T	T	T	T	T
F	T	F	F	F	T	F	F
F	F	T	F	F	F	T	F
F	F	F	F	F	F	F	F

Columns 5 and 8 of the above truth table show that the two statements have the same truth values, so they are equivalent.

44.

1	2	3	4	5	6	7	8
p	q	r	$q \vee r$	$p \wedge 4$	$p \wedge q$	$p \wedge r$	$6 \vee 7$
T	T	T	T	T	T	T	T
T	T	F	T	T	T	F	T
T	F	T	T	T	F	T	T
T	F	F	F	F	F	F	F
F	T	T	T	F	F	F	F
F	T	F	T	F	F	F	F
F	F	T	T	F	F	F	F
F	F	F	F	F	F	F	F

Columns 5 and 8 are identical. Thus, the two statements are equivalent.

45.

1	2	3	4	5	6	7
p	q	$p \vee q$	$\sim (3)$	$\sim p$	$\sim q$	$5 \wedge 6$
T	T	T	F	F	F	F
T	F	T	F	F	T	F
F	T	T	F	T	F	F
F	F	F	T	T	T	T

Columns 4 and 7 of the table show that the two statements have the same truth values, so they are equivalent.

46.

1	2	3	4	5	6	7
p	q	$\sim p$	$\sim q$	$p \wedge q$	~ 5	$3 \vee 4$
T	T	F	F	T	F	F
T	F	F	T	F	T	T
F	T	T	F	F	T	T
F	F	T	T	F	T	T

Columns 6 and 7 are identical. Thus, the two statements are equivalent.

47.

1	2	3	5	6	7
p	q	$p \wedge q$	$\sim p$	$3 \vee 5$	$q \vee \sim p$
T	T	T	F	T	T
T	F	F	F	F	F
F	T	F	T	T	T
F	F	F	T	T	T

Columns 5 and 6 of the table show that the two statements have the same truth values, so they are equivalent.

48.

1	2	3	4	5	6	7	8	9	10
p	q	$\sim p$	$\sim q$	$p \vee q$	$3 \vee 4$	$5 \wedge 6$	$1 \wedge 4$	$3 \wedge 2$	$8 \vee 9$
T	T	F	F	T	F	F	F	F	F
T	F	F	T	T	T	T	T	F	T
F	T	T	F	T	T	T	F	T	T
F	F	T	T	F	T	F	F	F	F

Since columns 7 and 10 are identical, the statement is true.

49. a. $p \wedge q$ is true only when p and q are both true. Thus, the truth values are $T\,F\,F\,F$ as in the table. $p \wedge \sim q$ is true only when p and $\sim q$ are both true, that is, when p is true and q is false. The truth values are $F\,T\,F\,F$ as in the table. $\sim p \wedge q$ is true only when p is false and q is true, so that the truth values are $F\,F\,T\,F$ as in the table. $\sim p \wedge \sim q$ is true only when p and q are both false, so the truth values are $F\,F\,F\,T$ as in the table.

b. The disjunction of two statements is true whenever at least one of the statements is true. Since $p \wedge q$ is true only in the first row and $\sim p \wedge \sim q$ is true only in the last row, the disjunction of these two has the truth values $T\,F\,F\,T$ as stated.

c. A statement with the truth values $F\,T\,T\,F$ is $\left(p \wedge \sim q\right) \vee \left(\sim p \wedge q\right)$. Similarly,

$$\left(p \wedge \sim q\right) \vee \left(\sim p \wedge q\right) \vee \left(\sim p \wedge \sim q\right)$$

has truth values $F\,T\,T\,T$. Since the given table has one F and three Ts, its negation will have one T and three Fs and will be a basic conjunction. Therefore a much simpler statement with truth values $F\,T\,T\,T$ is $\sim \left(p \wedge q\right)$, the negation of $p \wedge q$, as can be seen from the table.

50. It would be true when p is true, q is false, and r is true, or when p, q, r are all false. It would be false in all other cases.

51. None of the applicants is eligible. Statement (*d*) is false for Joe, (*t*) is false for Mary and (*m*) is false for Ellen.

52. None of the three qualifies. Mr. Perez and Ms. Jefferson both do not have enough combined income, and Tran Quang does not have assets of at least $10,000.

53. 7 is greater than or equal to 5

54. 8 is less than or equal to 9.

55. 0 is less than or equal to 3.

56. $\dfrac{1}{3}$ is less than 1.   **57.** $\dfrac{1}{2}$ is greater than $\dfrac{1}{8}$.

58. a. I will go fishing and the sun is shining.
b. The sun is not shining.
c. I will go fishing or the sun is shining.

59. I will not go fishing or the sun is not shining. This would be true if either or both of the statements: "I will not go fishing." and "The sun is not shining." is (are) true.

60. 1. $\left(e \wedge g\right) \vee a$ **2.** h **3.** $\left(c \vee n\right) \vee \sim t$

61. $\left[\left(e \wedge g\right) \vee a\right] \wedge h \wedge \left(c \vee n \vee \sim t\right)$

62. $a \wedge h \wedge n, \ a \wedge h \wedge \sim t$

63. Mr. Baker is the carpenter.

Section 3.3 The Conditional and the Biconditional

1.

1	2	3	4	5	6
p	q	$\sim q$	$\sim p$	$\sim q \to \sim p$	$p \to q$
T	T	F	F	T	T
T	F	T	F	F	F
F	T	F	T	T	T
F	F	T	T	T	T

Columns 5 and 6 are identical, so $\sim q \to \sim p$ is equivalent to $p \to q$.

2.

1	2	3	4	5	6	7
p	q	$\sim q$	$p \rightarrow 3$	$p \wedge q$	~ 5	$4 \Leftrightarrow 6$
T	T	F	F	T	F	T
T	F	T	T	F	T	T
F	T	F	T	F	T	T
F	F	T	T	F	T	T

Since columns 4 and 6 are identical,

$p \rightarrow \sim q$ and $\sim(p \vee q)$ are equivalent.

3.

1	2	3	4	5
p	q	$\sim p$	$\sim p \rightarrow q$	$p \vee q$
T	T	F	T	T
T	F	F	T	T
F	T	T	T	T
F	F	T	F	F

Since columns 4 and 5 are identical,

$\sim p \rightarrow q$ and $p \vee q$ are equivalent.

4. This is a statement of the form $p \rightarrow q$, with p being "$2 + 2 = 22$," and q being "$22 = 4$." Since p is false and q is false, the conditional has the truth value *True*.

5. This is a statement of the form $p \rightarrow q$, with p being "$2 + 2 = 4$," and q being "$8 = 5$." Since p is true and q is false, the conditional has the truth value *False*.

6. This is a statement of the form $p \rightarrow q$, with p being "$2 + 2 = 22$," and q being "$8 = 4 + 4$." Since p is false and q is true, the conditional has the truth value *True*.

7. This is a statement of the form $p \rightarrow q$, with p being "$2 + 2 = 22$," and q being "$4 = 26$." Since p is false, the conditional has the truth value *True*.

8. Since the antecedent, $2 + 2 = 4$, is true, the replacement for x must be a number that makes $x - 2 = 5$ true, so $x = 7$.

9. Since the antecedent, $2 + 2 = 22$, is false, x may be any number.

10. Since the consequent, $3 + 2 = 5$, is true, x may be any number.

11. Since the consequent, $2 + 2 = 32$, is false, x may be any number for which the antecedent is false, that is, any number except 4.

12. a. The statement $p \rightarrow q$ is false when p is true and q is false.

     b. The statement $\sim o \rightarrow (\sim n \vee b)$ is false when o is false, n is true and b is false.

13. a. $\sim o$ is true when o is false.

     b. $\sim n \vee b$ is false when n is true and b is false.

     c. The statement $\sim o \rightarrow (\sim n \vee b)$ is false when o is false, n is true and b is false.

14.

1	2	3	4	5
p	q	$p \rightarrow q$	$3 \rightarrow p$	$4 \rightarrow q$
T	T	T	T	T
T	F	F	T	F
F	T	T	F	T
F	F	T	F	T

The first two columns are filled out as usual to get all the possible combinations of p and q. The conditional, column 3, has F in the row where the antecedent p is true and the consequent q is false. The other rows are all T's. Column 4 has T's in the rows where p is true and has F's in the remaining rows. Column 5 has F in the row where column 4 has T and column 2 has F, and has T's in the remaining rows.

15.

1	2	3	4	5	6
p	q	r	$p \rightarrow q$	$p \vee r$	$4 \leftrightarrow 5$
T	T	T	T	T	T
T	T	F	T	T	T
T	F	T	F	T	F
T	F	F	F	T	F
F	T	T	T	T	T
F	T	F	T	F	F
F	F	T	T	T	T
F	F	F	T	F	F

The first three columns are filled out as usual to get all the possible combinations of p, q and r. The conditional, column 4, has F's in the rows where the antecedent p is true and the consequent q is false. The other rows are all T's. Column 5 has T's in the rows where either *p* or *r* is true and has *F*'s in the remaining rows. Column 6 has *T*'s in the rows where columns 4 and 5 both have *T*'s and has *F*'s in the remaining rows.

16.

1	2	3	4	5	6
p	*q*	~ *q*	*p* → *q*	*p* → ~ *q*	4 ↔ 5
T	*T*	*F*	*T*	*F*	*F*
T	*F*	*T*	*F*	*T*	*F*
F	*T*	*F*	*T*	*T*	*T*
F	*F*	*T*	*T*	*T*	*T*

The first two columns are filled out as usual to get all the possible combinations of *p* and *q*. Column 3 is the negation of *q*. The conditional, column 4, has *F* in the row where the antecedent *p* is true and the consequent *q* is false. The other rows are all *T*'s. Column 5, the conjunction of 1 and 3 has *T* in the row where p is true and ~q is true and has *F*'s in the other rows. Column 6 has *T*'s in the rows where both column 4 and 5 are true, the other rows are *F*.

17.

1	2	3	4	5
p	*q*	*r*	*q* ∧ *r*	*p* → (*q* ∧ *r*)
T	*T*	*T*	*T*	*T*
T	*T*	*F*	*F*	*F*
T	*F*	*T*	*F*	*F*
T	*F*	*F*	*F*	*F*
F	*T*	*T*	*T*	*T*
F	*T*	*F*	*F*	*T*
F	*F*	*T*	*F*	*T*
F	*F*	*F*	*F*	*T*

The first three columns are filled out as usual to get all the possible combinations of *p*, *q* and *r*. Column 4 is the conjunction of columns 2 and 3, so has *T*'s only in the rows where *q* and *r* are both *T*. Column 5, the conditional, has *F* in the rows where the antecedent *p* is true and the consequent *q* ∧ *r* is false (second, third and fourth rows). The remaining entries are *T*'s.

18.

1	2	3	4	5	6
p	*q*	*r*	*p* → *q*	*p* → *r*	4 ∧ 5
T	*T*	*T*	*T*	*T*	*T*
T	*T*	*F*	*T*	*F*	*F*
T	*F*	*T*	*F*	*T*	*F*
T	*F*	*F*	*F*	*F*	*F*
F	*T*	*T*	*T*	*T*	*T*
F	*T*	*F*	*T*	*T*	*T*
F	*F*	*T*	*T*	*T*	*T*
F	*F*	*F*	*T*	*T*	*T*

The first three columns are filled out as usual to get all the possible combinations of *p*, *q* and *r*. The conditional, column 4, has *F*'s in the rows where the antecedent *p* is true and the consequent *q* is false. The other rows are all *T*'s. The conditional, column 5, has *F*'s in the rows where the antecedent *p* is true and the consequent *r* is false. The other rows are all *T*'s. Column 6 has *T*'s in the rows where columns 4 and 5 both have *T*'s and has *F*'s in the remaining rows.

19. The final columns in the tables in problems 17 and 18 are identical, so the two statements are equivalent.

20. The antecedent is "It is a poodle," and the consequent is "I will adopt it." Thus, the symbolic form is *q* → *p* .

21. The antecedent is "I will adopt it," and the consequent is "It is a poodle." Thus, the symbolic form is *p* → *q* .

22. This is a biconditional. Thus, the symbolic form is *q* ↔ *p* .

23. The antecedent is "It is not a poodle," and the consequent is "I will not adopt it." Hence, the symbolic form is ~ *q* → ~ *p* .

24. The antecedent is "I will not adopt it," and the consequent is "It is not a poodle." Hence, the symbolic form is ~ *p* → ~ *q* .

25. The antecedent is "It is a poodle," and the consequent is "I will not adopt it." Thus, the symbolic form is *q* → ~ *p* .

26. The antecedent is "You are out of Schlitz," and the consequent is "You are out of beer." Thus, the symbolic form is $\sim s \rightarrow \sim b$.

27. The antecedent is "You are out of beer," and the consequent is "You are out of Schlitz." Thus, the symbolic form is $\sim b \rightarrow \sim s$.

28. This is a biconditional with b "You have beer" and s "You have Schlitz." Thus, the symbolic form is $b \leftrightarrow s$.

29. $\sim a \vee b$ The temperature is not above $80°$, or I would go to the beach.

30. $\sim h \vee r$ Mida is not home by 5 or dinner would be ready by 6.

31. $\sim a \vee g$ Eva does not have a day off, or she would go to the beach.

32. Let p be "You work," and q be "You have to pay taxes." Then $\sim p \vee q$ becomes "You do not work, or you have to pay taxes."

33. Let p be "You got the time," and q be "We got the beer." Then $\sim p \vee q$ becomes "You do not have the time, or we've got the beer."

34. Let p be "You find a better one," and q be "You buy it." Then $\sim p \vee q$ becomes "You do not find a better one, or you buy it."

35. If it is a dog, then it is a mammal.

36. If it is a cat, then it is a feline.

37. If it is a man, then it is created equal. (The equal refers to equal to each other, not to $10, not to a dog, etc.)

38. If it is a prime number greater than 2, then it is an odd number.

39. If it is a rectangle with perpendicular diagonals, then it is a square.

40.

1	2	3	4	5	6	7
p	q	$\sim p$	$\sim q$	$3 \vee q$	~ 5	$p \wedge 4$
T	T	F	F	T	F	F
T	F	F	T	F	T	T
F	T	T	F	T	F	F
F	F	T	T	T	F	F

Columns 6 and 7 are identical. Thus, the two statements are equivalent.

41.

1	2	3	4	5	6
p	q	$p \rightarrow q$	$\sim (3)$	$\sim q$	$p \wedge \sim q$
T	T	T	F	F	F
T	F	F	T	T	T
F	T	T	F	F	F
F	F	T	F	T	F

Since columns 4 and 6 are identical, $\sim (p \rightarrow q)$ and $p \wedge \sim q$ are equivalent.

42. You earn a lot of money, but you do not pay heavy taxes.

43. Johnny does not play quarterback, and his team does not lose.

44. Alice passes the test, but does not get the job.

45. I kiss you once, but I do not kiss you again.

46. Saturday is a hot day and I will not go to the beach.

47. Evel Knievel is careless, but he will not lose his life.

48. The truth table for $p \rightarrow q$ is T F T T.

49. If Johnny plays quarterback, then his team wins.

50. If Alice does not fail the test, then she gets the job.

51. If Joe had not had an accident, then he would be able to get car insurance.

52. a. Definition 1 shows truth values TFFF, which is the truth table for $p \wedge q$.
    b. Definition 2 shows truth values TFFT, which is the truth table for $p \leftrightarrow q$.
    c. Definition 3 shows truth values TFTF, which is the truth table for q.

53. The antecedent "You eat the spinach and the liver" is false, so the conditional is true. She has not broken her original promise.

54. The antecedent "You do not eat the spinach and the liver" is true but "You may not go out to play" is false, so the conditional is false. She has broken her original promise.

55. Let p be: "Mary is in Tampa," and q be: "Mary is in Florida." The given statement is $p \rightarrow q$, which is equivalent to $\sim p \vee q$. Statement (d) is symbolized by $\sim q \rightarrow \sim p$ which is equivalent to $\sim(\sim q) \vee \sim p$, that is, $q \vee \sim p$. Since $q \vee \sim p$ is equivalent to $\sim p \vee q$, statement (d) is logically equivalent to the given statement.

56. Let p be: "You want to buy organic food," and q be: "You have to let your grocer know." The given statement is $p \rightarrow q$, which is equivalent to $\sim p \vee q$. Statement (b) is symbolized by $\sim q \rightarrow \sim p$ which is equivalent to $\sim(\sim q) \vee \sim p$, that is, $q \vee \sim p$. Since $q \vee \sim p$ is equivalent to $\sim p \vee q$, statement (b) is logically equivalent to the given statement.

57. Let p be: "You studied hard," and q be: "You passed the course." The given statement is $p \rightarrow q$. The negation of $p \rightarrow q$ (See problem 17) is $p \wedge \sim q$, which is the symbolic form of statement (d).

58. Let p be: "It rains," and q be: "We will go to the beach." The given statement is $p \rightarrow \sim q$. The negation of $p \rightarrow \sim q$ is $p \wedge q$, which is the symbolic form of statement (d).

59. Answers may vary. Let p be: "You stop here," and q be: "Your pain will stop." Then the given statement is $p \rightarrow q$, which is false only if p is true and q is false. Thus, if p is false, then q can be true or false. Hence, the statement: "If you did not stop, your pain will not stop either,"

does not follow logically from the given statement.

60. Answers may vary. Let p be: "The loss is $50 or less," and q be: "We will make payment." Then the given statement is $p \rightarrow \sim q$, which is false only when p is true and $\sim q$ is false. If p is false, then $\sim q$ can be either truc or false. Thus, based only on the given excerpt, the insurance company can pay or not pay.

61. Answers may vary. The student has to take the placement examination only if the student is entering college for the first time even though this student may be admitted to sophomore standing due to satisfying freshman requirements (perhaps by advanced courses in high school, transfering from a different college, etc.).

62. Answers will vary.   63. Answers will vary.

64. Answers will vary.   65. Answers will vary.

66. $d \rightarrow r$ 67. $r \rightarrow a$ 68. $d \rightarrow (r \wedge a)$

69. No. It only says that an adjustment will definitely be made if a report is made in 10 days but doesn't speak to the situation where a late report is made.

70. Does the first road lead to freedom and are you telling the truth, or does the first road lead to freedom and are you lying?

71. A must see at least one black hat, or she would know that her hat is black since they are not all white. B also must see at least one black hat, and further, that hat had to be on C, otherwise she would know that her hat was black (since she knows A saw at least one black hat). So C knows that her hat is black, without even seeing the others' hats.

72. The fact that there are two is a red herring – you only need one of either type. You ask him the following question: "If I were to ask you if the left fork leads to Someplaceorother, would you say 'yes'?"

73. The one who fell silent, presumably the quickest of the three, reasoned that his head must be painted also. The argument goes as follows. Let's call the quick one Q, and the other two D and S. Let's assume Q's head is

untouched. Then D is laughing because S's head is painted, and vice versa. But eventually, D and S will realize that their head must be painted, because the other is laughing. So they will quit laughing as soon as they realize this. So, Q waits what he thinks is a reasonable amount of time for them to figure this out, and when they don't stop laughing, his worst fears are confirmed. He concludes that his assumption is invalid and he must be crowned in crimson too.

SKILL CHECKER

p	q	$\sim p$	$p \vee q$	$p \wedge q$
T	T	F	T	T
T	F	F	T	F
F	T	T	T	F
F	F	T	F	F

Collaborative Learning

1. $\left[(w \vee s \vee t \vee ts \vee g \vee c \vee d) \wedge \sim o \right] \to u$

2. Answers will vary.

3. Yes, provided you meet one of the other seven conditions.

4. No. Did not satisfy one of the seven conditions.

5. The IRS wants you to believe that $\sim w \to r$ is a tautology. The IRS wants you to believe that $\sim w \to\!\!\!\!/\, r$ is a contradiction.

Section 3.4 Variations of the Conditional and Implications

1. The *contrapositive* is: If n is divisible by 2, then n is an even number.

2. *Converse*: If you have no cavities, then you brush your teeth with Clean.
   Contrapositive: If you have cavities, then you do not brush your teeth with Clean.
   Inverse: If you do not brush your teeth with Clean, then you have cavities.

3. $q \to p$ 　4. $q \to p$ 　5. $q \to p$

6. If I kissed you once, then I will kiss you again.

7. If one is a mathematics major, then one takes calculus.

8. If Eva is convinced, then the argument is a good one.

9. If the measure gets a two-thirds vote, then it carries.

10. If we have rain, then we have clouds.

11. If we have a stable economy, then we have low unemployment.

12. If a person is a woman, then the person will join a women's club.

13. If birds are of a feather, then they flock together.

14. If it is a dog, then it is a canine.

15.

			Converse	Inverse
p	q	$p \to q$	$q \to p$	$\sim p \to \sim q$
T	T	T	T	T
T	F	F	T	T
F	T	T	F	F
F	F	T	T	T

The converse, $q \to p$, is true except when q is true and p is false (third row). The inverse, $\sim p$ is true and $\sim q$ is false (third row). Thus, the converse and the inverse have the same truth values, and hence are equivalent.

16. $u \to h$ 　17. $u \to h$ 　18. $h \to u$

19. $u \to h$ 　20. $h \to u$ 　21. $u \to h$

22. $u \to h$ 　23. $u \leftrightarrow h$

24. $h \to u$; $\sim u \to \sim h$; $\sim h \to\!\!\!\!/\, \sim u$

25. $u \to h$; $\sim h \to \sim u$; $\sim u \to \sim h$

26. $p \to s$ 　27. $p \leftrightarrow s$ 　28. $p \leftrightarrow s$

29. a. *Converse*: If you are not strong, then you do not eat your spinach.
    Inverse: If you eat your spinach, then you are strong.

Contrapositive: If you are strong, then you eat your spinach.

b. *Converse*: If you are strong, then you eat your spinach.
Inverse: If you do not eat your spinach, then you are not strong.
Contrapositive: If you are not strong, then you do not eat your spinach.

c. *Converse*: If you eat your spinach, then you are strong.
Inverse: If you are not strong, then you do not eat your spinach.
Contrapositive: If you do not eat your spinach, then you are not strong.

30. Statements (a) and (c) are contrapositives, thus are equivalent.

31. If the square of an integer is divisible by 4, the integer is even. Always true.

32. If there are clouds in the sky, then it is raining. Not always true.

33. If I am neat and well dressed, then I can get a date. Not always true.

34. If all our problems are over, then M is elected to office. Not always true.

35. If you pass this course, then you get passing grades on all the tests. Not always true.

36. If the three angles of a triangle are not equal, then the triangle is not equilateral.

37. If we cannot find a cure for cancer, then the research is inadequately funded.

38. If it is not beautiful, then it is not black.

39. If a person does not want to improve the world, then the person is not a radical.

40. If everyone does not want to buy it, then it is not a smartphone.

41. Let p be: "n is even," and q be: "$3n$ is even." Then, we see that the equivalence given in (c) makes the desired transformation.

42. Let p be: "It can be recycled," and q be: "Place it in this container." Then, we see that the equivalence given in (b) makes

the desired transformation.

43. Let p be: "The day is cool," and q be: "I will go fishing." Then the given statement is $p \to q$. Statement (b) translates into $q \to p$, which is not logically equivalent to $p \to q$.

44. Let p be: "The class is canceled," and q be: "Mary will go to the library." Then the given statement is $p \to q$. Statement (c) translates into $\sim q \to p$, which is not logically equivalent to $p \to q$.

45.

1	2	3	4
p	q	$p \wedge q$	$(p \wedge q) \to p$
T	T	T	T
T	F	F	T
F	T	F	T
F	F	F	T

Column 3 is the conjunction of columns 1 and 2, so has T only in the first row, both p and q are T. Therefore, column 4 is all T's, which shows that $(p \wedge q) \to p$ is a tautology.

46.

1	2	3	4	5	6	7	8
p	q	r	$p \to q$	$q \to r$	$4 \wedge 5$	$p \to r$	$6 \to 7$
T	T	T	T	T	T	T	T
T	T	F	T	F	F	F	T
T	F	T	F	T	F	T	T
T	F	F	F	T	F	F	T
F	T	T	T	T	T	T	T
F	T	F	T	F	F	T	T
F	F	T	T	T	T	T	T
F	F	F	T	T	T	T	T

Since column 8 is all T's, the statement is a tautology.

47.

1	2	3
p	$\sim p$	$p \leftrightarrow \sim p$
T	F	F
F	T	F

Since column 3 has all F's, the statement $p \leftrightarrow \sim p$ is a contradiction.

48.

1	2	3	4	5	6	7
p	q	$\sim p$	$\sim q$	$p \vee q$	~ 5	$3 \wedge 4$
T	T	F	F	T	F	F
T	F	F	T	T	F	F
F	T	T	F	T	F	F
F	F	T	T	F	T	T

Since column 6 and 7 are identical, the statements are equivalent.

49.

1	2	3	4	5	6
p	q	$\sim p$	$\sim p \wedge q$	$p \rightarrow q$	$4 \rightarrow 5$
T	T	F	F	T	T
T	F	F	F	F	T
F	T	T	T	T	T
F	F	T	F	T	T

Since column 6 is all T's, the first statement, $\sim p \wedge q$, implies the second, $p \rightarrow q$. (Columns 4 and 5 are not identical, so the statements are not equivalent.)

50.

1	2	3	4	5	6	7
p	q	$\sim p$	$\sim q$	$3 \rightarrow 4$	$3 \rightarrow 2$	$5 \leftrightarrow 6$
T	T	F	F	T	T	T
T	F	F	T	T	T	T
F	T	T	F	F	T	F
F	F	T	T	T	F	F

Neither implies the other. Since column 7 is not a tautology, neither of the statements implies the other.

51. If p is true, then the first statement is true, and if the first statement is true, then p is true. Hence, the two statements are equivalent as confirmed by the truth table.

1	2	3	4	5
p	q	$p \wedge q$	$p \vee 3$	$1 \leftrightarrow 4$
T	T	T	T	T
T	F	F	T	T
F	T	F	F	T
F	F	F	F	T

52.

1	2	3	4	5
p	q	$p \vee q$	$p \wedge 3$	$1 \leftrightarrow 4$
T	T	T	T	T
T	F	T	T	T
F	T	T	F	T
F	F	F	F	T

Since column 5 is all T's, the statements are equivalent.

53. If $p \wedge \sim q$ is true, then p is true and $\sim q$ is true, so that $\sim p \vee \sim q$ is also true. Thus: $p \wedge \sim q$ implies $\sim p \vee \sim q$. However, $\sim p \vee \sim q$ is true if p is false and $\sim q$ is true, in which case $p \wedge \sim q$ is false. Hence: $\sim p \vee \sim q$ does not imply $p \wedge \sim q$. Hence, the two statements are not equivalent nor does one statement imply the other as confirmed by the truth table.

1	2	3	4	5	6	7	8
p	q	$\sim p$	$\sim q$	$3 \vee 4$	$p \wedge 4$	$5 \rightarrow 6$	$6 \rightarrow 5$
T	T	F	F	F	F	T	F
T	F	F	T	T	T	T	T
F	T	T	F	T	F	F	T
F	F	T	T	T	F	F	T

54.

1	2	3	4	5	6	7	8	9
p	q	r	$\sim p$	$\sim q$	$p \wedge q$	$6 \rightarrow r$	$4 \vee 5 \vee r$	$7 \leftrightarrow 8$
T	T	T	F	F	T	T	T	T
T	T	F	F	F	T	F	F	T
T	F	T	F	T	F	T	T	T
T	F	F	F	T	F	T	T	T
F	T	T	T	F	F	T	T	T
F	T	F	T	F	F	T	T	T
F	F	T	T	T	F	T	T	T
F	F	F	T	T	F	T	T	T

Since column 9 is all T's, the statements are equivalent.

55. Answers will vary.

56. Answers may vary.
    (1) For q to be true, it is sufficient that p be true.
    (2) A sufficient condition for q to be true is that p be true.

57. Answers may vary.
    (1) For p to be true, it is necessary that q be true.

(2) A necessary condition for p to be true is that q be true.

58. Answers may vary.
(1) p is true only if q is true.
(2) q is false only if p is false.

59. Answers may vary. Should mention that the implication $\Rightarrow$ means that the conditional is a tautology.

60. Answers may vary. The conditional $p \rightarrow q$ is true whenever the consequent q is true. Thus, if q is true, then $p \rightarrow q$ is a tautology and p implies q whether p is true or false.

61. Answers may vary. The conditional $p \rightarrow q$ is true whenever the antecedent p is false. Thus, if p is false, then $p \rightarrow q$ is a tautology and p implies q whether q is true or false.

62.

Statement	Set
$\sim q$	Q'
$p \vee q$	$P \cup Q$
$p \wedge q$	$P \cap Q$
$p \Rightarrow q$	$P \subseteq Q$
$p \Leftrightarrow q$	$P = Q$
t, a tautology	U
C, a contradiction	$\varnothing$

63. a. The truth set of q is Q and the truth set of $\sim r$ is R'. Hence, the truth set of $q \wedge \sim r$ is $Q \cap R'$.

b. The truth set of $p \wedge q$ is $P \cap Q$ and the truth set of $\sim r$ is R'. Thus, the truth set of $(p \wedge q) \wedge \sim r$ is

$$(P \cap Q) \cap R'.$$

64. a. The truth set of p is P, of q is Q and the truth set of r is R. Hence, the truth set of $p \wedge \sim (q \vee r)$ is $P \cap (Q \cup R)'$.

b. The truth set of p is P, of q is Q and the truth set of r is R. Thus, the truth set of $(p \vee q) \wedge \sim (q \vee r)$ is

$$(P \cup Q) \cap (Q \cup R)'.$$

65. The contrapositive of $\sim q \rightarrow \sim p$ is

$$\sim (\sim p) \rightarrow \sim (\sim q), \text{ that is } p \rightarrow q.$$

66. The inverse of $\sim p \rightarrow \sim q$ is

$$\sim (\sim p) \rightarrow \sim (\sim q), \text{ that is } p \rightarrow q.$$

67. The inverse of $p \rightarrow q$ is $\sim p \rightarrow \sim q$, and the contrapositive of $\sim p \rightarrow \sim q$ is

$$\sim (\sim p) \rightarrow \sim (\sim q), \text{ that is } q \rightarrow p.$$

68. $r \vee s \vee \sim p \vee \sim q \Leftrightarrow \left[\sim (r \vee s) \rightarrow (p \wedge q) \right]$

This is true because:

$$\left[\sim (r \vee s) \rightarrow (p \wedge q) \right] \Leftrightarrow \left[(r \vee s) \vee \sim (p \wedge q) \right]$$
$$\Leftrightarrow \left[(r \vee s) \vee (\sim p \vee \sim q) \right]$$
$$\Leftrightarrow r \vee s \vee \sim p \vee \sim q$$

69. $(\sim r \wedge \sim s) \vee (p \vee q) \Leftrightarrow (r \vee s) \rightarrow (p \vee q)$; it is true because

$$(r \vee s) \rightarrow (p \vee q) \Leftrightarrow \sim (r \vee s) \vee (p \vee q)$$
$$\Leftrightarrow (\sim r \wedge \sim s) \vee (p \vee q)$$

and the converse of $(r \vee s) \rightarrow (p \vee q)$ is

$$(p \vee q) \rightarrow (r \vee s).$$

70. The direct statement

71. The direct statement

72. The inverse

73. The contrapositive

74. The converse

Collaborative Learning

4. a. $t \rightarrow b$ b. $i \rightarrow p$
   c. $m \rightarrow \sim l$ d. $w \rightarrow p$
   e. $r \rightarrow (p \wedge m)$

Section 3.5 Euler Diagrams: A Problem-Solving Tool

1. *Premises*: "No misers are generous," and "Some old persons are not generous."
   Conclusion: "Some old persons are misers."

2. *Premises*: "No thieves are honest," and "Some dishonest people are convicted."
   Conclusion: "Some thieves are convicted."

3. *Premises*: "All diligent students make A's," and "All lazy students are not successful."
   Conclusion: "All diligent students are lazy."

4. *Premises*: "All students like logic," and "Robin likes logic."
   Conclusion: "Robin is a student."

5. *Premises*: "No kitten that loves fish is unteachable," and "No kitten without a tail will play with a gorilla."
   Conclusion: "No unteachable kitten will play with a gorilla."

6. *Premises*: "No birds are proud of their tails," and "Some birds cannot sing."
   Conclusion: "Peacocks cannot sing."

7. In the diagram, the circle P (professors) must be inside the circle W (wise), and the point B (Ms. Brown) must be inside circle P, so the argument is valid.

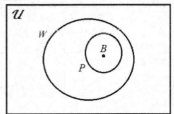

8. In the diagram, even though Mr. Smith is studious, not all studious people are students. Thus, the argument is invalid.

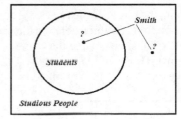

9. In the diagram, the circle D (drinkers) must be outside of both the circle H (healthy) and the circle J (joggers). The premises do not prevent the circles J and H from intersecting, so the argument is invalid.

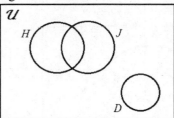

10. In the diagram, the circle *Students* must be inside *Dedicated People*, and the circle *Wealthy* must be inside the circle *Students*, so the argument is valid.

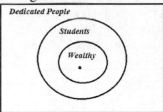

11. In the diagram, the circle M (men) must be inside the circle F (funny), and the dot J (Joey) must be inside the circle M, and so inside the circle F. Thus, the argument is valid.

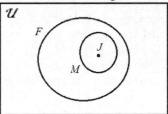

12. In the diagram, even though Jack is muscular, not all muscular people are football players. Thus, the argument is invalid.

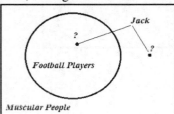

13. In the diagram, the circle *F* (felines) must be inside the circle *M* (mammals). The circle *D* (dogs) must not intersect the circle *F*, but the premises do not prevent circle *D* from intersecting circle *M*, so the argument is invalid.

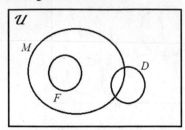

14. In the diagram, the circle *Beer Drinkers* must be inside circle *Dangerous*, the circle *Students* must intersect *Beer Drinkers* but the premises do not prevent the circle *Students* from being partially outside of circle *Dangerous*. Thus, the argument is invalid.

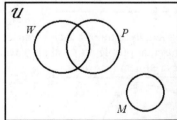

15. In the diagram, the circle *M* (Math teachers) must not intersect circle *W* (wealthy). The circle *P* (panthers) must not intersect the circle *M*, but may intersect the circle *W*, so the argument is invalid.

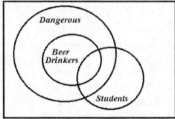

16. In the diagram, the circle *Yuppies* must be inside circle *Short-Haired People* and the circle *Athletes* must intersect *Yuppies*. Since premises do not require that the circle *Athletes* be inside circle *Short-Haired People,* the argument is valid.

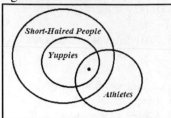

17. In the diagram, the circle *M* must be inside the circle *P* (publications). The *Ph* (Ph.D.) circle must intersect the circle *P*, but does not have to intersect the circle *M*, so the argument is invalid.

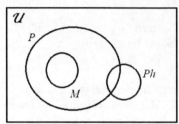

18. In the diagram, the circle *Beer Lovers* must be inside the circle *People Who Like Schlitz*, which in turn, must be inside the circle *People Who Get Drunk*. Thus, the argument is valid.

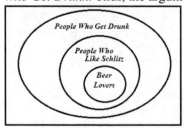

19. In the diagram, the circle *H* (heavy cars) must be inside the circle *C* (comfortable to ride in) and the circle *C* must be outside the circle *S* (shoddily built). Thus, circle *H* must lie outside of the circle *S*, so the argument is valid.

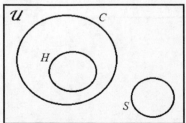

20. In the diagram, circles *Prius Owners* and *Fast Drivers* must intersect circle *People Who Save Money*. The premises do not require that circle *Prius Owners* and circle *Fast Drivers* intersect. Thus, the argument is invalid.

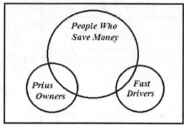

21. In the diagram, circle *B* (bulldogs) must be inside circle *U* (ugly). Point *D* (this dog) must be inside circle *U*, but not necessarily inside circle *B*, so the argument is invalid.

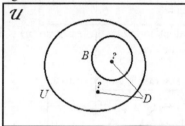

22. In this diagram, circle *Peacocks* must be in circle *Proud Birds*. *This Bird* must be outside circle *Proud Birds*. Thus, the argument is valid.

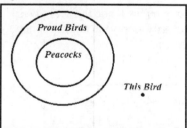

23. In the diagram, circle *A* (students who make A's) must be inside circle *S* (smart). The point *B* (student who made *B*) must be outside circle *A*, but can be inside or outside of circle *S*. Thus, the argument is invalid.

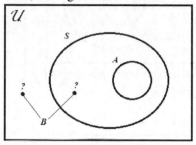

24. In this diagram, circles *Southerners* and *People Who Like Freezing Weather* do not intersect. Place *Joe* inside circle *People Who Like Freezing Weather*. Thus, the argument is valid.

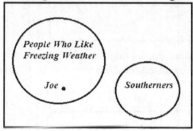

25. In the diagram, circle *F* (fishermen) must intersect circle *L* (lucky people) because some fishermen are lucky. Fred is unlucky, so he must be indicated outside of circle *L*, but the point Fred can be inside or outside the circle *F*. Thus, the argument is invalid.

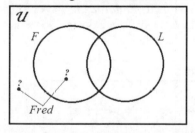

26. In this diagram, circles *Students* and *People Who Do Well In History* intersect. *Bobby* can be inside or outside of circle *Students*. Thus, the argument is invalid.

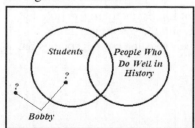

27. **b** is correct.

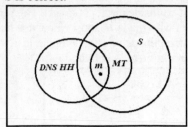

m is a salsero and does not sing hip-hop, so (**b**) is the correct conclusion.

28. **a** is correct.

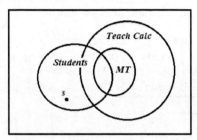

s is a student that is not a math teacher, so **a** is the correct conclusion.

29. **a** is correct.

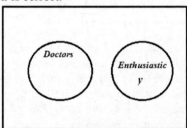

y (you) are inside *Enthusiastic* and outside *Doctors*, so you are not a doctor, so (**a**) is the correct conclusion.

30. **b** is correct.

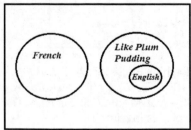

The set of Englishmen *English* does not intersect with the set of Frenchmen *French*, so (**b**) is the correct conclusion.

31. **b** is correct.

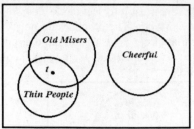

t is a thin person that is not cheerful so (**b**) is the correct conclusion.

32. **a** is correct.

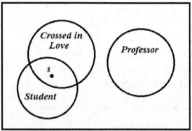

s is a student and not a professor so (**a**) is the correct conclusion.

33. Neither conclusion can be drawn.

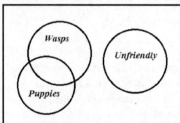

The set of puppies *P* and the set of wasps *W* is not necessarily empty, so neither conclusion can be drawn.

34. **a** is correct.

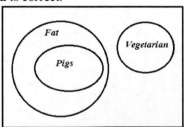

The sets *Fat* and *Vegetarian* do not intersect so the correct conclusion is (**a**).

35. **a** is correct.

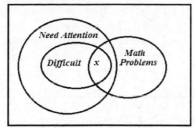

x is a difficult math problem that needs attention, so the correct conclusion is (**a**).

36. **a** is correct.

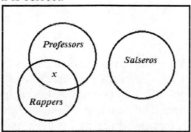

x is a rapper that is not a salsero so (**a**) is the correct conclusion.

37. Statement (**b**) can be logically deduced from the diagram.

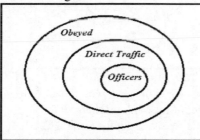

38. **b** is invalid as shown by the diagram.

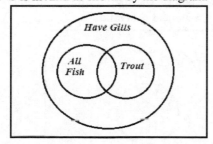

39. Answers may vary.
   a. An argument is valid if and only if the conclusion is true whenever all the premises are true. Thus, a valid argument reaches a true conclusion from true premises.
   b. No. By the definition stated in (a), if the premises are all true and the conclusion is false, then the argument is invalid.

40. Answers may vary.
   a. Yes. An invalid argument could result in a true conclusion even if all the premises are true. (See problem 38.)
   b. Yes. If all the premises are true and the conclusion is false, then the argument is invalid.

41. Answers may vary. No. It may be that the conclusion does not follow from the premises. Example 2 of this section is a good illustration.

42. Answers may vary.
   a. This is not necessarily true. Some of the premises might be true, but if the argument is valid, then at least one of the premises must be false.
   b. This is true if the argument is valid.
   c. If all the premises are true and the conclusion is false, then the argument must be invalid.

43. Answers may vary. By the definition of a valid argument, the conclusion is true whenever all the premises are true.

44. Answers may vary. Nothing. False premises can lead to any conclusion.

45. Draw a Venn diagram with two circles as shown: M for men and F for funny. The statement. "All men are funny," means that region 1 is empty. Thus, the point J (for Joey) must be in region 3. This shows that the argument is valid.

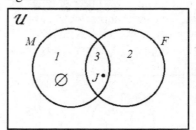

46. Draw a Venn diagram with two circles as shown: *M* for muscular and *F* for football players. The statement "All football players are muscular," means that region 1 is empty. Since Jack is muscular, the point *J* (for Jack) could be in regions 2 or 3. This shows that the argument is invalid.

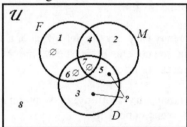

47. Draw a Venn diagram with three circles as shown: *F* for feline, *M* for mammals, and *D* for dogs. Because "All felines are mammals," regions 1 and 6 are empty. "No dog is a feline," makes region 7 empty. "This dog" can be in region 3 or 5, so the argument is invalid.

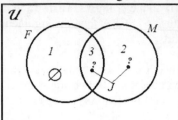

48. Draw a Venn diagram with three circles as shown: *S* for Students, *B* for Beer Drinkers, and *D* for Dangerous. The first premise "Some students drink beer" means that regions 4 or 7 are not empty. The second premise "All beer drinkers are dangerous" means that regions 2 and 4 must be empty. The premises do not require that region 1 is empty. Thus, the argument is invalid.

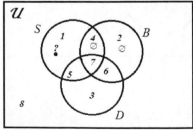

49. Draw a Venn diagram with three circles as shown: *M* for Math teachers, *W* for wealthy, and *P* for panthers. The first premise makes regions 4 and 7 empty. The second premise makes region 6 also empty. Since a given panther could be in region 3 or 5, the argument is invalid.

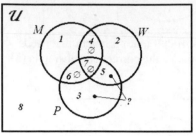

50. Draw a Venn diagram with three circles as shown: *Y* for Yuppies, *S* for Short Hair, and *A* for athletes. The first premise makes regions 1 and 5 empty. The statement "Some athletes are yuppies," means that region 7 is not empty. This shows that the argument is valid.

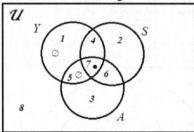

51. Draw a Venn diagram with three circles as shown: *M* for Math teachers, *P* for publications, and *Ph* for Ph.D's. The first premise makes regions 1 and 5 empty. The second premise means regions 6 and 7 can't both be empty. But region 7 might be empty, so the argument is invalid.

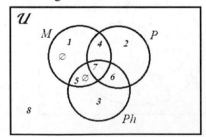

52. Draw a Venn diagram with three circles as shown: *B* for Beer Lovers, *S* for People Who Like Schlitz, and *D* for Drunk. The first premise makes regions 1 and 5 empty. The second premise makes regions 2 and 4 empty. Thus, region 7 is not empty. This shows that the argument is valid.

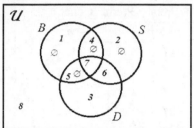

53. Draw a Venn diagram with three circles as shown: *H* for heavy cars, *C* for comfortable cars, and *S* for poorly-built cars. The first premise makes regions 1 and 5 empty, and the second premise makes regions 6 and 7 empty. Since the regions common to *H* and *S* (regions 6 and 7) are empty, the argument is valid.

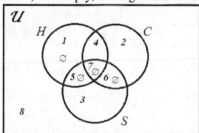

54. Draw a Venn diagram with three circles as shown: *P* for Prius Owners, *S* for Save Money, and *F* for Fast Drivers. The first premise could have either region 4 or 7 not empty. The second premise could have either region 6 or 7 not empty. Thus, the argument is invalid.

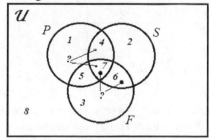

55. Draw a Venn diagram with three circles as shown: *W* (won't study), *A* (get A's), and *S* (students). The first premise makes regions 4 and 7 empty. The second means that region 5 is not empty, so the first conclusion is valid. Nothing in the premises makes region 6 or region 3 empty, so conclusions (b) and (c) are both invalid. Only conclusion **a** is valid.

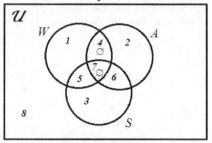

56. Draw a Venn diagram with three circles as shown: *R* (it rains), *G* (grass grows), and *C* (I cut it). The first premise makes regions 4 and 7 nonempty and regions 2 and 6 empty. The second premise means that region 4 is empty. The third premise means that regions 1, 5, or 7 are not empty. Thus, none of the conclusions are valid.

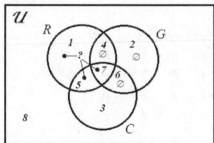

57. Yes, see the diagram. (If *x* is the empty set, then *y* and *z* could be disjoint.)

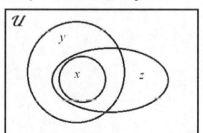

58. No *z* is *x*. See the diagram.

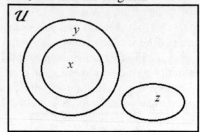

59. Some *z*'s are *y*'s. See the diagram.

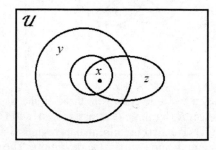

60. Yes. See problem 57.

Skill Checker

1.

1	2	3	4	5	6	7
p	q	$\sim p$	$\sim q$	$1 \to 4$	$1 \vee 4$	$3 \wedge 2$
T	T	F	F	F	T	F
T	F	F	T	T	T	F
F	T	T	F	T	F	T
F	F	T	T	T	T	F

2. a. $\sim q \to \sim p$ b. $\sim p \to q$
    c. $p \to q$ d. $q \to \sim p$

Section 3.6 Truth Tables and
Validity of Arguments

1. $e \to p$

      $\underline{\sim e}$

      $\therefore \sim p$

Using the symbolic form, make a truth table:

		Prem	Prem	Concl
e	p	$e \to p$	$\sim e$	$\sim p$
T	T	T	F	F
T	F	F	F	T
F	T	T	T	F
F	F	T	T	T

In the third row, the premises are true and the conclusion is false. Thus, the argument is invalid.

2. $e \to p$

      $\underline{\sim p}$

      $\therefore \sim e$

Using the symbolic form, make a truth table:

		Prem	Prem	Concl
e	p	$e \to p$	$\sim p$	$\sim e$
T	T	T	F	F
T	F	F	T	T
F	T	T	F	F
F	F	T	T	T

In the fourth row, the premises are true and the conclusion is true. Thus, the argument is valid.

3. $s \to e$

      $\underline{\sim e}$

      $\therefore \sim s$

Using the symbolic form, make a truth table:

		Prem	Prem	Concl
s	e	$s \to e$	$\sim e$	$\sim s$
T	T	T	F	F
T	F	F	T	F
F	T	T	F	T
F	F	T	T	T

In the fourth row, the premises are true and the conclusion is true. Thus, the argument is valid.

4. $m \vee e$

$\underline{\sim e}$

$\therefore m$

Using the symbolic form, make a truth table:

		Prem	Prem	Concl
m	e	$m \vee e$	$\sim e$	m
T	T	T	F	F
T	F	T	T	T
F	T	T	F	T
F	F	F	T	T

In the second row, the premises are true and the conclusion is true. Thus, the argument is valid.

5. $\underline{g}$

$\therefore g \wedge r$

Using the symbolic form, make a truth table:

		Prem	Concl
g	r	g	$g \wedge r$
T	T	T	T
T	F	T	F
F	T	F	F
F	F	F	F

In the second row, the premise is true and the conclusion is false, so the argument is invalid.

6. $u \rightarrow s$

$\underline{s \rightarrow t}$

$\therefore u \rightarrow t$

Using the symbolic form, make a truth table:

			Prem	Prem	Concl
u	s	t	$u \rightarrow s$	$s \rightarrow t$	$u \vee t$
T	T	T	T	T	T
T	T	F	T	F	F
T	F	T	F	T	F
T	F	F	F	T	F
F	T	T	T	T	T
F	T	F	T	F	F
F	F	T	T	T	T
F	F	F	T	F	F

Rows 1, 5, and 7 are the only rows where both premises are true. In these rows the conclusion is also true, so the argument is valid.

7. $w \rightarrow m$

$\underline{\sim w \rightarrow g}$

$\therefore m \vee g$

Using the symbolic form, make a truth table:

			Prem	Prem	Concl
w	m	g	$w \rightarrow m$	$\sim w \rightarrow g$	$m \vee g$
T	T	T	T	T	T
T	T	F	T	T	T
T	F	T	F	T	T
T	F	F	F	T	F
F	T	T	T	T	T
F	T	F	T	F	T
F	F	T	T	T	T
F	F	F	T	F	F

Rows 1, 2, 5, and 7 are the only rows where both premises are true. In these rows the conclusion is also true, so the argument is valid.

8. $b \to i$

   $m \to \sim d$

   $i \to d$

   $\therefore b \to \sim m$

Using the symbolic form, make a truth table:

| | | | | | | Prem | Prem | Prem | Concl |
b	d	i	m	$\sim d$	$\sim m$	$b \to i$	$m \to \sim d$	$i \to d$	$b \to \sim m$
T	T	T	T	F	F	T	F	T	F
T	T	T	F	F	T	T	T	T	T
T	T	F	T	F	F	F	F	T	F
T	T	F	F	F	T	F	T	T	T
T	F	T	T	T	F	T	T	F	T
T	F	T	F	T	T	T	T	F	T
T	F	F	T	T	F	F	T	T	F
T	F	F	F	T	T	F	T	T	T
F	T	T	T	F	F	T	F	T	T
F	T	T	F	F	T	T	T	T	T
F	T	F	T	F	F	T	F	T	T
F	T	F	F	F	T	T	T	T	T
F	F	T	T	T	F	T	T	F	T
F	F	T	F	T	T	T	T	F	T
F	F	F	T	T	F	T	T	T	T
F	F	F	F	T	T	T	T	T	T

Rows 2, 10, 12, 15, and 16 are the only rows where both premises are true. In these rows the conclusion is also true, so the argument is valid

9. $t \to b$

   t

   $\therefore b$

Using the symbolic form, make a truth table:

| | | Prem | Prem | Concl |
t	b	$t \to b$	t	b
T	T	T	T	T
T	F	F	T	F
F	T	T	F	T
F	F	T	F	F

The first row is the only one in which both premises are true. In that row, the conclusion is also true, so the argument is valid.

10. r

   $r \to \sim g$

   $\therefore \sim g$

Using the symbolic form, make a truth table:

| | | Prem | Prem | Concl |
r	g	$\sim g$	r	$r \to \sim g$	$\sim g$
T	T	F	T	F	F
T	F	T	T	T	T
F	T	F	F	T	F
F	F	T	F	T	T

The second row is the only one in which both premises are true. In that row, the conclusion is also true, so the argument is valid.

11. $s \rightarrow f$

$\underline{\quad s \quad}$

$\therefore f$

Using the symbolic form, make a truth table:

		Prem	Prem	Concl
s	f	$s \rightarrow f$	s	f
T	T	T	T	T
T	F	F	T	F
F	T	T	F	T
F	F	T	F	F

The first row is the only one where both premises are true. In that row, the conclusion is also true, so the argument is valid.

12. $(e \vee h) \rightarrow a$

$\underline{\quad \sim h \quad}$

$\therefore \sim a$

Using the symbolic form, make a truth table:

			Prem	Prem	Concl
e	h	a	$(e \vee h) \rightarrow a$	$\sim h$	$\sim a$
T	T	T	T	F	F
T	T	F	F	F	T
T	F	T	T	T	F
T	F	F	F	T	T
F	T	T	T	F	F
F	T	F	F	F	T
F	F	T	T	T	F
F	F	F	T	T	T

In the rows 2 and 5, the premises are true and the conclusion is false, so the argument is invalid.

13. $m \rightarrow e$

$\underline{\quad \sim m \quad}$

$\therefore \sim e$

Using the symbolic form, make a truth table:

		Prem	Prem	Concl
m	e	$m \rightarrow e$	$\sim m$	$\sim e$
T	T	T	F	F
T	F	F	F	T
F	T	T	T	F
F	F	T	T	T

In the third row, both premises are true and the conclusion is false, so the argument is invalid.

14. $p \rightarrow a$

$\underline{\quad \sim a \quad}$

$\therefore \sim p$

Using the symbolic form, make a truth table:

		Prem	Prem	Concl
p	a	$p \rightarrow a$	$\sim a$	$\sim p$
T	T	T	F	F
T	F	F	T	F
F	T	T	F	T
F	F	T	T	T

The third row is the only row where both premises are true. In that row, the conclusion is also true, so the argument is valid.

15. $f \rightarrow s$

$\underline{\quad \sim f \quad}$

$\therefore \sim s$

Using the symbolic form, make a truth table:

		Prem	Prem	Concl
f	s	$f \rightarrow s$	$\sim f$	$\sim s$
T	T	T	F	F
T	F	F	F	T
F	T	T	T	F
F	F	T	T	T

In the third row, both premises are true and the conclusion is false, so the argument is invalid.

16. $a \rightarrow m$

$\dfrac{m}{\therefore a}$

Using the symbolic form, make a truth table:

		Prem	Prem	Concl
a	m	$a \rightarrow m$	m	a
T	T	T	T	T
T	F	F	F	T
F	T	T	T	F
F	F	T	T	F

In rows 3 and 4, both premises are true and the conclusion is false, so the argument is invalid.

17. Using the symbolic form, make a truth table:

		Prem	Prem	Concl
p	q	$p \vee q$	$\sim p$	q
T	T	T	F	T
T	F	T	F	F
F	T	T	T	T
F	F	F	T	F

In the third row, both premises are true and the conclusion is true, so the argument is valid.

18. Using the symbolic form, make a truth table:

		Prem	Prem	Concl
p	q	$p \rightarrow q$	p	q
T	T	T	T	T
T	F	F	T	F
F	T	T	F	T
F	F	T	F	F

In the first row, both premises are true and the conclusion is true, so the argument is valid.

19. Using the symbolic form, make a truth table:

		Prem	Prem	Concl
p	q	$p \rightarrow q$	$\sim p$	q
T	T	T	F	T
T	F	F	F	F
F	T	T	T	T
F	F	T	T	F

In rows 3 and 4, both premises are true but the conclusion in row 4 is false, so the argument is invalid.

20. Using the symbolic form, make a truth table:

		Prem	Prem	Concl
p	q	$p \rightarrow q$	$\sim q$	$\sim p$
T	T	T	F	F
T	F	F	T	F
F	T	T	F	T
F	F	T	T	T

In the last row, both premises are true and the conclusion is true, so the argument is valid.

21. Using the symbolic form, make a truth table:

						Prem	Prem	Concl
p	q	r	$\sim p$	$\sim r$	$p \rightarrow q$	$q \rightarrow r$	$\sim r \rightarrow \sim p$	
T	T	T	F	F	T	T	T	
T	T	F	F	T	T	F	F	
T	F	T	F	F	F	T	T	
T	F	F	F	T	F	T	F	
F	T	T	T	F	T	T	T	
F	T	F	T	T	T	F	T	
F	F	T	T	F	T	T	T	
F	F	F	T	T	T	T	T	

Rows 1, 5, 7, and 8 are the only rows where both premises are true. In these rows the conclusion is also true, so the argument is valid.

22. The premises are $p \rightarrow q, q \rightarrow r, p \rightarrow \sim r$, so that a valid conclusion is $p \rightarrow \sim s$.

23. Use the hint and replace $\sim q \vee r$ by $q \rightarrow r$. The premises are then $p \rightarrow q$ and $q \rightarrow r$, so that a valid conclusion is $p \rightarrow r$.

24. Replace $\sim u \vee t$ by $u \rightarrow t$ and $s \rightarrow \sim r$ by $r \rightarrow \sim s$. The premises are then $p \rightarrow q$, $q \rightarrow u$, $u \rightarrow t$, $t \rightarrow r$, and $r \rightarrow \sim s$ so that a valid conclusion is $p \rightarrow \sim s$.

25. Replace the premise $\sim s \rightarrow \sim r$ by its contrapositive, $r \rightarrow s$. The premises can then be written p, $p \rightarrow q$, $q \rightarrow r$, and $r \rightarrow s$. Thus, a valid conclusion using all the premises is s.

26. Replace $p \rightarrow \sim q$ by $q \rightarrow \sim p$. The premises are then r, $r \rightarrow q$, and $q \rightarrow \sim p$, so that a valid conclusion is $\sim p$.

27. Replace the disjunction $\sim p \vee r$ by its equivalent, $\sim r \rightarrow \sim p$. The premises can then be written $\sim r$, $\sim r \rightarrow \sim p$, and $\sim p \rightarrow q$. Thus, a valid conclusion using all the premises is q.

28. $s \rightarrow p \rightarrow \sim l$ (p: people who assign work; $\sim l$: people who are not lovable; s: supervisor)
   Conclusion: No supervisors are lovable.

29. $p \rightarrow ro \rightarrow \sim r$ (p: politicians; ro: run for office; $\sim r$: not reliable)
   Conclusion: If you are a politician you are not reliable or equivalently, No politicians are reliable.

30. $(\sim e \rightarrow \sim p) \wedge \sim e$ ($\sim e$: employees who do not arrive for work on time; $\sim p$: people who are not promoted). The Law of Detachment gives the conclusion: Some employees will not be promoted.

31. Since there is at least one student that is intelligent, that student has to be a snob (because all intelligent people are snobs). Thus, we can conclude: Some students are snobs.

32. Let r be "It rains," g be "Grass will grow," c be "Cut grass," and h be "It is higher than 8 in." Then the symbolic forms of the given premises are: $r \rightarrow g$, $g \rightarrow c$, and $c \rightarrow h$. Thus a conclusion that uses all the premises: $r \rightarrow h$, or in words, "If it rains, then the grass is higher than 8 inches."

33. Let n be "I do not recommend them," h be "The books are healthy in tone," b be "The books are bound," w be "The books are well written," and r be "The books are

romances." Then the symbolic forms of the given premises are: $n \rightarrow \sim h$, $b \rightarrow w$, $r \rightarrow h$, and $\sim b \rightarrow n$. Replace the first and last of these premises by their contrapositives, $h \rightarrow \sim n$, and $\sim n \rightarrow b$. Then arrange the premises in the order: $r \rightarrow h$, $h \rightarrow \sim n$, $\sim n \rightarrow b$, $b \rightarrow w$.
You can now read a conclusion that uses all the premises: $r \rightarrow w$, or in words, "All romances are well written."

34. Let d be "It is a duck," f be "It can fly," b be "It is a land bird," and s be "It eats shrimp." Then, the symbolic forms of the given premises are: $d \rightarrow f$, $s \rightarrow \sim b$, and $\sim s \rightarrow \sim f$. Replace $\sim s \rightarrow \sim f$ with $f \rightarrow s$. Now arrange these in the order: $d \rightarrow f$, $f \rightarrow s$, $s \rightarrow \sim b$. A conclusion that uses all the premises is: $d \rightarrow \sim b$, or in words, "No land bird is a duck."

35. Let p be "You are patriotic," v be "You vote," a be "You are an aardvark," and e be "You have emotions." Then, the symbolic forms of the given premises are: $\sim p \rightarrow \sim v$, $a \rightarrow \sim e$, and $\sim e \rightarrow \sim p$. Now arrange these in the order: $a \rightarrow \sim e$, $\sim e \rightarrow \sim p$, $\sim p \rightarrow \sim v$. A conclusion that uses all the premises is: $a \rightarrow \sim v$, or in words, "Aardvarks do not vote."

36. There is at least a music student that doesn't practice but that music student will not learn to play well (because no music student who doesn't practice will learn to play well). Thus, we can conclude that: Some music students won't learn to play well (a).

37. There is at least a college student that does not go to class but that student will not pass the course (because no college student who doesn't go to class will pass the course). Thus, we can conclude that: Some college students will not pass the course, that is conclusion (c).

38. Let l: you work late, p: you are a party animal and s: you are a supervisor. The symbolic form of the premises is: $l \rightarrow \sim p$ and $s \rightarrow l$. Replace $l \rightarrow \sim p$ with $p \rightarrow \sim l$ and $s \rightarrow l$ with $\sim l \rightarrow \sim s$. Now arrange these in the order: $p \rightarrow \sim l$ and $\sim l \rightarrow \sim s$. We can

conclude that $p \rightarrow \sim s$, or written as the contrapositive, $s \rightarrow \sim p$. This means that if you are a supervisor, you are not a party animal or equivalently "No supervisors are party animals," that is, conclusion (c).

39. Let t: you are a teacher, tc: you teach classes and d: you are dumb. The symbolic form of the premises is:
    $tc \rightarrow \sim d$, $t \rightarrow tc$.
    We can conclude that $t \rightarrow \sim d$. This means that if you are a teacher you are not dumb or equivalently "No teacher is dumb," that is, conclusion (b).

40. Problem 2, modus tollens;
    Problem 4, disjunctive syllogism;
    Problem 6, hypothetical syllogism;
    Problem 11, modus ponens.

41. Conclusion (c) makes the argument valid. This can be seen by letting p be "I drive to work," q be "I will not be late," and n be "I do not lose any pay." Then the premises can be written as $p \rightarrow q$ and $q \rightarrow n$, from which it follows that $p \rightarrow n$, which is conclusion (c).

42. Conclusion (d) makes the argument valid. This can be seen by letting b be "Bears win the final game," p be "They will play in the NFL playoffs," and g be "The owners will make a good profit." Then the premises can be written as $b \rightarrow p$ and $p \rightarrow g$, from which it follows that $b \rightarrow g$, which is conclusion (d).

43. Let p be "All persons pay their bills on time," and q be "Some collection agencies are needed." Then the first premise is $p \rightarrow \sim q$ and the second premise is q. The contrapositive of the first premise is $q \rightarrow \sim p$. Thus, we have q and $q \rightarrow \sim p$, so a valid conclusion is ~p. This is conclusion (b).

44. Let s be ""All students learn from their books alone," and t be "Teachers are needed." Then the first premise is $s \rightarrow \sim t$ and the second premise is t. The contrapositive of the first premise is $t \rightarrow \sim s$. Thus, we have t and $t \rightarrow \sim s$, so a valid conclusion is ~s. This is conclusion (d).

45. Let e be "Bill studies economics," g be "Bill makes good money," b be "Bill studies business procedures." The premises are $e \rightarrow g, b \rightarrow g$, and $e \wedge \sim b$. If $e \wedge \sim b$ is true, then e is true and b is false. If b is false, then the second premise $b \rightarrow g$ with b false, allows g to be either true or false. However, if g is false $e \rightarrow g$ is also false, so g must be true. Thus, a logical conclusion is stated in (b). Note that statement (c) cannot be deduced from the given premises as a logical conclusion.

46. Let c be "You are a college graduate," e be "You are educated," d be "You dress neatly," and j be "You are Jackie." The premises are $c \rightarrow e, e \rightarrow d$, and $j \rightarrow d$. None of these statements is a logical conclusion.

47. You read X magazine.

48. You will be popular.

49. Answers may vary. "Affirming the consequent" means that the "then" statement is affirmed and the "if" statement is taken as a valid conclusion. This is a fallacy because the statement $p \rightarrow q$ is true if p is false and q is either true or false.

50. Answers may vary. In the statement, "If p then q," p is the antecedent and q is the consequent. "Denying the antecedent" assumes "If $\sim p$ then $\sim q$" is true.

51. Let f be "A kitten loves fish," u be "A kitten is unteachable," t be "A kitten has a tail," p be "A kitten will play with a gorilla," w be "A kitten has whiskers," and g be "A kitten has green eyes." Then, the symbolic forms of the given statements are: (1) $f \rightarrow \sim u$,
    (2) $\sim t \rightarrow \sim p$, (3) $w \rightarrow f$, (4) $\sim u \rightarrow \sim g$,
    (5) $\sim w \rightarrow \sim t$. Now replace statements (2) and (5) by their respective contra-positives: (2') $p \rightarrow t$ (5') $t \rightarrow w$. Then arrange the premises in the order (2'), (5'), (3), (1), (4):
    $p \rightarrow t$. $t \rightarrow w$, $w \rightarrow f$, $f \rightarrow \sim u$,
    $\sim u \rightarrow \sim g$. A conclusion using all these premises is: $p \rightarrow \sim g$ or, in words, "Kittens that will play with a gorilla do not have green eyes." (An equivalent conclusion is, "No kitten

with green eyes will play with a gorilla.")

Collaborative Learning

1. The Megarian logician Eubulides of Miletus.

2. Three.

3. Answers will vary.

4. Answers will vary.

5. Answers will vary.

You can read more about sorites and see the three different types at:
http://plato.stanford.edu/entries/sorites-paradox/

Chapter 3 Practice Test

1. (b), (c), (d), and (e) are statements. Each is either true or false. (a) is not a statement because people do not agree on what is good. (f) is a question, so is neither true nor false.

2. a. d: The number of years is divisible by 4.
   p: The year is a presidential election year. The logical connective is *if ... then ...*, $d \rightarrow p$.
   b. b: I love Bill. $\sim m$: Bill does not love me. The logical connective is *and*, $b \wedge \sim m$.
   c. e: A candidate is elected president of the United States. m: He receives a majority of the electoral college votes. The logical connective is *if and only if*, $e \leftrightarrow m$.
   d. s: Janet can make sense out of symbolic logic. f: She fails this course. The logical connective is *or*, $s \vee f$.
   e. s: Janet can make sense out of symbolic logic. The logical modifier is *not*, $\sim s$.

3. a. It is not the case that he is a gentleman and a scholar.
   b. He is not a gentleman, but he is a scholar.

4. a. I will go neither to the beach nor to the movies.
   b. I will either not stay in my room or not do my homework.
   c. Pluto is a planet.

5. a. Some cats are not felines.
   b. No dog is well trained.
   c. Some dogs are afraid of a mouse.

6. a. Joey does not study, and he will not fail this course.
   b. Sally studies hard, but she does not get an A in this course.

7. a. $p \leftrightarrow q$ b. $p \wedge q$ c. $\sim p$
   d. $p \rightarrow q$ e. $p \vee q$

8.
1	2	3	4	5	6	7
p	q	$\sim p$	$\sim q$	$p \vee q$	$3 \vee 4$	$5 \wedge 6$
T	T	F	F	T	F	F
T	F	F	T	T	T	T
F	T	T	F	T	T	T
F	F	T	T	F	T	F

9.
1	2	3	4	5
p	q	$\sim p$	$p \vee q$	$(p \vee q) \rightarrow \sim p$
T	T	F	T	F
T	F	F	T	F
F	T	T	T	T
F	F	T	F	T

10. Make a truth table for the given statement and statements a and b:

1	2	3	4	5	6	7	8
p	q	$\sim p$	$3 \vee 2$	$\sim q$	$3 \wedge 5$	$1 \wedge 5$	~ 7
T	T	F	T	F	F	F	T
T	F	F	F	T	F	T	F
F	T	T	T	F	F	F	T
F	F	T	T	T	T	F	T

Since columns 4 and 8 show the same truth values, $T F T T$, statement (b) is equivalent to the given statement.

11. When at least one of the statements "Sally is naturally beautiful," and "Sally knows how to use makeup," is true.

12. The premise, "$2 + 2 = 5$," is false, so the statement (a conditional) is true.

13. In making the truth table, keep in mind that a biconditional is true when both components have the same truth value, and is false in the other cases.

1	2	3	4	5	6
p	q	$p \to q$	$\sim p$	$2 \vee 4$	$3 \leftrightarrow 5$
T	T	T	F	T	T
T	F	F	F	F	T
F	T	T	T	T	T
F	F	T	T	T	T

14. You should keep in mind that, starting with $p \to q$, the converse is $q \to p$, the inverse is $\sim p \to \sim q$, and the contrapositive is $\sim q \to \sim p$.

a. If you make a golf score of 62 again, then you made it once.

b. If you do not make a golf score of 62 once, then you will not make it again.

c. If you do not make a golf score of 62 again, then you did not make it once.

15. a. $m \to p$ b. $p \to m$ c. $p \leftrightarrow m$

16. a. $b \to c$ b. $c \to b$ c. $b \leftrightarrow c$

17. b implies a; b implies c; c implies a.

18. Statement (b), $p \vee \sim p$, is always true, so it is a tautology.

Statement (a), $p \wedge \sim p$, is always false, so it is not a tautology, but is known as a contradiction.

Statement (c), $(p \to q) \leftrightarrow (\sim q \vee p)$, is not always true. For example, if p is false and q is true, then $p \to q$ is true, but $\sim q \vee p$ is false, so the biconditional is false. Thus, it is not a tautology.

19. Nothing in the premises tells whether the J (for John) is inside or outside of circle H. Thus, the argument is invalid.

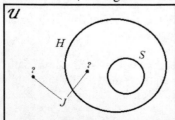

20. Nothing in the premises tells whether S (for Sally) goes inside the circle L or not. Thus, the argument is invalid.

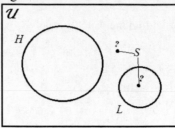

21. With s for "He is a student," and h for "He studies hard," the argument can be symbolized and a truth table constructed.

$s \to h$

$\underline{\sim s}$

$\therefore \sim h$

		Prem	Prem	Concl
s	h	$s \to h$	$\sim s$	$\sim h$
T	T	T	F	F
T	F	F	F	T
F	T	T	T	F
F	F	T	T	T

In the third row, both premises are true and the conclusion is false, so the argument is invalid.

22. With f for "Sally is a loafer," and h for "Sally works hard," the argument can be symbolized and a truth table constructed.

$f \to \sim h$

$\underline{\sim h}$

$\therefore f$

		Prem	Prem	Concl
f	h	$f \to \sim h$	$\sim h$	f
T	T	F	F	T
T	F	T	T	T
F	T	T	F	F
F	F	T	T	F

In the fourth row of the truth table, the premises are both true and the conclusion is false, so the argument is invalid.

23. With *w* for "You win the race," and *r* for "You are a good runner", the argument can be symbolized and a truth table constructed.

$$w \rightarrow r$$

$$\underline{w}$$

$$\therefore r$$

		Prem	Prem	Concl
r	*w*	$w \rightarrow r$	*w*	*r*
T	T	T	T	T
T	F	T	F	T
F	T	F	T	F
F	F	T	F	F

The first row of the table is the only row where the premises are both true. In this row the conclusion is also true, so the argument is valid.

24. Write the contrapositive of 2 which is $r \rightarrow p$, 1 which is $p \rightarrow q$ and the contrapositive of 3 which is $q \rightarrow \sim s$.

We then have: $r \rightarrow p$, $p \rightarrow q$, $q \rightarrow \sim s$.

A valid conclusion is $r \rightarrow \sim s$, or its contrapositive $s \rightarrow \sim r$.

Chapter 4 Numeration Systems

Section 4.1 Egyptian, Babylonian, and Roman Numeration Systems

1. ∩∩||||

2. ∩∩∩||||
   ∩∩

3. 𝟫∩∩∩∩||

4. 𝄃 𝟫𝟫∩∩∩∩||||||

5. 𝟫𝟫𝟫𝟫∩∩∩|||
   𝟫𝟫𝟫𝟫 ||

6. 𝒪 𝄃 𝟫𝟫 |||||
              ||||

7. 113   8. 1904   9. 322

10. 45   11. 11,232   12. 655

13.   ∩∩∩||||
    + ∩∩ |||
    ─────────────
      ∩∩∩∩∩||||||||

14.   𝟫∩∩∩∩∩|||| ||
    + ∩∩∩∩ ||||
    ─────────────
      𝟫∩∩∩∩∩
        ∩∩∩∩|||

15. Step 1. Subtract one coil, two heel bones, and two strokes:

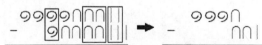

Step 2. In the top line, replace one coil by ten heel bones and one heel bone by ten strokes. This lets you do the remainder of the subtraction. Subtract two heel bones and one stroke. The answer is given as two coils, eight heel bones, and nine strokes.

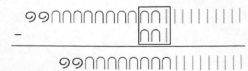

16. Step 1. Subtract two coils and two strokes:

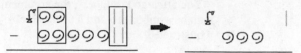

Step 2. In the top line, replace the lotus flower with ten coils. Subtract three coils. The answer is given as seven coils and one stroke.

$$\begin{array}{l} 𝟫𝟫𝟫𝟫𝟫𝟫\boxed{𝟫𝟫𝟫}| \\ - \qquad\quad \boxed{𝟫𝟫𝟫} \\ \hline 𝟫𝟫𝟫𝟫| \\ 𝟫𝟫𝟫 \end{array}$$

17.			18.		
\1	40		\1	15	
\2	80		2	30	
\4	160		4	60	
\8	320		\8	120	
15	600		\16	240	
			25	375	

19.			20.		
1	51		\1	63	
\2	102		2	126	
\4	204		\4	252	
8	408		8	504	
\16	816		\16	1008	
22	1122		21	1323	

21.			22.		
18	32		15	32
9	64		7	64
4	128		3	128
2	256		1	256
1	512			480
	576			

23.			24.		
12	51		40	61
6	102		20	122
3	204		10	244
1	408		5	488
	612		2	976
			1	1952
				2440

25. ▼▼▼▼▼▼   26. ≪ ≺▼▼▼▼

27. $32 = 3 \times 10 + 2 =$ ≺≺≺▼▼

28. $64 = 1 \times 60 + 4 =$ ▼   ▼▼▼▼

29. $123 = 2 \times 60 + 3 =$ ▼▼   ▼▼▼

30. $144 = 2 \times 60 + 2 \times 10 + 4 =$ ▼▼ ≺≺▼▼▼▼

31. $258 = 4 \times 60 + 1 \times 10 + 8 =$
▼▼▼▼ ≺▼▼▼▼▼▼▼▼

32. $192 = 3 \times 60 + 1 \times 10 + 2 =$ ▼▼▼ ≺▼▼

33. $3733 = 1 \times 3600 + 2 \times 60 + 1 \times 10 + 3 =$
▼   ▼▼   ≺▼▼▼

34. $3883 = 1 \times 3600 + 4 \times 60 + 4 \times 10 + 3 =$
▼   ▼▼▼▼   ≺▼▼▼

35. One 60 plus three 10's plus two 1's = 92

36. Thirteen 60's plus one 10 plus two 1's = 792

37. Three 60's plus one 10 plus two 1's = 192

38. Fourteen 60's plus three 1's = 843

39. One 3600 plus twelve 60's plus two 1's
= 4322

40. Two 3600's plus eleven 60's plus four 1's
= 7864

41. First add, then replace six 10's by one 60.
≺≺≺▼▼
+ ≺≺≺≺▼▼▼
≺≺≺≺≺≺≺▼▼▼▼▼ = ▼ ≺▼▼▼▼▼

42. Add. No replacements can be made.
▼   ▼▼▼
+ ▼   ≺≺▼
▼▼   ≺≺▼▼▼▼▼

43. First add, then replace ten 1's by one 10.
▼▼ ≺▼▼▼
+ ▼ ▼▼▼▼▼▼▼▼
▼▼▼ ≺▼▼▼▼▼▼▼▼▼▼▼ = ▼▼▼ ≺≺▼

44. Add. No replacement can be made.
▼▼▼▼ ▼▼
+ ▼▼▼ ▼
▼▼▼▼▼▼▼ ▼▼▼

45. $CXXVI = 100 + 2 \times 10 + 5 + 1 = 126$

46. $DCXVII = 500 + 100 + 10 + 5 + 2 = 617$

47. $\overline{XLII} = \left[(50 - 10) + 2 \right] \times 1000 = 42{,}000$

48. $\overline{XXXDCI}$
$= \left[(10 + 10 + 10) \cdot 1000 \right] + 500 + 100 + 1$
$= 30{,}601$

49. $\overline{XCCDV} = \overline{XC}(CD)V$
$= (100 - 10) \times 1000 + (500 - 100) + 5$
$= 90{,}405$

50. $\overline{LDDC} = \left[(500 - 50) \cdot 1000 \right] + 500 + 100$
$= 450{,}600$

51. $72 = 50 + 10 + 10 + 2 = LXXII$

52. $631 = 500 + 100 + 10 + 10 + 10 + 1$
$= DCXXXI$

53. $145 = 100 + (50 - 10) + 5 = CXLV$

54. $1709 = 1000 + 500 + 100 + 100 + (10 - 1)$
$= MDCCIX$

55. $32{,}503 = (3 \times 10 + 2) \times 1000 + 500 + 3$
$= \overline{XXXII}\,DIII$

56. $49{,}231 = \left[(50 - 10) + (10 - 1) \right] \cdot 1000 + 100$
$+ 100 + 10 + 10 + 10 + 1 = \overline{XLIX}CCXXXI$

57. J   o   h   n
$1 + 6 + 8 + 5 = 20 \rightarrow 2 + 0 = 2$
F   i   t   z   g   e   r   a   l   d
$6 + 9 + 2 + 8 + 7 + 5 + 9 + 1 + 3 + 4 = 54$
$\rightarrow 5 + 4 = 9$
K   e   n   n   e   d   y
$2 + 5 + 5 + 5 + 5 + 4 + 7 = 33 \rightarrow 3 + 3 = 6$
$2 + 9 + 6 = 17 \rightarrow 1 + 7 = 8$
$\rightarrow \rightarrow$ Lonely, misunderstood

58. S   o   n   y   a
$1 + 6 + 5 + 7 + 1 = 20 \rightarrow 2 + 0 = 2$
K   o   v   a   l   e   v   s   k   i
$2 + 6 + 4 + 1 + 3 + 5 + 4 + 1 + 2 + 9 = 37 \rightarrow$
$3 + 7 = 10 \rightarrow 1 + 0 = 1$
$\rightarrow \rightarrow 2 + 1 = 3$: Ambitious, proud,
independent

59. R   i   n   g   o
$9 + 9 + 5 + 7 + 6 = 36 \rightarrow 3 + 6 = 9$
S   t   a   r   r
$1 + 2 + 1 + 9 + 9 = 22 \rightarrow 2 + 2 = 4$
$4 + 9 = 13 \rightarrow 1 + 3 = 4$
$\rightarrow \rightarrow$ Rebels, unconventional

60. Answers will vary.

61. Answers may vary. No. C is more than two
steps larger than I, so this subtraction is not
allowed. I may be subtracted from V or X
only.

62. Answers may vary. Our decimal system is
positional and the Egyptian system is not
positional. In our system the symbols 21 and
12 represent different numbers, but in the
Egyptian system, both ∩|| and ||∩ represent
twelve. Also, we use different symbols for the
digits from 1 to 9, while the Egyptian system
uses just the corresponding number of vertical
strokes for these numbers; the Egyptians use
different symbols for other numbers, the
powers of 10. Finally, the Egyptians had no
symbol for 0.

63. Answers may vary. The Babylonian system is
a base 60 system and our decimal system is a
base 10 system. Another important difference
is the lack of a symbol for zero in the
Babylonian system. The Babylonian system
was not a good place system, it depended on
spacing. The symbol for 1 was the same as that
for 60, and only the spacing could show which
was intended.

64. Answers may vary. The Roman system of
numeration uses both an addition and a
subtraction principle to write numbers. For
example, XI means 10 + 1, while IX means
10 – 1. Our decimal system uses the addition
principle (for instance, 12 means 10 + 2), but
we do not use a subtraction principle. The
decimal system is positional while the Roman
system is not. For large numbers, the Roman
system uses an overbar. We do not use a
corresponding symbol.

65. Answers may vary. The Egyptian system was
based on 10 and the Babylonian on 60. The
Egyptian system was not a positional system;
it depended essentially on the addition of the
symbol values. The Babylonian system used
spacing to change symbol values.

66. Answers may vary. The spacing between the
symbol for 10 and the five wedges for 5 is the
only difference between 605 and 15. Unless
this spacing is very distinct, the number would
be read as 15, or 10 + 5, rather than 605,
$10 \times 60 + 5$.

67. Assume the answer is 6. $6 + \dfrac{1}{6} \cdot 6 = 7$, and
$21 \div 7 = 3$. Hence, the correct answer is
$3 \cdot 6 = 18$.

68. Assume that the answer is 8.
$8 + \frac{1}{2} \cdot 8 + \frac{1}{4} \cdot 8 = 14$ and $28 \div 14 = 2$. Therefore,
the correct answer is $2 \cdot 8 = 16$. (This could
also be accomplished by using the smallest
integer that is a multiple of the divisors. In this
case, assume a value of 4. Then
$4 + \frac{1}{2} \cdot 4 + \frac{1}{4} \cdot 4 = 7$ and $28 = 4 \cdot 7$, so the
correct answer is $4 \cdot 4 = 16$.)

69. Assume the answer is 3. $3 + \dfrac{2}{3} \cdot 3 = 5$, and
$5 - \dfrac{1}{3} \cdot 5 = \dfrac{10}{3}$ and $10 \div \dfrac{10}{3} = 3$. Hence, the
correct answer is $3 \times 3 = 9$.
(To avoid fractions, assume the answer is a
multiple of 3, so start with 9. Then
$9 + \dfrac{2}{3} \cdot 9 = 15$, and
$15 - \dfrac{1}{3} \cdot 15 = 10$ and $10 \div 10 = 1$. Hence, the
correct answer is $9 \times 1 = 9$.)

70. If you calculated $n^3 + n^2$ for $n = 9$, you found the result to be $729 + 81 = 810$. Thus, the answer is $n = 9$.

71. If you calculated $n^3 + n^2$ for $n = 8$, you found the result to be $5121 + 64 = 576$. Thus, the answer is $n = 8$.

72. Substitute $2x$ for n:
$(2x)^3 + 2(2x)^2 - 3136 = 0$, which can be written as $8x^3 + 8x^2 - 3136 = 0$. Divide by 8:
$x^3 + x^2 - 392 = 0$. If you calculated
$x^3 + x^2$ for $x = 7$, you found the result to be $343 + 49 = 392$. Thus, the answer is $x = 7$.
Thus, $n = 2x = 2 \cdot 7 = 14$.

Section 4.2 The Hindu-Arabic (Decimal) System

1. $432 = (4 \times 10^2) + (3 \times 10^1) + (2 \times 10^0)$

2. $549 = (5 \times 10^2) + (4 \times 10^1) + (9 \times 10^0)$

3. $2307 = (2 \times 10^3) + (3 \times 10^2) + (0 \times 10^1)$
$\qquad + (7 \times 10^0)$

4. $3047 = (3 \times 10^3) + (0 \times 10^2) + (4 \times 10^1)$
$\qquad + (7 \times 10^0)$

5. $12,349 = (1 \times 10^4) + (2 \times 10^3) + (3 \times 10^2)$
$\qquad + (4 \times 10^1) + (9 \times 10^0)$

6. $10,950 = (1 \times 10^4) + (0 \times 10^3) + (9 \times 10^2)$
$\qquad + (5 \times 10^1) + (0 \times 10^0)$

7. $5^0 = 1$

8. $(3 \times 10) + (4 \times 10^0) = 34$

9. $(4 \times 10) + (5 \times 10^0) = 45$

10. $(4 \times 10^2) + (3 \times 10) + (2 \times 10^0) = 432$

11. $(9 \times 10^3) + (7 \times 10) + (1 \times 10^0) = 9071$

12. $(7 \times 10^4) + (2 \times 10^0) = 70,002$

13. $(7 \times 10^5) + (4 \times 10^4) + (8 \times 10^3)$
$\qquad + (3 \times 10^2) + (8 \times 10^0) = 748,308$

14. $(8 \times 10^9) + (3 \times 10^5) + (2 \times 10^2) + (4 \times 10^0)$
$\qquad = 8,000,300,204$

15. $(4 \times 10^6) + (3 \times 10) + (1 \times 10^0) = 4,000,031$

16.
$$
\begin{array}{r}
32 \\
+15 \\
\hline
47
\end{array}
\qquad
\begin{array}{l}
(3 \times 10) + (2 \times 10^0) \\
+(1 \times 10) + (5 \times 10^0) \\
\hline
(4 \times 10) + (7 \times 10^0)
\end{array}
$$

17.
$$
\begin{array}{r}
23 \\
+13 \\
\hline
36
\end{array}
\qquad
\begin{array}{l}
(2 \times 10) + (3 \times 10^0) \\
+(1 \times 10) + (3 \times 10^0) \\
\hline
(3 \times 10) + (6 \times 10^0)
\end{array}
$$

18.
$$
\begin{array}{r}
21 \\
+34 \\
\hline
55
\end{array}
\qquad
\begin{array}{l}
(2 \times 10) + (1 \times 10^0) \\
+(3 \times 10) + (4 \times 10^0) \\
\hline
(5 \times 10) + (5 \times 10^0)
\end{array}
$$

19.
$$
\begin{array}{r}
71 \\
+23 \\
\hline
94
\end{array}
\qquad
\begin{array}{l}
(7 \times 10) + (1 \times 10^0) \\
+(2 \times 10) + (3 \times 10^0) \\
\hline
(9 \times 10) + (4 \times 10^0)
\end{array}
$$

20.
$$
\begin{array}{r}
34 \\
-21 \\
\hline
13
\end{array}
\qquad
\begin{array}{l}
(3 \times 10) + (4 \times 10^0) \\
-\left[(2 \times 10) + (1 \times 10^0)\right] \\
\hline
(1 \times 10) + (3 \times 10^0)
\end{array}
$$

21.
$$
\begin{array}{r}
76 \\
-54 \\
\hline
22
\end{array}
$$
$$
\begin{array}{r}
(7\times10)+(6\times10^0) \\
-\left[(5\times10)+(4\times10^0)\right] \\
\hline
(2\times10)+(2\times10^0)
\end{array}
$$

22.
$$
\begin{array}{r}
45 \\
-22 \\
\hline
23
\end{array}
$$
$$
\begin{array}{r}
(4\times10)+(5\times10^0) \\
-\left[(2\times10)+(2\times10^0)\right] \\
\hline
(2\times10)+(3\times10^0)
\end{array}
$$

23.
$$
\begin{array}{r}
84 \\
-31 \\
\hline
53
\end{array}
$$
$$
\begin{array}{r}
(8\times10)+(4\times10^0) \\
-\left[(3\times10)+(1\times10^0)\right] \\
\hline
(5\times10)+(3\times10^0)
\end{array}
$$

24. $3^5 \times 3^9 = 3^{5+9} = 3^{14}$

25. $7^8 \times 7^3 = 7^{8+3} = 7^{11}$

26. $4^5 \times 4^2 = 4^{5+2} = 4^7$

27. $6^{19} \times 6^{21} = 6^{19+21} = 6^{40}$

28. $5^8 \div 5^3 = 5^{8-3} = 5^5$

29. $6^{10} \div 6^3 = 6^{10-3} = 6^7$

30. $7^{15} \div 7^3 = 7^{15-3} = 7^{12}$

31. $6^{12} \div 6^0 = 6^{12-0} = 6^{12}$

32. $\left(3^2\right)^4 = 3^{2\times4} = 3^8$

33. $\left(5^4\right)^3 = 5^{4\times3} = 5^{12}$

34. $\left(7^3\right)^5 = 7^{3\times5} = 7^{15}$

35. $\left(10^3\right)^{10} = 10^{3\times10} = 10^{30}$

36.
$$
\begin{array}{r}
41 \\
\times23 \\
\hline
123 \\
82 \\
\hline
943
\end{array}
$$
$$
\begin{array}{r}
(4\times10)+(1\times10^0) \\
\times(2\times10)+(3\times10^0) \\
\hline
(1\times10^2)+(2\times10)+(3\times10^0) \\
(8\times10^2)+(2\times10) \\
\hline
(9\times10^2)+(4\times10)+(3\times10^0)
\end{array}
$$

37.
$$
\begin{array}{r}
25 \\
\times51 \\
\hline
25 \\
125 \\
\hline
1275
\end{array}
$$
$$
\begin{array}{r}
(2\times10)+(5\times10^0) \\
\times(5\times10)+(1\times10^0) \\
\hline
(2\times10)+(5\times10^0) \\
(10\times10^2)+(25\times10) \\
\hline
10^3+(27\times10)+(5\times10^0)
\end{array}
$$

$= 1\times10^3 + 2\times10^2 + 7\times10 + 5\times10^0 = 1275$

38.
$$
\begin{array}{r}
91 \\
\times24 \\
\hline
364 \\
182 \\
\hline
2184
\end{array}
$$

$$
\begin{array}{r}
(9\times10)+(1\times10^0) \\
\times(2\times10)+(4\times10^0) \\
\hline
(3\times10^2)+(6\times10)+(4\times10^0) \\
(1\times10^3)+(8\times10^2)+(2\times10) \\
\hline
(1\times10^3)+(11\times10^2)+(8\times10)+(4\times10^0)
\end{array}
$$

$= (2\times10^3)+(1\times10^2)+(8\times10)+(4\times10^0)$

39.
$$
\begin{array}{r}
62 \\
\times25 \\
\hline
310 \\
124 \\
\hline
1550
\end{array}
$$
$$
\begin{array}{r}
(6\times10)+(2\times10^0) \\
\times(2\times10)+(5\times10^0) \\
\hline
(30\times10)+(10\times10^0) \\
(12\times10^2)+(4\times10) \\
\hline
12\times10^2+(34\times10)+(10\times10^0)
\end{array}
$$

$= 1\times10^3 + 5\times10^2 + 5\times10 + 0\times10^0 = 1550$

40.

$$\begin{array}{r} 12 \\ 4\overline{)48} \\ \underline{4} \\ 8 \\ \underline{8} \\ 0 \end{array}$$

$$4\times10^0\overline{)\,(4\times10)+(8\times10^0)}\quad (1\times10)+(2\times10^0)$$
$$\underline{(4\times10)}$$
$$(8\times10^0)$$
$$\underline{(8\times10^0)}$$
$$0$$

41.

$$\begin{array}{r} 8 \\ 8\overline{)64} \\ \underline{64} \\ 0 \end{array}$$

$$8\times10^0\overline{)\,(6\times10)+(4\times10^0)}\quad 8\times10^0$$
$$\underline{(6\times10)+(4\times10^0)}$$
$$0$$

42.

$$\begin{array}{r} 31 \\ 3\overline{)93} \\ \underline{9} \\ 3 \\ \underline{3} \\ 0 \end{array}$$

$$3\times10^0\overline{)\,(9\times10)+(3\times10^0)}\quad (3\times10)+(1\times10^0)$$
$$\underline{(9\times10)}$$
$$(3\times10^0)$$
$$\underline{(3\times10^0)}$$
$$0$$

43.

$$\begin{array}{r} 12 \\ 6\overline{)72} \\ \underline{6} \\ 12 \\ \underline{12} \\ 0 \end{array}$$

$$6\times10^0\overline{)\,(7\times10)+(2\times10^0)}\quad (1\times10)+(2\times10^0)$$
$$\underline{(6\times10)}$$
$$(1\times10)+(2\times10^0)$$
$$\underline{(1\times10)+(2\times10^0)}$$
$$0$$

44. $5\times(3\times10^8)=15\times10^8=1.5\times10^9$ lb

45. $4\times75,000=300,000=3\times10^5$ trees saved

46. $2.5\times(4.4\times10^6)=11\times10^6$
$$=1.1\times10^7 \text{ pet reptiles}$$

47. $1.7\times(45.5\times10^6)=77.35\times10^6$
$$=7.735\times10^7 \text{ dogs}$$

48. $(7.2\times10^7)\div30=0.24\times10^7$
$$=2.4\times10^6 \text{ searches/day}$$

49. $\dfrac{4.8\times10^7}{30}=0.16\times10^7=1.6\times10^6$ searches/day

50. $400\times(3.20\times10^8)=1280\times10^6$
$$=1.28\times10^9 \text{ lb/yr}$$

51. $200\times(3.20\times10^8)=640\times10^6$
$$=6.4\times10^8 \text{ lb/yr}$$

52. $20.2\times(3.20\times10^8)=64.64\times10^8$
$$=6.464\times10^9 \text{ lb/yr}$$

53. $58.8\times(3.20\times10^8)=188.16\times10^8$
$$=1.8816\times10^{10} \text{ lb/yr}$$

54. $13.9\times(3.20\times10^8)=44.48\times10^8$
$$=4.448\times10^9 \text{ lb/yr}$$

55. $24\times(3.20\times10^8)=76.8\times10^8$
$$=7.68\times10^9 \text{ gal/yr}$$

56. $50\times(3.20\times10^8)=160\times10^8$
$$=1.6\times10^{10} \text{ gal/yr}$$

57. $\dfrac{(2.7\times10^8)\times(2\times10^3)}{(3\times10^8)\times(3.6\times10^2)}=\dfrac{5.4\times10^{11}}{10.8\times10^{10}}$
$$=0.5\times10=5 \text{ lb}$$

58. $(1.8\times10^3)\times(4.7\times10^6)=8.46\times10^9$
$$=8,460,000,000 \text{ lb}$$

59. $(1.8\times10^3)\times(4.2\times10^6)=7.56\times10^9$
$$=7,560,000,000 \text{ lb}$$

60. $\dfrac{1.02\times10^{19}}{\left(5.1\times10^{8}\right)\times10^{10}} = \dfrac{1.02\times10^{19}}{5.1\times10^{18}} = 0.2\times10^{1} = 2$

61. Answers may vary. You must add the exponents to obtain a^{m+n}.

62. Answers may vary. Write a with the exponent $m-n$.

63. Answers may vary. You must multiply the exponent m by n to obtain a^{mn}.

64. Answers may vary. The answer should be 1 if $a \neq 0$. Thus, if we write $\dfrac{a^{m}}{a^{n}} = a^{m-n} = a^{0}$, then we should define a^{0} to be 1.

65. 7 women, $7^2 = 49$ mules. $7^3 = 343$ sacks. $7^4 = 2401$ loaves. $7^5 = 16,807$ knives. $7^6 = 117,649$ sheaths. Thus there were: $7 + 49 + 343 + 2401 + 16,807 + 117,649 = 137,256$ in all on the road to Rome.

66. There was only one going to St. Ives (if the traveler meets the others going in the opposite direction). If all travelers were going to St. Ives the total would be 1 + 1 + 2800 = 2802. If only the kits, cats, sacks and wives are counted, 2800 were going to St. Ives.

Section 4.3 Number Systems with Bases Other Than 10

1. 22_{three}

2. 33_{five}

3. 31_{four}

4. 36_{ten}

5. $\boxed{********}\ \ ******* = 17_{eight}$

6. $\boxed{*****}\boxed{*****}\boxed{*****} = 30_{five}$

7. $\boxed{*******}\boxed{*******}\ * = 21_{seven}$

8. $\boxed{************}\ *** = 13_{twelve}$

9. $42_{five} = 4\times5 + 2 = 22$

10. $31_{five} = 3\times5 + 1 = 16$

11. $213_{eight} = 2\times8^{2} + 1\times8 + 3$
$= 128 + 8 + 3 = 139$

12. $563_{eight} = 5\times8^{2} + 6\times8 + 3$
$= 320 + 48 + 3 = 371$

13. $11011_{two} = 2^{4} + 2^{3} + 2 + 1$
$= 16 + 8 + 2 + 1 = 27$

14. $101001_{two} = 2^{5} + 2^{3} + 1$
$= 32 + 8 + 1 = 41$

15. $123_{sixteen} = 1\times16^{2} + 2\times16 + 3$
$= 256 + 32 + 3 = 291$

16. $ACE_{sixteen} = 10\times16^{2} + 12\times16 + 14$
$= 2560 + 192 + 14 = 2766$

17. $5\overline{)15}$
$\quad 3\,|\,0 \qquad 15 = 30_{five}$

18. $5\overline{)27}$
$5\overline{)5\,|\,2}$
$5\overline{)1\,|\,0} \qquad 27 = 102_{five}$

19. $2\overline{)28}$
$2\overline{)14\,|\,0}$
$2\overline{)\ 7\,|\,0}$
$2\overline{)\ 3\,|\,1}$
$\quad 1\,|\,1 \qquad 28 = 11100_{two}$

20. $2\,)\,43$

    $2\,)\,21\,|\,1$

    $2\,)\,10\,|\,1$

    $2\,)\,\ \ 5\,|\,0$

    $2\,)\,\ \ 2\,|\,1$

    $\qquad 1\,|\,0 \qquad 43 = 101011_{\text{two}}$

21. $16\,)\,25$

    $\qquad 1\,|\,9 \qquad 25 = 19_{\text{sixteen}}$

22. $16\,)\,121$

    $\qquad 7\,|\,9 \qquad 121 = 79_{\text{sixteen}}$

23. $6\,)\,25$

    $\qquad 4\,|\,1 \qquad 25 = 41_{\text{six}}$

24. $6\,)\,38$

    $6\,)\,6\,|\,2$

    $\qquad 1\,|\,0 \qquad 38 = 102_{\text{six}}$

25. $7\,)\,64$

    $7\,)\,\ \ 9\,|\,1$

    $\qquad 1\,|\,2 \qquad 64 = 121_{\text{seven}}$

26. $7\,)\,123$

    $7\,)\,\ \ 17\,|\,4$

    $\qquad 2\,|\,3 \qquad 123 = 234_{\text{seven}}$

27. $8\,)\,38$

    $\qquad 4\,|\,6 \qquad 38 = 46_{\text{eight}}$

28. $8\,)\,135$

    $8\,)\,\ \ 16\,|\,7$

    $\qquad 2\,|\,0 \qquad 135 = 207_{\text{eight}}$

29. $16\,)\,1467$

    $16\,)\,\ \ 91\,|\,11$

    $\qquad 5\,|\,11 \qquad 1467 = 5BB_{\text{sixteen}}$

30. $16\,)\,145,263$

    $16\,)\,9078\,|\,15$

    $16\,)\,\ \ 567\,|\,6$

    $16\,)\,\ \ \ 35\,|\,7$

    $\qquad 2\,|\,3 \qquad 145,263 = 2376F_{\text{sixteen}}$

31. $2\,)\,73$

    $2\,)\,36\,|\,1$

    $2\,)\,18\,|\,0$

    $2\,)\,\ \ 9\,|\,0$

    $2\,)\,\ \ 4\,|\,1$

    $2\,)\,\ \ 2\,|\,0$

    $\qquad 1\,|\,0 \qquad 73 = 1001001_{\text{two}}$

    $\qquad 8\,)\,73$

    $\qquad 8\,)\,\ \ 9\,|\,1$

    $\qquad \qquad 1\,|\,1 \qquad 73 = 111_{\text{eight}}$

32. $8\,)\,87$

    $8\,)\,107$

    $\qquad 1\,|\,2 \qquad 87 = 127_{\text{eight}}$

    $\qquad 16\,)\,87$

    $\qquad \qquad 5\,|\,7 \qquad 87 = 57_{\text{sixteen}}$

33. | 00110 | 01010 | 00101 | 00011 | 01100 |
    |-------|-------|-------|-------|-------|
    | 3 | 5 | 2 | 1 | 6 |

34. | 01010 | 00110 | 01001 | 00011 | 01010 |
    |-------|-------|-------|-------|-------|
    | 5 | 3 | 4 | 1 | 5 |

35. | 01001 | 00101 | 00011 | 00110 | 01010 |
    |-------|-------|-------|-------|-------|
    | 4 | 2 | 1 | 3 | 5 |

36. | 10010 | 11000 | 10001 | 01001 | 00110 |
    |-------|-------|-------|-------|-------|
    | 8 | 0 | 7 | 4 | 3 |

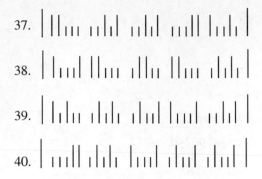

37.

38.

39.

40.

41. Answers may vary. Yes. The Zip Code + 4 consists of 9 numbers and each number is represented by 5 bars, so there should only be 45 bars and the two long bars at the beginning and the end of the Zip Code + 4 numbers for a total of 47 bars. As it turns out, the other 5 bars are the *checking* digit.

42. a. The extra digit is |||||, so the checking digit is 6.
    b. Answers may vary.
    $3 + 3 + 6 + 7 + 5 = 24$
    $2 + 4 = 6 \leftarrow$ Check digit

43. Answers may vary. One of the meanings of binary is "based on two." The prefix bi means "two."

44. Answers may vary. Octal means related to or being a number in the base 8 number system. The prefix oct means "eight."

45. Answers may vary. Hexadecimal means "based on 16." The prefix hexa means "six" and the "deci" means ten to make sixteen.

46. Answers may vary. We can't use more than one decimal digit because in the base 16 system, $10_{16} = 16$, $11_{16} = 16 + 1 = 17$, and so on. Thus, we use letters to correspond to the base 10 numbers 10, 11, 12, 13, 14, and 15.

47. The trick works because the columns correspond to the binary digits in the number. For instance, $6 = 110_{two}$ and this corresponds to the number $6 = 2 + 4$, the numbers that head columns *B* and *C*. Note that 6 occurs in columns *B* and *C*, but not in *A*.

48. The binary number for 15 is 1111_{two}. Since there are four places, you would need four columns to extend this trick.

49. Use the same procedure as for the numbers from 1 to 7, but with five columns instead of three. If you label the columns *A, B, C, D, E*, then the numbers 1, 2, 4, 8, and 16 would head these columns. The number 13, for example, would be put into columns *A, C*, and *D* because $13 = 01101_{two}$ which means that $13 = 1 + 4 + 8$, the numbers that head these three columns.

Calculator Corner

1. Key in the following and the calculator will show the answer 13:
   $\boxed{1}\boxed{\times}\boxed{2}\boxed{+}\boxed{1}\boxed{=}\boxed{\times}\boxed{2}\boxed{+}\boxed{0}\boxed{=}\boxed{\times}\boxed{2}\boxed{+}\boxed{1}\boxed{=}$

2. Key in the following and the calculator will show the answer 45:
   $\boxed{2}\boxed{\times}\boxed{4}\boxed{+}\boxed{3}\boxed{=}\boxed{\times}\boxed{4}\boxed{+}\boxed{1}\boxed{=}$

3. Key in the following and the calculator will show the answer 113:
   $\boxed{4}\boxed{\times}\boxed{5}\boxed{+}\boxed{2}\boxed{=}\boxed{\times}\boxed{5}\boxed{+}\boxed{3}\boxed{=}$

4. Key in the following and the calculator will show the answer 490:
   $\boxed{7}\boxed{\times}\boxed{8}\boxed{+}\boxed{5}\boxed{=}\boxed{\times}\boxed{8}\boxed{+}\boxed{2}\boxed{=}$

5. Key in the following and the calculator will show the answer 1914:
   $\boxed{3}\boxed{\times}\boxed{8}\boxed{+}\boxed{5}\boxed{=}\boxed{\times}\boxed{8}\boxed{+}\boxed{7}\boxed{=}\boxed{\times}\boxed{8}\boxed{+}\boxed{2}\boxed{=}$

6. Key in the following and the calculator will show the answer 714:
   $\boxed{8}\boxed{\times}\boxed{9}\boxed{+}\boxed{7}\boxed{=}\boxed{\times}\boxed{9}\boxed{+}\boxed{3}\boxed{=}$

Collaborative Learning

1. 36 (Base 1, Base 2... Base 10, Base 11 (using A), Base 12 (using A, B), etc).

2. Answers will vary.　3. Answers will vary.

4. Answers will vary.

You can read more about prime words by visiting **http://www.cut-the-knot.org/recurrence/word_primes.shtml**

Section 4.4 Binary, Octal, and Hexadecimal Arithmetic

1. $\begin{array}{r} {}^{1}111_2 \\ +\ 10_2 \\ \hline 1001_2 \end{array}$

2. $\begin{array}{r} {}^{1}1{}^{1}11_2 \\ +1\ 01_2 \\ \hline 1100_2 \end{array}$

3. $\begin{array}{r} {}^{1}1101_2 \\ +110_2 \\ \hline 10011_2 \end{array}$

4. $\begin{array}{r} {}^{1}1{}^{1}1{}^{1}11_2 \\ +11\ 01_2 \\ \hline 11100_2 \end{array}$

5. $\begin{array}{r} {}^{1}1{}^{1}10_2 \\ 1\ 01_2 \\ +1\ 11_2 \\ \hline 10010_2 \end{array}$

6. $\begin{array}{r} {}^{1}1{}^{1}1{}^{1}01_2 \\ 11\ 10_2 \\ +\ \ 101_2 \\ \hline 100000_2 \end{array}$

7. $\begin{array}{r} {}^{1}5{}^{1}31_8 \\ +47_8 \\ \hline 600_8 \end{array}$

8. $\begin{array}{r} {}^{1}4{}^{1}25_8 \\ +\ \ 364_8 \\ \hline 1011_8 \end{array}$

9. $\begin{array}{r} {}^{1}7{}^{1}2{}^{1}56_8 \\ +634_8 \\ \hline 10112_8 \end{array}$

10. $\begin{array}{r} {}^{1}5{}^{1}7{}^{1}32_8 \\ +\ \ 747_8 \\ \hline 6701_8 \end{array}$

11. $\begin{array}{r} {}^{1}3{}^{1}CB_{16} \\ +4C_{16} \\ \hline 417_{16} \end{array}$

12. $\begin{array}{r} {}^{1}4{}^{1}FE_{16} \\ +\ \ 35_{16} \\ \hline 533_{16} \end{array}$

13. $\begin{array}{r} 9{}^{1}8D_{16} \\ +2B_{16} \\ \hline 9B8_{16} \end{array}$

14. $\begin{array}{r} {}^{1}C{}^{1}BD_{16} \\ +\ \ AF_{16} \\ \hline D6C_{16} \end{array}$

15. $\begin{array}{r} 111_2 \\ -10_2 \\ \hline 101_2 \end{array}$

16. $\begin{array}{r} \cancel{1}{}^{10}\cancel{1}{}^{1}0_2 \\ -\ \ 1\ 1_2 \\ \hline 11_2 \end{array}$

17. $\begin{array}{r} \cancel{1}{}^{1}0{}^{1}0{}^{1}0_2 \\ -1\ 1\ 1_2 \\ \hline 1_2 \end{array}$

18. $\begin{array}{r} \cancel{1}{}^{10}\cancel{1}{}^{1}01_2 \\ -\ \ 1\ 11_2 \\ \hline 110_2 \end{array}$

19. $\begin{array}{r} 1111_2 \\ -101_2 \\ \hline 1010_2 \end{array}$

20. $\begin{array}{r} \cancel{1}{}^{1}0{}^{0}\cancel{1}{}^{1}0_2 \\ -\ 1\ 0\ 1_2 \\ \hline 101_2 \end{array}$

21. $\begin{array}{r} 5{}^{2}\cancel{3}{}^{1}4_8 \\ -\ \ 25_8 \\ \hline 507_8 \end{array}$

22. $\begin{array}{r} {}^{5}\cancel{6}{}^{1}17_8 \\ -\ \ 47_8 \\ \hline 550_8 \end{array}$

23. $\begin{array}{r} {}^{2}\cancel{3}{}^{1}2{}^{5}\cancel{6}{}^{1}4_8 \\ -\ \ 756_8 \\ \hline 2306_8 \end{array}$

24. $\begin{array}{r} 47{}^{5}\cancel{6}{}^{1}3_8 \\ -65\ 4_8 \\ \hline 4107_8 \end{array}$

25. $\begin{array}{r} 110_2 \\ \times 11_2 \\ \hline 110_2 \\ 1100_2 \\ \hline 10010_2 \end{array}$

26. $\begin{array}{r} 101_2 \\ \times 10_2 \\ \hline 1010_2 \end{array}$

27. $\begin{array}{r} 1111_2 \\ \times\ 11_2 \\ \hline 1111_2 \\ 11110_2 \\ \hline 101101_2 \end{array}$

28. $\begin{array}{r} 1110_2 \\ \times\ 111_2 \\ \hline 1110_2 \\ 11100_2 \\ 111000_2 \\ \hline 1100010_2 \end{array}$

29. $\begin{array}{r} 1011_2 \\ \times 101_2 \\ \hline 1011_2 \\ 101100_2 \\ \hline 110111_2 \end{array}$

30. $\begin{array}{r} 1011_2 \\ \times 111_2 \\ \hline 1011_2 \\ 10110_2 \\ 101100_2 \\ \hline 1001101_2 \end{array}$

31. $\begin{array}{r} 57_8 \\ \times 6_8 \\ \hline 432_8 \end{array}$

32. $\begin{array}{r} {}^{4}45_8 \\ \times\ 7_8 \\ \hline 403_8 \end{array}$

33. 216_8
$\times 32_8$
434
652
7154_8

34. 312_8
$\times 65_8$
1762
22740
24722_8

35. $2C5_{16}$
$\times 3B_{16}$
37
84
16
F
24
6
$A367_{16}$

36. $4DE_{16}$
$\times 12_{16}$
1C
1A
8
E
D
4
$579C_{16}$

37. $6F3_{16}$
$\times AB_{16}$
21
A5
42
1E
96
3C
$4A451_{16}$

38. $29A_{16}$
$\times E0F_{16}$
96
87
1E
8C
7E
1C
249306_{16}

39. $\dfrac{110_2\,R1_2}{10_2\,)\,1101_2}$
10
10
10
01

40. $\dfrac{100_2\,R1_2}{11_2\,)\,1101_2}$
11
01

41. $\dfrac{100_2\,R10_2}{11_2\,)\,1110_2}$
11
010

42. $\dfrac{1001_2}{11_2\,)\,11011_2}$
11
011
11
0

43. $\dfrac{1011_2\,R100_2}{101_2\,)\,111011_2}$
101
1001
101
1001
101
100

44. $\dfrac{10001_2}{111_2\,)\,1110111_2}$
111
0111
111
0

45. $\dfrac{35_8\,R4_8}{7_8\,)\,317_8}$
25
47
43
4

46. $\dfrac{711_8}{5_8\,)\,4355_8}$
43
55
50
5
5
0

47. $\dfrac{250_8\,R5_8}{15_8\,)\,4215_8}$
32
101
101
05

48. $\dfrac{230_8\,R12_8}{31_8\,)\,7342_8}$
62
1142
93
12

49. Answers will vary. The main reason is that there are only two digits in the binary system contrasted with 16 digits in the hexadecimal system. Compare the addition and multiplication tables for the two systems.

50. Answers will vary. Powers of 10 are easier to work with than powers of 2 or powers of 16 probably because we are accustomed to base 10, and have used that representation since we were exceedingly young. If the number is given to us in decimal form, the conversion is direct since each power of 10 is a position in the number.

51. Answers will vary depending on the numbers chosen.

52. a. The number of orifices (holes) in the human head is 7.
    b. The atomic number of sodium is 11.

c. Using numerology, the number 7 is associated with each word.

d. There are 7 dwarfs in the Snow White tale.

e. Using numerology, the number 11 is associated with each word.

f. There are 7 stars in the Big Dipper.

g. The atomic number of argon is 18.

h. Using numerology, the number 18 is associated with each word.

i. The atomic number of nitrogen is 7.

j. James Polk was the 11th president of the United States of America, Andrew Jackson was the 7th president, and Ulysses S. Grant was the 18th president.

53. $110111_2 = 2^5 + 2^4 + 2^2 + 2 + 1$
$$= 32 + 16 + 4 + 2 + 1 = 55$$

54. It represents a shade closer to black.

55. Since white is represented by 000000_2, the next smallest number, 000001_2, would represent the lightest shade of gray that is not white.

56. The darkest shade of gray that is not black is represented by the binary number 111110_2.

Collaborative Learning

1. Yes.   No.

2. Yes. Answers will vary.

3. *Supercalifragilisticexpialidocious* has 34 letters: $34 \times 8 = 272$ bits

Chapter 4 Practice Test

1. a. ∩∩∩ ||| / ∩∩∩

   b. 9999∩∩||| / 999 ∩ ||

2. a. $10 + 10 + 1 + 1 + 1 = 23$
   b. $100 + 10 + 10 + 1 = 121$

3. a. ▼ ▼▼▼

   b. ◄ ▼▼ ◄▼▼▼▼▼

4. a. $60 + 10 + 10 + 1 + 1 = 82$
   b. $60 + 60 + 10 + 1 = 131$

5. a.
\1	21
\2	42
\4	84
8	168
\16	336
23	483

   b.
23	21
11	42
5	84
2	168
1	336
	483

6. a. 67   b. 48,000

7. a. LIII   b. XLII   c. $\overline{\text{XXII}}$

8. a. $2 \times 10^3 + 5 \times 10^2 + 0 \times 10 + 7 \times 10^0$
   b. $1 \times 10^2 + 8 \times 10 + 9 \times 10^0$

9. a. 3702   b. 59,040

10. a.
$$
\begin{array}{r}
75 \\
+32 \\
\hline
107
\end{array}
$$
$$
\begin{array}{l}
(7 \times 10) + (5 \times 10^0) \\
+(3 \times 10) + (2 \times 10^0) \\
\hline
(10 \times 10) + (7 \times 10^0)
\end{array}
$$
$$= (1 \times 10^2) + (7 \times 10^0) = 107$$

   b.
$$
\begin{array}{r}
56 \\
-24 \\
\hline
32
\end{array}
$$
$$
\begin{array}{l}
(5 \times 10) + (6 \times 10^0) \\
-(2 \times 10) + (4 \times 10^0) \\
\hline
(3 \times 10) + (2 \times 10^0) = 32
\end{array}
$$

11. a. $3^4 \times 3^8 = 3^{4+8} = 3^{12}$
    b. $2^9 \div 2^3 = 2^{9-3} = 2^6$

12. a.
$$
\begin{array}{r}
83 \\
\times 21 \\
\hline
83 \\
166 \\
\hline
1743
\end{array}
$$
$$
\begin{array}{l}
(8 \times 10) + (3 \times 10^0) \\
\times (2 \times 10) + (1 \times 10^0) \\
\hline
(8 \times 10) + (3 \times 10^0) \\
(16 \times 10^2) + (6 \times 10) \\
\hline
16 \times 10^2 + (14 \times 10) + (3 \times 10^0)
\end{array}
$$
$$= 1 \times 10^3 + 7 \times 10^2 + 4 \times 10 + 3 \times 10^0 = 1743$$

b. $\dfrac{7\,R\,5}{7)\overline{54}}$ $\quad 7\times10^0\overline{)\dfrac{(7\times10^0)\,R\,(5\times10^0)}{(5\times10)+(4\times10^0)}}$

$\quad\quad \dfrac{49}{5}$ $\quad\quad\quad \dfrac{(4\times10)+(9\times10^0)}{5\times10^0}$

b.

$2)\overline{527}$

$2)\overline{263}|1$

$2)\overline{131}|1$

$2)\overline{\;65}|1$

$2)\overline{\;32}|1$

$2)\overline{\;16}|0$

$2)\overline{\quad 8}|0$

$2)\overline{\quad 4}|0$

$2)\overline{\quad 2}|0$

$\quad\quad 1|0 \quad\quad 527 = 1000001111_{\text{two}}$

13. a. $203_4 = 2\times4^2 + 0\times4 + 3 = 32 + 3 = 35$

b. $143_5 = 1\times5^2 + 4\times5 + 3$

$\quad\quad = 25 + 20 + 3 = 48$

c. $1101_2 = 1\times2^3 + 1\times2^2 + 0\times2 + 1$

$\quad\quad = 8 + 4 + 1 = 13$

14. a. $152_8 = 1\times8^2 + 5\times8 + 2$

$\quad\quad = 64 + 40 + 2 = 106$

b. $A2C_{16} = 10\times16^2 + 2\times16 + 12$

$\quad\quad\quad = 2560 + 32 + 12 = 2604$

17. a. $8)\overline{47}$

$\quad\quad 5|7 \quad\quad 47 = 57_{\text{eight}}$

b. $16)\overline{47}$

$\quad\quad 2|15 \quad\quad 47 = 2F_{\text{sixteen}}$

15. a. $5)\overline{33}$

$\quad 5)\overline{\;6}|3$

$\quad\quad 1|1 \quad\quad 33 = 113_{\text{five}}$

b. $6)\overline{33}$

$\quad\quad 5|3 \quad\quad 33 = 53_{\text{six}}$

18. a. $\begin{array}{r} {}^{1}11{}^{1}01_2 \\ +\ 101_2 \\ \hline 10010_2 \end{array}$
b. $\begin{array}{r} {}^{1}1{}^{0}\not{1}{}^{1}01_2 \\ -\ 11\,1_2 \\ \hline 110_2 \end{array}$

16. a. $2)\overline{39}$

$\quad 2)\overline{19}|1$

$\quad 2)\overline{\,9}|1$

$\quad 2)\overline{\;4}|1$

$\quad 2)\overline{\;2}|0$

$\quad\quad 1|0 \quad\quad 39 = 100111_{\text{two}}$

19. a. $\begin{array}{r} 1101_2 \\ \times\,11_2 \\ \hline 1101_2 \\ 11010_2 \\ \hline 100111_2 \end{array}$
b. $\begin{array}{r} 10110_2 \\ \times\,101_2 \\ \hline 10110_2 \\ 1011000_2 \\ \hline 1101110_2 \end{array}$

20. a. $\dfrac{111_2\,R1_2}{11_2)\overline{10110_2}}$
b. $\dfrac{1001_2\,R1_2}{110_2)\overline{110111_2}}$

a.
$\quad \dfrac{11}{101}$
$\quad \dfrac{11}{100}$
$\quad \dfrac{11}{1}$

b.
$\quad \dfrac{110}{0111}$
$\quad \dfrac{110}{1}$

21. $^16{}^132_8$
    $\underline{+\ 46_8}$
    700_8

22. 37_8
    $\underline{\times 5_8}$
    43
    $\underline{17}$
    233_8

23. $^5\cancel{6}\ ^{12}\cancel{3}\ ^1 2_8$
    $\underline{-\ \ 4\ \ 6_8}$
    564_8

24. $\quad\ \ 77_8$
    $6_8\overline{)572_8}$
    $\quad\ \underline{52}$
    $\quad\ \ 52$
    $\quad\ \underline{52}$
    $\quad\ \ \ 0$

25. a. $\quad ^12{}^1BC_{16}$
    $\quad\underline{+\ 5D_{16}}$
    $\quad 319_{16}$

    b. $\quad 3C4_{16}$
    $\quad\underline{\times\ 2B_{16}}$
    $\quad\ 2C$
    $\quad\ 84$
    $\quad\ 21$
    $\quad\quad 8$
    $\quad 18$
    $\quad\ \underline{6}$
    $\quad A1EC_{16}$

Chapter 5 Number Theory and the Real Numbers

Section 5.1 Number Theory: Primes and Composites

1. For identification only

2. Ordinal number

3. A cardinal number (used for counting)

4. Cardinal numbers

5. The "First" is for identification; the "one" is an ordinal number.

6. 14, an ordinal number; 5696, a cardinal number; 0166, for identification.

7. The sieve is constructed in the same way as it was for the numbers from 1 to 50. We cross out all the multiples of 2, of 3, of 5, and of 7. The remaining numbers are all primes. We don't have to go beyond 7, because the next prime is 11 and its square is greater than 100. The primes in the table are boxed.

8. There are 9 primes between 1 and 25: 2, 3, 5, 7, 11, 13, 17, 19, 23.

9. There are 6 primes between 25 and 50: 29, 31, 37, 41, 43, 47.

10. There are 6 primes between 50 and 75: 53, 59, 61, 67, 71, 73.

11. There are 4 primes between 75 and 100: 79, 83, 89, 97.

12. a. The smallest prime is 2.
    b. The only even prime is 2.

13. a. 2 and 3 are both primes and are consecutive counting numbers.
    b. No. If any pair of consecutive counting numbers greater than 2 is selected, one of the pair must be an even number (divisible by 2) and hence, not a prime. Thus, there cannot be a second pair of primes that are consecutive counting numbers .

14. Possible answers: 5 and 7, 11 and 13, 17 and 19, 29 and 31, 41 and 43

15. a. The product part of m is exactly divisible by 2, so that m divided by 2 would have a remainder of 1.
    b. The product part of m is exactly divisible by 3, so that m divided by 3 would have a remainder of 1.
    c. and d. Exactly the same reasoning as in parts a and b applies here. If m is divided by any prime from 2 to P, there is remainder of 1.
    e. Because P was assumed to be the largest prime.
    f. Because m is not divisible by any of the primes from 2 to P.

16. $28 = 2 \cdot 2 \cdot 7$. Thus, the divisors of 28 are 1, 2, 4 (or $2 \cdot 2$), 7, 14 (or $2 \cdot 7$), and 28 (or $2 \cdot 2 \cdot 7$).

17. $50 = 2 \cdot 5 \cdot 5$. Thus, the divisors of 50 are 1, 2, 5, 10 (or $2 \cdot 5$), 25 (or $5 \cdot 5$), and 50 (or $2 \cdot 5 \cdot 5$).

18. $119 = 7 \cdot 17$. Thus, the divisors of 119 are 1, 7, 17, and 119 (or $7 \cdot 17$).

19. $128 = 2 \cdot 2 \cdot 2 \cdot 2 \cdot 2 \cdot 2 \cdot 2 = 2^7$. Thus, the divisors of 128 are 1, 2, 4 (or $2 \cdot 2$), 8 (or $2 \cdot 4$), 16 (or $2 \cdot 8$), 32 (or $2 \cdot 16$), 64 (or $2 \cdot 32$), and 128 (or $2 \cdot 64$).

20. $1365 = 3 \cdot 5 \cdot 7 \cdot 13$. Thus, the divisors of 1365 are 1, 3, 5, 7, 13, 15 (or $3 \cdot 5$), 21 (or $3 \cdot 7$), 35 (or $5 \cdot 7$), 39 (or $3 \cdot 13$), 65 (or $5 \cdot 13$), 91 (or $7 \cdot 13$), 105 (or $3 \cdot 5 \cdot 7$), 195 (or $3 \cdot 5 \cdot 13$), 273 (or $3 \cdot 7 \cdot 13$), 455 (or $5 \cdot 7 \cdot 13$), and 1365 (or $3 \cdot 5 \cdot 7 \cdot 13$).

21. $1001 = 7 \cdot 11 \cdot 13$. Thus, the divisors of 1001 are 1, 7, 11, 13, 77 (or $7 \cdot 11$), 91 (or $7 \cdot 13$), 143 (or $11 \cdot 13$), and 1001 (or $7 \cdot 11 \cdot 13$).

22. $24 = 2^3 \cdot 3$

23. 41 is a prime.

24. $82 = 2 \cdot 41$

25. $91 = 7 \cdot 13$

26. 191 is a prime.

27. $148 = 2^2 \cdot 37$

28. $2 \cdot 3^2 \cdot 5^2 = 450$

29. $2 \cdot 5 \cdot 7^2 = 490$

30. $2 \cdot 3 \cdot 5 \cdot 11 = 330$

31. $2^4 \cdot 3 \cdot 5^2 = 1200$

32. a. 468 is an even number, so is divisible by **2**. The sum of the digits is 18, so the number is divisible by **3**. The number does not end in 5, so is not divisible by 5.
    b. 580 ends in 0, so is divisible by **2** and by **5**. The sum of the digits is 13, so the number is not divisible by 3.
    c. 795 is not an even number, so is not divisible by 2. The sum of the digits is 21, so the number is divisible by **3**. The number ends in 5, so is divisible by **5**.
    d. 3942 is an even number, so is divisible by **2**. The sum of the digits is 18, so the number is divisible by **3**. The number does not end in 5, so is not divisible by 5.

33. a. 6345 is not an even number, so is not divisible by 2. The sum of the digits is 18, so the number is divisible by **3**. The number ends in 5, so is divisible by **5**.
    b. 8280 ends in 0, so is divisible by **2** and by **5**. The sum of the digits is 18, so the number is divisible by **3**.
    c. 11,469,390 ends in 0, so is divisible by **2** and by **5**. The sum of the first three digits is 6, which is divisible by 3, and the other digits are all multiples of 3; thus, the number is divisible by **3**.

34. The smallest number that when divided by either 5 or 7, that has a remainder of 1 must be the lcm (5, 7) + 1 = 35 + 1 = 36: $\boxed{36} = 9 \cdot 4 = 5 \cdot 7 + 1 = 7 \cdot 5 + 1$.

35. In order to leave a remainder of 1 when divided into 23, the divisor must be an exact divisor of 22; 2, 11 or 22. All three of these leave a remainder of 1 when divided into 45. Thus, there are three whole numbers, 2, 11 and 22, that satisfy the given condition.

36. $14 = 2 \cdot 7$; $210 = 2 \cdot 3 \cdot 5 \cdot 7$.
    GCF (14, 210) = 14

37. $135 = 3^3 \cdot 5$; $351 = 3^3 \cdot 13$.
    GCF $(135, 351) = 3^3 = 27$

38. $315 = 5 \cdot 3^2 \cdot 7$; $350 = 2 \cdot 5^2 \cdot 7$.
    GCF (315, 350) = 35

39. $147 = 3 \cdot 7^2$; $260 = 2^2 \cdot 5 \cdot 13$.
    GCF (147, 260) = 1, so 147 and 260 are relatively prime.

40. $368 = 2^4 \cdot 23$; $80 = 2^4 \cdot 5$. GCF (368, 80) = 16

41. $282 = 2 \cdot 3 \cdot 47$; $329 = 7 \cdot 47$.
    GCF (282, 329) = 47

42. $12 = 2^2 \cdot 3$; $18 = 2 \cdot 3^2$; $30 = 2 \cdot 3 \cdot 5$.
    GCF (12, 18, 30) = 6

43. $12 = 2^2 \cdot 3$; $15 = 3 \cdot 5$; $20 = 2^2 \cdot 5$.
    GCF (12, 15, 20) = 1, so 12, 15 and 20 are relatively prime.

44. $285 = 3 \cdot 3 \cdot 19$; $315 = 3^2 \cdot 5 \cdot 7$;
    $588 = 2^2 \cdot 3 \cdot 7^2$. GCF (285, 315, 588) = 3

45. $100 = 2^2 \cdot 5^2$; $200 = 2^3 \cdot 5^2$; $320 = 2^6 \cdot 5$.
    GCF $(100, 200, 320) = 2^2 \cdot 5 = 20$.

46. $\dfrac{80}{92} = \dfrac{4 \cdot 20}{4 \cdot 23} = \dfrac{20}{23}$

47. $\dfrac{62}{88} = \dfrac{2 \cdot 31}{2 \cdot 44} = \dfrac{31}{44}$

48. $\dfrac{140}{280} = \dfrac{140 \cdot 1}{140 \cdot 2} = \dfrac{1}{2}$

49. $156 = 2^2 \cdot 3 \cdot 13$; $728 = 2^3 \cdot 7 \cdot 13$.
    GCF $(156, 728) = 2^2 \cdot 13 = 52$. So,
    $\dfrac{156}{728} = \dfrac{52 \cdot 3}{52 \cdot 14} = \dfrac{3}{14}$

50. $315 = 3^2 \cdot 5 \cdot 7$; $420 = 2^2 \cdot 3 \cdot 5 \cdot 7$.
    GCF $(315, 420) = 3 \cdot 5 \cdot 7 = 105$. So,
    $\dfrac{315}{420} = \dfrac{105 \cdot 3}{105 \cdot 4} = \dfrac{3}{4}$

51. $96 = 2^5 \cdot 3; \quad 384 = 2^7 \cdot 3.$

    $GCF\,(96, 384) = 2^5 \cdot 3 = 96.$ Thus,

    $$\frac{96}{384} = \frac{96 \cdot 1}{96 \cdot 4} = \frac{1}{4}$$

52. $\dfrac{716}{4235}$ is already in lowest terms.

53. $15 = 3 \cdot 5; \quad 55 = 5 \cdot 11.$

    $LCM\,(15, 165) = 3 \cdot 5 \cdot 11 = 165.$

    $$\frac{1}{15} + \frac{1}{55} = \frac{11}{165} + \frac{3}{165} = \frac{14}{165}$$

54. $17 = 17; \quad 136 = 2^3 \cdot 17.$ $LCM\,(17, 136) =$

    $136; \quad \dfrac{1}{17} + \dfrac{1}{136} = \dfrac{1 \cdot 8}{136} + \dfrac{1}{136} = \dfrac{9}{136}$

55. $32 = 2^5; \quad 124 = 2^2 \cdot 31.$

    $LCM = 2^5 \cdot 31 = 992.$

    $$\frac{3}{32} + \frac{1}{124} = \frac{3 \cdot 31}{992} + \frac{1 \cdot 8}{992} = \frac{93}{992} + \frac{8}{992}$$

    $$= \frac{101}{992}$$

56. $124 = 2^2 \cdot 31; \quad 155 = 5 \cdot 31.$

    $LCM\,(124, 155) = 2^2 \cdot 5 \cdot 31 = 620.$

    $$\frac{3}{124} + \frac{1}{155} = \frac{3 \cdot 5}{620} + \frac{1 \cdot 4}{620} = \frac{15}{620} + \frac{4}{620}$$

    $$= \frac{19}{620}$$

57. $180 = 2^2 \cdot 3^2 \cdot 5; \quad 240 = 2^4 \cdot 3 \cdot 5.$

    $LCM\,(180, 240) = 2^4 \cdot 3^2 \cdot 5 = 720.$

    $$\frac{1}{180} + \frac{1}{240} = \frac{4}{720} + \frac{3}{720} = \frac{7}{720}$$

58. $284 = 2^2 \cdot 71; \quad 568 = 2^3 \cdot 71.$

    $LCM\,(284, 568) = 2^3 \cdot 71 = 568.$

    $$\frac{3}{284} + \frac{1}{568} = \frac{3 \cdot 2}{568} + \frac{1}{568} = \frac{6}{568} + \frac{1}{568} = \frac{7}{568}$$

59. $12 = 2^2 \cdot 3; \quad 18 = 2 \cdot 3^2; \quad 30 = 2 \cdot 3 \cdot 5$

    $LCM\,(12, 18, 30) = 2^2 \cdot 3^2 \cdot 5 = 180$

$$\frac{1}{12} + \frac{1}{18} + \frac{1}{30} = \frac{15}{180} + \frac{10}{180} + \frac{6}{180} = \frac{31}{180}$$

60. $12 = 2^2 \cdot 3; \quad 15 = 3 \cdot 5; \quad 20 = 2^2 \cdot 5$

    $LCM\,(12, 15, 20) = 2^2 \cdot 3 \cdot 5 = 60$

    $$\frac{1}{12} + \frac{1}{15} + \frac{1}{20} = \frac{1 \cdot 5}{60} + \frac{1 \cdot 2^2}{60} + \frac{1 \cdot 3}{60}$$

    $$= \frac{5}{60} + \frac{4}{60} + \frac{3}{60} = \frac{12}{60} = \frac{1}{5}$$

61. $285 = 3 \cdot 5 \cdot 19; \quad 315 = 3^2 \cdot 5 \cdot 7;$

    $588 = 2^2 \cdot 3 \cdot 7^2$

    $LCM\,(285, 315, 588) = 2^2 \cdot 3^2 \cdot 5 \cdot 7^2 \cdot 19 = 167,580$

    $$\frac{1}{285} + \frac{1}{315} + \frac{1}{588}$$

    $$= \frac{2^2 \cdot 3 \cdot 7^2}{167,580} + \frac{2^2 \cdot 7 \cdot 19}{167,580} + \frac{3 \cdot 5 \cdot 19}{167,580}$$

    $$= \frac{588 + 532 + 285}{167,580} = \frac{1405}{167,580} = \frac{281}{33,516}$$

62. $100 = 2^2 \cdot 5^2; \quad 200 = 2^3 \cdot 5^2; \quad 320 = 2^6 \cdot 5$

    $LCM\,(100, 200, 300) = 2^6 \cdot 5^2 = 1600$

    $$\frac{1}{100} + \frac{1}{200} + \frac{1}{320} = \frac{1 \cdot 2^4}{1600} + \frac{1 \cdot 2^3}{1600} + \frac{1 \cdot 5}{1600}$$

    $$= \frac{16}{1600} + \frac{8}{1600} + \frac{5}{1600} = \frac{29}{1600}$$

63. $200 = 2^3 \cdot 5^2; \quad 300 = 2^2 \cdot 3 \cdot 5^2;$

    $420 = 2^2 \cdot 3 \cdot 5 \cdot 7$

    $LCM\,(200, 300, 420) = 2^3 \cdot 3 \cdot 5^2 \cdot 7 = 4200$

    $$\frac{1}{200} + \frac{1}{300} + \frac{1}{420} = \frac{21}{4200} + \frac{14}{4200} + \frac{10}{4200}$$

    $$= \frac{45}{4200} = \frac{3}{280}$$

64. To determine in how many hours you will need to take all three medications again, find the LCM of 6, 2, and 4.

    $6 = 2 \cdot 3; \quad 2 = 2; \quad 4 = 2^2$

    $LCM\,(6, 2, 4) = 2^2 \cdot 3 = 12$

    You will take all three medications again in 12 hours.

65. To determine in how many hours you will need to take all four medications again, find the LCM of 6, 2, 4, and 12.

$6 = 2 \cdot 3; \ 2 = 2; \ 4 = 2^2; 12 = 2^2 \cdot 3$

$\text{LCM } (6, 2, 4, 12) = 2^2 \cdot 3 = 12$

You will take all our medications again in 12 hours.

66. To determine in how many hours there will be fresh tamales and fresh pastries filled with fresh meat, find the LCM of 2, 5, and 4.

$2 = 2; \ 5 = 5; \ 4 = 2^2$

$\text{LCM } (2, 5, 4) = 2^2 \cdot 5 = 20$

You will fresh items again in 20 days.

67. To determine in how many hours there will be fresh tamales and fresh pastries, find the LCM of 5 and 4.

$5 = 5; \ 4 = 2^2$

$\text{LCM } (5, 4) = 2^2 \cdot 5 = 20$

You will fresh items again in 20 days.

68. $1 - \dfrac{1}{5} - \dfrac{1}{10} - \dfrac{1}{4} - \dfrac{1}{8}$

$= \dfrac{40}{40} - \dfrac{8}{40} - \dfrac{4}{40} - \dfrac{10}{40} - \dfrac{5}{40} = \dfrac{13}{40}$

$\dfrac{13}{40}$ of the garbage is paper and cardboard.

69. $1 - \dfrac{3}{10} - \dfrac{1}{5} - \dfrac{1}{20} - \dfrac{3}{20}$

$= \dfrac{20}{20} - \dfrac{6}{20} - \dfrac{4}{20} - \dfrac{1}{20} - \dfrac{3}{20} = \dfrac{6}{20} = \dfrac{3}{10}$

$\dfrac{3}{10}$ of the water is used for toilet flushing.

70. a. For $n = 4$, $4^2 - 4 + 41 = 53$.

b. For $n = 5$, $5^2 - 5 + 41 = 61$.

c. For $n = 41$, $41^2 - 41 + 41 = 1681$.

d. No. $1681 = 41^2$.

71. a. This can be done in several ways:
$100 = 3 + 97 = 11 + 89 = 17 + 83$
$= 29 + 71 = 41 + 59 = 47 + 53$.

b. This can also be done in several ways:

$200 = 3 + 197 = 7 + 193 = 19 + 181$
$= 37 + 163 = 43 + 157 = 61 + 139$
$= 73 + 127 = 97 + 103$

72. a. $20 = 2 + 7 + 11$ or $20 = 2 + 5 + 13$
b. $43 = 2 + 7 + 11 + 23$ or
$43 = 2 + 2 + 2 + 37$

73. Answers may vary. The number 1 has only one divisor, itself. It is not a prime because a prime must have exactly *two distinct divisors*, 1 and itself. It is not a composite number because it has only one divisor.

74. Answers may vary. The number 1 is neither prime nor composite.

75. Answers may vary. The largest prime that you need to try is 13, because the next prime is 17 and $17^2 = 289$ which is greater than 211.

76. Answers may vary. If there were only a finite number of primes, we could select the largest. Since Euclid proved that there is no largest prime, the number of primes must be infinite.

77. All the other digits are multiples of 3, so their sum is divisible by 3. Hence, only the sum of 2 and 7 needs to be checked.

78. No. $5 + 7 + 1 = 13$, not divisible by 3.

79. Since 999 and 99 and 9 are all divisible by 9, only the sum $2 \cdot 1 + 8 \cdot 1 + 5 \cdot 1 + 3$, which is exactly the sum of the digits, needs to be checked. If this sum is divisible by 9, the original number is divisible by 9 and not otherwise.

80. a. 405 is divisible by 9 because the sum of the digits of the number $(4 + 0 + 5 = 9)$ is divisible by **9**. 405 is not divisible by 6 because it is not divisible by 2.

b. 676 is not divisible by 9 because the sum of the digits of the number $(6 + 7 + 6 = 19)$ is not divisible by 9. 676 is not divisible by 6 because it is not divisible by 3.

c. 7488 is divisible by 9 because the sum of the digits of the number $(7 + 4 + 8 + 8 = 27)$ is divisible by **9**. 7488 is divisible by **6** because it is divisible by 2 and divisible by 3.

d. 309,907,452 is not divisible by 9 because the sum of the digits of the number $(6 + 0 + 9 + 9 + 0 + 7 + 4 + 5 + 2 = 42)$ is not divisible by 9. 309,907,452 is divisible by **6** because it is divisible by 2 and divisible by 3.

81. a. 1436 is divisible by 4 because 36 is divisible by **4**. 1436 is not divisible by 8 because 436 is not divisible by 8.
    b. 21,408 is divisible by 8 because 408 is divisible by **8**. Being divisible by 8, the number is also divisible by **4**.
    c. 347,712 is divisible by 8 because 712 is divisible by **8**. Since the number is divisible by 8, it is also divisible by **4**.
    d. 40,924 is divisible by 4 because 24 is divisible by **4**. The number is not divisible by 8 because 924 is not divisible by 8.

82. a. 4920 is divisible by **10** because the number ends in 0. 4920 is divisible by **12** because it is divisible by both 3 and 4.
    b. 943 is not divisible by 10 because the number does not end in 0. 943 is not divisible by 12 because it is not divisible by either 3 or 4.
    c. 52,341,120 is divisible by **10** because the number ends in 0. 52,341,120 is divisible by **12** because it is divisible by both 3 and 4.
    d. 60,210 is divisible by **10** because the number ends in 0. 60,210 is not divisible by 12 because it is not divisible by 4.

83. None of the numbers 1, 2, 3, 4, 5 is the sum of its proper divisors. Therefore, 6 is the smallest perfect number.

84. The next perfect number is 28. The proper divisors of 28 are 1, 2, 4, 7, 14 and $1 + 2 + 4 + 7 + 14 = 28$.

85. $496 = 2^4 \cdot 31$ Thus, the proper divisors of 496 are 1, 2, 4, 8, 16, 31, 62, 124, and 248. The sum of these divisors is 496, so 496 is a perfect number.

86. 8 is not a perfect number because $1 + 2 + 4 = 7 < 8$.

87. The only proper divisor of a prime is the number 1. Thus, a prime is always greater than the sum of its proper divisors. Consequently, all primes are deficient.

88. Yes. This is so because all primes are deficient.

89. They end in 6 or 28. Also, they are sums of powers of 2. $6 = 2 + 2^2$, $28 = 2^4 + 2^3 + 2^2$, and so on.

90. 111111111111100000000. No.

Collaborative Learning

1. $2^{17} - 1$ and $2^{19} - 1$ are prime.

2. 23, 29, and 37 do not produce primes in $2^n - 1$.

3. In 1644 Mersenne claimed that $2^n - 1$ is prime if $n = 2, 3, 5, 7, 13, 17, 19, 31, 67, 127$ and 257 but composite for the other 44 primes smaller than 257.
   Over the years it has been found that Mersenne was wrong about 5 of the primes less than or equal to 257 (he claimed two that didn't lead to a prime (67 and 257) and missed 3 that did: 61, 89, 107).

4. Answers will vary.

Section 5.2 Whole Numbers, Integers, and Order of Operations

1. Because $9 + (-9) = 0$, the additive inverse of 9 is –9.

2. Because $11 + (-11) = 0$, the additive inverse of 11 is –11.

3. Because $-10 + 10 = 0$, the additive inverse of –10 is 10.

4. Because $-17 + 17 = 0$, the additive inverse of –17 is 17.

5. Because $0 + 0 = 0$, the additive inverse of 0 is 0.

6. $|14| = 14$ because 14 is 14 units from zero.

7. $|27| = 27$ because 27 is 27 units from zero.

8. $|-24| = 24$ because –24 is 24 units from zero.

9. $\left|-16\right| = 16$ because -16 is 16 units from zero.

10. $\left|-19\right| = 19$ because -19 is 19 units from zero.

11. $-3 + 5 = 5 - 3 = 2$

12. $-18 + 21 = 21 - 18 = 3$

13. $8 + (-1) = 8 - 1 = 7$

14. $19 + (-6) = 19 - 6 = 13$

15. $-8 + 13 = 13 - 8 = 5$

16. $-9 + 11 = 11 - 9 = 2$

17. $-17 + 4 = -(17 - 4) = -13$

18. $-18 + 9 = -(18 - 9) = -9$

19. Add the positives 8 and 6 and the negatives (–4) and (–2); then add the results.
$$-4 + 8 + 6 + (-2) = 8 + 6 + (-4) + (-2)$$
$$= 14 + (-6) = 14 - 6 = 8$$

20. Add the positives 5 and 7 and the negatives (–17) and (–6); then add the results.
$$-17 + 5 + (-6) + 7 = 5 + 7 + (-17) + (-6)$$
$$= 12 + (-23)$$
$$= -(23 - 12) = -11$$

21. $3 - 8 = 3 + (-8) = -5$

22. $8 - 3 = 8 + (-3) = 5$

23. $3 - 4 = 3 + (-4) = -1$

24. $-3 - 4 = -3 + (-4) = -7$

25. $-5 - 2 = -5 + (-2) = -7$

26. $-3 - 5 = -3 + (-5) = -8$

27. $5 - (-6) = 5 + (+6) = 11$

28. $6 - (-3) = 6 + (+3) = 9$

29. $-3 - (-4) = -3 + (+4) = 1$

30. $-5 - (-6) = -5 + (+6) = 1$

31. The product of like-signed numbers is a positive number: $16 \cdot 2 = 32$

32. The product of like-signed numbers is a positive number: $9 \cdot 4 = 36$

33. The product of unlike-signed numbers is a negative number: $-7 \cdot 8 = -(7 \cdot 8) = -56$

34. The product of unlike-signed numbers is a negative number: $-10 \cdot 4 = -(10 \cdot 4) = -40$

35. The product of unlike-signed numbers is a negative number: $2 \cdot (-5) = -(2 \cdot 5) = -10$

36. The product of unlike-signed numbers is a negative number: $9 \cdot (-9) = -(9 \cdot 9) = -81$

37. The product of like-signed numbers is a positive number: $-4 \cdot (-5) = 4 \cdot 5 = 20$

38. The product of like-signed numbers is a positive number: $-6 \cdot (-3) = 6 \cdot 3 = 18$

39. The product of like-signed numbers is a positive number: $-7 \cdot (-10) = 7 \cdot 10 = 70$

40. The product of like-signed numbers is a positive number: $-9 \cdot (-2) = 9 \cdot 2 = 18$

41. The quotient of like-signed numbers is a positive number: $10 \div 2 = 5$

42. The quotient of like-signed numbers is a positive number: $\dfrac{14}{2} = 7$

43. The quotient of unlike-signed numbers is a negative number: $\dfrac{-20}{5} = -\left(\dfrac{20}{5}\right) = -4$

44. The quotient of unlike-signed numbers is a negative number: $-50 \div 10 = -(50 \div 10) = -5$

45. The quotient of unlike-signed numbers is a negative number: $-40 \div 8 = -(40 \div 8) = -5$

46. The quotient of unlike-signed numbers is a negative number: $\dfrac{-30}{10} = -\left(\dfrac{30}{10}\right) = -3$

47. The quotient of unlike-signed numbers is a negative number:
$150 \div (-15) = -(150 \div 15) = -10$

48. The quotient of unlike-signed numbers is a negative number:
$96 \div (-6) = -(96 \div 6) = -16$

49. The quotient of unlike-signed numbers is a negative number: $\dfrac{140}{-7} = -\left(\dfrac{140}{7}\right) = -20$

50. The quotient of unlike-signed numbers is a negative number: $\dfrac{91}{-13} = -\left(\dfrac{91}{13}\right) = -7$

51. The quotient of like-signed numbers is a positive number:
$-98 \div (-14) = 98 \div 14 = 7$

52. The quotient of like-signed numbers is a positive number:
$-120 \div (-30) = 120 \div 30 = 4$

53. The quotient of like-signed numbers is a positive number: $\dfrac{-98}{-7} = \dfrac{98}{7} = 14$

54. The quotient of like-signed numbers is a positive number: $\dfrac{-92}{-4} = \dfrac{92}{4} = 23$

55. Division by zero is not allowed.
$\dfrac{3}{0}$ is not defined.

56. Zero divided by any number is 0.
$\dfrac{0}{-9} = 0$

57. Zero divided by any number is 0.
$\dfrac{0}{-33} = 0$

58. Division by zero is not allowed.
$-10 \div 0$ is not defined.

59. Division by zero is not allowed.
$-19 \div 0$ is not defined.

60. Zero divided by any number is 0.
$0 \div (-11) = 0$

61. $(-8)^2 = (-8) \cdot (-8) = 64$

62. $-8^2 = -(8 \cdot 8) = -64$

63. $-6^2 = -(6 \cdot 6) = -36$

64. $(-6)^2 = (-6) \cdot (-6) = 36$

65. $-6^3 = -(6 \cdot 6 \cdot 6) = -216$

66. $(-6)^3 = (-6) \cdot (-6) \cdot (-6) = 36 \cdot (-6) = -216$

67. $(-3)^4 = (-3) \cdot (-3) \cdot (-3) \cdot (-3)$
$= 9 \cdot (-3) \cdot (-3) = -27 \cdot (-3) = 81$

68. $-3^4 = -(3 \cdot 3 \cdot 3 \cdot 3) = -81$

69. $(-4)^3 = (-4) \cdot (-4) \cdot (-4) = 16 \cdot (-4) = -64$

70. $-4^3 = -(4 \cdot 4 \cdot 4) = -64$

71. a. $-3(4 + 5) = -3(9) = -27$
    b. $-4(4 - 5) = -4(-1) = 4$

72. a. $-2(-3 + 1) = -2(-2) = 4$
    b. $-5(-4 + 2) = -5(-2) = 10$

73. a. $-5 + (-5 + 1) = -5 + (-4) = -9$
    b. $-8 + (-2 + 5) = -8 + (3) = -5$

74. a. $-2(4 - 8) - 9 = -2(-4) - 9 = 8 - 9 = -1$
    b. $-3(5 - 7) - 11 = -3(-2) - 11 = 6 - 11 = -5$

75. $(-2-4)(-3)-8(5-4)=-6(-3)-8(1)$
$$=18-8=10$$

76. $(-3-5)(-2)+8(3+4-5)$
$$=(-8)(-2)+8(7-5)$$
$$=(-8)(-2)+8(2)$$
$$=16+16=32$$

77. $6\times2\div3+6\div2\times(-3)=12\div3+3\times(-3)$
$$=4+(-9)=-5$$

78. $8\div2\times4-8\times2\div4=4\times4-8\times2\div4$
$$=16-8\times2\div4$$
$$=16-16\div4=16-4=12$$

79. $4\times9\div3\times10^3-2\times10^2$
$$=4\times9\div3\times1000-2\times100$$
$$=36\div3\times1000-200$$
$$=12\times1000-200$$
$$=12,000-200$$
$$=11,800$$

80. $5\cdot(-2)\cdot3^2+6\div3\cdot5\cdot3^2$
$$=5\cdot(-2)\cdot9+6\div3\cdot5\cdot9$$
$$=-10\cdot9+6\div3\cdot5\cdot9$$
$$=-90+2\cdot5\cdot9=-90+10\cdot9$$
$$=-90+90=0$$

81. $20\div5+\{3\cdot4-[4+(5-3)]\}$
$$=20\div5+\{3\cdot4-[4+(2)]\}$$
$$=20\div5+\{3\cdot4-6\}$$
$$=20\div5+\{12-6\}$$
$$=20\div5+6$$
$$=4+6$$
$$=10$$

82. $30\div6+\{4\div2\cdot3-[3+(5-4)]\}$
$$=30\div6+\{4\div2\cdot3-[3+1]\}$$
$$=30\div6+\{4\div2\cdot3-4\}$$
$$=30\div6+\{2\cdot3-4\}$$
$$=30\div6+\{6-4\}$$
$$=30\div6+2$$
$$=5+2=7$$

83. $(20-15)\cdot[20\div2-(2\cdot2+2)]$
$$=(20-15)\cdot[20\div2-(4+2)]$$
$$=5\cdot[20\div2-6]$$
$$=5\cdot[10-6]$$
$$=5\cdot4=20$$
$$=20$$

84. $(30-10)\cdot[52\div4-(3\cdot3+3)]$
$$=(30-10)\cdot[52\div4-(9+3)]$$
$$=20\cdot[52\div4-12]$$
$$=20\cdot[13-12]$$
$$=20\cdot1=20$$
$$=20$$

85. $-14;\ 506-14=492$

86. $-23;\ 514-23=491$

87. $+19;\ 506+19=525$

88. $+19;\ 514+19=533$

89. $+53;\ 506+53=559$

90. $-95-(-76)=-95+76=-(95-76)=-19$

91.

Altitude in (1000 ft)	Altitude × Rate of Change	Temperature Change
5	5(−4)	−20

92.

Altitude in (1000 ft)	Altitude × Rate of Change	Temperature Change
10	10(−4)	−40°F

93.

Altitude in (1000 ft)	Altitude × Rate of Change	Temperature Change
15	15(–4)	–60°F

94.

Altitude in Kilometers	Altitude × Rate of Change	Temperature Change
3	3(–7)	–21°C

95.

Altitude in Kilometers	Altitude × Rate of Change	Temperature Change
5	5(–7)	–35°C

96.

Altitude in Kilometers	Altitude × Rate of Change	Temperature Change
6	6(–7)	–42°C

97. 14,000 ft is 14 thousands and the rate of change is $-4°F$ for each 1000 ft of altitude. The temperature change is $70 + 14(-4) = 70 - 56 = 14°F$.

98. 20,000 ft is 20 thousands and the rate of change is $-4°F$ for each 1000 ft of altitude. The temperature at the top is $70 + 20(-4) = 70 + (-80) = -10°F$.

99. 6000 m is 6 kilometers and the rate of change is $-7°C$ for each kilometer of altitude. The temperature at the top is $20 + 6(-7) = 20 + (-42) = -22°C$.

100. 8000 m is 8 kilometers and the rate of change is $-7°C$ for each kilometer of altitude. The expression for temperature at the top is $20°C + 8(-7°C)$. The temperature at the top is $20 + 8(-7) = 20 + (-56) = -36°C$.

101. Answers may vary. The product of two positive numbers is a positive number.

102. Answers may vary. The product of two numbers of opposite signs is a negative number.

103. Answers may vary. The product of two negative numbers is a positive number.

104. $5 + 4 \cdot (-2) = 5 + (-8) = -3$

105. $2 \cdot 1 + 2 \cdot 6 + 7 \cdot (-2) = 2 + 12 - 14 = 0$

106. $1 + 1 + 4 + 3(-2) = 6 + (-6) = 0$

Collaborative Learning

1. 1089 or –1089; No

Section 5.3 Operations with Rational Numbers, Expanded and Scientific Notation

1. The numerator is 3; the denominator is 4.

2. Numerator 4, denominator 5

3. The numerator is 3; the denominator is –5.

4. Numerator –4, denominator 5

5. $\dfrac{17}{41} \overset{?}{=} \dfrac{289}{697}$; $17 \cdot 697 = 11{,}849 = 41 \cdot 289$ and

   $\dfrac{17}{41} \overset{?}{=} \dfrac{714}{1682}$; $17 \cdot 1682 = 28{,}594$

   $\neq 29{,}274 = 41 \cdot 714$

   Thus, $\dfrac{17}{41} = \dfrac{289}{697}$.

6. $\dfrac{19}{23} \overset{?}{=} \dfrac{323}{391}$; $19 \cdot 391 = 7429 = 23 \cdot 323$ and

   $\dfrac{438}{529} \overset{?}{=} \dfrac{19}{23}$; $438 \cdot 23 = 10{,}074$

   $\neq 10{,}051 = 529 \cdot 19$

   Thus, $\dfrac{19}{23} = \dfrac{323}{391}$.

7. $\dfrac{11}{91} \overset{?}{=} \dfrac{253}{2093}$; $11 \cdot 2093 = 23{,}023 = 91 \cdot 253$ and

   $\dfrac{11}{91} \overset{?}{=} \dfrac{111}{911}$; $11 \cdot 911 = 10{,}021 \neq 10{,}101 = 91 \cdot 111$

   Thus, $\dfrac{11}{91} = \dfrac{253}{2093}$.

8. $\dfrac{14}{21} = \dfrac{2 \cdot 7}{3 \cdot 7} = \dfrac{2}{3}$ 9. $\dfrac{95}{38} = \dfrac{5 \cdot 19}{2 \cdot 19} = \dfrac{5}{2}$

28. $\dfrac{2}{7} - \dfrac{3}{11} = \dfrac{22}{77} - \dfrac{21}{77} = \dfrac{1}{77}$

10. $\dfrac{42}{86} = \dfrac{21 \cdot 2}{43 \cdot 2} = \dfrac{21}{43}$ 11. $\dfrac{21}{48} = \dfrac{3 \cdot 7}{3 \cdot 16} = \dfrac{7}{16}$

29. $\dfrac{3}{4} - \dfrac{5}{6} = \dfrac{9}{12} - \dfrac{10}{12} = -\dfrac{1}{12}$

12. $\dfrac{15}{12} = \dfrac{5 \cdot 3}{4 \cdot 3} = \dfrac{5}{4}$ 13. $\dfrac{30}{28} = \dfrac{2 \cdot 15}{2 \cdot 14} = \dfrac{15}{14}$

30. $\dfrac{7}{18} - \dfrac{1}{12} = \dfrac{14}{36} - \dfrac{3}{36} = \dfrac{11}{36}$

14. $\dfrac{22}{33} = \dfrac{2 \cdot 11}{3 \cdot 11} = \dfrac{2}{3}$ 15. $\dfrac{52}{78} = \dfrac{2 \cdot 26}{3 \cdot 26} = \dfrac{2}{3}$

31. $\dfrac{7}{19} - \dfrac{3}{17} = \dfrac{119}{323} - \dfrac{57}{323} = \dfrac{62}{323}$

16. $\dfrac{224}{84} = \dfrac{8 \cdot 28}{3 \cdot 28} = \dfrac{8}{3}$

32. $\dfrac{3}{4} \times \dfrac{2}{7} = \dfrac{3}{\cancel{4}_{2}} \times \dfrac{\cancel{2}^{1}}{7} = \dfrac{3}{14}$

17. $\dfrac{2}{9} + \dfrac{1}{6} + \dfrac{7}{18} = \dfrac{4}{18} + \dfrac{3}{18} + \dfrac{7}{18} = \dfrac{14}{18}$

18. $\dfrac{7}{3} + \dfrac{7}{9} + \dfrac{5}{6} = \dfrac{42}{18} + \dfrac{14}{18} + \dfrac{15}{18} = \dfrac{71}{18}$

33. $\dfrac{2}{5} \times \dfrac{5}{3} = \dfrac{2}{\cancel{5}_{1}} \times \dfrac{\cancel{5}^{1}}{3} = \dfrac{2}{3}$

19. $\dfrac{1}{3} + \dfrac{1}{6} + \dfrac{1}{9} = \dfrac{6}{18} + \dfrac{3}{18} + \dfrac{2}{18} = \dfrac{11}{18}$

34. $\dfrac{7}{9} \times \dfrac{3}{8} = \dfrac{7}{\cancel{9}_{3}} \times \dfrac{\cancel{3}^{1}}{8} = \dfrac{7}{24}$

20. $\dfrac{1}{7} + \dfrac{1}{3} = \dfrac{3}{21} + \dfrac{7}{21} = \dfrac{10}{21}$

21. $\dfrac{1}{7} + \dfrac{1}{9} = \dfrac{9}{63} + \dfrac{7}{63} = \dfrac{16}{63}$

35. $\dfrac{3}{4} \div \dfrac{2}{7} = \dfrac{3}{4} \times \dfrac{7}{2} = \dfrac{21}{8}$

22. $\dfrac{2}{7} + \dfrac{3}{11} = \dfrac{22}{77} + \dfrac{21}{77} = \dfrac{43}{77}$

36. $\dfrac{2}{5} \div \dfrac{5}{3} = \dfrac{2}{5} \times \dfrac{3}{5} = \dfrac{6}{25}$

23. $\dfrac{3}{4} + \dfrac{5}{6} = \dfrac{9}{12} + \dfrac{10}{12} = \dfrac{19}{12}$

37. $\dfrac{7}{9} \div \dfrac{3}{8} = \dfrac{7}{9} \times \dfrac{8}{3} = \dfrac{56}{27}$

24. $\dfrac{1}{12} + \dfrac{7}{18} = \dfrac{3}{36} + \dfrac{14}{36} = \dfrac{17}{36}$

38. $\left(\dfrac{-2}{5}\right) \times \left(\dfrac{4}{9}\right) = -\dfrac{8}{45}$

39. $\left(-\dfrac{6}{7}\right) \times \left(-\dfrac{3}{11}\right) = \dfrac{18}{77}$

25. $\dfrac{3}{17} + \dfrac{7}{19} = \dfrac{57}{323} + \dfrac{119}{323} = \dfrac{176}{323}$

40. $\left(\dfrac{4}{5}\right) \div \left(\dfrac{-7}{9}\right) = \left(\dfrac{4}{5}\right) \cdot \left(\dfrac{9}{-7}\right) = -\dfrac{36}{35}$

26. $\dfrac{1}{3} - \dfrac{1}{7} = \dfrac{7}{21} - \dfrac{3}{21} = \dfrac{4}{21}$

41. $\left(-\dfrac{3}{4}\right) \div \left(-\dfrac{7}{6}\right) = \left(-\dfrac{3}{\cancel{4}_{2}}\right)\left(-\dfrac{\cancel{6}^{3}}{7}\right) = \dfrac{9}{14}$

27. $\dfrac{1}{7} - \dfrac{1}{9} = \dfrac{9}{63} - \dfrac{7}{63} = \dfrac{2}{63}$

42. $\left(\dfrac{3}{4}\right) \div \left(-\dfrac{1}{5}\right) = \left(\dfrac{3}{4}\right) \cdot \left(-\dfrac{5}{1}\right) = -\dfrac{15}{4}$

43. $\dfrac{1}{8} \div \left(-\dfrac{3}{4}\right) = \dfrac{1}{\cancel{8}_{2}} \cdot \left(-\dfrac{\cancel{4}^{1}}{3}\right) = -\dfrac{1}{6}$

44. $\left(-\dfrac{1}{4}\right) + \left(-\dfrac{1}{7}\right) = -\dfrac{7}{28} + \left(-\dfrac{4}{28}\right) = -\dfrac{11}{28}$

45. $\left(-\dfrac{1}{8}\right) + \dfrac{1}{4} = -\dfrac{1}{8} + \dfrac{2}{8} = \dfrac{1}{8}$

46. $\left(\dfrac{1}{3} + \dfrac{1}{4}\right) + \dfrac{7}{8} = \left(\dfrac{8}{24} + \dfrac{6}{24}\right) + \dfrac{21}{24}$

$\qquad = \dfrac{14}{24} + \dfrac{21}{24} = \dfrac{35}{24}$

47. $\dfrac{3}{8} - \left(\dfrac{1}{4} - \dfrac{1}{8}\right) = \dfrac{3}{8} - \left(\dfrac{2}{8} - \dfrac{1}{8}\right) = \dfrac{3}{8} - \dfrac{1}{8}$

$\qquad = \dfrac{2}{8} = \dfrac{1}{4}$

48. $\left(\dfrac{1}{5} \times \dfrac{1}{4}\right) \times \dfrac{3}{7} = \dfrac{1}{20} \times \dfrac{3}{7} = \dfrac{3}{140}$

49. $\dfrac{1}{2} \times \left(\dfrac{7}{8} \times \dfrac{7}{5}\right) = \dfrac{1}{2} \times \dfrac{49}{40} = \dfrac{49}{80}$

50. $\dfrac{1}{2} \div \left(\dfrac{1}{8} \div \dfrac{1}{4}\right) = \dfrac{1}{2} \div \left(\dfrac{1}{8} \times \dfrac{4}{1}\right)$

$\qquad = \dfrac{1}{2} \div \dfrac{1}{2} = \dfrac{1}{2} \times \dfrac{2}{1} = 1$

51. $\left(\dfrac{1}{2} \div \dfrac{1}{8}\right) \div \dfrac{1}{4} = \left(\dfrac{1}{2} \cdot \dfrac{8}{1}\right) \cdot \dfrac{4}{1} = 4 \cdot 4 = 16$

52. $\dfrac{3}{4} + \dfrac{1}{2}\left(\dfrac{3}{2} + \dfrac{1}{4}\right) = \dfrac{3}{4} + \dfrac{1}{2}\left(\dfrac{6}{4} + \dfrac{1}{4}\right)$

$\qquad = \dfrac{3}{4} + \dfrac{1}{2}\left(\dfrac{7}{4}\right) = \dfrac{3}{4} + \dfrac{7}{8} = \dfrac{6}{8} + \dfrac{7}{8} = \dfrac{13}{8}$

53. $\dfrac{2}{3}\left(\dfrac{1}{2} + \dfrac{3}{4}\right) + \dfrac{2}{3} = \dfrac{2}{3}\left(\dfrac{2}{4} + \dfrac{3}{4}\right) + \dfrac{2}{3}$

$\qquad = \dfrac{2}{3}\left(\dfrac{5}{4}\right) + \dfrac{2}{3} = \dfrac{5}{6} + \dfrac{4}{6} = \dfrac{9}{6} = \dfrac{3}{2}$

54. $\dfrac{1}{2}\left(\dfrac{3}{4} - \dfrac{1}{2}\right) - \dfrac{1}{12} = \dfrac{1}{2}\left(\dfrac{3}{4} - \dfrac{2}{4}\right) - \dfrac{1}{12}$

$\qquad = \dfrac{1}{2}\left(\dfrac{1}{4}\right) - \dfrac{1}{12} = \dfrac{1}{8} - \dfrac{1}{12}$

$\qquad = \dfrac{3}{24} - \dfrac{2}{24} = \dfrac{1}{24}$

55. $\dfrac{1}{3}\left(\dfrac{3}{2} - \dfrac{1}{5}\right) - \dfrac{1}{30} = \dfrac{1}{3}\left(\dfrac{15}{10} - \dfrac{2}{10}\right) - \dfrac{1}{30}$

$\qquad = \dfrac{1}{3}\left(\dfrac{13}{10}\right) - \dfrac{1}{30} = \dfrac{13}{30} - \dfrac{1}{30} = \dfrac{12}{30} = \dfrac{2}{5}$

56. $\dfrac{1}{2}\left(\dfrac{5}{2} - \dfrac{1}{3}\right) - \dfrac{5}{12} = \dfrac{1}{2}\left(\dfrac{15}{6} - \dfrac{2}{6}\right) - \dfrac{5}{12}$

$\qquad = \dfrac{1}{2}\left(\dfrac{13}{6}\right) - \dfrac{5}{12} = \dfrac{13}{12} - \dfrac{5}{12} = \dfrac{8}{12} = \dfrac{2}{3}$

57. $1\dfrac{1}{2} + \dfrac{1}{7} = \dfrac{3}{2} + \dfrac{1}{7} = \dfrac{21}{14} + \dfrac{2}{14} = \dfrac{23}{14} = 1\dfrac{9}{14}$

58. $5 - 1\dfrac{1}{3} = 5 - \dfrac{4}{3} = \dfrac{15}{3} - \dfrac{4}{3} = \dfrac{11}{3} = 3\dfrac{2}{3}$

59. $\dfrac{1}{4} \times 1\dfrac{1}{7} = \dfrac{1}{4} \cdot \dfrac{8}{7} = \dfrac{2}{7}$

60. $5 \div \left(-2\dfrac{1}{2}\right) = 5 \div \left(-\dfrac{5}{2}\right) = 5 \cdot \left(-\dfrac{2}{5}\right) = -2$

61. $3\dfrac{1}{4} + \dfrac{1}{6} = 3 + \dfrac{1}{4} + \dfrac{1}{6} = 3 + \dfrac{3}{12} + \dfrac{2}{12} = 3\dfrac{5}{12}$

62. $4 - 2\dfrac{1}{4} = 4 - \dfrac{9}{4} = \dfrac{16}{4} - \dfrac{9}{4} = \dfrac{7}{4} = 1\dfrac{3}{4}$

63. $\dfrac{1}{5} \cdot 2\dfrac{1}{7} = \dfrac{1}{5} \cdot \dfrac{15}{7} = \dfrac{3}{7}$

64. $6 \div \left(-1\frac{1}{5}\right) = 6 \div \left(-\frac{6}{5}\right) = 6 \cdot \left(-\frac{5}{6}\right) = -5$

65. $-3 + 2\frac{1}{4} = -3 + 2 + \frac{1}{4} = -1 + \frac{1}{4} = -\frac{3}{4}$

66. $-\frac{2}{3} - (-2) = -\frac{2}{3} + 2 = -\frac{2}{3} + \frac{6}{3} = \frac{4}{3} = 1\frac{1}{3}$

67. $(-8) \cdot 2\frac{1}{4} = (-8) \cdot \frac{9}{4} = (-2) \cdot 9 = -18$

68. $7 \div \left(-2\frac{1}{3}\right) = 7 \div \left(-\frac{7}{3}\right) = 7 \cdot \left(-\frac{3}{7}\right) = -3$

69. $-2 + 1\frac{1}{5} = -2 + 1 + \frac{1}{5} = -1 + \frac{1}{5} = -\frac{4}{5}$

70. $-\frac{3}{4} - (-3) = -\frac{3}{4} + 3 = -\frac{3}{4} + \frac{12}{4} = \frac{9}{4} = 2\frac{1}{4}$

71. $(-9) \times 3\frac{1}{3} = (-9) \cdot \frac{10}{3} = (-3) \times 10 = -30$

72. $\left(-\frac{1}{6}\right) \div \left(-\frac{5}{7}\right) = \left(-\frac{1}{6}\right) \times \left(-\frac{7}{5}\right) = \frac{7}{30}$

73. $7\frac{1}{4} + \left(-\frac{1}{8}\right) = 7 + \frac{1}{4} - \frac{1}{8} = 7 + \frac{2}{8} - \frac{1}{8}$

$= 7 + \frac{1}{8} = 7\frac{1}{8}$

74. $-3\frac{1}{8} - (-2) = -\frac{25}{8} + 2 = -\frac{25}{8} + \frac{16}{8}$

$= -\frac{9}{8} = -1\frac{1}{8}$

75. $\left(-1\frac{1}{4}\right) \times \left(-2\frac{1}{10}\right) = \left(-\frac{5}{4}\right) \times \left(-\frac{21}{10}\right)$

$= \left(-\frac{1}{4}\right) \times \left(-\frac{21}{2}\right) = \frac{21}{8} = 2\frac{5}{8}$

76. $\left(-1\frac{1}{8}\right) \div \left(-2\frac{1}{4}\right) = \left(-\frac{9}{8}\right) \div \left(-\frac{9}{4}\right)$

$= \left(-\frac{9}{8}\right) \times \left(-\frac{4}{9}\right) = \frac{1}{2}$

77. $\frac{1}{2} \times \frac{1}{6} - \frac{1}{3} + \frac{1}{4} = \frac{1}{12} - \frac{4}{12} + \frac{3}{12} = \frac{0}{12} = 0$

78. $\frac{3}{8} - 6\left(\frac{1}{4} - \frac{1}{8}\right) = \frac{3}{8} - 6\left(\frac{2}{8} - \frac{1}{8}\right) = \frac{3}{8} - 6\left(\frac{1}{8}\right)$

$= \frac{3}{8} - \frac{6}{8} = -\frac{3}{8}$

79. $\frac{1}{3} - \frac{1}{3} \times \frac{2}{3} \div \frac{2}{5} = \frac{1}{3} - \frac{2}{9} \div \frac{2}{5} = \frac{1}{3} - \frac{2}{9} \times \frac{5}{2}$

$= \frac{3}{9} - \frac{5}{9} = -\frac{2}{9}$

80. $\frac{1}{2} \div \frac{1}{4} - \frac{3}{4} = \frac{1}{2} \times \frac{4}{1} - \frac{3}{4} = 2 - \frac{3}{4}$

$= \frac{8}{4} - \frac{3}{4} = \frac{5}{4} = 1\frac{1}{4}$

81. $\left(2\frac{1}{2}\right) \times \left(-3\frac{1}{4}\right) - \left(-7\frac{1}{8}\right) \div 3$

$= \frac{5}{2} \cdot \left(-\frac{13}{4}\right) - \left(-\frac{57}{8}\right) \times \frac{1}{3}$

$= -\frac{65}{8} - \left(-\frac{19}{8}\right) = -\frac{65}{8} + \frac{19}{8}$

$= -\frac{46}{8} = -\frac{23}{4} = -5\frac{3}{4}$

82. $\left(-6\frac{2}{5}\right) \div (-4) + \left(2\frac{1}{10}\right) \times (-2)$

$= \left(-\frac{32}{5}\right) \times \left(-\frac{1}{4}\right) + \left(\frac{21}{10}\right) \times (-2)$

$= \left(-\frac{\overset{8}{\cancel{32}}}{5}\right) \times \left(-\frac{1}{\cancel{4}_{1}}\right) + \left(\frac{21}{\cancel{10}_{5}}\right) \times \left(-\frac{\cancel{2}^{1}}{}\right)$

$= \frac{8}{5} - \frac{21}{5} = -\frac{13}{5} = -2\frac{3}{5}$

83. $12 \div 6 - \left(\dfrac{1}{3} + \dfrac{1}{2}\right) = 12 \div 6 - \left(\dfrac{2}{6} + \dfrac{3}{6}\right)$

$= 12 \div 6 - \left(\dfrac{5}{6}\right) = \dfrac{12}{6} - \dfrac{5}{6} = \dfrac{7}{6} = 1\dfrac{1}{6}$

84. $18 \div 9 - \left(\dfrac{1}{4} + \dfrac{1}{6}\right) = 18 \div 9 - \left(\dfrac{3}{12} + \dfrac{2}{12}\right)$

$= 18 \div 9 - \dfrac{5}{12} = 2 - \dfrac{5}{12} = \dfrac{24}{12} - \dfrac{5}{12} = \dfrac{19}{12} = 1\dfrac{7}{12}$

85. $\dfrac{1}{3} \cdot \dfrac{1}{4} \div \dfrac{1}{2} + \left(\dfrac{5}{6} - \dfrac{1}{2}\right) = \dfrac{1}{3} \cdot \dfrac{1}{4} \div \dfrac{1}{2} + \left(\dfrac{5}{6} - \dfrac{3}{6}\right)$

$= \dfrac{1}{3} \cdot \dfrac{1}{4} \div \dfrac{1}{2} + \dfrac{2}{6} = \dfrac{1}{12} \cdot \dfrac{2}{1} + \dfrac{2}{6}$

$= \dfrac{1}{6} + \dfrac{2}{6} = \dfrac{3}{6} = \dfrac{1}{2}$

86. $\dfrac{1}{3} \cdot \dfrac{1}{6} \div \dfrac{1}{2} + \left(\dfrac{4}{5} - \dfrac{1}{2}\right)$

$= \dfrac{1}{3} \cdot \dfrac{1}{6} \div \dfrac{1}{2} + \left(\dfrac{8}{10} - \dfrac{5}{10}\right)$

$= \dfrac{1}{3} \cdot \dfrac{1}{6} \div \dfrac{1}{2} + \dfrac{3}{10} = \dfrac{1}{18} \div \dfrac{1}{2} + \dfrac{3}{10}$

$= \dfrac{1}{18} \cdot \dfrac{2}{1} + \dfrac{3}{10} = \dfrac{1}{9} + \dfrac{3}{10}$

$= \dfrac{10}{90} + \dfrac{27}{90} = \dfrac{37}{90}$

87. $\dfrac{1}{6} \div \dfrac{1}{3} \cdot \dfrac{1}{3} \cdot \dfrac{1}{3} + \left(\dfrac{1}{4} - \dfrac{1}{9}\right)$

$= \dfrac{1}{6} \div \dfrac{1}{3} \cdot \dfrac{1}{3} \cdot \dfrac{1}{3} + \left(\dfrac{9}{36} - \dfrac{4}{36}\right)$

$= \dfrac{1}{6} \div \dfrac{1}{3} \cdot \dfrac{1}{3} \cdot \dfrac{1}{3} + \dfrac{5}{36}$

$= \dfrac{1}{6} \cdot \dfrac{3}{1} \cdot \dfrac{1}{3} \cdot \dfrac{1}{3} + \dfrac{5}{36}$

$= \dfrac{1}{18} + \dfrac{5}{36} = \dfrac{2}{36} + \dfrac{5}{36} = \dfrac{7}{36}$

88. $\dfrac{1}{10} \div \dfrac{1}{2} \cdot \dfrac{1}{2} \cdot \dfrac{1}{2} + \left(\dfrac{2}{3} - \dfrac{1}{2}\right)$

$= \dfrac{1}{10} \div \dfrac{1}{2} \cdot \dfrac{1}{2} \cdot \dfrac{1}{2} + \left(\dfrac{4}{6} - \dfrac{3}{6}\right)$

$= \dfrac{1}{10} \div \dfrac{1}{2} \cdot \dfrac{1}{2} \cdot \dfrac{1}{2} + \dfrac{1}{6} = \dfrac{1}{10} \cdot \dfrac{2}{1} \cdot \dfrac{1}{2} \cdot \dfrac{1}{2} + \dfrac{1}{6}$

$= \dfrac{1}{10} \cdot \dfrac{\overset{1}{\cancel{2}}}{1} \cdot \dfrac{1}{\underset{1}{\cancel{2}}} \cdot \dfrac{1}{2} + \dfrac{1}{6} = \dfrac{1}{20} + \dfrac{1}{6}$

$= \dfrac{6}{120} + \dfrac{20}{120} = \dfrac{26}{120} = \dfrac{13}{60}$

89. $8 \div \dfrac{1}{2} \cdot \dfrac{1}{2} \cdot \dfrac{1}{2} - \left(\dfrac{1}{3} + \dfrac{1}{5}\right)$

$= 8 \div \dfrac{1}{2} \cdot \dfrac{1}{2} \cdot \dfrac{1}{2} - \left(\dfrac{5}{15} + \dfrac{3}{15}\right)$

$= 8 \div \dfrac{1}{2} \cdot \dfrac{1}{2} \cdot \dfrac{1}{2} - \dfrac{8}{15}$

$= 8 \cdot \dfrac{2}{1} \cdot \dfrac{1}{2} \cdot \dfrac{1}{2} - \dfrac{8}{15} = 4 - \dfrac{8}{15} = 3\dfrac{7}{15}$

90. $6 \div \dfrac{1}{3} \cdot \dfrac{1}{3} \cdot \dfrac{1}{3} - \left(\dfrac{1}{3} + \dfrac{1}{5}\right)$

$= 6 \div \dfrac{1}{3} \cdot \dfrac{1}{3} \cdot \dfrac{1}{3} - \left(\dfrac{5}{15} + \dfrac{3}{15}\right)$

$= 6 \div \dfrac{1}{3} \cdot \dfrac{1}{3} \cdot \dfrac{1}{3} - \dfrac{8}{15}$

$= 6 \cdot \dfrac{\overset{1}{\cancel{3}}}{1} \cdot \dfrac{1}{\underset{1}{\cancel{3}}} \cdot \dfrac{1}{3} - \dfrac{8}{15}$

$= 2 - \dfrac{8}{15} = \dfrac{30}{15} - \dfrac{8}{15} = \dfrac{22}{15} = 1\dfrac{7}{15}$

91. $692.087 = 6 \times 10^2 + 9 \times 10 + 2 \times 10^0$
$\qquad\qquad + 0 \times 10^{-1} + 8 \times 10^{-2} + 7 \times 10^{-3}$

92. $30.2959 = (3 \times 10) + (2 \times 10^{-1}) + (9 \times 10^{-2})$
$\qquad\qquad + (5 \times 10^{-3}) + (9 \times 10^{-4})$

93. $0.00107 = 1 \times 10^{-3} + 7 \times 10^{-5}$

94. $4.30008 = (4 \times 10^0) + (3 \times 10^{-1}) + (8 \times 10^{-5})$

95. 5020.39

96. 405.0609

97. 0.004702

98. 0.2504

99. $935 = 9.35 \times 10^2$

100. $0.372 = 3.72 \times 10^{-1}$

101. $0.0012 = 1.2 \times 10^{-3}$

102. $3,453,000 = 3.453 \times 10^6$

103. $8.64 \times 10^4 = 86,400$

104. $9.01 \times 10^7 = 90,100,000$

105. $6.71 \times 10^{-3} = 0.00671$

106. $4.02 \times 10^{-7} = 0.000000402$

107. $0.0346 \div 1,730,000$
$$= \left(3.46 \times 10^{-2}\right) \div \left(1.73 \times 10^6\right)$$
$$= \left(3.46 \div 1.73\right) \times \left(10^{-2} \div 10^6\right)$$
$$= 2 \times 10^{-8}$$

108. $0.00741 \times 225,000$
$$= \left(7.41 \times 10^{-3}\right) \times \left(2.25 \times 10^5\right)$$
$$= \left(7.41 \times 2.25\right) \times \left(10^{-3} \times 10^5\right)$$
$$= 16.6725 \times 10^2$$
$$= 1.66725 \times 10^1 \times 10^2 = 1.667 \times 10^3$$

109. $\left(3.1 \times 10^5\right) \times \left(2.2 \times 10^{-6}\right)$
$$= \left(3.1 \times 2.2\right) \times \left(10^5 \times 10^{-6}\right)$$
$$= 6.82 \times 10^{-1}$$

110. $\left(4.9 \times 10^{-2}\right) \times \left(3.5 \times 10^{-1}\right)$
$$= \left(4.9 \times 3.5\right) \times \left(10^{-2} \times 10^{-1}\right)$$
$$= 17.15 \times 10^{-3} = 1.715 \times 10^1 \times 10^{-3}$$
$$= 1.715 \times 10^{-2}$$

111. $\dfrac{\left(2 \times 10^6\right)\left(6 \times 10^{-5}\right)}{4 \times 10^3} = \dfrac{\left(2 \cdot 6\right) \cdot \left(10^6 \times 10^{-5}\right)}{4 \times 10^3}$
$$= \dfrac{12 \times 10^1}{4 \times 10^3} = 3 \times 10^{-2}$$

112. $\dfrac{\left(8 \times 10^2\right)\left(3 \times 10^{-2}\right)}{24 \times 10^{-3}} = \dfrac{\left(8 \cdot 3\right) \cdot \left(10^2 \times 10^{-2}\right)}{24 \times 10^{-3}}$
$$= \dfrac{24 \times 10^0}{24 \times 10^{-3}} = 1 \times 10^3$$

113. a. $3.81 + 0.93 = 4.74$
   b. $-3.81 + \left(-0.93\right) = -4.74$

114. a. $18.64 - 0.983 = 17.657$
   b. $-18.64 - 0.983 = -19.623$

115. a. $2.08 - 6.238 = -4.158$
   b. $3.07 - 8.934 = -5.864$

116. a. $2.48 \times 2.7 = 6.696$
   b. $\left(-2.48\right) \times \left(-2.7\right) = 6.696$

117. a. $\left(-0.03\right) \times \left(-1.5\right) = 0.045$
   b. $\left(-3.2\right) \times \left(-0.04\right) = 0.128$

118. a. $10.25 \div 0.05 = 205$
   b. $2.16 \div 0.06 = 36$

119. a. $\left(-0.07\right) \div 1.4 = -0.05$
   b. $\left(-0.09\right) \div \left(-4.5\right) = 0.02$

120. a. $\left(-1.8\right) \div \left(0.09\right) = -20$
   b. $\left(3.6\right) \div \left(-0.012\right) = -300$

121. $\dfrac{1}{12}$ of the time was spent eating.

122. $\dfrac{2}{12} = \dfrac{1}{6}$ of the time was spent watching TV.

123. $\dfrac{1}{12}$ of the time was spent doing homework.

124. a. $4.8 \times \left(4.6 \times 10^6\right) \times \left(3.65 \times 10^2\right)$

$\qquad = \left(4.8 \times 4.6 \times 3.65\right) \times \left(10^6 \times 10^2\right)$

$\qquad = 80.592 \times 10^8 = 8.0592 \times 10^1 \times 10^8$

$\qquad = 8.0592 \times 10^9$

   b. From part a,

$\qquad 8.0592 \times 10^9 = 8,059,200,000$

125. a. $4.8 \times \left(5.6 \times 10^6\right) \times \left(3.65 \times 10^2\right)$

$\qquad = \left(4.8 \times 5.6 \times 3.65\right) \times \left(10^6 \times 10^2\right)$

$\qquad = 98.112 \times 10^8 = 9.8112 \times 10^1 \times 10^8$

$\qquad = 9.8112 \times 10^9$

   b. From part a,

$\qquad 9.8112 \times 10^9 = 9,811,200,000$

126. To determine the octane rating, use

$\dfrac{R+M}{2}$,

where $R = 92$ and $M = 82$.

$\dfrac{R+M}{2} = \dfrac{92+82}{2} = \dfrac{174}{2} = 87$

The octane rating is 87.

127. a. To determine minimum pulse rate for a 20-year old, use $0.72(220 - A)$, $A = 20$. $0.72(220 - 20) = 0.72(200) = 144$ The minimum pulse rate is 144.

   b. To determine minimum pulse rate for a 45-year old, use $0.72(220 - A)$, $A = 20$. $0.72(220 - 45) = 0.72(175) = 126$ The minimum pulse rate is 126.

128. a. To determine monthly cost for a talker that used 1000 minutes, use $C = \$59.99 + 0.40(m - 900)$, where $m = 1000$.
$C = \$59.99 + 0.40(1000 - 900) = 99.99$
The monthly cost is \$99.99.

   b. To determine monthly cost for a talker that used 945 minutes, use $C = \$59.99 + 0.40(m - 900)$, where $m = 945$.
$C = \$59.99 + 0.40(945 - 900) = 77.99$
The monthly cost is \$77.99.

129. 2007 CO_2 concentration is 384.42 ppm and 1967 CO_2 concentration is 322.16 ppm. The difference is $384.42 - 322.16 = $ 62.26 ppm.

130. 2008 CO_2 concentration is 385.96 ppm and 1968 CO_2 concentration is 323.04 ppm. The difference is $385.96 - 323.04 = 62.92$ ppm.

131. 2009 CO_2 concentration is 388.79 ppm and 1969 CO_2 concentration is 324.62 ppm. The difference is $388.79 - 324.62 = 64.17$ ppm.

132. Yes, the CO_2 concentration was increasing in the 1960s . Yes, the CO_2 concentration was increasing in the 2000s .

133. Answers may vary.

134. Answers may vary. In order for this 'rule' to hold, do not drop trailing zeros. For instance, write $0.5 \cdot 0.2 = 0.10$ not 0.1, or $5 \cdot 0.2 = 1.0$ not 1.

135. Special K provides $\dfrac{4}{70}$ of the recommended daily protein needs. Rounded to the hundredths, $\dfrac{4}{70} \approx 0.06$.

136. Spinach (1 cup) provides $\dfrac{5}{70} = \dfrac{1}{14}$ of the recommended daily protein needs. Expressed as a decimal rounded to the hundredths:

$\dfrac{1}{14} \approx 0.07$

137. One egg provides $\dfrac{7}{70} = \dfrac{1}{10}$ of the recommended daily protein needs. Expressed as a decimal, $\dfrac{1}{10} = 0.10$.

Collaborative Learning

1. Answers will vary. Based on the items chosen, the group may find that brand-name items are not always more expensive than generic.

2. Answers will vary. Based on the items chosen, the group may find that the bigger size is not always cheaper.

Section 5.4 Rationals and Irrationals as Decimals: Percents

1. $\dfrac{9}{10} = 0.9$

2. $\dfrac{3}{10} = 0.3$

3. $\dfrac{11}{10} = 1.1$

4. $\dfrac{27}{10} = 2.7$

5. $\dfrac{17}{100} = 0.17$

6. $\dfrac{38}{100} = 0.38$

7. $\dfrac{121}{100} = 1.21$

8. $\dfrac{3520}{100} = 35.20$

9. $\dfrac{3}{1000} = 0.003$

10. $\dfrac{143}{1000} = 0.143$

11. $\dfrac{1243}{1000} = 1.243$

12. $\dfrac{25,360}{1000} = 25.360$

13. $\dfrac{3}{5} = 0.6$

14. $\dfrac{7}{8} = 0.875$

15. $\dfrac{9}{16} = 0.5625$

16. $\dfrac{15}{32} = 0.46875$

17. $\dfrac{5}{8} = 0.625$

18. $\dfrac{5}{4} = 1.25$

19. $\dfrac{5}{7} = 0.714285714285... = 0.\overline{714285}$

20. $\dfrac{7}{6} = 1.1666... = 1.1\overline{6}$

21. $\dfrac{4}{15} = 0.2666... = 0.2\overline{6}$

22. $6\dfrac{1}{4} = 6.25$

23. $7\dfrac{1}{7} = 7.142857142857... = 7.\overline{142857}$

24. $3\dfrac{2}{3} = 3.666... = 3.\overline{6}$

25. $\dfrac{3}{16} = 0.1875$

26. $\dfrac{3}{14}$: no terminating decimal expansion.

27. $\dfrac{1}{64} = 0.015625$

28. $\dfrac{4}{28}$: no terminating decimal expansion.

29. $\dfrac{31}{3125} = 0.00992$

30. $\dfrac{9}{250} = 0.036$

31. $0.555555\cdots = 0.\overline{5}$

32. $0.777777\cdots = 0.\overline{7}$

33. $0.646464\cdots = 0.\overline{64}$

34. $0.737373\cdots = 0.\overline{73}$

35. $0.235235\cdots = 0.\overline{235}$

36. $0.930930\cdots = 0.\overline{930}$

37. $0.215555\cdots = 0.21\overline{5}$

38. $0.7132222\cdots = 0.713\overline{2}$

39. $0.079353535\cdots = 0.079\overline{35}$

40. $0.23515151\cdots = 0.235\overline{51}$

41. $5.070707\cdots = 5.\overline{07}$

42. $9.23373737\cdots = 9.23\overline{37}$

43. To change $0.\overline{8}$ to a fraction:

$10x = 8.88888\cdots$

$\underline{-\ x = .88888\cdots}$

$9x = 8$

$x = \dfrac{8}{9}$

44. To change $0.\overline{6}$ to a fraction:

$10x = 6.66666\cdots$

$\underline{-\ x = .66666\cdots}$

$9x = 6$

$x = \dfrac{6}{9} = \dfrac{2}{3}$

45. To change $0.\overline{31}$ to a fraction:

$100x = 31.313131\cdots$

$\underline{-\ x = .313131\cdots}$

$99x = 31$

$x = \dfrac{31}{99}$

46. To change $0.\overline{21}$ to a fraction:

$100x = 21.212121\cdots$

$\underline{-\ x = .212121\cdots}$

$99x = 21$

$x = \dfrac{21}{99} = \dfrac{7}{33}$

47. To change $0.\overline{114}$ to a fraction:

$1000x = 114.114114\cdots$

$\underline{-\ x = .114114\cdots}$

$999x = 114$

$x = \dfrac{114}{999} = \dfrac{38}{333}$

48. To change $0.\overline{102}$ to a fraction:

$1000x = 102.102102\cdots$

$\underline{-\ x = .102102\cdots}$

$999x = 102$

$x = \dfrac{102}{999} = \dfrac{34}{333}$

49. To change $2.\overline{31}$ to a fraction, rewrite as $2 + 0.\overline{31}$ and then

$100x = 31.313131\cdots$

$\underline{-\ x = .313131\cdots}$

$99x = 31$

$x = \dfrac{31}{99}$

$2.\overline{31} = 2 + \dfrac{31}{99} = \dfrac{229}{99}$

50. To change $5.\overline{672}$ to a fraction, rewrite as $5 + 0.\overline{672}$ and then

$1000x = 672.672672\cdots$

$\underline{-\ x = .672672\cdots}$

$999x = 672$

$x = \dfrac{672}{999}$

$5.\overline{672} = 5 + \dfrac{672}{999} = \dfrac{5667}{999} = \dfrac{1889}{333}$

51. To change $1.\overline{234}$ to a fraction, rewrite as $1 + 0.\overline{234}$ and then

$1000x = 234.234234\cdots$

$\underline{-\ x = .234234\cdots}$

$999x = 234$

$x = \dfrac{234}{999}$

$1.\overline{234} = 1 + \dfrac{234}{999} = \dfrac{1233}{999} = \dfrac{137}{111}$

52. To change $0.\overline{017}$ to a fraction:

$1000x = 17.017017\cdots$

$\underline{-\ x = .017017\cdots}$

$999x = 17$

$x = \dfrac{17}{999}$

53. To change $1.\overline{27}$ to a fraction, rewrite as $1 + 0.\overline{27}$ and then

$$100x = 27.272727\cdots$$
$$-\quad x = .272727\cdots$$
$$99x = 27$$

$$x = \frac{27}{99} = \frac{3}{11}$$

$$1.\overline{27} = 1 + \frac{3}{11} = \frac{14}{11}$$

54. To change $2.4\overline{8}$ to a fraction, rewrite as $2 + 0.\overline{8}$ and then

$$100x = 48.88888\cdots$$
$$-10x = 4.88888\cdots$$
$$90x = 44$$

$$x = \frac{44}{90} = \frac{22}{45}$$

$$2.4\overline{8} = 2 + \frac{22}{45} = \frac{112}{45}$$

55. To change $0.45\overline{75}$ to a fraction:

$$10,000x = 4575.757575\cdots$$
$$-\quad 100x = 45.757575\cdots$$
$$9900x = 4530$$

$$x = \frac{4530}{9900} = \frac{151}{330}$$

56. To change $0.23\overline{15}$ to a fraction:

$$10,000x = 2315.151515\cdots$$
$$-\quad 100x = 23.151515\cdots$$
$$9900x = 2292$$

$$x = \frac{2292}{9900} = \frac{191}{825}$$

57. To change $0.\overline{2016}$ to a fraction:

$$10,000x = 2016.20162016\cdots$$
$$-\quad x = 0.20162016\cdots$$
$$9999x = 2016$$

$$x = \frac{2016}{9999} = \frac{224}{1111}$$

58. To change $0.20\overline{16}$ to a fraction:

$$10,000x = 2016.666666\cdots$$
$$-\quad 1000x = 201.666666\cdots$$
$$9000x = 1996$$

$$x = \frac{1815}{9000} = \frac{121}{600}$$

For problems 59 – 67, to change a percent to a decimal, move the decimal point two places to the left and omit the % symbol.

59. $29\% = 0.29$ 60. $23.4\% = 0.234$

61. $0.9\% = 0.009$ 62. $56.9\% = 0.569$

63. $45.69\% = 0.4569$ 64. $0.008\% = 0.00008$

65. $34.15\% = 0.3415$ 66. $93.56\% = 0.9356$

67. $0.0234\% = 0.000234$

For problems 68 – 76, to change a decimal to a percent, move the decimal point two places to the right and attach the % symbol.

68. $0.38 = 38\%$ 69. $3.45 = 345\%$

70. $9.998 = 999.8\%$ 71. $0.567 = 56.7\%$

72. $0.00452 = 0.452\%$ 73. $9.003 = 900.3\%$

74. $0.0004 = 0.04\%$ 75. $0.0045 = 0.45\%$

76. $0.0008 = 0.08\%$ 77. $\dfrac{3}{5} = 0.6 = 60\%$

78. $\dfrac{4}{7} \approx 0.5714 \approx 57.1\%$

79. $\dfrac{5}{6} \approx 0.8333 \approx 83.3\%$

80. $\dfrac{7}{8} = 0.875 = 87.5\%$

81. $\sqrt{120}$ is an irrational number because 120 is not a perfect square.

82. $\sqrt{121} = 11$ is a rational number because 121 is a perfect square.

83. $\sqrt{125}$ is an irrational number because 125 is not a perfect square.

84. $\sqrt{169} = 13$ is a rational number because 169 is a perfect square.

85. $\sqrt{\dfrac{9}{16}} = \dfrac{3}{4}$ is a rational number because 9 and 16 are perfect squares.

86. $\sqrt{\dfrac{9}{15}} = \dfrac{3}{\sqrt{15}}$ is an irrational number because 15 is not a perfect square.

87. $\dfrac{3}{5}$ is a rational number.

88. $-\dfrac{22}{7}$ is a rational number.

89. $-\dfrac{5}{3}$ is a rational number.

90. -0 is a rational number as it can be rewritten as $-\dfrac{0}{a}$, where a is any integer except 0.

91. $0.2323\cdots$ is a repeating decimal, so is a rational number.

92. $0.023002300023\cdots$ is nonrepeating and nonterminating, so is an irrational number.

93. $0.121231234\ldots$ is a nonterminating, nonrepeating decimal, so is an irrational number.

94. 0.121231234 is a terminating decimal, so is a rational number.

95. $6\dfrac{1}{4} = \dfrac{25}{4} = 6.25$ is a terminating decimal, so is a rational number.

96. $\sqrt{6\dfrac{1}{4}} = 2.5$ is a terminating decimal, so is a rational number.

97. $\sqrt{3\dfrac{1}{4}} = 1.802995638\cdots$ is a nonrepeating, nonterminating decimal, so is an irrational number.

98. $0.24681012\cdots$ is a nonterminating, nonrepeating decimal, so is an irrational number.

99. 0.1122334455 is a terminating decimal, so is a rational number.

100. 3.1415 is a terminating decimal, so is a rational number.

101. $\pi = 3.141592654\cdots$ is a nonrepeating, nonterminating decimal, so is an irrational number.

102. $3 < 4$

103. $17 > 11$

104. $\dfrac{1}{5} < \dfrac{1}{4}$

105. $\dfrac{12}{19} < \dfrac{11}{17}$

106. $\dfrac{5}{7} = \dfrac{10}{14}$

107. $1\dfrac{2}{3} > \dfrac{8}{6}$

108. $4.5^2 = 20.25$, so $\sqrt{20} < 4.5$

109. $3.777\cdots < \sqrt{15}$

110. $0.333\cdots < 0.333444\cdots$

111. $0.101001000 < 0.1101001000\cdots$

112. $0.999\cdots = 1$

113. $0.333\cdots + 0.666\cdots = 1$

114. $3(0.333\cdots) = 0.999\cdots = 1$

115. $0.112233 > 0.111222333\cdots$

For problems 116 – 129, other answers are possible.

116. 0.315

117. 0.2825

118. $0.311212345\cdots$

119. $0.28101001000\cdots$

120. 0.1011

121. 0.3031

122. 0.101101001000⋯

123. 0.303103003000⋯

124. $\dfrac{7}{22}$; This is the average (one-half the sum) of the given numbers.

125. $\dfrac{79}{99}$; This is the average (one-half the sum) of the given numbers.

126. $\dfrac{4}{9} = 0.444\cdots$ and $\dfrac{5}{9} = 0.555\cdots$, so 0.5101001000⋯

127. $\dfrac{2}{11} = 0.1818\cdots$ and $\dfrac{3}{11} = 0.2727\cdots$, so 0.2273101001000⋯

128. $0.\overline{5} = 0.555\cdots = \dfrac{5}{9} = \dfrac{10}{18}$ and $\dfrac{2}{3} = \dfrac{12}{18}$, so $\dfrac{11}{18}$

129. $0.1 = \dfrac{1}{10}$ and $0.\overline{1} = 0.111\cdots = \dfrac{1}{9}$, so $\dfrac{19}{180}$. This is the average (one-half the sum) of the two fractions.

130. a. False; All repeating decimals can be written in the form $\dfrac{a}{b}$, where a and b are integers and $b \neq 0$, which is the definition of a rational number.
   b. True; A counting number a is an integer and can be written as $\dfrac{a}{1}$. The form $\dfrac{a}{b}$, where a and b are integers (1 is an integer) and $b \neq 0$, defines a rational number. Thus, all counting numbers are rational numbers.
   c. False; All integers can be written as $\dfrac{a}{1}$, where a is an integer. The form

$\dfrac{a}{b}$, where a and b are integers (1 is an integer) and $b \neq 0$, defines a rational number. Thus, all integers are rational numbers.
   d. False; 0.20200200020000⋯ is not a repeating decimal as the number of 0s increases.
   e. True; All terminating decimals can be written in the form $\dfrac{a}{b}$, where a and b are integers and $b \neq 0$, so are rational numbers.

131. Slightly wicked: $(0.54)(-2.5) = -1.35$

132. Decidedly average: $(1.16)(-0.8) = -0.928$

133. Rather lovable: $(0.84)(2.4) = 2.016$

134. Very good: $(1.25)(3.1) = 3.875$

135. $0.\overline{4} = 0.444\cdots = \dfrac{4}{9}$

136. $0.\overline{4321} = \dfrac{4321}{9999}$

Section 5.5 Radicals and Real Numbers

1. $\sqrt{90} = \sqrt{9 \cdot 10} = 3\sqrt{10}$

2. $\sqrt{72} = \sqrt{36 \cdot 2} = 6\sqrt{2}$

3. $\sqrt{122}$ is in simplest form.

4. $\sqrt{175} = \sqrt{25 \cdot 7} = 5\sqrt{7}$

5. $\sqrt{180} = \sqrt{36 \cdot 5} = 6\sqrt{5}$

6. $\sqrt{162} = \sqrt{81 \cdot 2} = 9\sqrt{2}$

7. $\sqrt{200} = \sqrt{100 \cdot 2} = 10\sqrt{2}$

8. $\sqrt{191}$ is in simplest form.

9. $\sqrt{384} = \sqrt{64 \cdot 6} = 8\sqrt{6}$

10. $\sqrt{486} = \sqrt{81 \cdot 6} = 9\sqrt{6}$

11. $\sqrt{588} = \sqrt{196 \cdot 3} = 14\sqrt{3}$

12. $\sqrt{5000} = \sqrt{2500 \cdot 2} = 50\sqrt{2}$

13. $\dfrac{3}{\sqrt{7}} = \dfrac{3}{\sqrt{7}} \cdot \dfrac{\sqrt{7}}{\sqrt{7}} = \dfrac{3\sqrt{7}}{7}$

14. $\dfrac{6}{\sqrt{5}} = \dfrac{6}{\sqrt{5}} \cdot \dfrac{\sqrt{5}}{\sqrt{5}} = \dfrac{6\sqrt{5}}{5}$

15. $-\dfrac{\sqrt{2}}{\sqrt{5}} = -\dfrac{\sqrt{2}}{\sqrt{5}} \cdot \dfrac{\sqrt{5}}{\sqrt{5}} = -\dfrac{\sqrt{10}}{5}$

16. $-\dfrac{\sqrt{3}}{\sqrt{7}} = \dfrac{\sqrt{3}}{\sqrt{7}} \cdot \dfrac{\sqrt{7}}{\sqrt{7}} = -\dfrac{\sqrt{21}}{7}$

17. $\dfrac{4}{\sqrt{8}} = \dfrac{4}{\sqrt{8}} \cdot \dfrac{\sqrt{2}}{\sqrt{2}} = \dfrac{4\sqrt{2}}{\sqrt{16}} = \dfrac{4\sqrt{2}}{4} = \sqrt{2}$

18. $\dfrac{3}{\sqrt{27}} = \dfrac{3}{\sqrt{27}} \cdot \dfrac{\sqrt{3}}{\sqrt{3}} = \dfrac{3\sqrt{3}}{\sqrt{81}} = \dfrac{3\sqrt{3}}{9} = \dfrac{\sqrt{3}}{3}$

19. $\sqrt{\dfrac{3}{49}} = \dfrac{\sqrt{3}}{\sqrt{49}} = \dfrac{\sqrt{3}}{7}$

20. $\sqrt{\dfrac{7}{16}} = \dfrac{\sqrt{7}}{\sqrt{16}} = \dfrac{\sqrt{7}}{4}$

21. $\sqrt{\dfrac{4}{3}} = \dfrac{\sqrt{4}}{\sqrt{3}} = \dfrac{2}{\sqrt{3}} \cdot \dfrac{\sqrt{3}}{\sqrt{3}} = \dfrac{2\sqrt{3}}{3}$

22. $\sqrt{\dfrac{25}{11}} = \dfrac{25}{\sqrt{11}} = \dfrac{5}{\sqrt{11}} \cdot \dfrac{\sqrt{11}}{\sqrt{11}} = \dfrac{5\sqrt{11}}{11}$

23. $\sqrt{\dfrac{8}{49}} = \dfrac{\sqrt{8}}{\sqrt{49}} = \dfrac{\sqrt{4 \cdot 2}}{\sqrt{49}} = \dfrac{2\sqrt{2}}{7}$

24. $\sqrt{\dfrac{18}{25}} = \dfrac{\sqrt{18}}{\sqrt{25}} = \dfrac{\sqrt{9 \cdot 2}}{\sqrt{25}} = \dfrac{3\sqrt{2}}{5}$

25. $\sqrt{\dfrac{18}{50}} = \sqrt{\dfrac{9}{25}} = \dfrac{3}{5}$

26. $\sqrt{\dfrac{24}{75}} = \sqrt{\dfrac{8}{25}} = \dfrac{\sqrt{8}}{\sqrt{25}} = \dfrac{\sqrt{4 \cdot 2}}{\sqrt{25}} = \dfrac{2\sqrt{2}}{5}$

27. $\sqrt{\dfrac{32}{125}} = \dfrac{\sqrt{16 \cdot 2}}{\sqrt{25 \cdot 5}} = \dfrac{4\sqrt{2}}{5\sqrt{5}} = \dfrac{4\sqrt{2}}{5\sqrt{5}} \cdot \dfrac{\sqrt{5}}{\sqrt{5}}$

$= \dfrac{4\sqrt{10}}{5 \cdot 5} = \dfrac{4\sqrt{10}}{25}$

28. $\sqrt{7} \cdot \sqrt{8} = \sqrt{56} = \sqrt{4 \cdot 14} = 2\sqrt{14}$

29. $\sqrt{5} \cdot \sqrt{50} = \sqrt{250} = \sqrt{25 \cdot 10} = 5\sqrt{10}$

30. $\sqrt{10} \cdot \sqrt{5} = \sqrt{50} = \sqrt{25 \cdot 2} = 5\sqrt{2}$

31. $\dfrac{\sqrt{28}}{\sqrt{2}} = \sqrt{\dfrac{28}{2}} = \sqrt{14}$

32. $\dfrac{\sqrt{22}}{\sqrt{2}} = \sqrt{\dfrac{22}{2}} = \sqrt{11}$

33. $\dfrac{\sqrt{10}}{\sqrt{250}} = \sqrt{\dfrac{10}{250}} = \sqrt{\dfrac{1}{25}} = \dfrac{1}{5}$

34. $\dfrac{\sqrt{10}}{\sqrt{490}} = \sqrt{\dfrac{10}{490}} = \sqrt{\dfrac{1}{49}} = \dfrac{1}{7}$

35. $\dfrac{\sqrt{33}}{\sqrt{22}} = \sqrt{\dfrac{33}{22}} = \sqrt{\dfrac{3}{2}} = \dfrac{\sqrt{3}}{\sqrt{2}} \cdot \dfrac{\sqrt{2}}{\sqrt{2}} = \dfrac{\sqrt{6}}{2}$

36. $\dfrac{\sqrt{18}}{\sqrt{12}} = \sqrt{\dfrac{18}{12}} = \sqrt{\dfrac{3}{2}} = \dfrac{\sqrt{3}}{\sqrt{2}} \cdot \dfrac{\sqrt{2}}{\sqrt{2}} = \dfrac{\sqrt{6}}{2}$

37. $\sqrt{3} + \sqrt{12} = \sqrt{3} + \sqrt{4 \cdot 3} = \sqrt{3} + 2\sqrt{3} = 3\sqrt{3}$

38. $\sqrt{32} - \sqrt{8} = \sqrt{16 \cdot 2} - \sqrt{4 \cdot 2}$

$= 4\sqrt{2} - 2\sqrt{2} = 2\sqrt{2}$

39. $\sqrt{125} + \sqrt{80} = \sqrt{25 \cdot 5} + \sqrt{16 \cdot 5}$

$= 5\sqrt{5} + 4\sqrt{5} = 9\sqrt{5}$

40. $\sqrt{24} - \sqrt{150} = \sqrt{4 \cdot 6} - \sqrt{25 \cdot 6}$

$= 2\sqrt{6} - 5\sqrt{6} = -3\sqrt{6}$

41. $\sqrt{3^2 + 4^2} = \sqrt{9 + 16} = \sqrt{25} = 5$

42. $\sqrt{5^2 + (12)^2} = \sqrt{25 + 144} = \sqrt{169} = 13$

43. $\sqrt{13^2 - 12^2} = \sqrt{169 - 144} = \sqrt{25} = 5$

44. $\sqrt{(25)^2 - (24)^2} = \sqrt{625 - 576} = \sqrt{49} = 7$

45. $6\sqrt{7} + \sqrt{7} - 2\sqrt{7} = (6 + 1 - 2)\sqrt{7} = 5\sqrt{7}$

46. $\sqrt{3} + 11\sqrt{3} - 3\sqrt{3} = (1 + 11 - 3)\sqrt{3} = 9\sqrt{3}$

47. $5\sqrt{7} - 3\sqrt{28} - 2\sqrt{63}$
$$= 5\sqrt{7} - 3\sqrt{4 \cdot 7} - 2\sqrt{9 \cdot 7}$$
$$= 5\sqrt{7} - 3 \cdot 2\sqrt{7} - 2 \cdot 3\sqrt{7}$$
$$= 5\sqrt{7} - 6\sqrt{7} - 6\sqrt{7} = -7\sqrt{7}$$

48. $3\sqrt{28} - 6\sqrt{7} - 2\sqrt{175}$
$$= 3\sqrt{4 \cdot 7} - 6\sqrt{7} - 2\sqrt{25 \cdot 7}$$
$$= 3 \cdot 2\sqrt{7} - 6\sqrt{7} - 2 \cdot 5\sqrt{7}$$
$$- 6\sqrt{7} - 6\sqrt{7} - 10\sqrt{7} = -10\sqrt{7}$$

49. $-3\sqrt{45} + \sqrt{20} - \sqrt{5}$
$$= -3\sqrt{9 \cdot 5} + \sqrt{4 \cdot 5} - \sqrt{5}$$
$$= -3 \cdot 3\sqrt{5} + 2\sqrt{5} - \sqrt{5}$$
$$= -9\sqrt{5} + 2\sqrt{5} - \sqrt{5} = -8\sqrt{5}$$

50. $-5\sqrt{27} + \sqrt{12} - 5\sqrt{48}$
$$= -5\sqrt{9 \cdot 3} + \sqrt{4 \cdot 3} - 5\sqrt{16 \cdot 3}$$
$$= -5 \cdot 3\sqrt{3} + 2\sqrt{3} - 5 \cdot 4\sqrt{3}$$
$$= -15\sqrt{3} + 2\sqrt{3} - 20\sqrt{3} = -33\sqrt{3}$$

51. a. To determine how long (t) a storm 6 mi in diameter will last, let $d = 6$ in the formula $t = \sqrt{\left(\dfrac{d}{6}\right)^3}$:
$$t = \sqrt{\left(\frac{d}{6}\right)^3} = \sqrt{\left(\frac{6}{6}\right)^3} = \sqrt{(1)^3} = 1$$
The storm will last 1 hour.

b. To determine how long (t) a storm 10 mi in diameter will last, let $d = 10$ in the formula $t = \sqrt{\left(\dfrac{d}{6}\right)^3}$:
$$t = \sqrt{\left(\frac{d}{6}\right)^3} = \sqrt{\left(\frac{10}{6}\right)^3} = \sqrt{\left(\frac{5}{3}\right)^3} = \sqrt{\frac{5^3}{3^3}}$$
$$= \frac{\sqrt{5^3}}{\sqrt{3^3}} = \frac{5\sqrt{5}}{3\sqrt{3}}$$
$$= \frac{5\sqrt{5}}{3\sqrt{3}} \cdot \frac{\sqrt{3}}{\sqrt{3}} = \frac{5\sqrt{15}}{9} \approx 2.15$$
The storm will last about 2.15 hours.

52. a. To determine how long (t) a storm 3 mi in diameter will last, let $d = 3$ in the formula $t = \sqrt{\left(\dfrac{d}{6}\right)^3}$:
$$t = \sqrt{\left(\frac{d}{6}\right)^3} = \sqrt{\left(\frac{3}{6}\right)^3} = \sqrt{\left(\frac{1}{2}\right)^3} = \sqrt{\frac{1^3}{2^3}}$$
$$= \frac{\sqrt{1^3}}{\sqrt{2^3}} = \frac{1}{2\sqrt{2}}$$
$$= \frac{1}{2\sqrt{2}} \cdot \frac{\sqrt{2}}{\sqrt{2}} = \frac{\sqrt{2}}{4}$$
The storm will last $\dfrac{\sqrt{2}}{4}$ hour.

b. The game will be resumed; it was only delayed 0.35 hr, or about 21 minutes.

53. a. To determine the average speed S of a tsunami when the average depth d of the water is 40 m, let $d = 40$ in the formula $S = \sqrt{10} \cdot \sqrt{d}$:
$$S = \sqrt{10} \cdot \sqrt{d} = \sqrt{10} \cdot \sqrt{40} = \sqrt{400} = 20$$
The average speed of the tsunami is 20 m/sec.

b. To determine the average speed S of this tsunami when the average depth d of the water is 4267 m, let $d = 4267$ in the formula $S = \sqrt{10} \cdot \sqrt{d}$, round to the nearest meter:
$$S = \sqrt{10} \cdot \sqrt{d} = \sqrt{10} \cdot \sqrt{4267}$$
$$= \sqrt{42670} \approx 207$$
The average speed of this tsunami is 207 m/sec.

54. To determine the average speed S of this tsunami when the average depth d of the water is 30 m, let $d = 30$ in the formula $S = \sqrt{10} \cdot \sqrt{d}$, round to the nearest meter:

$$S = \sqrt{10} \cdot \sqrt{d} = \sqrt{10} \cdot \sqrt{30}$$
$$= \sqrt{300} = \sqrt{100 \cdot 3} = 10\sqrt{3}$$

The average speed of this tsunami is $10\sqrt{3}$ m/sec.

55. $r = \sqrt{\dfrac{144}{100}} - 1 = \dfrac{12}{10} - 1 = 1.2 - 1 = 0.20$

$= 20\%$

56. a. Let $a = 123{,}800$ in the formula

$$V_m = \sqrt{\dfrac{3}{2}a} \;:$$

$$V_m = \sqrt{\dfrac{3}{2}(123{,}800)} = \sqrt{185{,}700} = 10\sqrt{1857}$$

The view would be $10\sqrt{1857}$ mi.

b. The view would be about 430 mi.

57. $v = \sqrt{20 \cdot 10 + 25} = \sqrt{225} = 15$ m/sec

58. $v = \sqrt{20 \cdot 45 + 0} = \sqrt{900} = 30$ m/sec

59. $v = \sqrt{64 \cdot 12 + 16} = \sqrt{784} = 28$ ft/sec

60. $v = \sqrt{64 \cdot 25 + 0} = \sqrt{1600} = 40$ ft/sec

61. $\sqrt{5^2 - 4 \cdot 1 \cdot 4} = \sqrt{25 - 16} = \sqrt{9} = 3$

62. $\sqrt{3^2 - 4 \cdot 1 \cdot 2} = \sqrt{9 - 8} = \sqrt{1} = 1$

63. $\sqrt{(-3)^2 - 4 \cdot 2 \cdot (-20)} = \sqrt{9 + 160}$

$$= \sqrt{169} = 13$$

64. $\sqrt{\left(-\dfrac{1}{12}\right)^2 - 4 \cdot \dfrac{1}{2} \cdot (-1)}$

$$= \sqrt{\dfrac{1}{144} + 2} = \sqrt{\dfrac{1}{144} + \dfrac{288}{144}} = \sqrt{\dfrac{289}{144}} = \dfrac{17}{12}$$

65. $\sqrt{\left(\dfrac{1}{3}\right)^2 - 4 \cdot \dfrac{1}{12} \cdot (-1)} = \sqrt{\dfrac{1}{9} + \dfrac{1}{3}} = \sqrt{\dfrac{4}{9}} = \dfrac{2}{3}$

66. $\sqrt{\left(\dfrac{1}{2}\right)^2 - 4 \cdot \dfrac{1}{12} \cdot \dfrac{2}{3}} = \sqrt{\dfrac{1}{4} - \dfrac{2}{9}} = \sqrt{\dfrac{1}{36}} = \dfrac{1}{6}$

67. 4.2: check Rational numbers, Real numbers

68. $-\dfrac{3}{8}$: check Rational numbers, Real numbers

69. 0: check Whole numbers, Integers, Rational numbers, Real numbers

70. $\sqrt{3}$: check Irrational numbers, Real numbers

71. $\sqrt{9}$: check Natural numbers, Whole numbers, Integers, Rational numbers, Real numbers

72. 5: check Integer numbers, Whole numbers, Integers, Rational numbers, Real numbers

73. $0.\overline{66}$: check Rational numbers, Real numbers

74. $1\dfrac{5}{8}$: check Rational numbers, Real numbers

75. $\sqrt{20}$: check Irrational numbers, Real numbers

76. π : check Irrational numbers, Real numbers

77. Answers may vary. Try an example. Suppose $a = -2$ and $b = -3$. Then, by definition, $\sqrt{-2}$ and $\sqrt{-3}$ are not real numbers but $\sqrt{-2}\sqrt{-3} = \sqrt{(-2)(-3)} = \sqrt{6}$, which is a real number. How can the product of two undefined numbers yield a real number?

78. Answers may vary. Every integer can be written in the form $\dfrac{a}{b}$ where $b = 1$.

79. $40 - 36 = 4$

$\sqrt{36} = 6$

$\sqrt{40} = \boxed{6\dfrac{4}{13} \approx 6.31}$

$\sqrt{49} = 7$

$49 - 36 = 13$

(Calculator gives 6.32.)

80. $68 - 64 = 4$

$\sqrt{64} = 8$

$\sqrt{68} = \boxed{8\dfrac{4}{17} \approx 8.24}$

$\sqrt{81} = 9$

$81 - 64 = 17$

(Calculator gives 8.25.)

81. $85 - 81 = 4$

$\sqrt{81} = 9$

$\sqrt{85} = \boxed{9\dfrac{4}{19} \approx 9.21}$

$\sqrt{100} = 10$

$100 - 81 = 19$

(Calculator gives 9.22.)

82. $108 - 100 = 8$

$\sqrt{100} = 10$

$\sqrt{108} = \boxed{10\dfrac{8}{21} \approx 10.38}$

$\sqrt{121} = 11$

$121 - 100 = 21$

(Calculator gives 10.39.)

Collaborative Learning

$\sqrt{10} \approx 3.16227766$

$\sqrt{867} \approx 29.44486373$

$\sqrt{900} = 30$

$\sqrt{40} \approx 6.32455532$

$\sqrt{68} \approx 8.246211251$

$\sqrt{85} \approx 9.219544457$

$\sqrt{108} \approx 10.39230485$

Section 5.6 Number Sequences

1. a. $a_1 = 7$ b. $d = 6$
    c. $a_{10} = a_1 + 9d = 7 + 9 \cdot 6 = 7 + 54 = 61$
    d. $a_n = a_1 + (n-1)d = 7 + (n-1)6$
        $= 7 + 6n - 6 = 6n + 1$

2. a. $a_1 = 3$ b. $d = 3$
    c. $a_{10} = a_1 + 9d = 3 + 9 \cdot 3 = 3 + 27 = 30$
    d. $a_n = a_1 + (n-1)d = 3 + (n-1)3$
        $= 3 + 3n - 3 = 3n$

3. a. $a_1 = 43$ b. $d = -9$
    c. $a_{10} = a_1 + 9d = 43 + 9 \cdot (-9)$
        $= 43 - 81 = -38$
    d. $a_n = a_1 + (n-1)d = 43 + (n-1)(-9)$
        $= 43 - 9n + 9 = 52 - 9n$

4. a. $a_1 = 3$ b. $d = -4$
    c. $a_{10} = a_1 + 9d = 3 + 9 \cdot (-4)$
        $= 3 - 36 = -33$
    d. $a_n = a_1 + (n-1)d = 3 + (n-1)(-4)$
        $= 3 - 4n + 4 = 7 - 4n$

5. a. $a_1 = 2$ b. $d = -5$
    c. $a_{10} = a_1 + 9d = 2 + 9 \cdot (-5)$
        $= 2 - 45 = -43$
    d. $a_n = a_1 + (n-1)d = 2 + (n-1)(-5)$
        $= 2 - 5n + 5 = 7 - 5n$

6. a. $a_1 = \dfrac{2}{3}$ b. $d = \dfrac{1}{6}$
    c. $a_{10} = a_1 + 9d = \dfrac{2}{3} + 9 \cdot \dfrac{1}{6}$
        $= \dfrac{2}{3} + \dfrac{9}{6} = \dfrac{4}{6} + \dfrac{9}{6} = \dfrac{13}{6}$
    d. $a_n = a_1 + (n-1)d = \dfrac{2}{3} + (n-1)\dfrac{1}{6}$
        $= \dfrac{2}{3} + \dfrac{1}{6}n - \dfrac{1}{6} = \dfrac{4}{6} + \dfrac{1}{6}n - \dfrac{1}{6} = \dfrac{n+3}{6}$

7. a. $a_1 = -\dfrac{5}{6}$ b. $d = \dfrac{1}{2}$

c. $a_{10} = a_1 + 9d = -\dfrac{5}{6} + 9 \cdot \dfrac{1}{2}$

$= -\dfrac{5}{6} + \dfrac{9}{2} = \dfrac{22}{6} = \dfrac{11}{3}$

d. $a_n = a_1 + (n-1)d = -\dfrac{5}{6} + (n-1)\left(\dfrac{1}{2}\right)$

$= -\dfrac{5}{6} + \dfrac{1}{2}n - \dfrac{1}{2} = \dfrac{1}{2}n - \dfrac{4}{3} = \dfrac{3n-8}{6}$

8. a. $a_1 = -\dfrac{1}{4}$ b. $d = \dfrac{1}{2}$

c. $a_{10} = a_1 + 9d = -\dfrac{1}{4} + 9 \cdot \dfrac{1}{2}$

$= -\dfrac{1}{4} + \dfrac{9}{2} = -\dfrac{1}{4} + \dfrac{18}{4} = \dfrac{17}{4}$

d. $a_n = a_1 + (n-1)d$

$= -\dfrac{1}{4} + (n-1)\left(\dfrac{1}{2}\right)$

$= -\dfrac{1}{4} + \dfrac{1}{2}n - \dfrac{1}{2} = \dfrac{1}{2}n - \dfrac{3}{4} = \dfrac{2n-3}{4}$

9. a. $a_1 = 0.6$ b. $d = -0.4$

c. $a_{10} = a_1 + 9d = 0.6 + 9 \cdot (-0.4)$

$= 0.6 - 3.6 = -3$

d. $a_n = a_1 + (n-1)d$

$= 0.6 + (n-1)(-0.4)$

$= 0.6 - 0.4n + 0.4 = 1 - 0.4n$

10. a. $a_1 = 0.7$ b. $d = -0.5$

c. $a_{10} = a_1 + 9d = 0.7 + 9 \cdot (-0.5)$

$= 0.7 - 4.5 = -3.8$

d. $a_n = a_1 + (n-1)d$

$= 0.7 + (n-1)(-0.5)$

$= 0.7 - 0.5n + 0.5 = 1.2 - 0.5n$

11. $S_{10} = \dfrac{10(7+61)}{2} = 5(68) = 340$

$S_n = \dfrac{n(7+6n+1)}{2} = \dfrac{n(6n+8)}{2}$

$= n(3n+4) = 3n^2 + 4n$

12. $S_{10} = \dfrac{10(3+30)}{2} = 5(33) = 165$

$S_n = \dfrac{n(3+3n)}{2} = \dfrac{n(3n+3)}{2}$

$= \dfrac{3n(n+1)}{2} = \dfrac{3}{2}(n^2 + n)$

13. $S_{10} = \dfrac{10(43+(-38))}{2} = 5(5) = 25$

$S_n = \dfrac{n(43+52-9n)}{2} = \dfrac{n(95-9n)}{2}$

$= \dfrac{95n - 9n^2}{2}$

14. $S_{10} = \dfrac{10(3+(-33))}{2} = 5(-30) = -150$

$S_n = \dfrac{n(3+7-4n)}{2} = \dfrac{n(10-4n)}{2}$

$= n(5-2n) = 5n - 2n^2$

15. $S_{10} = \dfrac{10(2+(-43))}{2} = 5(-41) = -205$

$S_n = \dfrac{n(2+7-5n)}{2} = \dfrac{n(9-5n)}{2}$

$= \dfrac{9n - 5n^2}{2}$

16. $S_{10} = \dfrac{10\left(\dfrac{2}{3} + \dfrac{13}{6}\right)}{2} = 5\left(\dfrac{17}{6}\right) = \dfrac{85}{6} = 14\dfrac{1}{6}$

$S_n = \dfrac{n\left(\dfrac{2}{3} + \dfrac{n+3}{6}\right)}{2} = \dfrac{1}{2}n\left(\dfrac{4}{6} + \dfrac{n+3}{6}\right)$

$= \dfrac{1}{2}n\left(\dfrac{n+7}{6}\right) = \dfrac{n(n+7)}{12} = \dfrac{n^2 + 7n}{12}$

17. $S_{10} = \dfrac{10\left(-\frac{5}{6} + \frac{11}{3}\right)}{2} = 5\left(\frac{17}{6}\right) = \dfrac{85}{6} = 14\frac{1}{6}$

$S_n = \dfrac{n\left(-\frac{5}{6} + \frac{3n-8}{6}\right)}{2} = \dfrac{n\left(\frac{3n-13}{6}\right)}{2}$

$= \dfrac{n(3n-13)}{12} = \dfrac{3n^2 - 13n}{12}$

18. $S_{10} = \dfrac{10\left(-\frac{1}{4} + \frac{17}{4}\right)}{2} = 5(4) = 20$

$S_n = \dfrac{n\left(-\frac{1}{4} + \frac{2n-3}{4}\right)}{2} = \dfrac{n\left(\frac{1}{2}n - 1\right)}{2}$

$= \dfrac{1}{4}n(n-2) = \dfrac{1}{4}n^2 - \dfrac{1}{2}n$

19. $S_{10} = \dfrac{10(0.6 + (-3))}{2} = 5(-2.4) = -12$

$S_n = \dfrac{n(0.6 + 1 - 0.4n)}{2} = \dfrac{n(1.6 - 0.4n)}{2}$

$= n(0.8 - 0.2n)$

$= 0.8n - 0.2n^2$, or $\dfrac{n}{5}(4-n)$

20. $S_{10} = \dfrac{10(0.7 + (-3.8))}{2} = 5(-3.1) = -15.5$

$S_n = \dfrac{n(0.7 + 1.2 - 0.5n)}{2} = \dfrac{n(1.9 - 0.5n)}{2}$

$= \dfrac{1}{4}n(3.8 - n) = 0.95n - \dfrac{1}{4}n^2$

21. a. $a_1 = 3$ b. $r = 2$
    c. $a_{10} = a_1 \cdot r^{n-1} = 3 \cdot 2^9 = 3 \cdot 512 = 1536$
    d. $a_n = 3 \cdot 2^{n-1}$

22. a. $a_1 = 5$ b. $r = 3$
    c.
    $a_{10} = a_1 \cdot r^{n-1} = 5 \cdot 3^9 = 5 \cdot 19,683 = 98,415$

    d. $a_n = 5 \cdot 3^{n-1}$

23. a. $a_1 = \dfrac{1}{3}$ b. $r = 3$

    c. $a_{10} = a_1 \cdot r^{n-1} = \dfrac{1}{3} \cdot 3^9 = 3^8 = 6561$

    d. $a_n = \dfrac{1}{3} \cdot 3^{n-1} = 3^{n-2}$

24. a. $a_1 = \dfrac{1}{5}$ b. $r = 5$

    c. $a_{10} = a_1 \cdot r^{n-1} = \dfrac{1}{5} \cdot 5^9 = \dfrac{1}{5} \cdot 1,953,125$
    $= 390,625$

    d. $a_n = \dfrac{1}{5} \cdot 5^{n-1} = 5^{n-2}$

25. a. $a_1 = 16$ b. $r = -\dfrac{1}{4}$

    c. $a_{10} = a_1 \cdot r^{n-1} = 16 \cdot \left(-\dfrac{1}{4}\right)^9 = -4^2 \cdot 4^{-9}$

    $= -4^{-7} = -\dfrac{1}{16,384}$

    d. $a_n = 16 \cdot \left(-\dfrac{1}{4}\right)^{n-1} = 4^2 (-1)^{n-1} \left(4^{1-n}\right)$

    $= (-1)^{n-1}\left(4^{3-n}\right) = \dfrac{(-1)^{n-1}}{4^{n-3}}$

26. a. $a_1 = 3$ b. $r = -\dfrac{1}{3}$

    c. $a_{10} = a_1 \cdot r^{n-1} = 3 \cdot \left(-\dfrac{1}{3}\right)^9 = -3 \cdot 3^{-9}$

    $= -3^{-8} = -\dfrac{1}{6561}$

    d. $a_n = 3 \cdot \left(-\dfrac{1}{3}\right)^{n-1} = 3 \cdot (-1)^{n-1}\left(3^{1-n}\right)$

    $= (-1)^{n-1}\left(3^{2-n}\right) = \dfrac{(-1)^{n-1}}{3^{n-2}}$

27. $S_{10} = \dfrac{3\left(1 - 2^{10}\right)}{1-2} = \dfrac{3(-1023)}{-1} = 3069$

$S_n = \dfrac{3\left(1 - 2^n\right)}{1-2} = \dfrac{3\left(1 - 2^n\right)}{-1} = 3\left(2^n - 1\right)$

28. $S_{10} = \dfrac{5\left(1-3^{10}\right)}{1-3} = \dfrac{5}{2}\left(3^{10}-1\right)$

$\qquad = \dfrac{5}{2}(59{,}048) = 147{,}620$

$\qquad S_n = \dfrac{5\left(1-3^n\right)}{1-3} = \dfrac{5\left(1-3^n\right)}{-1} = \dfrac{5}{2}\left(3^n-1\right)$

29. $S_{10} = \dfrac{\frac{1}{3}\left(1-3^{10}\right)}{1-3} = \dfrac{\frac{1}{3}\left(1-3^{10}\right)}{-2}$

$\qquad = \dfrac{1}{6}\left(3^{10}-1\right)$

$\qquad = \dfrac{1}{6}(59{,}048) = 9841\dfrac{1}{3}$

$\qquad S_n = \dfrac{\frac{1}{3}\left(1-3^n\right)}{1-3} = \dfrac{\frac{1}{3}\left(1-3^n\right)}{-2} = \dfrac{1}{6}\left(3^n-1\right)$

30. $S_{10} = \dfrac{\frac{1}{5}\left(1-5^{10}\right)}{1-5} = \dfrac{\frac{1}{5}\left(1-(5)^{10}\right)}{-4}$

$\qquad = \dfrac{1}{20}\left(5^{10}-1\right)$

$\qquad = \dfrac{1}{20}(9{,}765{,}624) = 488{,}281\dfrac{1}{5}$

$\qquad S_n = \dfrac{\frac{1}{5}\left(1-5^n\right)}{1-5} = \dfrac{\frac{1}{5}\left(1-5^n\right)}{-4} = \dfrac{1}{20}\left(5^n-1\right)$

31.
$S_{10} = \dfrac{16\left(1-\left(-\frac{1}{4}\right)^{10}\right)}{1-\left(-\frac{1}{4}\right)} = \dfrac{16\left(1-\frac{1}{4^{10}}\right)}{\frac{5}{4}}$

$\qquad = \dfrac{64}{5}\left(\dfrac{4^{10}-1}{4^{10}}\right) = \dfrac{4^3}{5}\left(\dfrac{4^{10}-1}{4^{10}}\right) = \dfrac{4^{10}-1}{5 \cdot 4^7}$

$\qquad = \dfrac{1{,}048{,}575}{81{,}920} = \dfrac{209{,}715}{16{,}384}$

$S_n = \dfrac{16\left(1-\left(-\frac{1}{4}\right)^n\right)}{1-\left(-\frac{1}{4}\right)} = \dfrac{16\left(1-\dfrac{(-1)^n}{4^n}\right)}{\frac{5}{4}}$

$\qquad = \dfrac{64}{5}\left(\dfrac{4^n-(-1)^n}{4^n}\right) = \dfrac{4^3}{5}\left(\dfrac{4^n-(-1)^n}{4^n}\right)$

$\qquad = \dfrac{4^n-(-1)^n}{5 \cdot 4^{n-3}}$

32. $S_{10} = \dfrac{3\left(1-\left(-\frac{1}{3}\right)^{10}\right)}{1-\left(-\frac{1}{3}\right)} = \dfrac{3\left(1-\left(-\frac{1}{3}\right)^{10}\right)}{\frac{4}{3}}$

$\qquad = \dfrac{3\left(1-\dfrac{1}{3^{10}}\right)}{\frac{4}{3}} = \dfrac{9}{4}\left(1-\dfrac{1}{3^{10}}\right)$

$\qquad = \dfrac{59{,}048}{26{,}244} = \dfrac{14{,}762}{6561}$

$\qquad S_n = \dfrac{3\left(1-\left(-\frac{1}{3}\right)^n\right)}{1-\left(-\frac{1}{3}\right)} = \dfrac{3\left(1-\left(-\frac{1}{3}\right)^n\right)}{\frac{4}{3}}$

$\qquad = \dfrac{9}{4}\left(1-\left(-\dfrac{1}{3}\right)^n\right)$

33. $a_1 = 6,\ r = \dfrac{1}{2}$

$\qquad S = \dfrac{a_1}{1-r} = \dfrac{6}{1-\frac{1}{2}} = \dfrac{6}{\frac{1}{2}} = 12$

34. $a_1 = 12,\ r = \dfrac{1}{3}$

$\qquad S = \dfrac{a_1}{1-r} = \dfrac{12}{1-\frac{1}{3}} = \dfrac{12}{\frac{2}{3}} = 18$

35. $a_1 = -8$, $r = \dfrac{1}{2}$

$$S = \dfrac{a_1}{1-r} = \dfrac{-8}{1-\dfrac{1}{2}} = \dfrac{-8}{\dfrac{1}{2}} = -16$$

36. $a_1 = 9$, $r = -\dfrac{1}{3}$

$$S = \dfrac{a_1}{1-r} = \dfrac{9}{1-\left(-\dfrac{1}{3}\right)} = \dfrac{9}{\dfrac{4}{3}} = \dfrac{27}{4}$$

37. $a_1 = 0.7$, $r = 0.1$

$$S = \dfrac{a_1}{1-r} = \dfrac{0.7}{1-0.1} = \dfrac{0.7}{0.9} = \dfrac{7}{9}$$

38. Rewrite $1.555\cdots$ as $1 + 0.555\cdots$, then for the decimal part:

$a_1 = 0.5$, $r = 0.1$

$$S = \dfrac{a_1}{1-r} = \dfrac{0.5}{1-0.1} = \dfrac{0.5}{0.9} = \dfrac{5}{9}$$

The number is: $1 + \dfrac{5}{9} = \dfrac{14}{9}$

39. First write this as $2 + 0.101010\cdots$. Then for the decimal part:

$a_1 = 0.10$, $r = 0.01$

$$S = \dfrac{a_1}{1-r} = \dfrac{0.1}{1-0.01} = \dfrac{0.1}{0.99} = \dfrac{10}{99}$$

The number is: $2 + \dfrac{10}{99} = \dfrac{208}{99}$

40. First write this as $1 + 0.272727\cdots$. Then for the decimal part:

$a_1 = 0.27$, $r = 0.01$

$$S = \dfrac{a_1}{1-r} = \dfrac{0.27}{1-0.01} = \dfrac{0.27}{0.99} = \dfrac{27}{99}$$

The number is: $1 + \dfrac{27}{99} = \dfrac{126}{99} = \dfrac{14}{11}$

41. This results in an arithmetic sequence with $a_1 = 1380$ and $d = -40$.

a. $a_{10} = a_1 + (n-1)d = 1380 + 9(-40)$

$= 1380 - 360 = 1020$

Thus, the depreciation the tenth year will be $1020.

b. The total depreciation for the ten years is obtained as the sum of the first ten terms of the sequence:

$$S_{10} = \dfrac{n}{2}(a_1 + a_{10}) = \dfrac{10}{2}(1380 + 1020)$$

$$= 5(2400) = 12,000$$

Thus, the value of the property at the end of ten years will be
$30,000 - 12,000 = \$18,000$.

42. This will be an arithmetic sequence with $a_1 = 100$ and $d = 50$. First find the fine for day 10.

$a_{10} = a_1 + (n-1)d = 100 + 9(50)$

$= 100 + 450 = 550$

The total fine is obtained as the sum of the first ten terms of the sequence.

$$S_{10} = \dfrac{n}{2}(a_1 + a_{10}) = \dfrac{10}{2}(100 + 550)$$

$$= 5(650) = 3250$$

Thus, the total fine will be $3250.

43. The costs per foot form an arithmetic progression with $a_1 = 50$ and $d = 5$.

a. The cost of the tenth foot is

$a_{10} = a_1 + (n-1)d = 50 + 9(5)$

$= 50 + 45 = 95$

So the cost is $95.

b. $a_{50} = a_1 + (n-1)d = 50 + 49(5)$

$= 50 + 245 = 295$

The total cost for the 50 ft is obtained from the sum

$$S_{50} = \dfrac{n}{2}(a_1 + a_{10}) = \dfrac{50}{2}(50 + 295)$$

$$= 25(345) = 8625$$

Thus, the total cost for a 50 foot well is $8625.

44. a. This is a geometric sequence with $a_1 = 10$ and $r = 0.9$. The term a_{11} represents how high the ball bounces on the tenth bounce.

$$a_{11} = a_1 \cdot r^{n-1} = 10 \cdot (0.9)^{10} = \dfrac{9^{10}}{10^9}$$

$= 3.487$

After the tenth bounce, the ball bounces about 3.5 ft.

b. For each bounce, the ball travels a

distance up and then a distance down. Since the ball initially falls a distance of 10 ft, the total distance traveled would be 10 ft plus twice the sum of the infinite series, where a_1 will be $10 \cdot 0.9$ and $r = 0.9$.

$$D = 10 + 2\left(\frac{10 \cdot 0.9}{1 - 0.9}\right) = 10 + \frac{20 \cdot 0.9}{0.1}$$

$$= 10 + \frac{18}{0.1} = 10 + 180 = 190$$

The total distance traveled is 190 ft.

45. Here, the sequence is geometric with $a_1 = 100$ and $r = 1.10$. The sum of the first five terms is

$$S_5 = 100\left(\frac{1 - 1.10^5}{1 - 1.10}\right) = 100\left(\frac{1 - 1.10^5}{-0.10}\right)$$

$$= 100\left(\frac{1.10^5 - 1}{0.10}\right) = 1000\left(1.10^5 - 1\right)$$

$$= 1000(1.61051 - 1) = 1000(0.61051)$$

$$= 610.51$$

Thus, the final amount is $610.51.

46. a. a_3 is the amount taken on the third day. So, $a_3 = 4$.

b. – c. To determine a_6, find the arithmetic sequence with $a_1 = 6$ and $d = -1$. Substituting into

$$a_n = a_1 + (n - 1)d$$, we

have $a_n = 6 + (n - 1)(-1) = 7 - n$.

$$a_6 = 7 - 6 = 1$$

d. $S_n = \dfrac{n(a_1 + a_n)}{2}$ so

$$S_6 = \frac{6(6 + 1)}{2} = \frac{6(7)}{2} = \frac{42}{2} = 21$$

The total number of pills taken is 21.

e. On the fourth day, you will take

$a_4 = 7 - 4 = 3$ pills. The total mg will

be $3(60) = 180$ mg.

f. On the nth day, you will take

$a_n = 7 - n$ pills. (Technically, this

formula would only be valid for only a week, otherwise, the patient will be giving back pills!) The total mg will be

$$60(7 - n) = (420 - 60n) \text{ mg.}$$

47. Assume that n is an even number. Then there are $\dfrac{n}{2}$ pairs and the sum of each pair is $n + 1$.

Thus, the sum of the sequence is $\dfrac{n}{2}(n + 1)$. If n is an odd number, first consider the sequence $1 + 2 + 3 + \cdots + (n - 3) + (n - 2) + (n - 1)$. Here there are $\dfrac{n - 1}{2}$ pairs with n as the sum of each pair. So the sum is $\dfrac{n - 1}{2}(n) = \dfrac{n(n - 1)}{2}$.

Adding the term n that was omitted, the final sum is

$$\frac{n(n - 1)}{2} + n = \frac{n(n - 1) + 2n}{2} = \frac{n(n - 1 + 2)}{2}$$

$$= \frac{n}{2}(n + 1) \text{ as before.}$$

48. a. The sum of each pair is $2n + 2$ and there are $\dfrac{n}{2}$ pairs. Thus, the total sum is $n(n + 1)$.

b. Each term of the sequence here is double the corresponding term of the sequence in problem 47.

49. Answers may vary. In an arithmetic sequence, each term after the first is obtained by adding the constant difference d to the preceding term. In a geometric sequence, each term after the first is obtained by multiplying the preceding term by the constant ratio r.

50. Answers may vary. In the Fibonacci sequence, the difference between successive terms is not constant and the ratio of successive terms is not constant. Thus, the sequence is neither an arithmetic nor a geometric sequence.

51. $a_n = 0 + (n - 1)4.5 = 4.5n - 4.5$

52. $n = 2016 - 2007 = 9$

$$a_9 = 4.5(9) - 4.5 = 8(4.5) = 36$$

The forecast share of Tablet computers in 2016 is 36%.

53. $a_n = 45 + (n-1)0.5 = -0.5n + 45.5$

54. $n = 2016 - 2007 = 9$

$a_9 = -0.5(9) + 45.5 = 41$

The forecast share of Notebook computers in 2016 is 41%.

Chapter 5 Practice Test

1. a. The <u>third</u> is an ordinal number.
   b. The <u>two</u> is a cardinal number.
   c. The <u>270–891</u> is used for identification only.

2. a. A prime number is a natural number with exactly two distinct divisors: itself and 1.
   b. A composite number is a natural number with more than two distinct divisors.

3. 2)$\overline{1220}$

   2)$\overline{\ 610}$

   5)$\overline{\ 305}$

   $\qquad 61$

   Thus, $1220 = 2^2 \cdot 5 \cdot 61$

4. 53, 59, 61 and 67

5. $143 = 11 \cdot 13$, so 143 is composite.

6. a. 436 and 1530 are divisible by **2**.
   b. $3 + 8 + 7 = 18$, which is divisible by 3, so 387 is divisible by **3**.
      $1 + 5 + 3 = 9$, which is divisible by 3, so 1530 is divisible by **3**.
   c. 2345 ends in a 5 and 1530 ends in a 0, so these are both divisible by **5**.

7. $216 = 2 \cdot 2 \cdot 2 \cdot 3 \cdot 3 \cdot 3 = 2^3 \cdot 3^3$

   $254 = 2 \cdot 127$
   The GCF is 2.
   $\dfrac{216}{254} = \dfrac{2 \cdot 108}{2 \cdot 127} = \dfrac{108}{127}$

8. $18 = 2 \cdot 3^2$

   $54 = 2 \cdot 3^3$

   $60 = 2^2 \cdot 3 \cdot 5$

$\text{LCM} = 2^2 \cdot 3^3 \cdot 5 = 4 \cdot 27 \cdot 5 = 540$

$\dfrac{1}{18} + \dfrac{1}{54} - \dfrac{1}{60} = \dfrac{30}{540} + \dfrac{10}{540} - \dfrac{9}{540} = \dfrac{31}{540}$

9. $1 - \dfrac{1}{4} - \dfrac{1}{2} - \dfrac{1}{8} = \dfrac{8 - 2 - 4 - 1}{8} = \dfrac{1}{8}$

10. a. -27 b. 41

11. a. $8 - 19 = 8 + (-19) = -11$
    b. $8 - (-19) = 8 + (+19) = 27$
    c. $-8 - 19 = -8 + (-19) = -27$
    d. $-8 - (-19) = -8 + (+19) = 11$

12. a. $6 \cdot 7 = 42$ b. $-8 \cdot 9 = -72$
    c. $-3 \cdot (-7) = 21$ d. $5 \cdot (-8) = -40$

13. a. $(-7)^2 = 49$ b. $-7^2 = -49$
    c. $(-4)^3 = -64$ d. $-4^3 = -64$

14. a. $81 \div 9 = 9$ b. $\dfrac{-15}{5} = -3$
    c. $12 \div (-2) = -6$ d. $\dfrac{-20}{-10} = 2$
    e. $\dfrac{0}{15} = 0$ f. $\dfrac{15}{0}$ is not defined.

15. a. $4 \times 12 \div 3 \times 10^3 - 2(-6 + 4) \times 10^4$

   $= 4 \times 12 \div 3 \times 10^3 - 2(-2) \times 10^4$

   $= 4 \times 12 \div 3 \times 1000 - 2(-2) \times 10,000$

   $= 48 \div 3 \times 1000 + 4 \times 10,000$

   $= 16 \times 1000 + 4 \times 10,000$

   $= 16,000 + 40,000 = 56,000$

   b. $\left(\dfrac{1}{2}\right)^3 \div \dfrac{1}{4} \cdot \dfrac{1}{2} + \dfrac{1}{3}\left(\dfrac{7}{2} - \dfrac{3}{2}\right) - \dfrac{1}{2} \cdot \dfrac{1}{3}$

   $= \left(\dfrac{1}{2}\right)^3 \div \dfrac{1}{4} \cdot \dfrac{1}{2} + \dfrac{1}{3}\left(\dfrac{4}{2}\right) - \dfrac{1}{2} \cdot \dfrac{1}{3}$

   $= \dfrac{1}{8} \div \dfrac{1}{4} \cdot \dfrac{1}{2} + \dfrac{1}{3}(2) - \dfrac{1}{2} \cdot \dfrac{1}{3}$

   $= \dfrac{1}{8} \cdot \dfrac{4}{1} \cdot \dfrac{1}{2} + \dfrac{1}{3}(2) - \dfrac{1}{2} \cdot \dfrac{1}{3}$

$$= \frac{1}{4} + \frac{2}{3} - \frac{1}{6} = \frac{3}{12} + \frac{8}{12} - \frac{2}{12}$$

$$= \frac{9}{12} = \frac{3}{4}$$

16. $\dfrac{3}{4} = \dfrac{3 \cdot 4}{4 \cdot 4} = \dfrac{12}{16}$

17. a. $\dfrac{3}{2}$ b. $-\dfrac{7}{4}$ c. $\dfrac{8}{21}$ d. $-\dfrac{1}{8}$

18. a. $\dfrac{7}{8} \times \left(-\dfrac{5}{16} \right) = -\dfrac{35}{128}$

  b. $-\dfrac{7}{8} \div \left(-\dfrac{5}{16} \right) = -\dfrac{7}{8} \cdot \left(-\dfrac{16}{5} \right) = \dfrac{14}{5}$

19. a. 23.508
   $= 2 \times 10 + 3 \times 10^0 + 5 \times 10^{-1} + 8 \times 10^{-3}$
   b. 803.04

20. $\left(6 \times 10^4 \right) \times \left(8 \times 10^{-6} \right) = 6 \times 8 \times 10^{4-6}$

   $= 48 \times 10^{-2} = 4.8 \times 10^{-1}$

21. a. $6.73 + 2.8 = 9.53$
   b. $9.34 - 4.71 = 4.63$
   c. $0.29 \times 6.7 = 1.943$
   d. $17.36 \div 3.1 = 5.6$

22. a. $\dfrac{3}{4} = 0.75$ b. $\dfrac{1}{15} = 0.0\overline{6}$

23. a. $0.\overline{12} = \dfrac{12}{99} = \dfrac{4}{33}$

   b. $2.6555... = \dfrac{26}{10} + \dfrac{5}{90} = \dfrac{234 + 5}{90} = \dfrac{239}{90}$

24. a. $21\% = 0.21$ b. $9.35\% = 0.0935$
   c. $0.26\% = 0.0026$

25. a. $0.52 = 52\%$ b. $2.765 = 276.5\%$

   c. $\dfrac{3}{5} = 0.60 = 60\%$

   d. $\dfrac{2}{11} = 0.1818... \approx 18.2\%$

26. a. $\sqrt{49} = 7$, a rational number.

b. $\sqrt{45}$ is an irrational number because 45 is not a perfect square.

c. $\sqrt{121} = 11$, a rational number.

d. $0.41252525...$ is a nonterminating, repeating decimal, so is a rational number.

e. $0.212112111...$ is a nonterminating, nonrepeating decimal, so is an irrational number.

f. $0.246810...$ is a nonterminating, nonrepeating decimal, so is an irrational number.

27. a. $\sqrt{59} < 7.7$ b. $\sqrt{31} > 5.5$

28. $0.\overline{2} = 0.222...$ so 0.24 is a rational number between $0.\overline{2}$ and 0.25 . (Other answers are possible.)

29. $0.23456...$ is a nonterminating, nonrepeating decimal, so is an irrational number. Also, it is between 0.222 . . . and 0.25. (Other answers are possible.)

30. a. $\sqrt{96} = \sqrt{16 \cdot 6} = 4\sqrt{6}$
   b. $\sqrt{58}$ is in simplest form.

31. a. $\dfrac{4}{\sqrt{20}} = \dfrac{4}{\sqrt{4 \cdot 5}} = \dfrac{4}{2\sqrt{5}} \cdot \dfrac{\sqrt{5}}{\sqrt{5}} = \dfrac{2\sqrt{5}}{5}$

   b. $\sqrt{\dfrac{48}{49}} = \dfrac{\sqrt{16 \cdot 3}}{\sqrt{49}} = \dfrac{4\sqrt{3}}{7}$

32. a. $\sqrt{8} \cdot \sqrt{6} = \sqrt{48} = \sqrt{16 \cdot 3} = 4\sqrt{3}$

   b. $\dfrac{\sqrt{56}}{\sqrt{7}} = \sqrt{\dfrac{56}{7}} = \sqrt{8} = \sqrt{4 \cdot 2} = 2\sqrt{2}$

33. a. $\sqrt{90} - \sqrt{40} = \sqrt{9 \cdot 10} - \sqrt{4 \cdot 10}$

   $= 3\sqrt{10} - 2\sqrt{10} = \sqrt{10}$

   b. $\sqrt{32} + \sqrt{18} - \sqrt{50}$

   $= \sqrt{16 \cdot 2} + \sqrt{9 \cdot 2} - \sqrt{25 \cdot 2}$

   $= 4\sqrt{2} + 3\sqrt{2} - 5\sqrt{2} = 2\sqrt{2}$

34. $c = \sqrt{4^2 + 6^2} = \sqrt{16 + 36} = \sqrt{52}$

   $= \sqrt{4 \cdot 13} = 2\sqrt{13}$

35. a. Check Natural numbers, Whole numbers, Integers, Rational numbers and Real

        Numbers.

  b. Check Rational numbers and Real numbers.

  c. Check Irrational numbers and Real numbers.

  d. Check Rational numbers and Real numbers.

  e. Check Rational numbers and Real numbers.

36. a. Each term is 2 times the preceding term, so this is a geometric sequence.

     b. Each term is 3 plus the preceding term so this is an arithmetic sequence.

37. This is an arithmetic sequence with

$a_1 = 9$ and $d = 4$. So,

$$a_{10} = 9 + 9(4) = 9 + 36 = 45$$

$$S_{10} = \frac{10}{2}(9 + 45) = 5(54) = 270$$

38. This is a geometric sequence with

$a_1 = 1$ and $r = \dfrac{1}{2}$. So,

$$S_5 = \frac{1\left(1 - \left(\frac{1}{2}\right)^5\right)}{1 - \frac{1}{2}} = \frac{1 - \frac{1}{32}}{\frac{1}{2}} = 2\left(1 - \frac{1}{32}\right)$$

$$= 2 - \frac{1}{16} = \frac{31}{16}$$

39. a. $a_5 = \dfrac{1}{3}\left(\dfrac{1}{2}\right)^4 = \dfrac{1}{3} \cdot \dfrac{1}{16} = \dfrac{1}{48}$

     b. $S_5 = \dfrac{\frac{1}{3}\left(1 - \left(\frac{1}{2}\right)^5\right)}{1 - \frac{1}{2}} = \dfrac{\frac{1}{3}\left(1 - \frac{1}{32}\right)}{\frac{1}{2}}$

$$= \frac{2}{3}\left(1 - \frac{1}{32}\right) = \frac{2}{3} \cdot \frac{31}{32} = \frac{31}{48}$$

40. a. $S = \dfrac{0.4}{1 - 0.1} = \dfrac{0.4}{0.9} = \dfrac{4}{9}$

     b. $S = \dfrac{0.21}{1 - 0.01} = \dfrac{0.21}{0.99} = \dfrac{21}{99} = \dfrac{7}{33}$

     c. $S = 2 + \dfrac{0.5}{1 - 0.1} = 2 + \dfrac{0.5}{0.9} = 2 + \dfrac{5}{9} = \dfrac{23}{9}$

Chapter 6 Equations, Inequalities, and Problem Solving

Section 6.1 Solutions of First-Degree Sentences

1. $2 + x \le 2 - x$
   a. Substitute 2 for x: $2 + 2 = 4$; $2 - 2 = 0$ and $4 > 0$. So 2 is not a solution.
   b. Substitute -2 for x: $2 + (-2) = 0$, $2 - (-2) = 4$ and $0 < 4$. So -2 is a solution.
   c. Substitute 0 for x: $2 + 0 = 2$; $2 - 0 = 2$ and $2 = 2$. So 0 is a solution.
   d. Substitute 5 for x: $2 + 5 = 7$; $2 - 5 = -3$ and $7 > -3$. So 5 is not a solution.
   Thus, the only solutions are -2 and 0.

2. $3x + 1 < 2x + 4$
   a. Substitute $\dfrac{1}{3}$ for x:
   $$3\left(\frac{1}{3}\right) + 1 < 2\left(\frac{1}{3}\right) + 4;\ 1 + 1 < \frac{2}{3} + 4\ ;$$
   $2 < 4\dfrac{2}{3}$. So $\dfrac{1}{3}$ is a solution.
   b. Substitute 4 for x:
   $3(4) + 1 < 2(4) + 4;$
   $12 + 1 < 8 + 4$; and $13 < 12$. So 4 is not a solution.
   c. Substitute 0 for x:
   $3(0) + 1 < 2(0) + 4;\ 0 + 1 < 0 + 4;$ and $1 < 4$. So 0 is a solution.
   d. Substitute 3 for x: $3(3) + 1 < 2(3) + 4;$
   $9 + 1 < 6 + 4$; and $10 < 10$. So 5 is not a solution.

   Thus, the only solutions are $\dfrac{1}{3}$ and 0.

3. $3x - 2 \ge 2x - 1$
   a. Substitute 0 for x: $3 \cdot 0 - 2 = -2$; $2 \cdot 0 - 1 = -1$ and $-2 < -1$. So 0 is not a solution.
   b. Substitute 3 for x: $3 \cdot 3 - 2 = 7$; $2 \cdot 3 - 1 = 5$ and $7 > 5$. So 3 is a solution.
   c. Substitute -2 for x: $3(-2) - 2 = -8$; $2(-2) - 1 = -5$ and $-8 < -5$. So -2 is not a solution.

   d. Substitute 1 for x: $3 \cdot 1 - 2 = 1$; $2 \cdot 1 - 1 = 1$ and $1 = 1$. So 1 is a solution.
   Thus, the only solutions are 3 and 1.

4. $x > 3 - 2x$
   a. Substitute 1 for x: $1 > 3 - 2(1)$; $1 > 3 - 2$; and $1 > 1$. So 1 is not a solution.
   b. Substitute 2 for x: $1 > 3 - 2(2)$; $1 > 3 - 4$; and $1 > -1$. So 2 is a solution.
   c. Substitute 0 for x: $1 > 3 - 2(0)$; $1 > 3 - 0$; and $1 > 3$. So 0 is not a solution.
   d. Substitute -2 for x: $1 > 3 - 2(-2)$; $1 > 3 + 4$; and $1 > 7$. So -2 is not a solution.
   Thus, the only solution is 2.

5. a. Substitute -1 for x: $2(-1) - 1 = 3$; $-2 - 1 = 3$; and $-3 = 3$. So -1 is not a solution.
   b. Substitute 1 for x: $2(1) - 1 = 3$; $2 - 1 = 3$; and $1 = 3$. So 1 is not a solution.
   c. Substitute 2 for x: $2(2) - 1 = 3$; $4 - 1 = 3$; and $3 = 3$. So 2 is a solution.
   d. Substitute 0 for x: $2(0) - 1 = 3$; $0 - 1 = 3$; and $-1 = 3$. So 0 is not a solution.
   2 is the only solution of $2x - 1 = 3$.

6. a. Substitute -1 for x: $\dfrac{1}{5}(3(-1) - 2) = 2$;
   $\dfrac{1}{5}(-3 - 2) = 2$; $\dfrac{1}{5}(-5) = 2$; and $-1 = 2$.
   So -1 is not a solution.
   b. Substitute 0 for x: $\dfrac{1}{5}(3(0) - 2) = 2$;
   $\dfrac{1}{5}(-2) = 2$; and $-\dfrac{2}{5} = 2$.
   So 0 is not a solution.
   c. Substitute 2 for x: $\dfrac{1}{5}(3(2) - 2) = 2$;
   $\dfrac{1}{5}(6 - 2) = 2$; $\dfrac{1}{5}(4) = 2$; and $\dfrac{4}{5} = 2$.
   So 2 is not a solution.
   d. Substitute 4 for x: $\dfrac{1}{5}(3(4) - 2) = 2$;
   $\dfrac{1}{5}(12 - 2) = 2$; $\dfrac{1}{5}(10) = 2$; and $2 = 2$.
   So 4 is a solution.

4 is the only solution of $\frac{1}{5}(3x-2)=2$.

For problems 7 – 32, checking the answer (step 7 of the procedure to solve linear equations) is left to the student.

7. The given equation is: $x+10=15$
    Subtract 10 from both sides:
    $$x+10-10=15-10$$
    Simplify: $x=5$

8. The given equation is: $x-5=8$
    Add 5 to both sides:
    $$x-5+5=8+5$$
    Simplify: $x=13$

9. The given equation is: $2x-1=5$
    Add 1 to both sides:
    $$2x-1+1=5+1$$
    Simplify: $2x=6$
    Divide both sides by 2: $x=3$

10. The given equation is: $3x+1=4$
    Add –1 to both sides:
    $$3x+1-1=4-1$$
    Simplify: $3x=3$
    Divide both sides by 3: $x=1$

11. The given equation is: $2x+2=x+4$
    Subtract x from both sides:
    $$2x+2-x=x+4-x$$
    Simplify: $x+2=4$
    Subtract 2 from both sides: $x=2$

12. The given equation is: $3x+1=x-3$
    Subtract x from both sides:
    $$3x+1-x=x-3-x$$
    Simplify: $2x+1=-3$
    Add –1 to both sides, then divide by 2:
    $$2x+1-1=-3-1$$
    $$x=-2$$

13. The given equation is: $3x+1=4x-8$
    Subtract $3x$ from both sides:
    $$3x+1-3x=4x-8-3x$$
    Simplify: $1=x-8$
    Add 8 to both sides: $9=x$

14. The given equation is: $2x+3=3x-1$
    Subtract $2x$ from both sides:
    $$2x+3-2x=3x-1-2x$$
    Simplify: $3=x-1$

Add 1 to both sides: $x=4$

15. The given equation is: $7=3x+4$
    Subtract 4 from both sides:
    $$7-4=3x+4-4$$
    Simplify: $3=3x$
    Divide both sides by 3: $1=x$

16. The given equation is: $22=4x+2$
    Subtract 2 from both sides:
    $$22-2=4x+2-2$$
    Simplify: $20=4x$
    Divide both sides by 4: $x=5$

17. The given equation is: $4=3x-2$
    Add 2 to both sides: $4+2=3x-2+2$
    Simplify: $6=3x$
    Divide both sides by 3: $2=x$

18. The given equation is: $1=5x-8$
    Add 8 to both sides: $1+8=5x-8+8$
    Simplify: $9=5x$
    Divide both sides by 5: $x=\dfrac{9}{5}=1\dfrac{4}{5}$

19. The given equation is:
    $$7n+10-2n=4n-2+3n$$
    Simplify: $5n+10=7n-2$
    Subtract $5n$ from both sides:
    $$5n+10-5n=7n-2-5n$$
    Simplify: $10=2n-2$
    Add 2 to both sides: $10+2=2n-2+2$
    Simplify: $12=2n$
    Divide both sides by 2: $6=n$

20. The given equation is:
    $$13a-6+a=5a+3+3a$$
    Simplify: $14a-6=8a+3$
    Subtract $8a$ from both sides:
    $$14a-6-8a=8a+3-8a$$
    Simplify: $6a-6=3$
    Add 6 to both sides: $6a-6+6=3+6$
    Simplify: $6a=9$
    Divide both sides by 6: $a=\dfrac{9}{6}=\dfrac{3}{2}=1\dfrac{1}{2}$

21. The given equation is: $2(x+5)=13$
    Simplify: $2x+10=13$
    Subtract 10 from both sides:
    $$2x+10-10=13-10$$
    Simplify: $2x=3$

Divide both sides by 3:

$$x = \frac{3}{2} = 1\frac{1}{2}$$

22. The given equation is: $6(x+2) = 17$

    Simplify: $6x + 12 = 17$
    Subtract 12 from both sides:
    $$6x + 12 - 12 = 17 - 12$$
    Simplify: $6x = 5$

    Divide both sides by 6: $x = \frac{5}{6}$

23. The given equation is: $\frac{1}{2}(x-2) = 5$

    Multiply both sides by 2: $x - 2 = 10$
    Add 2 to both sides: $x = 12$

24. The given equation is: $\frac{2}{3}(5x-4) = 1$

    Multiply both sides by 3: $2(5x-4) = 3$
    Simplify: $10x - 8 = 3$
    Add 8 to both sides: $10x - 8 + 8 = 3 + 8$
    Simplify: $10x = 11$

    Divide both sides by 10: $x = \frac{11}{10} = 1\frac{1}{10}$

25. The given equation is:
    $$3(x+1) - x = 2(9-x)$$
    Multiply: $3x + 3 - x = 18 - 2x$
    Simplify: $2x + 3 = 18 - 2x$
    Add $2x$ to both sides: $4x + 3 = 18$
    Subtract 3 from both sides: $4x = 15$

    Divide both sides by 4: $x = \frac{15}{4} = 3\frac{3}{4}$

26. The given equation is:
    $$14y - 14 - 3y = 10y - 6(1-y)$$
    Multiply: $14y - 14 - 3y = 10y - 6 + 6y$
    Simplify: $11y - 14 = 16y - 6$
    Subtract $11y$ from both sides:
    $$11y - 14 - 11y = 16y - 6 - 11y$$
    Simplify: $-14 = 5y - 6$
    Add 6 to both sides: $-14 + 6 = 5y - 6 + 6$
    Simplify: $-8 = 5y$

    Divide both sides by 5: $y = -\frac{8}{5} = -1\frac{3}{5}$

27. The given equation is: $8(x-1) = x + 2$

    Multiply: $8x - 8 = x + 2$
    Subtract x from both sides: $7x - 8 = 2$
    Add 8 to both sides: $7x = 10$

    Divide both sides by 7: $x = \frac{10}{7} = 1\frac{3}{7}$

28. The given equation is: $x + 6 = 6(x-1)$

    Multiply: $x + 6 = 6x - 6$
    Subtract x from both sides: $6 = 5x - 6$
    Add 6 to both sides: $12 = 5x$

    Divide both sides by 5: $x = \frac{12}{5} = 2\frac{2}{5}$

29. The given equation is: $\frac{1}{4}(x-2) = \frac{1}{3}(x-4)$

    Multiply both sides by 12:
    $$3(x-2) = 4(x-4)$$
    Simplify: $3x - 6 = 4x - 16$
    Subract $3x$ from both sides: $-6 = x - 16$
    Add 16 to both sides: $10 = x$

30. The given equation is:
    $$\frac{1}{2}(3x-1) = \frac{2}{5}(3x+1)$$
    Multiply both sides by 10:
    $$5(3x-1) = 4(3x+1)$$
    Simplify: $15x - 5 = 12x + 4$
    Subract $12x$ from both sides: $3x - 5 = 4$
    Add 5 to both sides: $3x = 9$
    Divide both sides by 3: $x = 3$

31. The given equation is:
    $$3 \times 2p + 5 = 37 - \frac{4p^2}{2p}$$
    Multiply and divide: $6p + 5 = 37 - 2p$
    Add $2p$ to both sides: $8p + 5 = 37$
    Subtract 5 from both sides: $8p = 32$
    Divide both sides by 8: $p = 4$

32. The given equation is:
    $$15 + \frac{12t^2}{3t} = 3 \times 3t - 5$$
    Multiply and divide: $15 + 4t = 9t - 5$
    Subtract $9t$ from both sides: $15 - 5t = -5$
    Subtract 15 from both sides: $-5t = -20$
    Divide both sides by -5: $t = 4$

33. Given: $V = \pi r^2 h$; solve for h:

Divide both sides by πr^2: $h = \dfrac{V}{\pi r^2}$

34. Given: $V = \dfrac{1}{3}\pi r^2 h$; solve for h:

Divide both sides by $\dfrac{1}{3}\pi r^2$: $h = \dfrac{3V}{\pi r^2}$

35. Given: $V = LWH$; solve for W:

Divide both sides by LH : $W = \dfrac{V}{LH}$

36. Given: $V = LWH$; solve for H:

Divide both sides by LW : $H = \dfrac{V}{LW}$

37. Given: $P = s_1 + s_2 + b$; solve for b:

Subtract $s_1 + s_2$ from both sides:

$b = P - s_1 - s_2$

38. Given: $P = s_1 + s_2 + b$; solve for s_2:

Subtract $s_1 + b$ from both sides:

$s_2 = P - s_1 - b$

39. Given: $D = RT$
    a. Solve for T:

Divide both sides by R: $T = \dfrac{D}{R}$

    b. $D = 220$ mi, $R = 55$ mph

$T = \dfrac{220}{55} = 4$ hr

40. Given: $W = 5H - 190$
    a. Solve for H:
       Add 190 to both sides:
       $W + 190 = 5H$

Divide both sides by 5: $\dfrac{W + 190}{5} = H$

    b. $W = 160$ lb

$H = \dfrac{160 + 190}{5} = 70$ in.

41. Given: $H = 17 - \dfrac{A}{2}$

    a. Solve for A:
       Multiply each term by 2:
       $2H = 34 - A$

Add A and subtract $2H$: $A = 34 - 2H$

    b. $H = 8$ hr
       $A = 34 - 2 \cdot 8 = 34 - 16 = 18$ years old

42. Given: $A = \dfrac{1}{2}h(a + b)$

    a. Solve for b:
       Multiply each term by 2: $2A = h(a + b)$

       Distribute h: $2A = ha + hb$
       Subtract ha and divide by h:

       $b = \dfrac{2A - ah}{h}$

    b. $A = 60$, $h = 10$, $a = 7$

       $b = \dfrac{2(60) - 7(10)}{10} = 5$ units

43. The given inequality is: $x - 3 < 1$
    Add 3 to both sides: $x < 4$
    The solution is $\{x \mid x < 4\}$.

44. The given inequality is: $x - 2 < 2$
    Add 2 to both sides: $x < 4$
    The solution is $\{x \mid x < 4\}$.

45. The given inequality is: $x - 4 > -1$
    Add 4 to both sides: $x > 3$
    The solution is $\{x \mid x > 3\}$.

46. The given inequality is: $x + 3 > -2$
    Subtract 3 from both sides: $x > -5$
    The solution is $\{x \mid x > -5\}$.

47. The given inequality is: $2x - 1 > x + 2$
    Subtract x from both sides: $x - 1 > 2$
    Add 1 to both sides: $x > 3$
    The solution is $\{x \mid x > 3\}$.

48. The given inequality is: $3x - 3 > 2x + 1$
    Subtract $2x$ from both sides: $x - 3 > 1$
    Add 3 to both sides: $x > 4$
    The solution is $\{x \mid x > 4\}$.

49. The given inequality is: $2x + 3 \le 9 + 5x$
    Subtract $2x$ from both sides: $3 \le 9 + 3x$
    Subtract 9 from both sides: $-6 \le 3x$
    Divide both sides by 3: $-2 \le x$
    The solution is $\{x \mid x \ge -2\}$.

50. The given inequality is: $\quad x+8 \geq 2x-1$

    Subtract x from both sides: $\quad 8 \geq x-1$

    Add 1 to both sides: $\quad\quad\quad 9 \geq x$

    The solution is $\{x \mid x \leq 9\}$.

51. The given inequality is: $\quad x+1 > \dfrac{1}{2}x-1$

    Multiply both sides by 2: $\ 2x+2 > x-2$

    Subtract x from both sides: $x+2 > -2$

    Subtract 2 from both sides: $\quad x > -4$

    The solution is $\{x \mid x > -4\}$.

52. The given inequality is: $\quad x-1 < \dfrac{1}{2}x+2$

    Multiply both sides by 2: $\quad 2x-2 < x+4$

    Subtract x from both sides: $\ x-2 < 4$

    Add 2 to both sides: $\quad\quad\quad x < 6$

    The solution is $\{x \mid x < 6\}$.

53. The given inequality is: $\quad x \geq 4+3x$

    Subtract x from both sides: $\quad 0 \geq 4+2x$

    Subtract 4 from both sides: $-4 \geq 2x$

    Divide both sides by 2: $\quad\quad -2 \geq x$

    The solution is $\{x \mid x \leq -2\}$.

54. The given inequality is: $\quad x-1 \leq 5+3x$

    Subtract x from both sides: $\quad -1 \leq 5+2x$

    Subtract 5 from both sides: $\quad -6 \leq 2x$

    Divide both sides by 2: $\quad\quad -3 \leq x$

    The solution is $\{x \mid x \geq -3\}$.

55. The given inequality is: $\ \dfrac{1}{3}x-2 \geq \dfrac{2}{3}x+1$

    Multiply both sides by 3: $\ x-6 \geq 2x+3$

    Subtract x from both sides: $\ -6 \geq x+3$

    Subtract 3 from both sides: $\ -9 \geq x$

    The solution is $\{x \mid x \leq -9\}$.

56. The given inequality is:

    $\dfrac{1}{4}x+1 \leq \dfrac{3}{4}x-1$

    Multiply both sides by 4: $\quad x+4 \leq 3x-4$

    Subtract x from both sides: $\quad 4 \leq 2x-4$

    Add 4 to both sides: $\quad\quad\quad 8 \leq 2x$

    Divide both sides by 2: $\quad\quad\quad 4 \leq x$

    The solution is $\{x \mid x \geq 4\}$.

57. The given inequality is: $\quad 2x-2 > x+1$

    Subtract x from both sides: $\quad x-2 > 1$

    Add 2 to both sides: $\quad\quad\quad x > 3$

    The solution is $\{x \mid x > 3\}$.

58. The given inequality is: $\quad 3x-2 > 2x+2$

    Subtract $2x$ from both sides: $\quad x-2 > 2$

    Add 2 to both sides: $\quad\quad\quad x > 4$

    The solution is $\{x \mid x > 4\}$.

59. The given inequality is: $\quad x+3 > \dfrac{1}{2}x+1$

    Multiply both sides by 2: $\quad 2x+6 > x+2$

    Subtract x from both sides: $\quad x+6 > 2$

    Subtract 6 from both sides: $\quad x > -4$

    The solution is $\{x \mid x > -4\}$.

60. The given inequality is: $\quad x+1 < \dfrac{1}{2}x+4$

    Multiply both sides by 2: $\quad 2x+2 < x+8$

    Subtract x from both sides: $\quad x+2 < 8$

    Subtract 2 from both sides: $\quad x < 6$

    The solution is $\{x \mid x < 6\}$.

61. The given inequality is: $\quad x \geq 2+4x$

    Subtract x from both sides: $\quad 0 \geq 2+3x$

    Subtract 2 from both sides: $\quad -2 \geq 3x$

    Divide both sides by 3: $\quad\quad -\dfrac{2}{3} \geq x$

    The solution is $\left\{x \mid x \leq -\dfrac{2}{3}\right\}$.

62. The given inequality is: $\quad x-2 \leq 6+3x$

    Subtract x from both sides: $\quad -2 \leq 6+2x$

    Subtract 6 from both sides: $\quad -8 \leq 2x$

    Divide both sides by 2: $\quad\quad -4 \leq x$

    The solution is $\{x \mid x \geq -4\}$.

63. The given inequality is: $\quad 2x+1 < 2x$

    Subtract $2x$ from both sides: $\quad 1 < 0$

    which is false for any value of x. There is no value of x for which the given inequality is true. The solution is $\varnothing$.

64. The given inequality is: $\quad 5x \leq 5x+4$

    Subtract $5x$ from both sides: $\quad 0 \leq 4$

    which is true for any value of x. The solution is R, the set of all real numbers: $\{x \mid x \in R\}$

65. The given inequality is: $8x+2 \le 3(x+4)$

Multiply: $\qquad 8x+2 \le 3x+12$

Subtract $3x$ from both sides:

$\qquad 5x+2 \le 12$

Subtract 2 from both sides: $5x \le 10$

Divide both sides by 5: $\qquad x \le 2$

The solution is $\{x | x \le 2\}$.

66. The given inequality is: $9x+3 \le 4(x+2)$

Multiply: $\qquad 9x+3 \le 4x+8$

Subtract $4x$ from both sides:

$\qquad 5x+3 \le 8$

Subtract 3 from both sides: $5x \le 5$

Divide both sides by 5: $\qquad x \le 1$

The solution is $\{x | x \le 1\}$.

67. The given inequality is:

$$3(x+4) > -5x-4$$

Multiply: $\qquad 3x+12 > -5x-4$

Add $5x$ to both sides: $\quad 8x+12 > -4$

Subtract 12 from both sides: $8x > -16$

Divide both sides by 8: $\qquad x > -2$

The solution is $\{x | x > -2\}$.

68. The given inequality is:

$$5(x+2) < -3x+2$$

Multiply: $\qquad 5x+10 < -3x+2$

Add $5x$ to both sides: $\quad 8x+10 < 2$

Subtract 10 from both sides: $8x < -8$

Divide both sides by 8: $\qquad x < -1$

The solution is $\{x | x < -1\}$.

69. The given inequality is:

$$-2(x+1) \ge 3x-4$$

Multiply: $\qquad -2x-2 \ge 3x-4$

Add $2x$ to both sides: $\qquad -2 \ge 5x-4$

Add 4 to both sides: $\qquad 2 \ge 5x$

Divide both sides by 5: $\qquad \dfrac{2}{5} \ge x$

The solution is $\left\{x \middle| x \le \dfrac{2}{5}\right\}$.

70. The given inequality is:

$$-3(2-x) \ge 5x-7$$

Multiply: $\qquad -6+3x \ge 5x-7$

Subtract $3x$ from both sides: $\quad -6 \ge 2x-7$

Add 7 to both sides: $\qquad 1 \ge 2x$

Divide both sides by 2: $\qquad \dfrac{1}{2} \ge x$

The solution is $\left\{x \middle| x \le \dfrac{1}{2}\right\}$.

71. The given inequality is: $a(x-1) \le a(2x+3)$

Divide by a: $\qquad x-1 \ge 2x+3$

(reverse inequality since $a < 0$)

Subtract x from both sides: $\quad -1 \ge x+3$

Subtract 3 from both sides: $\quad -4 \ge x$

The solution is $\{x | x \le -4\}$.

72. The given inequality is: $b(1-2x) > 5b-4bx$

Multiply: $\qquad b-2bx > 5b-4bx$

Add $4bx$ to both sides: $\quad b+2bx > 5b$

Subtract b from both sides: $\quad 2bx > 4b$

Divide by $2b$: $\qquad x < 2$

(reverse inequality since $b < 0$)

The solution is $\{x | x < 2\}$.

73. Use the equation $0.01 \cdot r \cdot n = p$. In this problem, $r = 40, n = 80,$ and p is unknown. Thus, the equation becomes

$0.01 \cdot 40 \cdot 80 = p$

$\qquad 32 = p$

The number is 32.

74. Use the equation $0.01 \cdot r \cdot n = p$. In this problem, $r = 15, n = 60,$ and p is unknown. Thus, the equation becomes

$0.01 \cdot 15 \cdot 60 = p$

$\qquad 9 = p$

The number is 9.

75. Use the equation $0.01 \cdot r \cdot n = p$. In this problem, $n = 3150, p = 315,$ and r is unknown. Thus, the equation becomes

$0.01 \cdot r \cdot 3150 = 315$

$\qquad 31.50r = 315$ Divide by 31.50.

$\qquad r = 10$

The percent is 10%.

76. Use the equation $0.01 \cdot r \cdot n = p$. In this problem, $n = 4, p = 8,$ and r is unknown. Thus, the equation becomes
$0.01 \cdot r \cdot 4 = 8$

$0.04r = 8$ Divide by 0.04.

$r = 200$
The percent is 200%.

77. Use the equation $0.01 \cdot r \cdot n = p$. In this problem, $n = 40, p = 5,$ and r is unknown. Thus, the equation becomes
$0.01 \cdot r \cdot 40 = 5$

$0.4r = 5$ Divide by 0.4.

$r = 12.5$
The percent is 12.5%.

78. Use the equation $0.01 \cdot r \cdot n = p$. In this problem, $n = 30, p = 20,$ and r is unknown. Thus, the equation becomes
$0.01 \cdot r \cdot 30 = 20$

$0.3r = 20$ Divide by 0.3.

$r = 66\dfrac{2}{3}$

The percent is $66\dfrac{2}{3}\%$.

79. Use the equation $0.01 \cdot r \cdot n = p$. In this problem, $r = 30, p = 60,$ and n is unknown. Thus, the equation becomes
$0.01 \cdot 30 \cdot n = 60$

$0.30n = 60$ Divide by 0.30.

$n = 200$
The number is 200.

80. Use the equation $0.01 \cdot r \cdot n = p$. In this problem, $r = 40, p = 10,$ and n is unknown. Thus, the equation becomes
$0.01 \cdot 40 \cdot n = 10$

$0.4n = 10$ Divide by 0.4.

$n = 25$
The number is 25.

81. a. Determine 10% of 20 mpg: $0.1 \cdot 20 = 2$
   Since this is an increase, add to
   20 mpg: $2 + 20 = 22$ mpg
   b. Currently, you drive $20 \cdot 600 = 12,000$
   miles per year. Divide by the new

mpg: $12,000 \div 22 \approx 545$ gal/yr

82. a. Ditching 100 lb of junk will decrease the amount of gas used in a year by 2%. The decrease is $0.02 \cdot 600 = 12$ gal of gas per year.
   b. Determine the new mpg when you ditch the 100 lb of junk in the trunk. Let e equal the mileage without any junk and m is the mileage with 100 lb of junk in the car. Since the additional junk lowers the amount of gas used in a year by 2%, we have the equation $m = (1 - 0.02)e = 0.98e$. Substitute $m = 20$ and solve for e.
   $20 = 0.98e$

   $e = 20 \div 0.98 \approx 20.40816$
   Currently, you drive $20 \cdot 600 = 12,000$ miles per year. With the new mpg, you will use $12,000 \div 20.40816 = 588$ gal/yr.

83. Use the equation $0.01 \cdot r \cdot n = p$. In this problem, $n = 60, p = 40,$ and r is unknown. Thus, the equation becomes
$0.01 \cdot r \cdot 60 = 40$

$0.6r = 40$ Divide by 0.6.

$r \approx 67$
The students score was 67%.

84. Use the equation $0.01 \cdot r \cdot n = p$. In this problem, $r = 90, p = 18,$ and r is unknown. Thus, the equation becomes
$0.01 \cdot 90 \cdot n = 18$

$0.9r = 18$ Divide by 0.9.

$r = 20$
The regular price was $20.

85. Use the equation $0.01 \cdot r \cdot n = p$. In this problem, $r = 25, n = 140,$ and p is unknown. Thus, the equation becomes
$0.01 \cdot 25 \cdot 140 = p$

$35 = p$

The discount is $35, so the sale price at store A is $105. Store B at $100 has the lower price.

86. Use the equation $0.01 \cdot r \cdot n = p$. In this problem, $n = 48,000, p = 40,000,$ and p is unknown. Thus, the equation becomes
$0.01 \cdot r \cdot 48,000 = 40,000$

$480r = 40,000$

$$r = 83\frac{1}{3}$$

The percent of the purchase price that is the loan is $83\frac{1}{3}\%$.

87. Find when $B = M$. So solve the equation:
$$1.73x + 30 = 0.53x + 33$$
$$1.20x + 30 = 33$$
$$1.20x = 3$$
$$x = \frac{3}{1.20} = 2.5$$
The amounts are the same in 2.5 years.

88. a. Find when $I = A$. So solve the equation:
$$50.8x + 664.2 = 12.6x + 368.2$$
$$38.2x + 664.2 = 368.2$$
$$38.2x = -296$$
$$x = -\frac{296}{38.2} \approx -7.75 \approx -8$$

b. $I = A$ about 8 years before the study started. They will not be equal in the future.

89. a. Evaluate the equation when $N = 13$.
$$E = 0.15(13) + 7.77$$
$$= 1.95 + 7.77 = 9.72 \text{ million}$$
This value is within 0.18 million, or 180,000, of the value of the graph.

b. Evaluate the equation when $N = 25$.
$$E = 0.15(25) + 7.77$$
$$= 3.75 + 7.77 = 11.52 \text{ million}$$
This value is within 0.02 million, or 20,000, of the value of the graph.

c. Evaluate the equation when $N = 21$.
$$E = 0.15(21) + 7.77$$
$$= 3.15 + 7.77 = 10.92 \text{ million}$$

90. a. Evaluate the equation when $N = 13$.
$$E = 0.24(13) + 13.5$$
$$= 3.12 + 13.5 = 16.62 \text{ million}$$
students enrolled. This is very close to the graph value.

b. Evaluate the equation when $N = 25$.
$$E = 0.24(25) + 13.5$$
$$= 6 + 13.5 = 19.5 \text{ million}$$
students enrolled. This is exactly the graph value.

c. Evaluate the equation when $N = 30$.
$$E = 0.24(30) + 13.5$$
$$= 7.2 + 13.5 = 20.7 \text{ million}$$
students enrolled in 2019.

91. Solve the men's equation for $S = 11$.
$$11 = 3L - 22$$
$$33 = 3L$$
$$11 = L$$
Tyrone's foot is 11 in. long.

92. Solve the women's equation for $S = 7$.
$$7 = 3L - 21$$
$$28 = 3L$$
$$9\frac{1}{3} = L$$
Maria's foot is $9\frac{1}{3}$ in. long.

93. Solve the men's equation for $S = 7$.
$$7 = 3L - 22$$
$$29 = 3L$$
$$L = \frac{29}{3} = 9\frac{2}{3}$$
Sam's foot is $9\frac{2}{3}$ in. long. So Sue's foot is also $9\frac{2}{3}$ in. long. Solve the women's equation for S:
$$S = 3\left(\frac{29}{3}\right) - 21 = 29 - 21 = 8$$
Sue's shoe size is 8.

94. Solve the men's equation for $S = 42$.
$$42 = 3L - 22$$
$$64 = 3L$$
$$21\frac{1}{3} = L$$
Mr. Davidson's foot is $21\frac{1}{3}$ in. long.

95. Solve the men's equation for $S = 14$.
$$14 = 3L - 22$$
$$36 = 3L$$
$$12 = L$$
The foot is 12 in. long.

96. Let $S = L$ for each equation.
   a. Use the men's equation.
   $$L = 3L - 22$$
   $$22 = 2L$$
   $$11 = L$$
   For a man, shoe size is the same as foot length when foot length is 11 in.
   b. Use the women's equation.
   $$L = 3L - 21$$
   $$21 = 2L$$
   $$10.5 = L$$
   For a woman, shoe size is the same as foot length when foot length is 10.5 in.

97. a. For a snowman, solve the men's equation for $L = 23$:
   $$S = 3 \cdot 23 - 22 = 69 - 22 = 47$$
   The Abominable Snowman needs size 47 shoes.
   b. For a snowwoman, solve the women's equation for $L = 23$:
   $$S = 3 \cdot 23 - 21 = 69 - 21 = 48$$
   The Abominable Snowwoman needs size 48 shoes.

98. Solve the inequality $R > C$.
   $$20n > 12n + 160,000$$
   $$8n > 160,000$$
   $$n > 20,000$$
   More than 20,000 units must be sold to make a profit.

99. The U.S. Post Office price is cheaper when $\quad 0.44 + 0.20(x-1) < 5.00$
   $$0.44 + 0.20x - 0.20 < 5.00$$
   $$0.20x + 0.24 < 5.00$$
   $$0.20x < 4.76$$
   $$x < 23.8$$
   The Post Office is cheaper when the package weighs less than 23.8 oz, or 1 lb 7.8 oz.

100. Solve the inequality $C < 10$.
   $$1 + 0.75(h-1) < 10$$
   $$1 + 0.75h - 0.75 < 10$$
   $$0.75h + 0.25 < 10$$
   $$0.75h < 9.75$$
   $$h < 13$$
   When $h < 13$ hours the cost is less

than $10.

101. $N > A$ when
   $$0.165x + 4.68 > -0.185x + 5.38$$
   $$0.35x + 4.68 > 5.38$$
   $$0.35x > 0.70$$
   $$x > 2$$
   This will occur afer $1996 + 2$ or 1998.

102. Answers will vary. The replacement set is the set of numbers defined for a variable(s) in an equation or inequality.

103. Answers will vary. The solution set for an equation is the set of numbers taken from the replacement set that will make an open sentence a true statement when the number is substituted for the variable in the open sentence.

104. Answers will vary. No. A number may be part of the replacement set but not be a solution to the equation or inequality.

105. Answers will vary. Yes. In order to be in the solution set a number must be part of the replacement set.

106. Answers will vary.

107. Since 50% of the total calories c is 125 fat calories, we have:
   $$0.50c = 125$$
   $$c = 250 \quad \text{Divide by 0.50.}$$
   Thus, there are 250 calories in the apple pie.

108. Since 55% of the total calories c is 270 fat calories, we have:
   $$0.55c = 270$$
   $$c \approx 491 \quad \text{Divide by 0.55.}$$
   The total calories in the Big Mac are about 491 calories.

109. Since 50% of the calories is 355 of the total calories c, we have:
   $$0.50c = 355$$
   $$c = 710 \quad \text{Divide by 0.50.}$$
   Thus, there are 710 calories in a Whopper.

110. Let $F = 80$ and $N = 150$.

$$N \overset{?}{=} 4(F - 40)$$

$$150 \overset{?}{=} 4(80 - 40)$$

$$150 \overset{?}{=} 4(40)$$

$$150 \neq 160$$

No. For $F = 80$, $N = 160$.

111. $N = 4(77.5 - 40) = 4(37.5) = 150$ chirps per minute.

112. $0 = 4(F - 40)$

$0 = 4F - 160$

$160 = 4F$

$40 = F$

The cricket stops chirping at 40°F.

113. $S = \dfrac{1}{6}(10 - 4) = \dfrac{1}{6}(6) = 1$ cm/sec

114. $0 = \dfrac{1}{6}(C - 4)$

$0 = C - 4$

$4 = C$

4°C; the cricket stops chirping before the ant stops crawling as the temperature drops.

Section 6.2 Graphs of Algebraic Sentences

1. Subtract 2 from both sides to find the solution $x = 2$. The solution set is thus $\{2\}$, which is shown on the graph.

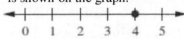

2. Add 1 to both sides to find the solution $x = 4$. The solution set is thus $\{4\}$, which is shown on the graph.

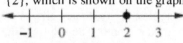

3. Subtract 1 from both sides to get $x \geq 1$. Thus, the solution set consists of all the positive integers as indicated on the graph.

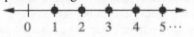

4. Subtract 2 from both sides to get $x < 3$. Thus, the solution set consists of all the positive integers as indicated on the graph.

5. Add 3 to both sides to get $x \neq 4$. This means that the solution consists of all the integers except 4, as indicated on the graph.

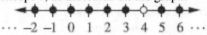

6. Since x is to be an integer, the inequality $-3 < x \leq 2$ has the solution set $\{-2, -1, 0, 1, 2\}$, as shown on the graph.

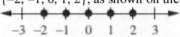

7. Since x is to be an integer, the inequality $-2 \leq x \leq 4$ has the solution set $\{-2, -1, 0, 1, 2, 3, 4\}$, as shown on the graph.

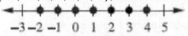

8. Since x is to be an integer, the inequality $-2 < x < 4$ has the solution set $\{-1, 0, 1, 2, 3\}$, as shown on the graph.

9. The solution set of $x < 4$ is the set of all real numbers less than 4, as shown on the graph.

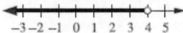

10. The solution set of $x \geq 2$ is the set of all real numbers less than 4, as shown on the graph.

11. Adding 2 to both sides gives the inequality $x \leq 2$ so the solution set consists of all the real numbers less than or equal to 2.

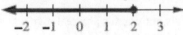

12. Adding 2 to both sides gives the inequality $x \geq 6$ so the solution set consists of all the real numbers less than or equal to 2.

13. The solution set of $-2 \leq x \leq 4$ consists of all the real numbers between -2 and $+4$, inclusive.

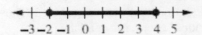

14. Adding 3 to both sides gives the equation $x \neq 4$ so the solution set consists of all the real numbers except 4.

15. Subtract 2 from both sides to get $x > 3$. The solution set is the set of all real numbers greater than 3.

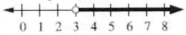

16. Adding 2 to both sides gives the equation $x = 3$ so the solution set consists of the number 3.

17. The solution set of $-1 < x < 2$ consists of all the real numbers between -1 and $+2$ with neither endpoint included.

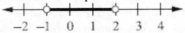

18. The solution is all real numbers greater than or equal to 3.

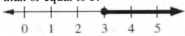

19. Subtracting 4 from both sides gives $x < 1$, so that the solution set consists of all the real numbers less than 1.

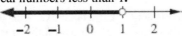

20. Subtracting 5 from both sides gives $x < -1$, so that the solution set consists of all the real numbers less than -1.

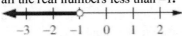

21. $x + 1 < x$ is not true for any real number. Thus, the solution set is $\varnothing$.

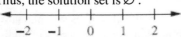

22. $x + 1 > x$ is true for any real number. Thus, the solution set is all real numbers.

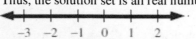

23. Subtract x from both sides to get $x + 3 < 1$. Then subtract 3 from both sides to get $x < -2$. Thus, the solution set consists of all the real numbers less than -2.

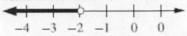

24. Add x to both sides to get $5 \leq 3x + 2$. Then subtract 2 from both sides to get $3 \leq 3x$. Then divide both sides by 3 to get $1 \leq x$, which can be written as $x \geq 1$. Thus, the solution set consists of all the real numbers greater than or equal to 1.

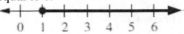

25. Add 7 to both sides to get $3x \geq 0$. Then divide both sides by 3 to get $x \geq 0$. The solution set consists of all the real numbers that are greater than or equal to 0.

26. Subtract 5 from both sides to get $2x < 0$. Then divide both sides by 2 to get $x < 0$. The solution set consists of all the real numbers that are less than 0.

27. Add 1 to both sides of the second inequality to get $x \geq -1$. The solution set of this inequality is the set of integers greater than or equal to -1. The solution set of $x \leq 4$ is the set of integers less than or equal to 4. So the solution set of $x \leq 4$ **and** $x \geq -1$ is the set of integers greater than or equal to -1 and less than or equal to 4, that is, $\{-1, 0, 1, 2, 3, 4\}$.

28. The solution set of the first inequality is the set of integers greater than 0. The solution set of $x \leq 5$ is the set of integers less than or equal to 5. So the solution set of $x > 0$ **and** $x \leq 5$ is the set of integers greater than 0 and less than or equal to 5, that is, $\{1, 2, 3, 4, 5\}$.

29. Subtract 1 from both sides of the first inequality to get $x \leq 6$. The solution set of this inequality is the set of integers less than or equal to 6. The solution set of $x > 2$ is the set of integers greater than 2. Thus, the solution set of $x > 2$ **and** $x \leq 6$ is the set of integers greater than 2 but less than or equal to 6, that

is, $\{3, 4, 5, 6\}$.

30. Add 1 to both sides of the second inequality to get $x < 1$. The solution set of this inequality is the set of integers less than 1. The solution set of $x > -5$ is the set of integers greater than –5. So the solution set of $x < 1$ **and** $x > -5$ is the set of integers less than 1 and greater than –5, that is, $\{-4, -3, -2, -1, 0\}$.

31. Add 1 to both sides of the first inequality to get $2x > 2$. Then divide both sides by 2 to obtain $x > 1$. The solution set of this inequality is the set of integers greater than 1. Now, subtract 1 from both sides of the second inequality to get $x < 3$. The solution set of this inequality is the set of integers less than 3. Thus, the solution set of $x > 1$ **and** $x < 3$ consists of the integer 2, that is, $\{2\}$.

32. Add 1 to both sides of the first inequality to get $x < 2$. The solution set of this inequality is the set of integers less than 2. Now, subtract 1 from both sides of the second inequality to get $3x > 12$. Then divide both sides by 3 to obtain $x > 4$. The solution set of this inequality is the set of integers greater than 4. Thus, the solution set of $x < 2$ **or** $x > 4$ consists of the all integers except 2, 3, and 4, that is, $\{\ldots, -2, -1, 0, 1, 5, 6, 7, \ldots\}$.

33. The solution set of $x < -5$ **or** $x > 5$ consists of all the integers except those between –5 and +5, inclusive, that is the set $\{\ldots, -8, -7, -6, 6, 7, 8, \ldots\}$.

34. The solution set of $x \geq 0$ **or** $x < -2$ consists of all the integers except –1 and –2, the set $\{\ldots, -5, -4, -3, 0, 1, 2, \ldots\}$.

35. Subtract 1 from both sides of the first inequality to get $x \geq 1$. The solution set of $x \geq 1$ **and** $x \leq 4$ is the set of all real numbers between 1 and 4, inclusive. This is shown on the graph.

36. The solution set of $x \leq 5$ **and** $x > -1$ is the set of all real numbers greater than –1 but

less than or equal to 5. This is shown on the graph.

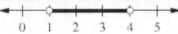

37. There are no numbers that are both greater than 2 and less than –2, so the solution set is the empty set, $\varnothing$.

38. Subtract 2 from both sides of the first inequality to get $x \leq 2$. Then, subtract 2 from both sides of the second inequality to get $x \geq 4$. The solution set of $x \leq 2$ **or** $x \geq 4$ is the set of all real numbers less than or equal to 2 or greater than or equal to 4. This is shown on the graph.

39. Add 1 to both sides of the first inequality to get $x > 1$. Then, subtract 1 from both sides of the second inequality to get $x < 4$. The solution set of $x > 1$ **and** $x < 4$ is the set of all real numbers between 1 and 4, not including the 1 and the 4. This is shown on the graph.

40. The solution set of $x \leq 0$ **or** $x > 3$ is the set of all real numbers less than or equal to 0 or greater than 3. This is shown on the graph.

41. The first inequality, $x \leq x + 1$, is satisfied by all real numbers. Therefore, only the inequality $x \geq 2$ must be satisfied, and the solution set of this inequality is the set of all real numbers greater than or equal to 2. The graph shows this set.

42. Subtract 2 from both sides of the first inequality to get $x \geq -4$. The solution set of $x \geq -4$ **or** $x < 0$ is the set of all real numbers. This is shown on the graph.

43. Add 2 to both sides of the first inequality to get $x \geq 4$. Since there is no real number that is both greater than or equal to 4 and less than 0, the solution set is the empty set, $\varnothing$.

44. Subtract 3 from both sides of the first inequality to get $x \le -3$. Then, add 1 to both sides of the second inequality to get $x > 1$. The solution set of $x \le -3$ **or** $x > 1$ is the set of all real numbers less than or equal to –3 or greater than 1. This is shown on the graph.

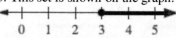

45. Add 1 to both sides of the second inequality to get $x \ge 3$. Then, the solution set of $x \ge 0$ **and** $x \ge 3$ is the set of all real numbers that are greater than or equal to 3. This set is shown on the graph.

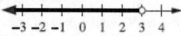

46. Add 1 to both sides of the second inequality to get $x \le 3$. Then, the solution set of $x \ge 0$ **and** $x \le 3$ is the set of all real numbers that are less than or equal to 3 and greater than or equal to 0. This set is shown on the graph.

47. Add 1 to both sides of the second inequality to get $x < 3$. Then, the solution set of $x < 0$ **or** $x < 3$ is the set of all real numbers that are less than 3. (Note that each number of this set satisfies at least one of the two inequalities.) The graph is shown below.

48. Add 1 to both sides of the second inequality to get $x > 3$. Since there is no real number that is both greater than 3 and less than 0, the solution set is the empty set, $\varnothing$.

49. Subtract 1 from both sides of the first inequality to get $x > 1$. Then, add 2 to both sides of the second inequality to get $x < 5$. The solution set of $x > 1$ **and** $x < 5$ is the set of all real numbers between 1 and 5, not including the 1 or the 5. The graph shows this set.

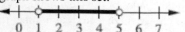

50. Add 1 to both sides of the first inequality to get $x > 4$. Then, subtract 1 from both sides of the second inequality to get $x > 1$. The solution set of $x > 4$ **and** $x > 1$ is the set of all real numbers greater than 4. The graph shows this set.

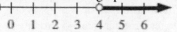

51. Add 1 to both sides of the first inequality and subtract 2 from both sides of the second inequality to get the system $x > 1$ **or** $x < 2$. Every real number is greater than 1 or less than 2, so the solution set consists of all the real numbers, as indicated by the graph.

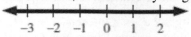

52. Subtract 1 from both sides of the first inequality and add 1 to both sides of the second inequality to get the system $x > 1$ **or** $x < 3$. Every real number is greater than 1 or less than 3, so the solution set consists of all the real numbers, as indicated by the graph.

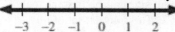

53. a. $C = 4953 + 0.12m$

   b. $6000 < 4953 + 0.12m < 6500$

   c. $6000 < 4953 + 0.12m < 6500$
      $1047 < 0.12m < 1547$

      $8725 < m < 12,892$
      To stay within the budget the car can be driven between 8725 mi and 12,892 mi annually.

54. a. $C = 6689 + 0.15m$

   b. $7000 < 6689 + 0.15m < 7500$

   c. $7000 < 6689 + 0.15m < 7500$
      $311 < 0.15m < 811$

      $2073 < m < 5406$
      To stay within the budget the car can be driven between 2073 mi and 5406 mi annually.

55. Solve for N when $E > 36$ and $E = 1.5N + 27$.
    $1.5N + 27 > 36$

    $1.5N > 9$

    $N > 6$

    $N > 6$ years after 2010, that is, 2016.

56. Solve for N when $E > 42$ and $E = 1.5N + 27$.

$$1.5N + 27 > 42$$

$$1.5N > 15$$

$$N > 10$$

$N > 10$ years after 2010, that is, 2020.

57. a. This represents all the real numbers between −1 and +2, including the 2 but not the −1.
    b. This represents all the real numbers between −1 and + 2, including the −1 but not the 2.
    c. This represents all the real numbers between −1 and + 2, not including the endpoints.
    d. This represents all the real numbers between −1 and + 2, including the endpoints.

58. a. The real numbers less than 1 or greater than 4.
    b. The real numbers less than or equal to 1 or greater than 4
    c. The real numbers less than or equal to 1 or greater than or equal to 4
    d. The real numbers less than 1 or greater than or equal to 4

59. a. This represents the set of all real numbers between, but not including −1 and 2.
    b. This represents the set of all real numbers between −1 and 2, including 2 but not −1.
    c. This represents the set of all real numbers between −1 and 2, including −1 but not 2.
    d. This represents the set of all real numbers between −1 and 2, including −1 and 2.

60. In interval notation, $\{x \mid x \geq -4\}$ is written

$[-4, \infty)$.

61. In interval notation, $\{x \mid x < 5\}$ is written

$(-\infty, 5)$.

62. In interval notation, $\{x \mid x \leq -6\}$ is written

$(-\infty, -6]$.

63. In interval notation, $\{x \mid x > 9\}$ is written

$(9, \infty)$.

64. In interval notation, $\{x \mid 3 < x < 7\}$ is written

$(3, 7)$.

65. In interval notation, $\{x \mid -4 \leq x < -1\}$ is written

$[-4, -1)$.

66. In interval notation, $\{x \mid 0 < x \leq 8\}$ is written

$(0, 8]$.

67. In interval notation, $\{x \mid -1 \leq x \leq 10\}$ is written

$[-1, 10]$.

68. $B > F > J$

69. Let J be Joe's height. Then $J = 60$ in.

70. $B > F$

71. Let F in. be Frank's height and S in. be Sam's height. Then, $F = S - 3$.

72. $F > J$

73. Let S be Sam's height. Then $S = 77$ in.

74. $B > F > J$

75. Let B be Bill's height. Then $B > 74$ in. (6 ft 2 in.)

Section 6.3 Sentences Involving Absolute Values

1. $|-10| = 10$ 2. $|15| = 15$

3. $\left|-\dfrac{1}{8}\right| = \dfrac{1}{8}$ 4. $\left|\dfrac{3}{4}\right| = \dfrac{3}{4}$

5. $|5 - 8| = |-3| = 3$ 6. $|8 - 5| = |3| = 3$

7. $|0| + |-2| = 0 + 2 = 2$

8. $|-2|-|-3| = 2 - 3 = -1$

9. $-|8| = -8$ 10. $-|3|+|-4| = -3 + 4 = 1$

11. a. For $x = 2$,
$$|1 - 3 \cdot 2| = |1 - 6| = |-5| = 5 > 3,$$
a solution.

   b. For $x = -\dfrac{1}{2}$,
$$\left|1 - 3\left(-\frac{1}{2}\right)\right| = \left|1 + \frac{3}{2}\right| = \left|\frac{5}{2}\right| = \frac{5}{2} \not> 3,$$
not a solution.

   c. For $x = \dfrac{5}{3}$,
$$\left|1 - 3 \cdot \frac{5}{3}\right| = |1 - 5| = |-4| = 4 > 3,$$
a solution.

   d. For $x = 0$,
$$|1 - 3 \cdot 0| = |1 - 0| = |1| = 1 \not> 3, \text{ not a}$$
solution.

12. a. For $x = 0$, $|0 - 2| = |-2| = 2 \not< 2$,
not a solution.

   b. For $x = 1$, $|1 - 2| = |-1| = 1 < 2$,
a solution.

   c. For $x = -1$, $|-1 - 2| = |-3| = 3 \not< 2$,
not a solution.

   d. For $x = -2$, $|-2 - 2| = |-4| = 4 \not< 2$,
not a solution.

13. $\{0\}$ 14. $\{\ldots, -2, -1, 0, 1, 2, \ldots\}$

15. $\{-5, 5\}$ 16. $\{-3, -2, -1, 0, 1, 2, 3\}$

17. $\{\ldots, -3, -2, -1, 1, 2, 3, \ldots\}$

18. $\{-3, -2, -1, 0, 1, 2, 3\}$

19. $|x| = 1$ is true for $x = -1$ and $x = 1$. These points are shown on the graph. There is no interval that satisfies this equation.

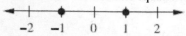

20. $|x| = 2.5$ is true for $x = -2.5$ and $x = 2.5$. These points are shown on the graph. There is no interval that satisfies this equation.

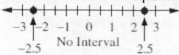

21. $|x| \le 4$ is true for all the real numbers between -4 and 4, inclusive. These numbers are shown on the graph. In interval notation, the solution is $[-4, 4]$.

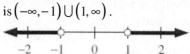

22. $|x| > 1$ is true for all the real numbers between -1 and 1, inclusive. These numbers are shown on the graph. In interval notation, the solution is $(-\infty, -1) \cup (1, \infty)$.

23. $|x + 1| < 3$ is equivalent to $-3 < x + 1 < 3$. Thus, by subtracting 1 from each side of this inequality, you get $-4 < x < 2$. The last inequality is true for all real numbers between -4 and 2, not including the -4 or the 2. This gives the required solution set, which is shown on the graph. In interval notation, the solution is $(-4, 2)$.

24. $|x - 2| < 1$ is equivalent to $-1 < x - 2 < 1$. Thus, by adding 2 to each side of this inequality, you get $1 < x < 3$. The last inequality is true for all real numbers between 1 and 3, not including the 1 or the 3. This gives the required solution set, which is shown on the graph. In interval notation, the solution is $(1, 3)$.

25. $|x| \ge 1$ is true if $x \ge 1$ or $x \le -1$. Thus, the solution set consists of all real numbers that are less than or equal to -1 or that are greater than or equal to 1. This set is shown on the graph. In interval notation, the solution is $(-\infty, -1] \cup [1, \infty)$.

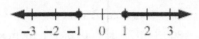

26. $|x| > -1$ is true for all real numbers. This set is shown on the graph. In interval notation, the solution is $(-\infty, \infty)$.

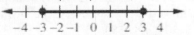

27. $|x - 1| > 2$ is true if $x - 1 > 2$ or $x - 1 < -2$. By adding 1 to both sides of the last two inequalities, you get $x > 3$ or $x < -1$. Thus, the solution set of the given inequality consists of all the real numbers that are less than -1 or are greater than 3. This set is shown on the graph. In interval notation, the solution is $(-\infty, -1) \cup (3, \infty)$.

28. $|x - 3| \geq 1$ is true if $x - 3 \geq 1$ or $x - 3 \leq -1$. By adding 3 to both sides of the last two inequalities, you get $x \geq 4$ or $x \leq 2$. Thus, the solution set of the given inequality consists of all the real numbers that are greater than or equal to 4 or are less than or equal to 2. This set is shown on the graph. In interval notation, the solution is $(-\infty, 2] \cup [4, \infty)$.

29. Divide both sides of the inequality $|2x| < 4$ by 2 to get $|x| < 2$. This inequality is satisfied by all the real numbers between -2 and 2, not including the -2 or the 2. This set is shown on the graph. In interval notation, the solution is $(-2, 2)$.

30. Divide both sides of the inequality $|3x| \leq 9$ by 3 to get $|x| \leq 3$. This inequality is satisfied by all the real numbers between -3 and 3. This set is shown on the graph. In interval notation, the solution is $(-3, 3)$.

31. Divide both sides of the inequality $|3x| \geq 6$ by 3 to get $|x| \geq 2$. This inequality is satisfied by all the real numbers that are less than or equal to -2 or that are greater than or equal to 2. The graph shows this set. In interval notation, the solution is $(-\infty, -2] \cup [2, \infty)$.

32. Divide both sides of the inequality $|2x| > 5$ by 3 to get $|x| > \dfrac{2}{5}$. This inequality is satisfied by all the real numbers that are less than $-\dfrac{2}{5}$ or that are greater than $\dfrac{2}{5}$. The graph shows this set. In interval notation, the solution is $\left(-\infty, -\dfrac{5}{2}\right) \cup \left(\dfrac{5}{2}, \infty\right)$.

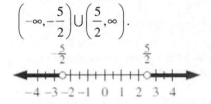

33. $|2x - 3| \leq 3$ is equivalent to $-3 \leq 2x - 3 \leq 3$. Add 3 to each member of this inequality to get $0 \leq 2x \leq 6$. Now divide by 2 to get the inequality $0 \leq x \leq 3$. This inequality is satisfied by all the real numbers between 0 and 3, inclusive. The solution set is shown on the graph. In interval notation, the solution is $[0, 3]$.

34. $|3x + 1| \leq 8$ is equivalent to $-8 \leq 3x + 1 \leq 8$. Subtract 1 from each member of this inequality to get $-9 \leq 3x \leq 7$. Now divide by 3 to get the inequality $-3 \leq x \leq \dfrac{7}{3}$. This inequality is satisfied by all the real numbers between -3 and $\dfrac{7}{3}$, inclusive. The solution set is shown on the graph. In interval notation, the

solution is $\left[-3, \dfrac{7}{3}\right]$.

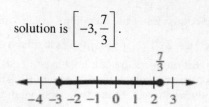

35. $|2x-3| > 3$ is equivalent to the system $2x-3 < -3$ or $2x-3 > 3$. Add 3 to both sides of these inequalities to get the system $2x < 0$ or $2x > 6$. Now divide by 2 to get $x < 0$ or $x > 3$. The solution set of these inequalities is the set of all real numbers that are less than 0 or that are greater than 3. The graph shows this set. In interval notation, the solution is $(-\infty, 0) \cup (3, \infty)$.

36. $|3x+1| > 8$ is equivalent to the system $3x+1 < -8$ or $3x+1 > 8$. Subtract 1 from both sides of these inequalities to get the system $3x < -9$ or $3x > 7$. Now divide by 3 to get $x < -3$ or $x > \dfrac{7}{3}$. The solution set of these inequalities is the set of all real numbers that are less than -3 or that are greater than $\dfrac{7}{3}$. The graph shows this set. In interval notation, the solution is $(-\infty, -3) \cup \left(\dfrac{7}{3}, \infty\right)$.

37. Substitute $b = 500$ and $c = 50$ to get $|500 - a| \le 50$. Since the absolute value is being used, we may write the equivalent as $|a - 500| \le 50$, and this is equivalent to $-50 \le a - 500 \le 50$. Add 500 to each member to get $450 \le a \le 550$. Thus, the company can spend any amount between $450 and $550, inclusive.

38. The variance c is $\$800 = 0.05 \cdot 800 = 40$. Substitute $b = 800$ and $c = 40$ to get

$|800 - a| \le 40$. This is equivalent to $-40 \le a - 800 \le 40$. Add 800 to each member to get $760 \le a \le 840$. Thus, the company can spend any amount between $760 and $840, inclusive.

39. Yes. Substitute $b = 300$ and $a = 290$ to get $|\$300 - \$290| = \$10$. Since 5% of the budgeted $\$300 = 0.05 \cdot \$300 = \$15$, George would have to spend within $15 of his budget to be within the 5% variance, and George only spent $10.

40. a. $\left|x - \dfrac{5}{2}\right| > \dfrac{3}{2}$ b. $\left|x - \dfrac{5}{2}\right| \le \dfrac{3}{2}$

    c. $x = 4$ or $\left|x - \dfrac{5}{2}\right| < \dfrac{3}{2}$

    d. $x = 1$ or $\left|x - \dfrac{5}{2}\right| > \dfrac{3}{2}$

41. a. $|w - 137| \le 7$ b. $-7 \le w - 137 \le 7$
                              $130 \le w \le 144$

42. a. $|w - 162| \le 10$ b. $-10 \le w - 162 \le 10$
                               $152 \le w \le 172$

43. a. $|L - 12| \le 0.02 \cdot 12 = 0.24$
    b. $-0.24 \le L - 12 \le 0.24$
       $11.76 \le L \le 12.24$

44. a. $|L - 1| \le 0.01$ b. $-0.01 \le L - 1 \le 0.01$
                               $0.99 \le L \le 1.01$

45. a. $|s - 505| \le 4$ b. $-4 \le s - 505 \le 4$
                              $501 \le s \le 509$

46. a. $|c - 186| \le 0.15 \cdot 186$
       $|c - 186| \le 27.9$
    b. $-27.9 \le c - 186 \le 27.9$
       $158.1 \le c \le 213.9$

47. Substitute $b = 500$ and $c = 50$ to get $|500 - a| \le 50$. This is equivalent to $-50 \le 500 - a \le 50$. Subtract 500 from each member to get $-550 \le -a \le -450$. Multiply each member by -1, and reverse the inequality, to get $\$450 \le a \le \$550$.

48. The variance c is $\$800 = 0.05 \cdot 800 = 40$.
Substitute $b = 800$ and $c = 40$ to get
$|800 - a| \le 40$. This is equivalent to
$-40 \le 800 - a \le 40$. Subtract 800 from each
member to get $-840 \le -a \le -760$. Multiply
each member by -1, and reverse the
inequality, to get $\$760 \le a \le \$840$.

49. A 5% variance of $\$300$ is
$\$300 = 0.05 \cdot 300 = \$15$. Substitute $a = 290$,
$b = 300$ and $c = 15$ into the inequality
$|300 - a| \le 15$.

$$|300 - 290| \overset{?}{\le} 15$$

$$|10| \overset{?}{\le} 15$$

$$10 \le 15$$

Yes, the actual expenses are within a 5%
budget variance.

50. Using the inequality from problem 49,
$|300 - a| \le 15$, substitute $a = 310$,
$b = 300$, and $c = 15$ into the inequality.

$$|300 - 310| \overset{?}{\le} 15$$

$$|-10| \overset{?}{\le} 15$$

$$10 \le 15$$

Yes, the actual expenses are within a 5%
budget variance.

51. Answers may vary. "The absolute value of
x is less than a." is equivalent to "x is
between $-a$ and a."

52. Answers may vary. "The absolute value of x
is greater than a" is equivalent to the system
"x is less than $-a$ or x is greater than a."

53. Answers may vary. The solution is the set
of all real numbers, since the absolute
value of an expression is always non
negative, the expression $|x - 2|$ is always
non-negative and has to be greater than
-5.

54. Answers may vary. $\varnothing$; The absolute value of
an expression cannot be negative.

Skill Checker

1. $\sqrt{(-2)^2 - 4(1)(-1)} = \sqrt{4 + 4} = \sqrt{8} = 2\sqrt{2}$

2. $\sqrt{1^2 - 4(3)(-5)} = \sqrt{1 + 60} = \sqrt{61}$

3. $\sqrt{(-2)^2 - 4(2)(-1)} = \sqrt{4 + 8} = \sqrt{12} = 2\sqrt{3}$

4. $\sqrt{(-3)^2 - 4(1)(-2)} = \sqrt{9 + 8} = \sqrt{17}$

5. $\sqrt{3^2 - 4(2)(-5)} = \sqrt{9 + 40} = \sqrt{49} = 7$

6. $\sqrt{5^2 - 4(2)(-7)} = \sqrt{25 + 56} = \sqrt{81} = 9$

7. $\sqrt{(-6)^2 - 4(9)(-2)} = \sqrt{36 + 72} = \sqrt{108}$
$$= \sqrt{36 \cdot 3} = 6\sqrt{3}$$

8. $\sqrt{(-8)^2 - 4(2)(5)} = \sqrt{64 - 40} = \sqrt{24} = 2\sqrt{6}$

9. $\sqrt{8^2 - 4(4)(-5)} = \sqrt{64 + 80} = \sqrt{144} = 12$

10. $\sqrt{2^2 - 4(2)(-5)} = \sqrt{4 + 40} = \sqrt{44} = 2\sqrt{11}$

Section 6.4 Quadratic Equations

1. $x^2 + 6x + 8 = (x + 2)(x + 4)$

2. $x^2 + 7x + 10 = (x + 2)(x + 5)$

3. $x^2 - x - 12 = (x - 4)(x + 3)$

4. $x^2 - 3x - 10 = (x - 5)(x + 2)$

5. $x^2 + 7x - 18 = (x + 9)(x - 2)$

6. $x^2 - 12x + 11 = (x - 11)(x - 1)$

7. $x^2 - 10x + 25 = (x - 5)(x - 5) = (x - 5)^2$

8. $x^2 - 8x + 16 = (x - 4)^2$

9. $x^2 + 10x + 25 = (x+5)(x+5) = (x+5)^2$

10. $x^2 + 16x + 64 = (x+8)(x+8) = (x+8)^2$

11. $2x^2 + x - 3 = (2x+3)(x-1)$

12. $3x^2 + 10x + 3 = (3x+1)(x+3)$

13. $6x^2 - 5x + 1 = (3x-1)(2x-1)$

14. $6x^2 - 11x + 3 = (2x-3)(3x-1)$

15. This equation is satisfied if and only if
    $x - 2 = 0$ or $x - 4 = 0$, that is, if and only
    if $x = 2$ or $x = 4$. The solution set is
    {2, 4}.

16. This equation is satisfied if and only if
    $x + 2 = 0$ or $x + 3 = 0$, that is, if and only if
    $x = -2$ or $x = -3$. The solution set is
    $\{-2, -3\}$.

17. This equation is satisfied if and only if
    $x + 2 = 0$ or $x - 3 = 0$, that is, if and only
    if $x = -2$ or $x = 3$. The solution set is
    {-2, 3}.

18. This equation is satisfied if and only if
    $x + 5 = 0$ or $x - 6 = 0$, that is, if and only
    if $x = -5$ or $x = 6$. The solution set is
    $\{-5, 6\}$.

19. This equation is satisfied if and only if
    $x = 0$ or $x - 1 = 0$ or $x + 1 = 0$, that is, if
    and only if $x = 0$ or $x = 1$ or $x = -1$. The
    solution set is {-1, 0, 1}.

20. This equation is satisfied if and only if
    $x + 1 = 0$ or $x + 2 = 0$ or $x - 3 = 0$, that is,
    if and only if $x = -1$ or $x = -2$ or $x = 3$.
    The solution set is $\{-1, -2, 3\}$.

21. This equation is satisfied if and only if
    $2x - 1 = 0$ or $x + 2 = 0$. Add 1 to both
    sides of the first equation to get $2x = 1$.
    Then, divide both sides by 2 to get $x = \dfrac{1}{2}$.
    The second equation is satisfied by
    $x = -2$. The solution set of the given

equation is $\left\{-2, \dfrac{1}{2}\right\}$.

22. This equation is satisfied if and only if
    $3x + 5 = 0$ or $4x + 7 = 0$. Subtract 5 from both
    sides of the first equation to get $3x = -5$.
    Then, divide both sides by 3 to get $x = -\dfrac{5}{3}$.
    Subtract 7 from both sides of the first equation
    to get $4x = -7$. Then, divide both sides by 4 to
    get $x = -\dfrac{7}{4}$. The solution set of the given
    equation is $\left\{-\dfrac{5}{3}, -\dfrac{7}{4}\right\}$.

23. Add 16 to both sides of the given equation to
    get $x^2 = 16$. Take the square root of both sides.
    The solution set of this equation is {–4, 4},
    because $(-4)^2 = 16$ and $4^2 = 16$.

24. Add 27 to both sides of the given equation to get
    $3x^2 = 27$, and then divide both sides by 3 to get
    $x^2 = 9$. Take the square root of both sides. The
    solution set of this equation is {–3, 3}, because
    $(-3)^2 = 9$ and $3^2 = 9$.

25. Divide both sides of the given equation by 5 to
    get $x^2 = 25$. Take the square root of both
    sides. The solution set of this equation is
    {–5, 5}, because $(-5)^2 = 25$ and $5^2 = 25$.

26. Subtract 1 from both sides of the given equation to get
    $4x^2 = 64$, and then divide both sides by 4 to get
    $x^2 = 16$. Take the square root of both sides. This
    equation is satisfied by $x = 4$ and by $x = -4$. The
    solution set is $\{-4, 4\}$.

27. The equation $(3x - 6)(2x + 3)(5x - 8) = 0$ is
    satisfied if and only if $3x - 6 = 0$ or
    $2x + 3 = 0$ or $5x - 8 = 0$. The equation
    $3x - 6 = 0$ can be solved by adding 6 to both
    sides and then dividing both sides by 3 to get
    $x = 2$. Similarly, the second equation can be
    solved by subtracting 3 from both sides and
    then dividing by 2 to get $x = -\dfrac{3}{2}$. The third
    equation is solved by adding 8 to both sides

and then dividing by 5 to get $x = \frac{8}{5}$. The solution set of the given equation is $\left\{ -\frac{3}{2}, \frac{8}{5}, 2 \right\}$.

28. The equation $2x(x+7)(2x-3)=0$ is satisfied if and only if $2x = 0$ or $x + 7 = 0$ or $2x - 3 = 0$. The equation $2x = 0$ can be solved by both sides by 2 to get $x = 0$. The second equation can be solved by subtracting 7 from both sides to get $x = -7$. The third equation is solved by adding 3 to both sides and then dividing by 2 to get $x = \frac{3}{2}$. The solution set of the given equation is $\left\{ -7, 0, \frac{3}{2} \right\}$.

29. To solve the equation $6x^2 - 1 = 215$, add 1 to both sides to get $6x^2 = 216$, and then divide both sides by 6 to get $x^2 = 36$. Take the square root of both sides. This equation is satisfied by –6 and by 6, because $(-6)^2 = 36$ and $6^2 = 36$. The solution set is {–6, 6}.

30. To solve the equation $4x^2 + 1 = 50$, subtract 1 from both sides to get $4x^2 = 49$, and then divide both sides by 4 to get $x^2 = \frac{49}{4}$. Take the square root of both sides. This equation is satisfied by $-\frac{7}{2}$ and by $\frac{7}{2}$, because $\left(-\frac{7}{2} \right)^2 = \frac{49}{4}$ and $\left(\frac{7}{2} \right)^2 = \frac{49}{4}$. The solution set is $\left\{ -\frac{7}{2}, \frac{7}{2} \right\}$.

31. Since $x^2 - 12x + 27 = (x-3)(x-9)$, the given equation can be rewritten as $(x-3)(x-9) = 0$, which is satisfied if and only if $x = 3$ or $x = 9$. The solution set of the given equation is {3, 9}.

32. Since $x^2 - 6x + 8 = (x-4)(x-2)$, the given equation can be rewritten as $(x-4)(x-2) = 0$, which is satisfied if and only if $x = 4$ or $x = 2$. The solution set of the given equation is $\{2, 4\}$.

33. Since $x^2 - 8x - 20 = (x+2)(x-10)$, the given equation can be rewritten as $(x+2)(x-10) = 0$, which is satisfied if and only if $x = -2$ or $x = 10$. The solution set is {–2, 10}.

34. First subtract 36 from both sides to get $x^2 - 9x - 36 = 0$. Since $x^2 - 9x - 36 = (x-12)(x+3)$, the given equation can be rewritten as $(x-12)(x+3) = 0$, which is satisfied if and only if $x = 12$ or $x = -3$. The solution set is $\{-3, 12\}$.

35. Since $10x^2 + 7x + 1 = (2x+1)(5x+1)$, the given equation can be rewritten as $(2x+1)(5x+1) = 0$, which is satisfied if and only if $x = -\frac{1}{2}$ or $x = -\frac{1}{5}$. The solution set is $\left\{ -\frac{1}{2}, -\frac{1}{5} \right\}$.

36. Since $6x^2 + 17x + 5 = (2x+5)(3x+1)$, the given equation can be rewritten as $(2x+5)(3x+1) = 0$, which is satisfied if and only if $x = -\frac{5}{2}$ or $x = -\frac{1}{3}$. The solution set is $\left\{ -\frac{5}{2}, -\frac{1}{3} \right\}$.

37. First subtract 5 from both sides to get $3x^2 + 2x - 5 = 0$. Since $3x^2 + 2x - 5 = (3x+5)(x-1)$ the given equation can be rewritten as $(3x+5)(x-1) = 0$, which is satisfied if and only if $x = -\frac{5}{3}$ or $x = 1$. The solution set is $\left\{ -\frac{5}{3}, 1 \right\}$.

38. First subtract 5 from both sides to get $2x^2 - x - 6 = 0$. Since $2x^2 - x - 6 = (2x+3)(x-2)$ the given equation can be rewritten as $(2x+3)(x-2)=0$, which is satisfied if and only if $x = -\dfrac{3}{2}$ or $x = 2$. The solution set is $\left\{-\dfrac{3}{2}, 2\right\}$.

39. For the equation $2x^2 + 3x - 5 = 0$, $a = 2$, $b = 3$, and $c = -5$. By substituting these numbers in the quadratic formula

$$x = \frac{-b \pm \sqrt{b^2 - 4ac}}{2a} \text{ we get}$$

$$x = \frac{-3 \pm \sqrt{3^2 - 4 \cdot 2(-5)}}{2 \cdot 2} = \frac{-3 \pm \sqrt{9 + 40}}{4}$$

$$= \frac{-3 \pm \sqrt{49}}{4} = \frac{-3 \pm 7}{4} = -\frac{10}{4} \text{ or } \frac{4}{4}$$

that is, $-\dfrac{5}{2}$ or 1. The solution set is

$$\left\{-\frac{5}{2}, 1\right\}.$$

40. For the equation $3x^2 - 7x + 2 = 0$, $a = 3$, $b = -7$, and $c = 2$. By substituting these numbers in the quadratic formula

$$x = \frac{-b \pm \sqrt{b^2 - 4ac}}{2a} \text{ we get}$$

$$x = \frac{-(-7) \pm \sqrt{(-7)^2 - 4 \cdot 3(2)}}{2 \cdot 3} = \frac{7 \pm \sqrt{49 - 24}}{6}$$

$$= \frac{7 \pm \sqrt{25}}{6} = \frac{7 \pm 5}{6} = \frac{2}{6} \text{ or } \frac{12}{6}$$

that is, $\dfrac{1}{3}$ or 2. The solution set is

$$\left\{\frac{1}{3}, 2\right\}.$$

41. For the equation $2x^2 + 5x - 7 = 0$, $a = 2$, $b = 5$, and $c = -7$. By substituting these numbers in the quadratic formula (see problem 39), we get

$$x = \frac{-5 \pm \sqrt{5^2 - 4 \cdot 2(-7)}}{2 \cdot 2} = \frac{-5 \pm \sqrt{25 + 56}}{4}$$

$$= \frac{-5 \pm \sqrt{81}}{4} = \frac{-5 \pm 9}{4} = -\frac{14}{4} \text{ or } \frac{4}{4}$$

that is, $-\dfrac{7}{2}$ or 1. The solution set is $\left\{-\dfrac{7}{2}, 1\right\}$.

42. For the equation $4x^2 - 7x - 15 = 0$, $a = 4$, $b = -7$, and $c = -15$. By substituting these numbers in the quadratic formula (see problem 40), we get

$$x = \frac{-(-7) \pm \sqrt{(-7)^2 - 4 \cdot 4(-15)}}{2 \cdot 4} = \frac{7 \pm \sqrt{49 + 240}}{8}$$

$$= \frac{7 \pm \sqrt{289}}{8} = \frac{7 \pm 17}{8} = -\frac{10}{8} \text{ or } \frac{24}{8}$$

that is, $-\dfrac{5}{4}$ or 3. The solution set is $\left\{-\dfrac{5}{4}, 3\right\}$.

43. For the equation $x^2 + 5x + 3 = 0$, $a = 1$, $b = 5$, and $c = 3$. By substituting these numbers in the quadratic formula (see problem 39), we get

$$x = \frac{-5 \pm \sqrt{5^2 - 4 \cdot 1(3)}}{2 \cdot 1} = \frac{-5 \pm \sqrt{25 - 12}}{2}$$

$$= \frac{-5 \pm \sqrt{13}}{2}$$

The solution set is $\left\{\dfrac{-5 - \sqrt{13}}{2}, \dfrac{-5 + \sqrt{13}}{2}\right\}$.

44. For the equation $2x^2 + 7x - 4 = 0$, $a = 2$, $b = 7$, and $c = -4$. By substituting these numbers in the quadratic formula (see problem 40), we get

$$x = \frac{-7 \pm \sqrt{7^2 - 4 \cdot 2(-4)}}{2 \cdot 2} = \frac{-7 \pm \sqrt{49 + 32}}{4}$$

$$= \frac{-7 \pm \sqrt{81}}{4} = \frac{-7 \pm 9}{4} = -\frac{16}{4} \text{ or } \frac{2}{4}$$

that is, -4 or $\dfrac{1}{2}$. The solution set is $\left\{-4, \dfrac{1}{2}\right\}$.

45. For the equation $5x^2 - 8x + 2 = 0$, $a = 5$, $b = -8$, and $c = 2$. By substituting these numbers in the quadratic formula (see problem 39), we get

$$x = \frac{-(-8) \pm \sqrt{(-8)^2 - 4 \cdot 5 \cdot 2}}{2 \cdot 5}$$

$$= \frac{8 \pm \sqrt{64-40}}{10} = \frac{8 \pm \sqrt{24}}{10}$$

$$= \frac{8 \pm 2\sqrt{6}}{10} = \frac{4 \pm \sqrt{6}}{5}$$

The solution set is $\left\{ \dfrac{4-\sqrt{6}}{5}, \dfrac{4+\sqrt{6}}{5} \right\}$.

46. For the equation $3x^2 + 5x + 1 = 0$, $a = 3$, $b = 5$, and $c = 1$. By substituting these numbers in the quadratic formula (see problem 40), we get

$$x = \frac{-5 \pm \sqrt{5^2 - 4 \cdot 3(1)}}{2 \cdot 3} = \frac{-5 \pm \sqrt{25-12}}{6}$$

$$= \frac{-5 \pm \sqrt{13}}{6} = \frac{-5 - \sqrt{13}}{6} \text{ or } \frac{-5+\sqrt{13}}{6}$$

The solution set is
$$\left\{ \frac{-5-\sqrt{13}}{6}, \frac{-5+\sqrt{13}}{6} \right\}.$$

47. By adding 1 to both sides, we can write the given equation in the standard form: $7x^2 - 6x + 1 = 0$, and $a = 7$, $b = -6$, and $c = 1$. By substituting these numbers in the quadratic formula (see problem 39), we

get $x = \dfrac{-(-6) \pm \sqrt{(-6)^2 - 4 \cdot 7 \cdot 1}}{2 \cdot 7}$

$$= \frac{6 \pm \sqrt{36-28}}{14} = \frac{6 \pm \sqrt{8}}{14}$$

$$= \frac{6 \pm 2\sqrt{2}}{14} = \frac{3 \pm \sqrt{2}}{7}$$

The solution set is $\left\{ \dfrac{3-\sqrt{2}}{7}, \dfrac{3+\sqrt{2}}{7} \right\}$.

48. By adding 5 to both sides, we can write the given equation in the standard form: $7x^2 - 12x + 5 = 0$, $a = 7$, $b = -12$, and $c = 5$. By substituting these numbers in the quadratic formula (see problem 40), we

get $x = \dfrac{-(-12) \pm \sqrt{(-12)^2 - 4 \cdot 7 \cdot 5}}{2 \cdot 7}$

$$= \frac{12 \pm \sqrt{144-140}}{14} = \frac{12 \pm \sqrt{4}}{14}$$

$$= \frac{12 \pm 2}{14} = \frac{10}{14} \text{ or } \frac{14}{14}$$

The solution set is $\left\{ \dfrac{5}{7}, 1 \right\}$.

49. For the equation $9x^2 - 6x - 2 = 0$, $a = 9$, $b = -6$, and $c = -2$. By substituting these numbers in the quadratic formula (see problem 39), we get

$$x = \frac{-(-6) \pm \sqrt{(-6)^2 - 4 \cdot 9(-2)}}{2 \cdot 9}$$

$$= \frac{6 \pm \sqrt{36+72}}{18} = \frac{6 \pm \sqrt{108}}{18}$$

$$= \frac{6 \pm 6\sqrt{3}}{18} = \frac{1 \pm \sqrt{3}}{3}$$

The solution set is $\left\{ \dfrac{1-\sqrt{3}}{3}, \dfrac{1+\sqrt{3}}{3} \right\}$.

50. For the equation $2x^2 - 8x + 5 = 0$, $a = 2$, $b = -8$, and $c = 5$. By substituting these numbers in the quadratic formula (see problem 40), we get

$$x = \frac{-(-8) \pm \sqrt{(-8)^2 - 4 \cdot 2 \cdot 5}}{2 \cdot 2}$$

$$= \frac{8 \pm \sqrt{64-40}}{4} = \frac{8 \pm \sqrt{24}}{4}$$

$$= \frac{8 \pm 2\sqrt{6}}{4} = \frac{8-2\sqrt{6}}{4} \text{ or } \frac{8+2\sqrt{6}}{4}$$

Simplifying, the solution set is
$$\left\{ \frac{4-\sqrt{6}}{2}, \frac{4+\sqrt{6}}{2} \right\}.$$

51. First subtract 1 from both sides to get $2x^2 + 2x - 1 = 0$, for which $a = 2$, $b = 2$, and $c = -1$. By substituting these numbers in the quadratic formula (see problem 39), we get

$$x = \frac{-2 \pm \sqrt{2^2 - 4 \cdot 2(-1)}}{2 \cdot 2} = \frac{-2 \pm \sqrt{4+8}}{4}$$

$$= \frac{-2 \pm \sqrt{12}}{4} = \frac{-2 \pm 2\sqrt{3}}{4} = \frac{-1 \pm \sqrt{3}}{2}$$

The solution set is $\left\{ \dfrac{-1-\sqrt{3}}{2}, \dfrac{-1+\sqrt{3}}{2} \right\}$.

52. First subtract 5 from both sides to get
$2x^2 - 6x - 5 = 0$, for which $a = 2$, $b = -6$, and $c = -5$. By substituting these numbers in the quadratic formula (see problem 40), we get

$$x = \frac{-(-6) \pm \sqrt{(-6)^2 - 4 \cdot 2(-5)}}{2 \cdot 2}$$

$$= \frac{6 \pm \sqrt{36 + 40}}{4} = \frac{6 \pm \sqrt{76}}{4}$$

$$= \frac{6 \pm 2\sqrt{19}}{4} = \frac{6 - 2\sqrt{19}}{4} = \frac{6 + 2\sqrt{19}}{2}$$

Simplifying, the solution set is

$$\left\{ \frac{3 - \sqrt{19}}{2}, \frac{3 + \sqrt{19}}{2} \right\}.$$

53. First, add $8x - 5$ to both sides to get
$4x^2 + 8x - 5 = 0$, $a = 4$, $b = 8$, and $c = -5$. By substituting these numbers in the quadratic formula (see problem 39), we get

$$x = \frac{-8 \pm \sqrt{8^2 - 4 \cdot 4(-5)}}{2 \cdot 4} = \frac{-8 \pm \sqrt{64 + 80}}{8}$$

$$= \frac{-8 \pm \sqrt{144}}{8} = \frac{-8 \pm 12}{8} = -\frac{20}{8} \text{ or } \frac{4}{8}$$

that is, $-\frac{5}{2}$ or $\frac{1}{2}$. The solution set is

$$\left\{ -\frac{5}{2}, \frac{1}{2} \right\}.$$

54. First, subtract $2x + 5$ to both sides to get
$2x^2 - 2x - 5 = 0$, $a = 2$, $b = -2$, and $c = -5$. By substituting these numbers in the quadratic formula (see problem 40), we get

$$x = \frac{-(-2) \pm \sqrt{(-2)^2 - 4 \cdot 2(-5)}}{2 \cdot 2}$$

$$= \frac{2 \pm \sqrt{4 + 40}}{4} = \frac{2 \pm \sqrt{44}}{4} = \frac{2 \pm 2\sqrt{11}}{4}$$

$$= \frac{2 - 2\sqrt{11}}{4} \text{ or } \frac{2 + 2\sqrt{11}}{4}$$

that is, $\frac{1 - \sqrt{11}}{2}$ or $\frac{1 + \sqrt{11}}{2}$. The solution

set is $\left\{ \dfrac{1 - \sqrt{11}}{2}, \dfrac{1 + \sqrt{11}}{2} \right\}$.

55. $(2ax + b)^2 = (2ax + b)(2ax + b)$

$$= 2ax(2ax + b) + b(2ax + b)$$

$$= (4a^2x^2 + 2axb) + (2abx + b^2)$$

$$= 4a^2x^2 + 4abx + b^2$$

Which is the left side of the equation, as stated. If we subtract b from both sides of

$$2ax + b = \pm\sqrt{b^2 - 4ac}$$

we get

$$2ax = -b \pm \sqrt{b^2 - 4ac}$$

If we divide both sides of this last equation by $2a$, we get the quadratic formula as given.

56. Let the shortest side be x. Then the the other leg is $x + 2$ and long hypotenuse is $x + 4$. By the Pythagorean theorem,

$$(x + 4)^2 = x^2 + (x + 2)^2$$

$x^2 + 8x + 16 = x^2 + x^2 + 4x + 4$ Multiply.

$0 = x^2 - 4x - 12$ Subtract

$x^2 + 8x + 16$.

$0 = (x - 6)(x + 2)$ Factor.

$x = 6$ or $x = -2$ Solve.

Since this is to be the side of a triangle, we discard the negative solution. The sides of the triangle are, respectively, 6, 8, and 10.

57. Let the shortest side be x cm long. Then the hypotenuse is $(x + 4)$ cm long and the other leg is $(x + 2)$ cm long. By the Pythagorean theorem,

$$(x + 4)^2 = x^2 + (x + 2)^2$$

$x^2 + 8x + 16 = x^2 + x^2 + 4x + 4$ Multiply.

$0 = x^2 - 4x - 12$ Subtract

$x^2 + 8x + 16$.

$0 = (x - 6)(x + 2)$ Factor.

$x = 6$ or $x = -2$ Solve.

Since this is to be the side of a triangle, we discard the negative solution. The sides of the triangle are, respectively, 6 cm, 6 + 2 = 8 cm, and 6 + 4 = 10 cm long.

58. Let the shortest side be x in. long. Then the hypotenuse is $(x + 16)$ in. long and the other leg is $(x + 14)$ in. long. By the Pythagorean theorem,

$$(x+16)^2 = x^2 + (x+14)^2$$

$x^2 + 32x + 256 = x^2 + x^2 + 28x + 196$ Multiply.

$0 = x^2 - 4x - 60$ Subtract $x^2 + 32x + 256$.

$0 = (x-10)(x+6)$ Factor.

$x = 10$ or $x = -6$ Solve.

Since this is to be the side of a triangle, we discard the negative solution. The sides of the triangle are, respectively, 10 in., $10 + 14 = 24$ in., and $10 + 16 = 26$ in. long.

59. Let the shortest side be x in. long. Then the hypotenuse is $(x + 8)$ in. long and the other leg is $(x + 7)$ in. long. By the Pythagorean theorem

$$(x+8)^2 = x^2 + (x+7)^2$$

$x^2 + 16x + 64 = x^2 + x^2 + 14x + 49$ Multiply.

$0 = x^2 - 2x - 15$ Subtract $x^2 + 16x + 64$.

$0 - (x-5)(x+3)$ Factor.

$x = 5$ or $x = -3$ Solve.

Since this is to be a side of a triangle, we discard the negative solution. The sides of the triangle are, respectively, 5 in., $5 + 7 = 12$ in. and $5 + 8 = 13$ in. long.

60. a. $x^2 + y^2 = (y+1)^2$

$x^2 + y^2 = y^2 + 2y + 1$

$x^2 = 2y + 1$

   b. 5, 12, 13; 7, 24, 25; 9, 40, 41; 11, 60, 61

61. Here $v_0 = 5, h = 10$ so we have:

$10 = 5t^2 + 5t$

$2 = t^2 + t$ Divide by 5.

$0 = t^2 + t - 2$ Subtract 2.

$0 = (t+2)(t-1)$ Factor.

$t = -2$ or $t = 1$ Solve.

Since time cannot be negative, we discard

$t = -2$ and use $t = 1$ second.

62. Here $v_0 = 4, h = 28$ so we have:

$28 = 5t^2 + 4t$

$0 = 5t^2 + 4t - 28$ Subtract 28.

$0 = (5t+14)(t-2)$ Factor.

$t = -\dfrac{14}{5}$ or $t = 2$ Solve.

Since time can not be negative, we discard

$t = -\dfrac{14}{5}$ and use $t = 2$ seconds.

63. Here $v_0 = 10, h = 15$ so we have:

$15 = 5t^2 + 10t$

$3 = t^2 + 2t$ Divide by 5.

$0 = t^2 + 2t - 3$ Subtract 3.

$0 = (t+3)(t-1)$ Factor.

$t = -3$ or $t = 1$ Solve.

Since time cannot be negative, we discard $t = -3$ and use $t = 1$ second.

64. Here $v_0 = 10, h = 175$ so we have:

$175 = 5t^2 + 10t$

$35 = t^2 + 2t$ Divide by 5.

$0 = t^2 + 2t - 35$ Subtract 35.

$0 = (t+7)(t-5)$ Factor.

$t = -7$ or $t = 5$ Solve.

Since time cannot be negative, we discard $t = -7$ and use $t = 5$ seconds.

65. a. $t^2 + 26t + 169$

$= (t+13)(t+13) = (t+13)^2$

   b. In 2020, the value of $t = 2020 - 1980 = 40$.

$E(40) = (40+13)^2 = 53^2 = 2809$

   In 2020, there will be 2809 endangered species.

66. a. $t^2 + 28t + 169 = (t+14)(t+14)$

$= (t+14)^2$

   b. In 2020, the value of $t = 2020 - 1980 = 40$.

$E(40) = (40+14)^2 = 54^2 = 2916$

In 2020, there will be 2916 threatened and endangered species.

67. a. $P - 2Pr + Pr^2 = P(1-2r+r^2)$

$= P(1-r)(1-r) = P(1-r)^2$

b. Let P = 25,000 and r = 0.15.

$P(1-r)^2 = 25,000(1-0.15)^2$

$= 25,000(0.85)^2$

$= 25,000(0.7225)$

$= 18,062.5$

In two years, the Prius will be worth $18,062.50.

68. a. $25,000r^2 - 50,000r + 25,000$

$= 25,000(r^2 - 2r + 1)$

$= 25,000(r-1)(r-1) = 25,000(r-1)^2$

b. Let r = 0.20.

$25,000(r-1)^2 = 25,000(0.2-1)^2$

$= 25,000(-0.8)^2$

$= 25,000(0.64)$

$= 16,000$

In two years, the Camry will be worth $16,000.

69. a. The $9,000 is lower.
   b. Let t = 15 in the equation

$H(t) = -3t^2 + 300t + 6300$

$H(15) = -3(15)^2 + 300(15) + 6300$

$= \$10,125$

This is lower than the $13,100 approximation in the graph.

70. a.   250 + 10n

   b. $(250+10n)(70-2n)$

$= 17,500 + 200n - 20n^2$

   c. $17,500 + 200n - 20n^2 = 17980$

$-480 + 200n - 20n^2 = 0$

$n^2 - 10n + 24 = 0$

$(n-6)(n-4) = 0$

$n - 6 = 0 \qquad n - 4 = 0$

$n = 6 \qquad\quad n = 4$

d.   For four $10 increases, the monthly rent will be $250 + 10(4) = \$290$. (for 62 apartments)
   For six $10 increases, the monthly rent will be $250 + 10(6) = \$310$. (for 58 apartments)

71. Answers will vary.   72.   Answers will vary.

73. Answers will vary.   74.   Answers will vary.

75. If $b^2 - 4ac = 0$, the two answers coincide. The only solution is $-\dfrac{b}{2a}$.

76. If $b^2 - 4ac > 0$, there will be two unequal real numbers.

77. If $b^2 - 4ac < 0$, there are no real number solutions.

78. When the ball hits the ground, the height is 0.

$-80t^2 + 340t - 260 = 0$

Use the quadratic formula with a = -80, b = 340, c = -260:

$x = \dfrac{-(340) \pm \sqrt{(340)^2 - 4 \cdot (-80)(-260)}}{2 \cdot (-80)}$

$= \dfrac{-340 \pm \sqrt{115,600 - 83,200}}{-160}$

$= \dfrac{-340 \pm \sqrt{32,400}}{-160} = \dfrac{-340 \pm 180}{-160}$

$= \dfrac{520}{160}$ or $\dfrac{160}{160}$

That is, 3.25 or 1. Use the larger value since we want when the ball hits the ground. Add 1 second since $H(t)$ is defined for one second after the ball leaves the bat. 1 + 3.25 = 4.25 sec will pass before the ball hits the ground.

79. From problem 78, t = 3.25 so

$D(3.25) = -5(3.25)^2 + 115(3.25) - 110$

$= 210.9375 \approx 211$ ft

80. For a high fly ball to hit the ground, let

$t = 6 \text{ s}$

$D(6) = -5(6)^2 + 115(6) - 110 = 400 \text{ ft}$

81. In the equation $x^2 = y^2 + 13^2$, we want y as large as possible relative to x, so we try putting $y = x - 1$. The equation becomes

$$x^2 = (x-1)^2 + 13^2$$

$$x^2 = x^2 - 2x + 1 + 169 \qquad \text{Multiply.}$$

$$0 = -2x + 170 \qquad \text{Subtract } x^2.$$

$$2x = 170 \qquad \text{Add } 2x.$$

$$x = 85 \qquad \text{Divide by 2.}$$

We can check this by noting that $85^2 = 7225$ and $84^2 = 7056$. Thus, $85^2 - 84^2 = 7225 - 7056 = 169 = 13^2$. So the maximum number of letters that Charlie could have received is $85^2 = 7225$.

Collaborative Learning

1. 1. $(x+2)(x+1); -2, -1$

    2. $(x+3)(x+2); -3, -2$

    3. $(x+4)(x+3); -4, -3$

    4. $(x-1)(x-2); 1, 2$

    5. $(x-2)(x-3); 2, 3$

    6. $(x-3)(x-4); 3, 4$

    7. $(x+1)(x-2); -1, 2$

    8. $(x+2)(x-3); -2, 3$

    9. $(x+3)(x-4); -3, 4$

2. If the integers whose product is ac are m and n, the roots of $ax^2 + bx + c = 0$ are:

    $-\dfrac{c}{m}$ and $-\dfrac{c}{n}$.

Section 6.5 Modeling and Problem Solving

1. $4m = m + 18$

2. $2n(2n+4) < (2n+2)^2$

3. If n is the first consecutive even integer, then $n + 2$ would be the next consecutive

integer. The equation is

$n(n+2) = 10(n+2) - 20$.

4. $x^2 - 2x = x + 10$

5. If x is the number, then the required equation is: $4x + 5 = 29$

    $4x = 24$ Subtract 5.

    $x = 6$ Divide by 4.

    Thus, the number is 6.

6. If x is the number, then the required equation is: $2x + 11 = 19$

    $2x = 8$ Subtract 11.

    $x = 4$ Divide by 2.

    Thus, the number is 4.

7. If x is the number, then the required equation is: $3x + 8 = 29$

    $3x = 21$ Subtract 8.

    $x = 7$ Divide by 3.

    Thus, the number is 7.

8. If x is the number, then the required equation is: $7x + 6 = 69$

    $7x = 63$ Subtract 6.

    $x = 9$ Divide by 7.

9. If x is the number, then the required equation is: $3x - 2 = 16$

    $3x = 18$ Add 2.

    $x = 6$ Divide by 3.

    Thus, the number is 6.

10. If x is the number, then the required equation is: $5x = 2x - 9$

    $3x = -9$ Subtract $2x$.

    $x = -3$ Divide by 3.

    Thus, the number is –3.

11. If x is the number, then the required equation is: $2x^2 = 2x + 12$

    $2x^2 - 2x - 12 = 0$ Subtract $2x + 12$.

    $x^2 - x - 6 = 0$ Divide by 2.

    $(x-3)(x+2) = 0$ Factor.

    $x = 3$ or $x = -2$ Solve.

    Thus, the number is –2 or 3.

12. If x is the number, then the required

    equation is: $\dfrac{1}{2}x^2 - 5 = x - 1$

    $$\dfrac{1}{2}x^2 - x - 4 = 0 \qquad \text{Subtract } x - 1.$$

    $$x^2 - 2x - 8 = 0 \qquad \text{Multiply by 2.}$$

    $$(x - 4)(x + 2) = 0 \qquad \text{Factor.}$$

    $$x = 4 \text{ or } x = -2 \qquad \text{Solve.}$$

    Thus, the number is –2 or 4.

13. If x is the number, then the required

    equation is: $\dfrac{1}{3}x^2 - 2 = 10$

    $$\dfrac{1}{3}x^2 = 12 \quad \text{Add 2.}$$

    $$x^2 = 36 \quad \text{Multiply by 3.}$$

    $$x = \pm 6 \quad \text{Take square roots.}$$

    Thus, the number is –6 or 6.

14. If x is the number, then the required

    equation is: $\dfrac{1}{5}x^2 + 2x = 15$

    $$\dfrac{1}{5}x^2 + 2x - 15 = 0 \qquad \text{Subtract 15.}$$

    $$x^2 + 10x - 75 = 0 \qquad \text{Multiply by 5.}$$

    $$(x + 15)(x - 5) = 0 \qquad \text{Factor.}$$

    $$x = -15 \text{ or } x = 5 \qquad \text{Solve.}$$

    Thus, the number is –15 or 5.

15. Let x million lb be the weight of the orbiter and fuel. Then the weight of the tank and the boosters is $(x - 1.26)$ million lb. The total weight of these components is 4.16 million lb, so the required equation

    is: $x + (x - 1.26) = 4.16$

    $$2x - 1.26 = 4.16 \qquad \text{Simplify.}$$

    $$2x = 5.42 \qquad \text{Add 1.26.}$$

    $$x = 2.71 \qquad \text{Divide by 2.}$$

    Check:
    2.71 – 1.26 = 1.45, and
    2.71 + 1.45 = 4.16.
    Thus, the weight of the orbiter and fuel is 2.71 million lb.

16. Let x million lb be the weight of the external tank. Then the weight of the boosters is $(x + 0.34)$ million lb. The

total weight of these components is 2.9 million lb, so the required equation is:

$$x + (x + 0.34) = 2.9$$

$$2x + 0.34 = 2.9 \qquad \text{Simplify.}$$

$$2x = 2.56 \qquad \text{Subtract 0.34.}$$

$$x = 1.28 \qquad \text{Divide by 2.}$$

Check:
1.28 + 0.34 = 1.62, and 1.28 + 1.62 = 2.9.
Thus, the weight of the xternal tank is 1.28 million lb and the boosters is 1.62 million lb.

17. Let x be Maria's age. Then Pedro is $2x$ years old. The sum of their ages is 30 less than 5 times Maria's, so the required equation is:

    $$x + 2x = 5x - 30$$

    $$3x = 5x - 30 \quad \text{Simplify.}$$

    $$-2x = -30 \qquad \text{Subtract } 5x.$$

    $$x = 15 \qquad \text{Divide by } -2.$$

    Check: $15 + 2(15) \overset{?}{=} 5(15) - 30$

    $$15 + 30 \overset{?}{=} 75 - 30$$

    $$45 = 45$$

    Thus, Pedro is 30 years old and Maria is 15 years old.

18. Let x be the number of years. Then in x years, Mary will be $12 + x$ and Joey will be $2 + x$. After x years, Mary will be twice as old as Joey, so the required equation is:

    $$12 + x = 2(2 + x)$$

    $$12 + x = 4 + 2x \qquad \text{Simplify.}$$

    $$8 = x \qquad \text{Subtract } 4 \text{ and } x.$$

    Check: $12 + 8 \overset{?}{=} 2(2 + 8)$

    $$20 \overset{?}{=} 2(10)$$

    $$20 = 20$$

    Thus, in 8 years Mary will be twice as old as Joey.

19. Let m be the number of miles that Margie traveled. Then, $0.20m$ is the number of dollars that her travel cost. Since the total cost was $44, the required equation is:

    $$0.20m + 18 = 44$$

    $$0.20m = 26 \qquad \text{Subtract 18.}$$

    $$m = 130 \qquad \text{Divide by 0.20.}$$

Check: 0.20(130) = 26 and 26 + 18 = 44.
Thus, Margie traveled 130 mi.

20. Let b be the number of times that José Cataña is at bat. The total number of bases is $2(4)+3+2(2)+9 = 24$ and his slugging average is 1.2. Since total bases divided by number of times of bat is the slugging average, the required equation is:

$$\frac{24}{b} = 1.2$$

$24 = 1.2b$ Mutliply by b.

$20 = b$ Divide by 1.2.

Check: $\dfrac{24}{20} \overset{?}{=} 1.2$

$1.2 = 1.2$

Thus, José Cataña has been 20 times at bat.

21. Let r be the annual interest rate in $I = Prt$. Then, the interest on \$10,000 for 3 months (one-fourth of a year) is $\dfrac{10000r}{4} = 2500r$.

Since the interest was \$50, the required equation is: $2500r = 50$

$r = 0.02$ Divide by 2500.

Check: (10,000)(0.02) = 200

$200 \div 4 = 50$

Thus, the interest rate was 2% per year.

22. Let r be the annual interest rate in $I = Prt$. Then, the interest on \$1400 for 2 years is $I = 1400(2)r$. Since the interest was \$84, the required equation is:

$1400(2)r = 84$

$2800r = 84$ Simplify.

$r = 0.03$ Divide by 2800.

Check: (1400)(2)(0.03) = 84.
Thus, the interest rate was 3% per year.

23. a.   If the total cost is \$71, then the required equation is:
$0.25m + 20 = 71$

$0.25m = 51$ Subtract 20.

$m = 204$ Divide by 0.25.

Check: (0.25)(204) = 51, and

$51 + 20 = 71$.

Thus, the answer is 204 miles.

b.   Using the mileage rate, the cost would be (0.25)(60) + 20, which comes to 35 dollars. The flat rate would be \$40, so use the mileage rate.

24. The flat rate is \$50. Let m be the number of miles traveled so that the other rate is $40 + .022m$. To determine how many miles can be traveled for \$50, the required equation is:
$40 + 0.22m = 50$

$0.22m = 10$ Subtract 40.

$m \approx 45$ Divide by 0.22.

Thus \$50 using the (40 + .022m) rate will only pay for 45 miles. Since they want to travel 50 mi, it will be less expensive to pay the flat rate.

25. Substitute $P = 1000$ and $A = 1040.40$ into the equation $A = P(1+r)^2$ to get the required equation:

$1040.40 = 1000(1+r)^2$

$1.0404 = (1+r)^2$ Divide by 1000.

$1.02 = 1+r$ Take square root.

$0.02 = r$ Subtract 1.

Thus, the rate is 0.02 or 2%.
    You can check this answer as follows: The interest for 1 yr would be 2% of \$1000, which is \$20. So the total amount at the end of the first year would be \$1000 + \$20 = \$1020. The interest for the second year would be 2% of \$1020, that is, \$20.40. Adding this interest to the \$1020 gives \$1040.40, which shows that the answer is correct.

26. Substitute $P = 1000$ and $A = 1060.90$ into the equation $A = P(1+r)^2$ to get the required equation:

$1060.90 = 1000(1+r)^2$

$1.0609 = (1+r)^2$ Divide by 1000.

$1.03 = 1+r$ Take square root.

$0.3 = r$ Subtract 1.

Thus, the rate is 0.03 or 3%.
You can check this answer as follows: The interest for 1 yr would be 3% of \$1000, which is \$30. So the total amount at the end of the first year would be \$1000 + \$30 = \$1030. The interest for the second year would be 3% of \$1030, that is, \$30.90. Adding this interest to the \$1030 gives \$1060.90, which shows that

the answer is correct.

27. Substitute $b = 54$ into the given formula to get the required equation:

$$54 = 0.06v^2$$

$$900 = v^2 \qquad \text{Divide by 0.06.}$$

$$30 = v \qquad \text{Take positive square root.}$$

Thus, the answer is 30 mph.

28. Substitute $v = 30$ and $r = 22.5$ into the given formula to get the required equation:

$$22.5 = 1.5(30)t$$

$$22.5 = 45t \qquad \text{Simplify.}$$

$$0.5 = t \qquad \text{Divide by 45.}$$

Thus, the drivers reaction time is 0.5 sec.

29. Substitute $v = 30$ and $t = 0.5$ into the given formula to get:

$$d = 1.5(0.5)(30) + 0.06(30)^2$$

$$= 22.5 + 54 = 76.5$$

Thus, the stopping distance is 76.5 ft.

30. Substitute $d = 187.5$ and $t = 0.5$ into the given formula to get:

$$187.5 = 1.5(0.5)v + 0.06v^2$$

$$0.75v + 0.06v^2 = 187.5$$

$$0.06v^2 + 0.75v - 187.5 = 0$$

Use the quadratic formula and substitute $a = 0.06$, $b = 0.75$, $c = -187.5$.

$$x = \frac{-0.75 \pm \sqrt{0.75^2 - 4 \cdot 0.06(-187.5)}}{2 \cdot 0.06}$$

$$= \frac{-0.75 \pm \sqrt{0.5625 + 45}}{0.12}$$

$$= \frac{-0.75 \pm \sqrt{45.5625}}{0.12} = \frac{-0.75 \pm 6.75}{0.12}$$

$$= -\frac{7.5}{0.12} \quad \text{or} \quad \frac{6}{0.12} = 50$$

Disregard the negative value. Thus, the car is going 50 mph.

31. Substitute $v = 20$ and $d = 42$ into the given formula to get:

$$42 = 1.5(20)t + 0.06(20)^2$$

$$42 = 30t + 24 \qquad \text{Simplify.}$$

$$18 = 30t \qquad \text{Subtract 24.}$$

$$0.6 = t \qquad \text{Divide by 30.}$$

Thus, the driver's reaction time is 0.6 sec.

32. Substitute $v = 50$ and $d = 200$ into the given formula to get:

$$200 = 1.5(50)t + 0.06(50)^2$$

$$200 = 75t + 150 \qquad \text{Simplify.}$$

$$50 = 75t \qquad \text{Subtract 150.}$$

$$\frac{2}{3} = t \qquad \text{Divide by 75.}$$

Thus, the driver's reaction time must be $\frac{2}{3}$ sec.

33. Substitute $t = \frac{2}{3}$ and $d = 44$ into the given formula to get the equation:

$$44 = 1.5\left(\frac{2}{3}\right)v + 0.06v^2$$

$$44 = v + 0.06v^2 \qquad \text{Simplify.}$$

$$4400 = 100v + 6v^2 \qquad \text{Multiply by 100.}$$

$$2200 = 50v + 3v^2 \qquad \text{Divide by 2.}$$

$$0 = 3v^2 + 50v - 2200 \qquad \text{Standard form}$$

In the last equation, you can read off: $a = 3$, $b = 50$, and $c = -2200$. Substitute these numbers into the quadratic formula to get:

$$v = \frac{-50 \pm \sqrt{50^2 - 4 \cdot 3(-2200)}}{2 \cdot 3}$$

$$= \frac{-50 \pm \sqrt{2500 + 26400}}{6}$$

$$= \frac{-50 \pm \sqrt{28900}}{6} = \frac{-50 \pm 170}{6}$$

Since a positive number is needed for the answer, use the plus sign to find

$$v = \frac{-50 + 170}{6} = \frac{120}{6} = 20.$$ Thus, Loren was going 20 mph at the instant of the stop signal.

34. Substitute $t = 0.4$ and $d = 120$ into the given formula to get the equation:

$$120 = 1.5(0.4)v + 0.06v^2$$

$$120 = 0.6v + 0.06v^2 \qquad \text{Simplify.}$$

$$0.06v^2 + 0.6v - 120 = 0 \qquad \text{Standard form}$$

In the last equation, you can read off:

$a = 0.06$, $b = 0.6$, and $c = -120$. Substitute these numbers into the quadratic formula to get:

$$v = \frac{-0.6 \pm \sqrt{0.6^2 - 4 \cdot 0.06(-120)}}{2 \cdot 0.06}$$

$$= \frac{-0.6 \pm \sqrt{0.36 + 28.8}}{0.12}$$

$$= \frac{-0.6 \pm \sqrt{29.16}}{0.12} = \frac{-0.6 \pm 5.4}{0.12}$$

Since a positive number is needed for the answer, use the plus sign to find

$$v = \frac{-0.6 + 5.4}{0.12} = \frac{4.8}{0.12} = 40 .$$ Thus, Pedro was going 40 mph at the instant of the stop signal.

35. Let the two consecutive integers be x and $x + 1$. Then the given condition says that $6x < 5(x+1)$. Simplify this inequality to get $6x < 5x + 5$. Then subtract $5x$ from both sides to get $x < 5$. Since 4 is the largest integer less than 5, take $x = 4$, so that $x + 1 = 5$. Thus, 4 and 5 are the largest integers for which 6 times the smaller is less than 5 times the larger.

36. Let the n represent the number of $1 bills with value $1n$ and m represent the number of $5 bills with value $5m$. Then the given condition says that $n + 5m < 80$. The total number of bills is $n + m = 20$, solving for n we have $n = 20 - m$. Substitute for n in the inequality and solve.

$$20 - m + 5m < 80$$

$$20 + 4m < 80$$

$$4m < 60$$

$$m < 15$$

Thus, the greatest possible number of $5 bills is 14. If there are 14 $5 bills, then there are 6 $1 bills so the largest total value of money is $5(14) + 6(1) = \$76$.

37. Let x billion cans be the number that are recycled. Then $\frac{2}{3}x$ billion cans are thrown away. Since the total number of billion cans is 100, we have the equation

$$x + \frac{2}{3}x = 100$$

$$\frac{5}{3}x = 100$$

$$x = \frac{3}{5} \cdot 100 = 60$$

So 60 billion cans are recycled and 40 billion cans are not recycled.

38. a. Determine break-even point:
costs + O = revenue, where $N = 15$ students and O = other costs. From Example 7: costs = $2000 + 15N$ and revenue = $330N$. Substituting, we have

$$2000 + 15(15) + O = 330(15)$$

$$2225 + O = 4950$$

$$O = 2725$$

The other costs are $2725.

b. Answers will vary.

c. Answers will vary.

39. a. Tuition = T

$$\text{State Contribution} = = \frac{3N}{40}(2800)$$

$$= 210N$$

Revenue to Institution = $T + 210N$

b. Costs to Institution:

(s) (40)($100)	=	$4,000
(U) (40)($150)	=	$6,000
(G) (40)($1000)	=	$40,000
(S) (3)($1000)	=	$3,000
Total Cost	=	$53,000

c. $T + 210N = 53{,}000$

d. $N = \dfrac{53000 - T}{210}$

e. If N is the number of students, then the total tuition revenue is
$T = 40 \cdot 3 \cdot N = 120N$.
To break even, $T + 210N = 53{,}000$, that is:
$120N + 210N = 53000$

$$330N = 53000$$

$$N = \frac{53000}{330} = 160.6060\ldots$$

Thus, to incur no loss, the least number of students required is 161.

40. a. $C_A = 20{,}000 + \dfrac{4m}{20}$

b. $C_B = 25{,}000 + \dfrac{4m}{25}$

c. Solve $C_A = C_B$ and solve for m.

$$20{,}000 + \frac{4m}{20} = 25{,}000 + \frac{4m}{25}$$

$$\frac{4m}{20} - \frac{4m}{25} = 5{,}000$$

$$\frac{m}{25} = 5{,}000$$

$$m = 125{,}000$$

The cost is the same when driving 125,000 mi.

d. For $m < 125{,}000$, $C_A < C_B$; buy car A if you plan to drive less than 125,000 mi. For $m > 125{,}000$, $C_B < C_A$; buy car B if you plan to drive over 125,000 mi.

41. a.   Identical Row Alignment

	Unit A	Unit B	Unit C
Cost per month	$25	$90	$128
Number per row	5	10	10
Rows	5	5	10
Layers	3	5	5
Total	75	250	500
Units Needed	5	2	1
Cost for 2 months	$250	$360	$256

Staggered Row Alignment

	Unit A	Unit B	Unit C
Cost per month	$25	$90	$128
Number per row	2-4s & 3-5s	3-10s & 2-9s	6-10s & 5-9s
Rows	5	5	11
Layers	3	5	5
Total	69	240	525
Units Needed	6	2	1
Cost for 2 months	$300	$360	$256

b. Rent 5 units A for a cost of $250.

c. Rent one unit C for a cost of $256.

d. Rent one unit A and one unit B for a cost of $230.

42. HOURS SPENT AND GRADE EARNED

	Math	Science	English	GPA
I	6(A)	4(A)	0(C)	$\dfrac{30}{9} = 3.33$
II	6(A)	2(B)	2(A)	$\dfrac{33}{9} = 3.67$
III	3(B)	4(A)	3(A)	$\dfrac{33}{9} = 3.67$

Computations:

I: $\dfrac{12 + 12 + 6}{9} = \dfrac{30}{9} = 3.33$

II: $\dfrac{12 + 9 + 12}{9} = \dfrac{33}{9} = 3.67$

III: $\dfrac{9 + 12 + 12}{9} = \dfrac{33}{9} = 3.67$

Either of the last two plans is best.

43. HOURS SPENT AND GRADE EARNED

	Math	Science	English	GPA
I	9(A)	2(C)	1(C)	$\dfrac{30}{11} = 2.73$
II	6(B)	4(B)	2(B)	$\dfrac{33}{11} = 3.00$
III	3(C)	6(A)	3(A)	$\dfrac{36}{11} = 3.23$

Computations:

I: $\dfrac{16 + 8 + 6}{11} = \dfrac{30}{11} = 2.73$

II: $\dfrac{12 + 12 + 9}{11} = \dfrac{33}{11} = 3.00$

III: $\dfrac{8 + 16 + 12}{11} = \dfrac{36}{11} = 3.23$

The table shows that you should spend 3 hr on Math, 6 hr on Science and 3 hours on English since the last row gives the best GPA.

44. a. **Rock-Busters**:

	Overdue 1 day	Overdue 2 days	Overdue 3 days
New	3 + 2.50 = $5.50	3 + 5 = $8	3 + 7.50 = $10.50
Old	3 + 1.50 = $4.50	3 + 3 = $6	3 + 4.50 = $7.50

Video Renters:

Overdue

	1 day	2 days	3 days
New	2.5 + 2 = $4.50	2.5 + 4 = $6.50	2.5 + 6 = $8.50
Old	2.5 + 2 = $4.50	2.5 + 4 = $6.50	2.5 + 6 = $8.50

b. $C_R = 6 + 4n$ (dollars)

$C_V = 5 + 4n$ (dollars)

c. $C_R = 6 + 4(5) = \$26$

$C_V = 5 + 4(5) = \$25$

45. a. **Blockbusters:**

Returned after

	2 days	3 days	4 days
New	3 + 2 = $5	3 + 4 = $7	3 + 6 = $9
Old	3 + 0 = $3	3 + 2 = $5	3 + 4 = $7

Red Rabbit:

Returned after

	2 days	3 days	4 days
New	3 + 3 = $6	3 + 6 = $9	3 + 9 = $12
Old	1.6 + 0 = $1.60	1.6 + 1.5 = $3.10	1.6 + 3 = $4.60

b. Returned after n days:

Blockbusters:

New $\qquad 3 + 2(n-1)$

Old $\qquad 3 + 2(n-2)$

New + Old $\quad 6 + 2n - 2 + 2n - 4 = \$4n$

Red Rabbit:

New $\qquad 3 + 3(n-1)$

Old $\qquad 1.60 + 1.50(n-2)$

New + Old $\quad 4.60 + 3n - 3 + 1.5n - 3$

$\qquad\qquad = \$4.5n - \$1.40$

c. Charges when a new movie and an old movie is returned after 5 days at

Blockbuster: $\$4(5) = \$20$

Charges when a new movie and an old movie is returned after 5 days at Red

Rabbit: $\$4.5(5) - \$1.40 = \$21.10$

46. a.

Hours of Parking

	1	2	3	4	5
Park & Shop	5.00	5.50	6.00	6.50	7.00
Safe Park	4.75	5.35	5.95	6.55	7.15

b. $C_{P\&S} = 5.00 + 0.50(n-1)$

$\qquad = 4.50 + 0.50n$ (dollars)

$C_{SP} = 4.75 + 0.60(n-1)$

$\qquad = 4.15 + 0.60n$ (dollars)

47. a. Average stopping distance in feet:

$d = 1.5(0.6)v + 0.06v^2$

$\qquad = 0.9v + 0.06v^2$

b. $d = 0.9(45) + 0.06(45)^2$

$\qquad = 40.5 + 121.5 = 162$ ft

c. 162 ft + 80 ft = 242 ft

d. $D = RT$

$242 = \dfrac{45(5280)T}{3600}$

$T = \dfrac{242(3600)}{45(5280)} \approx 3.67$ sec

48. Average stopping distance in feet:

$d = 1.5(1)v + 0.06v^2$

$\qquad = 1.5v + 0.06v^2$

Determine the nearest a car traveling 45 mph can be to the intersection and still stop safely:

$d = 1.5(45) + 0.06(45)^2$

$\qquad = 67.5 + 121.5 = 189$ ft

The total maximum distance a car must travel through the intersection: 189 ft + 80 ft = 269 ft

The minimum duration of the yellow light:

$D = RT$

$269 = \dfrac{45(5280)T}{3600}$

$T = \dfrac{269(3600)}{45(5280)} \approx 4.08$ sec

49. Answers may vary. You should try to determine the unknown, that is, what is wanted.

50. Answers may vary. You must check to see that the conditions of the problem are met.

51. $y = \dfrac{32(12)(28,000)}{(32-12)(30,000)(4.00)}$

$\qquad = \dfrac{32(12)(28)}{20(30)(4)} = \dfrac{10,752}{2400} = 4.48$ yr

52. $5 \text{ yr} = \dfrac{32(12)C}{(32-12)(30,000)(4.00)}$

$C = \dfrac{5(20)(30,000)(4.00)}{32(12)}$

$= \dfrac{12,000,000}{384} = 31,250$

If you have driven your car for 5 years, you could justify paying $31,250 for a new car.

53. If M is greater than G, then y would be negative, which is unrealistic. If $M = G$, then there is a zero denominator, which could be interpreted to mean that you should keep the old car and not buy the new one.

Section 6.6 Ratio, Proportion, and Variation

1. 7000 to 2000; 7000 : 2000; $\dfrac{7000}{2000}$;

or 7 to 2; 7:2; $\dfrac{7}{2}$

2. 700 to 800; 700:800; $\dfrac{700}{800}$ or 7 to 8; 7:8;

$\dfrac{7}{8}$

3. 70 to 4260; 70 : 4260; $\dfrac{70}{4260}$ or 7 to 426;

7:426; $\dfrac{7}{426}$

4. 28 to 34; 28:34; $\dfrac{28}{34}$ or 14 to 17; 14:17;

$\dfrac{14}{17}$

5. $\dfrac{2000}{600} = \dfrac{10}{3}$ 6. $\dfrac{6}{100}$ or 0.06

7. $\dfrac{12,000}{700} = \dfrac{120}{7} \approx 17$ mpg

8. a. $\dfrac{1.09}{8} = 0.13625 \approx 13.6¢$

b. $\dfrac{0.53}{4} = 0.1325 \approx 13.3¢$

c. The 4-oz generic can

d. The generic can here

9. a. $\dfrac{1.31}{22} = 0.0595 \approx \$0.06 = 6$ cents

b. $\dfrac{1.75}{32} = 0.0547 \approx \$0.05 = 5$ cents

c. Based on price per oz alone, White Magic is the better buy.

10. a. $\dfrac{0.79}{16} = 0.049375 \approx 5¢$

b. $\dfrac{1.25}{22} = 0.05682 \approx 6¢$

c. Based on price per oz alone, A&P Wool Washing Liquid is the better buy.

11. From the proportion $\dfrac{x}{9} = \dfrac{4}{3}$, you get $3x = 36$, by using "cross-products." Divide both sides by 3 to find $x = 12$.

12. From the proportion $\dfrac{x}{6} = \dfrac{5}{12}$, you get $12x = 30$, by using "cross-products." Divide both sides by 12 to find $x = 2.5$.

13. Use "cross-products" for the proportion $\dfrac{8}{x} = \dfrac{4}{3}$ to get $4x = 24$. Then, divide both sides by 4 to find $x = 6$.

14. Use "cross-products" for the proportion $\dfrac{6}{x} = \dfrac{18}{7}$ to get $18x = 42$. Then, divide both sides by 18 to find $x = \dfrac{7}{3}$.

15. Use "cross-products" for the proportion $\dfrac{3}{8} = \dfrac{9}{x}$ to get $3x = 72$. Then, divide both sides by 3 to find $x = 24$.

16. Use "cross-products" for the proportion

$\dfrac{3}{5} = \dfrac{9}{x}$ to get $3x = 45$. Then, divide both sides by 3 to find $x = 15$.

17. $\dfrac{n}{40} = \dfrac{9}{2}$ 18. $\dfrac{L}{10} = \dfrac{3}{2}$

19. $\dfrac{1 \text{ tank}}{\dfrac{1}{2} \text{ hr}} = \dfrac{x \text{ tanks}}{3 \text{ hr}}$

Cross multiply: $\dfrac{x}{2} = 3$

Solve for x: $x = 6$

Thus, you need 6 tanks for a 3 hr flight.

20. $\dfrac{\dfrac{1}{2} \text{ lb}}{3 \text{ servings}} = \dfrac{x \text{ lb}}{90 \text{ servings}}$

Cross multiply: $45 = 3x$

Solve for x: $x = 15$

Thus, you need 15 lb of cooked shrimp for 90 servings.

21. Let x be the length in inches. Then, you must have the proportion: $\dfrac{35}{x} = \dfrac{10}{19}$.

Now, use "cross-products" to get $10x = 35 \cdot 19 = 665$. Then divide both sides by 10 to find $x = 66.5$. Thus, the flag should be 66.5 in. long.

22. Let x be the number of tortillas. Then, you must have the proportion: $\dfrac{45}{x} = \dfrac{30}{74}$.

Now, use "cross-products" to get $30x = 45 \cdot 74 = 3330$. Then divide both sides by 30 to find $x = 111$. Thus, Tom could eat 111 tortillas in 45 minutes.

23. Let t be the number of trees. Then, you must have the proportion:

$\dfrac{t \text{ trees}}{7600 \text{ lb}} = \dfrac{1 \text{ tree}}{48 \text{ lb}}$.

Now, use "cross-products" to get $48t = 1 \cdot 7600 = 7600$. Then divide both sides by 48 to find $t = 158.\overline{3}$. Thus, 159 trees are needed to absorb 7600 lb of CO_2.

24. The ratio of tail to body length is $\dfrac{4}{5}$. Let x be the length of the tail. Then, you must have the proportion: $\dfrac{4}{5} = \dfrac{x}{10}$. Now, use "cross-products" to get $5x = 4 \cdot 10 = 40$. Then divide both sides by 5 to find $x = 8$. Thus, the length of the tail is 8 in.

25. Let x be the number of fish in the lake. Assuming that the ratio of the total number of fish to the total number tagged is the same as the corresponding ratio for the sample of 53 fish, we have the proportion $\dfrac{x}{250} = \dfrac{53}{5}$. Now, multiply both sides by 250 to get

$x = \dfrac{250 \cdot 53}{5} = 50 \cdot 53 = 2650.$

Thus, there are about 2650 fish in the lake.

26. a. $I = km$

   b. Substitute $I = 26.40$ and $m = 480$ into the equation in part a to get $480 = k \cdot 26.40$. Then divide both sides by 26.40 to find $k = 0.055$.

   c. Use $k = 0.055$ and $I = 750$ to get the equation $750 = 0.055t$. Then divide both sides by 0.055 to find $m = \$41.25$.

27. a. $S = kn$

   b. Substitute $S = 307{,}200$ and $n = 2$ into the equation in part a to get $307{,}200 = k \cdot 2$. Then divide both sides by 2 to find $k = 153{,}600$ bytes.

   c. Use $k = 153{,}600$ and $n = 20$ to get the equation $S = 153{,}600 \cdot 20$. Then simplify to find $t = 3{,}072{,}000$ bytes.

28. a. $d = ks^2$

   b. Substitute $d = 54$ and $s = 30$ into the equation in part a to get $54 = k \cdot 30^2$. Then divide both sides by 30^2 to find k:

   $k = \dfrac{54}{30^2} = \dfrac{54}{900} = 0.06.$

   c. $d = 0.06 \cdot 60^2 = 216$

   Thus, the stopping distance is 216 ft.

29. a. $T = kh^3$

   b. Substitute $T = 196$ and $h = 70$ into the equation in part a to get $196 = k \cdot 70^3$. Then divide both sides by 70^3 to find k:

$$k = \frac{196}{70^3} = \frac{196}{343000} \approx 0.0005714 \, .$$

c. $T = \frac{75^3}{1750} = \frac{421875}{1750} \approx 241.07$

Thus, the threshold weight is about 241 lb.

30. a. $s = \frac{k}{y}$

b. Substitute 30 $s = 50$ and $y = 3$ into the equation in part a to get $50 = \frac{k}{3}$. Then multiply both sides by 3 to find $k = 150$. The variation equation is $s = \frac{150}{y}$.

Now, substitute $s = 5$: $5 = \frac{150}{y}$.

Multiply both sides by y, then divide by 5 to get $y = 30$. A rock band will need 30 new songs after 5 years.

31. a. $f = \frac{k}{d}$

b. Substitute $f = 8$ and $k = \frac{1}{2}$ into the equation in part a to get $8 = \frac{k}{\frac{1}{2}}$. Then multiply both sides by $\frac{1}{2}$ to find $k = 4$.

c. Put $d = \frac{1}{4}$ and $k = 4$ into the equation in part a. This gives $f = \frac{4}{\frac{1}{4}} = 16$. So the f number is 16.

32. Since the pressure P varies inversely as the volume V, we write $P = \frac{k}{V}$ or $PV = k$.

To find k, substitute $P = 24$ and $V = 18$ to find $k = 18 \cdot 24 = 432$. This gives the equation $PV = 432$. For $V = 12$, we get $12P = 432$. Divide by 12 to find

$P = \frac{432}{12} = 36 \text{ lb/in}^2$.

33. Since the pressure P varies inversely as the volume V, we write $P = \frac{k}{V}$ or $PV = k$. To find k, substitute $P = 24$ and $V = 18$ to find $k = 18 \cdot 24 = 432$. This gives the equation $PV = 432$. For $P = 40$, we get $40V = 432$. Divide by 40 to find $V = \frac{432}{40} = 10.8 \text{ in}^3$.

34. a. $W = \frac{k}{d^2}$

b. Substitute $W = 121$ and $d = 3960$ into the equation in part a to get $121 = \frac{k}{3960^2}$. Then multiply both sides by 3960^2 to find k: $k = 121 \cdot 3960^2$.

c. Determine the distance from the center of Earth: $d = 3960 + 880 = 4848$ ft.

$W = \frac{121 \cdot 3960^2}{4848^2} \approx 81$

Thus, the astronaut weights approximately 81 lb.

35. a. $w = \frac{k}{s}$

b. Substitute $w = 600$ and $s = 12$ into the equation in part a to get $600 = \frac{k}{12}$. Then multiply both sides by 12 to find k: $k = 7200$.

c. $w = \frac{7200}{10} = 720$

Thus, 720 words can be typed on a page if a 10-point font were used.

36. a. $P = \frac{k}{S}$

b. Substitute $P = 100$ and $S = 25$ into the equation in part a to get $100 = \frac{k}{25}$. Then multiply both sides by 25 to find k: $k = 2500$.

c. $P = \frac{2500}{26} \approx 96.15$

Thus, the price of one barrel would be $96.15.

37. a. $b = \dfrac{k}{a}$

 b. Substitute $b = 110$ and $a = 27$ into the equation in part a to get $110 = \dfrac{k}{27}$. Then multiply both sides by 27 to find k: $k = 2970$.

 c. $b = \dfrac{2970}{33} = 90$; you would expect 90 births (per 1000 women) for 33-year old women.

38. a. $m = kg$

 b. Substitute $m = 1691.6$ and $g = 38.2$ into the equation in part a to get $1691.6 = k(38.2)$. Then dividing both sides by 38.2 to find k: $k \approx 44.3$.

 c. Miles per gallon is $k = \dfrac{m}{g}$. Thus, miles per gallon is 44.3 mpg.

39. a. $d = ks$

 b. Substitute $b = 500$ and $a = 28.41$ into the equation in part a to get $500 = k \cdot 28.41$. Then divide both sides by 28.41 to find k: $501 = k \cdot 28.41$ or $k \approx 17.63$.

 c. Since d is the distance, s the average speed and $k \approx 17.63$, $d = 17.63s$ and k is the number of hours needed to travel the distance d at the speed s.

40. a. Substitute $N = 40$ and $P = 100$ into the equation of variation $N = kP$ to get $40 = k \cdot 100$. Then divide both sides by 100 to find k: $k = 0.04$. The equation of variation is $N = 0.4P$.

 b. Substitute $P = 5000$:
 $N = 0.4(5000) = 2000$

41. a. $\text{BAC} = k(N-1)$

 b. According to the problem, the BAC is 0.052 when $N = 3$. Thus, $0.052 = k(3-1)$, that is, $0.052 = 2k$. Dividing by 2, $k = \dfrac{0.052}{2} = 0.026$.

 c. When $k = 0.026$, $\text{BAC} = k(N-1)$ becomes $\text{BAC} = 0.026(N-1)$. To find the BAC for $N = 5$ beers, $\text{BAC} = 0.026(5-1) = 0.104$.

 d. 4 beers: when $N = 4$, $\text{BAC} = 0.026(4-1) = 0.078$. Note that for $N = 5$, $\text{BAC} = 0.104$, which is over the limit!

42. a. $\text{BAC} = k(N-1)$

 b. According to the problem, the BAC is 0.06 when $N = 3$. Thus, $0.06 = k(3-1)$, that is, $0.06 = 2k$. Dividing by 2, $k = \dfrac{0.06}{2} = 0.03$.

 c. When $k = 0.03$, $\text{BAC} = k(N-1)$ becomes $\text{BAC} = 0.03(N-1)$. To find the BAC for $N = 5$ beers, $\text{BAC} = 0.03(5-1) = 0.12$.

 d. 3 beers: when $N = 3$, $\text{BAC} = 0.03(3-1) = 0.06$. Note that for $N = 4$, $\text{BAC} = 0.09$, which is over the limit!

43. a. $C = k(F - 37)$ According to the problem, when $C = 80$, $F = 57$ so we have $80 = k(57 - 37) = 20k$. Dividing by 20, $4 = k$. Thus, $C = 4(F - 37)$.

 b. Substituting $F = 90$,
 $C = 4(90 - 37) = 4 \cdot 53 = 212$.

44. Substitute $H = 25$, $N = 100$, and $t = 5$ into the equation of variation $H = k \cdot N(t + 10)$ to get $25 = k \cdot 100(5 + 10)$. Solving for k gives $k \approx 0.017$. The equation of variation is $H = 0.017N(t + 10)$. There are 20 cigarettes in one pack so $N = 2 \cdot 20 \cdot 360 \, \text{days} = 14,400$.
$H = 0.017(14,400)(5 + 10) \approx 3600$.
Thus, your life would be shortened by approximately 3600 hours or about 150 days.

45. a. $T = \dfrac{k}{n}$

 b. Substitute $T = 35$ and $n = 2$ into the equation in part a to get $35 = \dfrac{k}{2}$. Then multiply both sides by 2 to find k: $k = 70$.

c. $T = \dfrac{70}{48} = 1.458333\ldots$ min; Thus, it would take approximately 1.4583 minutes to completely read a 48X CD.

46.   Substitute $T = 1$ and $d = 4000$ into the equation of variation $T = \dfrac{k}{d}$ to get

$1 = \dfrac{k}{4000}$. Solving for k gives $k = 4000$.

The equation of variation is $T = \dfrac{4000}{d}$.

The temperature at 8000 m would be

$T = \dfrac{4000}{8000} = \dfrac{1}{2}\,{}^{\circ}\text{C}$.

47. $C = k\dfrac{w}{L}$. For the Rhodesian man, $w = 15$ and $L = 21$ and $C = 98$, so $98 = k\dfrac{15}{21}$.

Multiplying by 21 and dividing by 15 gives $k = 137.2$ so we rewrite the equation

as $C = 137.2\dfrac{w}{L}$. For Cro-Magnon, $L = 20$,

$w = 15, C = 137.2 \cdot \dfrac{15}{20} = 102.9$.

48.   a. $\text{BAC} = \dfrac{k}{W}$. When $W = 130$, and

$\text{BAC} = 0.06,\ 0.06 = \dfrac{k}{130}$. This means that $k = 130 \cdot 0.06 = 7.8$ and now

$\text{BAC} = \dfrac{7.8}{W}$.

b. $\text{BAC} = \dfrac{7.8}{W}$ where $W = 260$. Thus,

$\text{BAC} = \dfrac{7.8}{260} = 0.03$.

c.   According to the problem,

$\text{BAC} = 0.08 = \dfrac{7.8}{W}$. Multiplying both

sides by W and then dividing by 0.08

we get $W = \dfrac{7.8}{0.08} = 97.5$ lb.

d.   If you weigh more than 97.5 lb, BAC would be less than 0.08.

49.   a. $\text{BAC} = \dfrac{k}{W}$. When $W = 130$, and

$\text{BAC} = 0.066,\ 0.066 = \dfrac{k}{130}$. This means

that $k = 130 \cdot 0.066 = 8.58$ and now

$\text{BAC} = \dfrac{8.58}{W}$.

b. $\text{BAC} = \dfrac{8.58}{W}$ where $W = 260$. Thus,

$\text{BAC} = \dfrac{8.58}{260} \approx 0.033$.

c.   According to the problem,

$\text{BAC} = 0.08 = \dfrac{8.58}{W}$. Multiplying both

sides by W then dividing by 0.08 we get

$W = \dfrac{8.58}{0.08} = 107.25$ lb.

d.   If you weigh more than 107.25 lb, BAC would be less than 0.08.

50.   Answers may vary. A ratio is a quotient of two numbers. A proportion is an equality between two ratios.

51.   Answers may vary. In direct variation, as one quantity increases, a related quantity increases. In inverse variation as one quantity increases, a related quantity decreases.

52.   Answers may vary. To solve a proportion, cross-multiply and then solve for the variable.

53.   Answers may vary. The proportion $a/b = c/d$ can be solved by cross-multiplication means that $a/b = c/d$ can be rewritten as $ad = cb$.

54.   Answers may vary. No. A sum must be performed first.

55.   Answers may vary. As the number of miles that you drive increases, the number of gallons of gas that the car uses will increase.

56.   Answers may vary. The faster you drive the car, the more gas you use. This is a direct proportion.

57.   a. $T = 15S$
      b.   1 hour is 60 minutes, so substitute $T = 60$. $60 = 15S$, then divide both sides by 15 to get $S = 4$.

Chapter 6 Practice Test

1. a. $x + 7 = 2$; subtract 7 from both sides
        to get $x = -5$.
    b. $x - 4 = 9$; add 4 to both sides to get
        $x = 13$.

2. a. $x + 5 > 4$; subtract 5 from both sides
        to get $x > -1$. The set of integers
        satisfying this inequality is
        $\{0, 1, 2, 3, \ldots\}$.
    b. $2 + x \geq -x - 1$
        $2 + 2x \geq -1$ Add x to both sides.
        $\quad 2x \geq -3$ Subtract 2 from both
        $\qquad\qquad\qquad$ sides.

        $x \geq -\dfrac{3}{2}$ Divide both sides by 2.

        Thus, the solution set is
        $\{-1, 0, 1, 2, 3, \ldots\}$.

3. a. $2x + 2 = 3x - 2$
        $\quad 2 = x - 2$ Subtract $2x$ from
        $\qquad\qquad\quad$ both sides.
        $\quad 4 = x$ Add 2 to both sides.
    b. $\dfrac{x+3}{5} = \dfrac{x-1}{3} + \dfrac{6}{5}$

        $15 \cdot \dfrac{x+3}{5} = 15 \cdot \dfrac{x-1}{3} + 15 \cdot \dfrac{6}{5}$

        $3(x+3) = 5(x-1) + 18$ Multiply by 15.

        $3x + 9 = 5x - 5 + 18$ Simplify.

        $3x + 9 = 5x + 13$

        $\quad 9 = 2x + 13$

        $-4 = 2x$

        $x = -2$

4. a. Given: $S = 3L - 21$
        $S + 21 = 3L$ Add 21.

        $\dfrac{S + 21}{3} = L$ Divide by 3.

    b. Here $S = 6$, $L = \dfrac{6 + 21}{3} = \dfrac{27}{3} = 9$ in.

5. $\dfrac{x}{2} + 2 \geq \dfrac{-(x+1)}{4}$ Multiply by 4.

    $2x + 8 \geq -x - 1$ Add x.

    $3x + 8 \geq -1$ Subtract 8.

    $\quad 3x \geq -9$ Divide by 3.

    $\quad x \geq -3$

The solution set consists of all real numbers
greater than or equal to -3.

6. a. $x - 3 \leq 0$ Add 3 to both sides to get
        $x \leq 3$. This inequality is satisfied by all
        real numbers less than or equal to 3. The
        solution set is shown on the graph.

        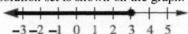

    b. $-2x + 4 > x + 1$

        $4 > 3x + 1$ Add $2x$.

        $3 > 3x$ Subtract 1.

        $1 > x$ Divide by 3.

        The last inequality is satisfied by all real
        numbers that are less than 1. This solution
        set is shown on the graph.

        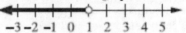

7. a. $x + 2 \geq 3$ and $x \leq 4$

        $x \geq 1$ and $x \leq 4$ Subtract 2.
        The solution set of this system of
        inequalities is the set of all real numbers
        between 1 and 4, inclusive. This set is
        shown on the graph.

        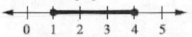

    b. $x - 3 \geq 1$ and $x \leq 0$

        $x \geq 4$ and $x \leq 0$ Add 3.

        There are no numbers that are greater than
        or equal to 4 and that are less than or
        equal to zero, so the solution set is empty.

8. a. $x < 0$ or $x - 2 < 1$

        $x < 0$ or $x < 3$ Add 2.
        The solution set of this system of inequalities
        is the set of all real numbers that are less than
        3. This set is shown on the graph.

        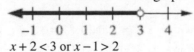

    b. $x + 2 < 3$ or $x - 1 > 2$

        $x < 1$ or $x > 3$

        (Subtract 2 from both sides of the first
        inequality and add 1 to both sides of the
        second inequality.) The solution set of
        this system of inequalities is the set of all
        real numbers that are less than 1 or that
        are greater than 3. This set is shown on
        the graph.

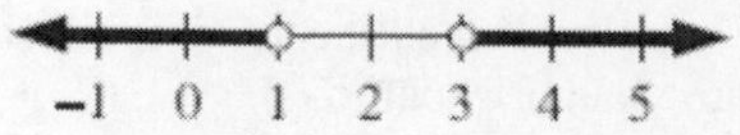

9. Since |3| = 3 and |–3| = 3, the solutions of |x| = 3 are $x = \pm 3$.

10. $|x| < 2$ means that $-2 < x < 2$, so the solution set consists of all the real numbers between –2 and 2, not including the –2 or the 2. The graph shows this set.

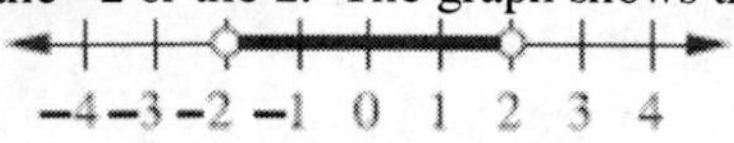

11. $|x-2| < 2$ means that $-2 < x-2 < 2$. By adding 2 to each side, we get $0 < x < 4$. The solution set of this system is the set of all real numbers that are between 0 and 4. The endpoints are not included.

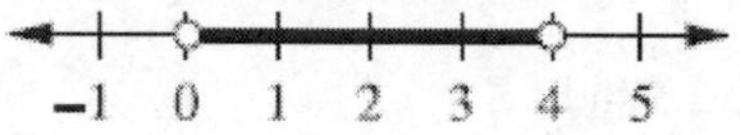

12. $|x| > 2$ is equivalent to the system $x < -2$ or $x > 2$. The solution set of this system is the set of all real numbers that are less than –2 or that are greater than +2. The graph shows this set.

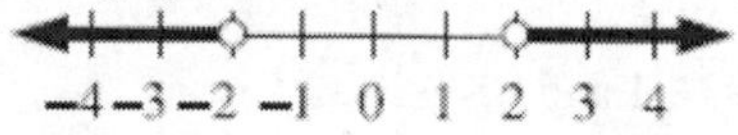

13. $|x-2| > 3$ is equivalent to the system $x-2 < -3$ or $x-2 > 3$. By adding 2 to both sides of these inequalities, we get the system $x < -1$ or $x > 5$. The solution set of this system is the set of all real numbers that are either less than –1 or that are greater than 5. The graph shows this set.

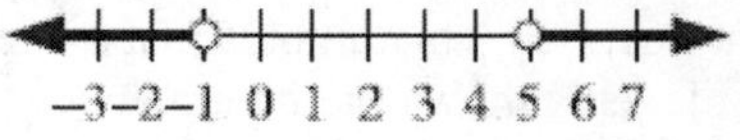

14. a. Since $1 \cdot 2 = 2$ and $1 + 2 = 3$, $x^2 + 3x + 2 = (x+1)(x+2)$.

b. Since $1 \cdot (-4) = -4$ and $1 + (-4) = -3$, $x^2 - 3x - 4 = (x+1)(x-4)$.

15. a. $(x-1)(x+2) = 0$ is satisfied if and only if $x - 1 = 0$ or $x + 2 = 0$, that is, if and only if $x = 1$ or $x = -2$.

b. $x(x-1) = 0$ is satisfied if and only if $x = 0$ or $x - 1 = 0$, that is, if and only if $x = 0$ or $x = 1$.

16. Since $x^2 + 7x + 10 = (x+5)(x+2)$, The given equation can be written as $(x+5)(x+2) = 0$ which is satisfied if and only if $x + 5 = 0$ or $x + 2 = 0$, that is, if and only if $x = -5$ or $x = -2$.

17. Since $x^2 - 3x - 10 = (x-5)(x+2)$, the given equation can be rewritten as $(x-5)(x+2) = 0$, which is satisfied if and only if $x - 5 = 0$ or $x + 2 = 0$, that is, if and only if $x = 5$ or $x = -2$.

18. a. $9x^2 - 16 = 0$

$9x^2 = 16$ Add 16.

$x^2 = \frac{16}{9}$ Divide by 9.

$x = \pm\frac{4}{3}$ Take square roots.

b. $25x^2 - 4 = 0$

$25x^2 = 4$ Add 4.

$x^2 = \frac{4}{25}$ Divide by 25.

$x = \pm\frac{2}{5}$ Take square roots.

19. In the equation $2x^2 + 3x - 5 = 0$, $a = 2$, $b = 3$, and $c = -5$. Substitute these values into the quadratic formula

$$x = \frac{-b \pm \sqrt{b^2 - 4ac}}{2a} \text{ to get}$$

$$x = \frac{-3 \pm \sqrt{3^2 - 4 \cdot 2(-5)}}{2 \cdot 2} = \frac{-3 \pm \sqrt{9 + 40}}{4}$$

$$= \frac{-3 \pm \sqrt{49}}{4} = \frac{-3 \pm 7}{4} = -\frac{10}{4} \text{ or } \frac{4}{4}$$

that is, $-\frac{5}{2}$ or 1. Thus, the solution set is

$\left\{-\frac{5}{2}, 1\right\}$.

20. Write the equation $x^2 - 2x = 2$, in the standard form $x^2 - 2x - 2 = 0$ with $a = 1$, $b = -2$, and $c = -2$. Substitute these values in the quadratic formula (see problem 18) to get

$$x = \frac{-(-2) \pm \sqrt{(-2)^2 - 4 \cdot 1 \cdot (-2)}}{2 \cdot 1}$$

$$= \frac{2 \pm \sqrt{4 + 8}}{2} = \frac{2 \pm \sqrt{12}}{2} = \frac{2 \pm 2\sqrt{3}}{2}$$

$$= 1 \pm \sqrt{3}$$

Thus, the solution set is $\left\{1 - \sqrt{3}, 1 + \sqrt{3}\right\}$.

21. Let x cm be the length of the shorter leg. Then the hypotenuse is of length $(x + 9)$ cm and the other leg is of length $(x + 7)$ cm. Thus,

$$(x + 9)^2 = x^2 + (x + 7)^2$$

$$x^2 + 18x + 81 = x^2 + x^2 + 14x + 49$$

$$0 = x^2 - 4x - 32$$

$$0 = (x - 8)(x + 4)$$

$$x = 8 \text{ or } x = -4$$

Since x must be positive, we discard the −4. If the shorter leg is 8 cm long, then the hypotenuse is 8 + 9 = 17 cm long and the other leg is 8 + 7 = 15 cm long. You can check that $17^2 = 8^2 + 15^2$.

22. Let m be the number of miles you could drive for a charge of $63. Then the required equation is

$$21 + 0.21m = 63$$

$$0.21m = 42 \qquad \text{Subtract 21.}$$

$$21m = 4200 \qquad \text{Multiply by 100.}$$

$$m = 200 \qquad \text{Divide by 21.}$$

200 miles could be driven for $63.

23. Let x and $x + 1$ be the integers. Then the required equation is

$$3(x + x + 1) = 45$$

$$3(2x + 1) = 45 \qquad \text{Simplify.}$$

$$2x + 1 = 15 \qquad \text{Divide by 3.}$$

$$2x = 14 \qquad \text{Subtract 1.}$$

$$x = 7 \qquad \text{Divide by 2.}$$

Thus, the two integers are 7 and 8. Check: $7 + 8 = 15$ and $3 \cdot 15 = 45$.

24. Let x and $x + 1$ be the integers.

$$12x > 9(x + 1)$$

$$12x > 9x + 9 \qquad \text{Simplify.}$$

$$3x > 9 \qquad \text{Subtract } 9x.$$

$$x > 3 \qquad \text{Divide by 3.}$$

Thus, the smaller integer must be greater than 3. Since the smallest such integer is 4, the two integers must be 4 and 5.
Check: $12 \cdot 4 = 48, 9 \cdot 5 = 45$ and $48 > 45$. That $x = 4$ is the smallest integer that satisfies the given condition is shown by trying $x = 3$. This gives $12 \cdot 3 = 36$, $9 \cdot 4 = 36$ so that $12 \cdot 3$ equals, but is not greater than, $9 \cdot 4$.

25. Let n be an odd number, then the next consecutive odd number is $n + 2$. Solve the equation $n(n + 2) = 10n - 7$.

$$n(n + 2) = 10n - 7$$

$$n^2 + 2n = 10n - 7 \qquad \text{Simplify.}$$

$$n^2 - 8n + 7 = 0 \qquad \text{Subtract } 10n \text{ and add 7.}$$

$$(n - 1)(n - 7) = 0 \qquad \text{Factor.}$$

$$n = 1 \text{ or } n = 7 \qquad \text{Solve.}$$

If $n = 1$, then the numbers are 1 and 3 or if $n = 7$, then the numbers are 7 and 9.

26. a. 801 to 688; 801:688; $\dfrac{801}{688}$

    b. $688 + 801 + 501 = 1990 = $ total number of stocks. So the ratio of losers to total number is $\dfrac{801}{1990}$.

27. a. $\dfrac{50}{8} = 6\dfrac{1}{4}$¢ per oz for the 8 oz box,

       $\dfrac{76}{12} = 6\dfrac{1}{3}$¢ per oz for the 12 oz box

    b. The 8 oz box is the better buy.

28. a. $\dfrac{x}{8} = \dfrac{9}{5}$

    b. Multiply both sides by 8 to get

       $x = \dfrac{72}{5} = 14.4$. So the second side is 14.4 ft long.

29. a. $C = kx^2$

b. Put $C = 100$ and $x = 150$ in the equation of part a to obtain

$100 = k(150)^2 = 22{,}500k$. Divide

both sides by 22,500 to get $k = \dfrac{1}{225}$.

c. Put $k = \dfrac{1}{225}$ and $x = 180$ in the equation of part a to get

$C = \dfrac{180^2}{225} = \dfrac{32400}{225} = 144$, so the cost is \$144 per hr.

30. a. $t = \dfrac{k}{I}$

b. Put $t = \dfrac{1}{30}$ and $I = 300$ in the equation of part a. This gives

$\dfrac{1}{30} = \dfrac{k}{300}$. Now multiply both sides by 300 to find $k = 10$.

c. Put $k = 10$ and $I = 600$ in the equation of part a to get $t = \dfrac{10}{600} = \dfrac{1}{60}$. Thus,

the correct exposure time is $\dfrac{1}{60}$ sec.

Chapter 7 Functions and Graphs

Section 7.1 Graphing Relations and Functions

1. The domain is the set of first numbers in the pairs of the relation: {1, 2, 3}. The range is the set of second numbers in these pairs: {2, 3, 4}.

2. The domain is the set of first numbers in the pairs of the relation: {1, 2, 3}. The range is the set of second numbers in these pairs: {1}.

3. The domain is the set of first numbers in the pairs of the relation: {1, 2, 3}. The range is the set of second numbers in these pairs: {1, 2, 3}.

4. The domain is the set of first numbers in the pairs of the relation: {4, 5, 6}. The range is the set of second numbers in these pairs: {1, 2}.

5. The domain is the set of x values: {x| x is a real number}. The range is the set of y values: {y| y is a real number}.

6. The domain is the set of x values: {x | x is a real number}. The range is the set of y values: {y | y is a real number}.

7. The domain is the set of x values: {x| x is a real number}. The range is the set of y values: {y| y is a real number}.

8. The domain is the set of x values: {x | x is a real number}. The range is the set of y values: {y | y is a real number}.

9. The domain is the set of x values: {x| x is a real number}. The range is the set of y values: {y| $y \geq 0$}.

10. The domain is the set of x values: {x | x is a real number}. The range is the set of y values: {y | y is a real number and $y \geq 2$}.

11. The domain is the set of x values: {x| $x > 0$}. The range is the set of y values: {y| y is a real number}.

12. The domain is the set of x values: {x | x is a real number and $x \geq 1$}. The range is the set of y values: {y | y is a real number}.

13. The domain is the set of x values: {x| $x \neq 0$}. The range is the set of y values: {y| $y \neq 0$}.

14. The domain is the set of x values: {x | x is a real number and $x \neq 2$}. The range is the set of y values: {y | y is a real number and $y \neq 0$}.

15. This is a function because one real value of y corresponds to each real value of x.

16. This is a function because one real value of y corresponds to each real value of x.

17. This is not a function, because two values of y correspond to each positive value of x. For instance, (4, 2) and (4, –2) both belong to this relation.

18. This is not a function. To each x greater than –1 in the domain, there correspond two values of y. For example, when $x = 3, y = \pm 2$.

19. This is a function. The domain is {x| $x \geq 0$}, and to each value of x in this domain there corresponds one y value, the nonnegative square root of the x-value.

20. This is a function. To each x in the domain, {x | $x \geq 0$}, there corresponds one value of y.

21. This is a function. The domain consists of the set of real numbers, and to each number in this domain there corresponds one y value, the cube root of x.

22. This is a function. To each real x, there corresponds one real y.

23. a. $f(0) = 3 \cdot 0 + 1 = 0 + 1 = 1$

    b. $f(2) = 3 \cdot 2 + 1 = 6 + 1 = 7$

    c. $f(-2) = 3(-2) + 1 = -6 + 1 = -5$

24. a. $g(0) = -2 \cdot 0 + 1 = 0 + 1 = 1$

    b. $g(1) = -2 \cdot 1 + 1 = -2 + 1 = -1$

    c. $g(-1) = -2 \cdot (-1) + 1 = 2 + 1 = 3$

25. a. $F(1) = \sqrt{1-1} = \sqrt{0} = 0$

    b. $F(5) = \sqrt{5-1} = \sqrt{4} = 2$

c. $F(26) = \sqrt{26-1} = \sqrt{25} = 5$

26. a. $G(0) = 0^2 + 2 \cdot 0 - 1 = 0 + 0 - 1 = -1$

b. $G(2) = 2^2 + 2 \cdot 2 - 1 = 4 + 4 - 1 = 7$

c. $G(-2) = (-2)^2 + 2(-2) - 1$
$= 4 - 4 - 1 = -1$

27. a. $f(x+h) = 3(x+h) + 1 = 3x + 3h + 1$

b. $f(x+h) - f(x)$
$= 3(x+h) + 1 - (3x+1)$
$= 3x + 3h + 1 - 3x - 1 = 3h$

c. $\dfrac{f(x+h) - f(x)}{h} = \dfrac{3h}{h} = 3$ for $h \neq 0$

28. $f(x) = \dfrac{1}{2}x$. The missing numbers are 15,

4.8, and $\dfrac{2}{7}$.

29. $g(x) = x^2$. The missing numbers are

$\dfrac{1}{16}, 4.41$, and ± 8.

30. a. $f(-1) = (-1)^3 - (-1)^2 + 2 \cdot (-1) = -4$

b. $f(-3) = (-3)^3 - (-3)^2 + 2 \cdot (-3) = -42$

c. $f(2) = 2^3 - 2^2 + 2 \cdot 2 = 8$

31. a. $g(0) = 2 \cdot 0^3 + 0^2 - 3 \cdot 0 + 1 = 1$

b. $g(-2) = 2(-2)^3 + (-2)^2 - 3(-2) + 1$
$= -16 + 4 + 6 + 1 = -5$

c. $g(2) = 2(2)^3 + (2)^2 - 3(2) + 1$
$= 16 + 4 - 6 + 1 = 15$

32.   a. Put $C = 15$ in the function

$F(C) = \dfrac{9}{5}C + 32$. This gives

$F(15) = \dfrac{9}{5}(15) + 32 = 59$. Thus, the
Farenheit temperature is 59°.

b. Put $C = 100$ in the function $F(C) = \dfrac{9}{5}C + 32$.

This gives $F(100) = \dfrac{9}{5}(100) + 32 = 212$.

Thus, the Fahrenheit temperature is 212°.

c. Put $C = -10$ in the function $F(C) = \dfrac{9}{5}C + 32$.

This gives $F(-10) = \dfrac{9}{5}(-10) + 32 = 14$.

Thus, $-10°$ C is $32 - 14 = 18°$ F below freezing.

d. Put $C = -273$ in the function $F(C) = \dfrac{9}{5}C + 32$.

This gives $F(-273) = \dfrac{9}{5}(-273) + 32 = -459.4$.

Thus, the temperature is $-459.4°$ F.

33.   a. Put $a = 50$ in the function
$U(a) = -a + 190$. This gives

$U(50) = -50 + 190 = 140$. Thus, the
upper limit is 140 beats per min.

b. Put $a = 60$ in the function
$U(a) = -a + 190$. This gives

$U(60) = -60 + 190 = 130$. Thus, the
upper limit is 130 beats per min.

34.   a. Put $a = 30$ in the function

$L(a) = -\dfrac{2}{3}a + 150$ and $U(a) = -a + 190$.

This gives $L(30) = -\dfrac{2}{3}(30) + 150 = 130$

$U(30) = -30 + 190 = 160$. Thus, the
target zone is $130 \leq R \leq 160$.

b. Put $a = 45$ in the function

$L(a) = -\dfrac{2}{3}a + 150$ and $U(a) = -a + 190$.

This gives $L(45) = -\dfrac{2}{3}(45) + 150 = 120$

$U(45) = -45 + 190 = 145$. Thus, the
target zone is $120 \leq R \leq 145$.

35. a.   Put $h = 70$ in the function
$w(h) = 5h - 190$. This gives

$w(70) = 5 \cdot 70 - 190 = 350 - 190 = 160$,
so his weight should be 160 lb.

b.   Put $w(h) = 200$ to get the equation

$200 = 5h - 190$. Then add 190 to both
sides to get $390 = 5h$. Now divide both
sides by 5 to find $h = 78$. Thus, his

height should be 78 in.

36. a. Put $m = 290$ in the function
$C(m) = 0.20m + 20$ to get
$C(290) = 0.20(290) + 20 = 78$. The
cost of renting the car is $78.

b. Put $C(m) = 60.60$ in the function
$C(m) = 0.20m + 20$ to get
$60.60 = 0.20(m) + 20$. Subtract 20 from
both sides, then divide by 0.20 to get
$m = 203$. The executive drove 203 mi.

37. a. Put $d = 10$ in the function $P(d) = 63.9d$
to get $P(10) = 63.9 \cdot 10 = 639$. The
pressure is 639 lb per sq ft.

b. Put $d = 100$ in the function
$P(d) = 63.9d$ to get
$P(100) = 63.9 \cdot 100 = 6390$. The
pressure is 6390 lb per sq ft.

38. a. Put $t = 2$ in the function $s(t) = 4.9t^2$ to get
$s(2) = 4.9(2)^2 = 19.6$. The distance the
ball falls is 19.6 m.

b. Put $t = 5$ in the function $s(t) = 4.9t^2$ to get
$s(5) = 4.9(5)^2 = 122.5$. The distance the ball
falls is 122.5 m.

39. $S(t) = \dfrac{1}{2}gt^2 = \dfrac{1}{2} \cdot 32t^2 = 16t^2$

a. $S(3) = 16 \cdot 3^2 = 16 \cdot 9 = 144$ ft

b. $S(5) = 16 \cdot 5^2 = 16 \cdot 25 = 400$ ft

40. Put $S(t) = 64.4$ and $t = 2$ in $S(t) = \dfrac{1}{2}gt^2$ to get
$64.4 = \dfrac{1}{2}g(2)^2$ Solving for g: $g = 32.2$ ft/sec^2.

41. The table of values and the graph for the
relation $\{(x, y) | y = x, x$ an integer
between -1 and 4, inclusive$\}$.

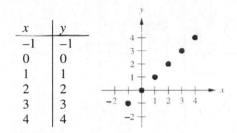

x	y
−1	−1
0	0
1	1
2	2
3	3
4	4

42. The table of values and the graph for the relation
$\{(x, y) | y = -x, x$ an integer between -1
and 4, inclusive$\}$

x	y
−1	1
0	0
1	−1
2	−2
3	−3
4	−4

43. The table of values and the graph for the
relation $\{(x, y) | y = 2x + 1, x$ an integer
between 0 and 5, inclusive$\}$.

x	y
0	1
1	3
2	5
3	7
4	9
5	11

44. The table of values and the graph for the
relation $\{(x, y) | x + 2y = 3, x$ an odd integer
between 0 and 10$\}$.

x	y
1	1
3	0
5	−1
7	−2
9	−3

45. The table of values and the graph for the
relation $\{(x, y) | 2x - y = 4, x$ an integer
between -2 and 2, inclusive$\}$.

x	y
-2	-8
-1	-6
0	-4
1	-2
2	0

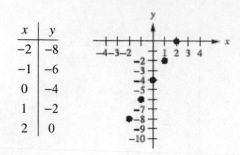

46. The table of values and the graph for the relation $\{(x,y)\mid y = x^2, x \text{ an integer between } -3 \text{ and } 3, \text{inclusive}\}$.

x	y
-3	9
-2	4
-1	1
0	0
1	1
2	4
3	9

47. The table of values and the graph for the relation
$\{(x,y)\mid y = \sqrt{x}, x = 0,1,4,9,16,25,36\}$.

x	y
0	0
1	1
4	2
9	3
16	4
25	5
36	6

48. The table of values and the graph for the relation $\{(x,y)\mid x = \sqrt{y}, x \text{ an integer between } 0 \text{ and } 3, \text{inclusive}\}$.

x	y
0	0
1	1
2	4
3	9

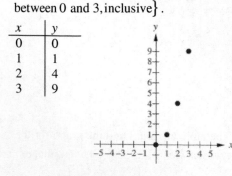

49. The table of values and the graph for the relation
$\{(x,y)\mid x + y < 5, x, y \text{ nonnegative integers}\}$.

x	$0 < y < 5 - x$
0	0,1,2,3,4
1	0,1,2,3
2	0,1,2
3	0,1
4	0

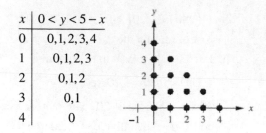

50. The table of values and the graph for the relation $\{(x,y)\mid y > x, x \text{ and } y \text{ positive integers less than } 4\}$.

x	$y > x$
1	2, 3
2	3
3	

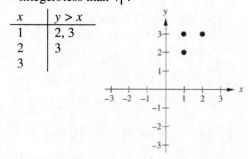

51. The table of values and the graph for the function given by $f(x) = x + 1$, x an integer between -3 and 3, inclusive.

x	$f(x) = x + 1$
-3	-2
-2	-1
-1	0
0	1
1	2
2	3
3	4

52. The table of values and the graph for the function given by $f(x) = 3x - 1$, x an integer between -1 and 3, inclusive.

x	$f(x) = 3x - 1$
-1	-4
0	-1
1	2
2	5
3	8

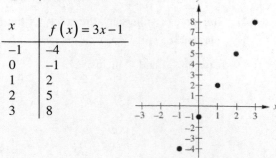

53. The table of values and the graph for the function given by $g(x) = x^2 + 1$, x an integer between -3 and 3, inclusive.

x	$g(x) = x^2 + 1$
-3	10
-2	5
-1	2
0	1
1	2
2	5
3	10

54. The table of values and the graph for the function given by $g(x) = -x^2$, x an integer between -3 and 3, inclusive.

x	$f(x) = 3x - 1$
-3	-9
-2	-4
-1	-1
0	0
1	-1
2	-4
3	-9

55. a. $h(x) = 2.89x + 70.64$

    b. $h(34) = 2.89(34) + 70.64 = 168.9$, so the height was about 169 cm.

56. a. $c(h) = 25h + 30$ b. $80; $105; $130

    c.

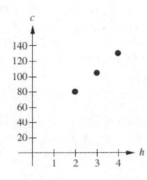

57. a. Let m be monthly data allowance and f be monthly access fee. The table of values and the graph for the data plan is

m	f
75-0.1	10
2	30
5	50
10	80

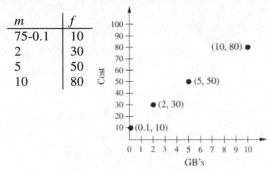

The graph is not a step function.

b. The access fee is $50 if you use 5 GB.

c. No, you cannot determine the fee for 8 GB.

d. The monthly allowance of 5 GB has a monthly access fee of $50. The access fee for 8 GB is determined by adding $10 for each GB over 5 GB, which is $8 - 5 = 3$ GB, to the monthly access fee of $50: $50 + 3(10) = 80. For 8.6 GB, we have $8.6 - 5 = 3.6$ GB and since even a fraction will incur an additional $10, the monthly access fee is $50 + 4(10) = 90.

58. a. Put $n = 100$ in the equation $u(n) = 504,000n$ to get $u(100) = 504,000(100) = 50,400,000$ gal spilled in 100 days.

    b. For a leak of 1.05 million gal per day, the function is $o(n) = 1.05n$ million gal per day.

    c. Put $n = 60$ in the function $o(n) = 1.05n$ to get $o(60) = 1.05(60) = 63$. Thus, there were 63 million gal spilled in 60 days.

59. a. Put $n = 100$ in the function $b(n) = 2.520n$ to get $b(100) = 2.520(100) = 252$. Thus, there were 252 million gal spilled in 100 days.

    b. For a leak of 4.2 million gal per day, the function is $e(n) = 4.2n$ million gal per day.

    c. Put $n = 60$ in the function $e(n) = 4.2n$ to get $e(60) = 4.2(60) = 252$. Thus, there were 252 million gal spilled in 60 days.

60. a. For a recovery of 441,000 gal per day, the function is $r(n) = 441,000n$ gal per day.

    b. Put $n = 60$ in the function $r(n) = 441,000n$ to get $r(60) = 441,000(60) = 26,460,000$. Thus, there were 26,460,000 gal recovered in 60 days.

61. a. Write the function $b(n) = 2.520n$ million gal per day as $b(n) = 2,520,000n$ gal. The actual amount of oil that spilled daily is

$$a(n) = 2,520,000n - 441,000n$$
$$= 2,079,000n \text{ gal per day.}$$

b. Put $n = 60$ in the function $a(n) = 2,079,000n$ to get

$$a(n) = 2,079,000(60) = 124,740,000.$$

Thus, there were 124,740,000 gal spilled in 60 days.

62. Answers may vary. $x = -1$ and $x = 1$. These values would result in a zero denominator.

63. Answers may vary. $g(x) = \sqrt{x-1}$ is real if and only if $x - 1 \geq 0$, that is, if $x \geq 1$. Thus, we would exclude all values of x less than 1 if g is to have real values.

64. Answers may vary. $h(x) = \dfrac{x}{\sqrt{x+1}}$ is real if and only if $x + 1 > 0$, that is, if $x > -1$. Thus, we would exclude all values of x less than or equal to -1, $x \leq -1$, if h is to have real values.

65. Answers may vary. The graph of a function $f(x)$ is a picture of the set of points $\{(x, y) \mid y = f(x), x \text{ an element of the domain of } f\}$.

66. Answers may vary. No. A relation is any set of ordered pairs. A function is a relation such that for every element in the domain there is exactly one corresponding element in the range. For example, since $(4, 2)$ and $(4, -2)$ both belong to the relation $x = y^2$, this relation is not a function.

67. Answers may vary. Yes. A function is a relation in which there is exactly one value of y for each value of x in the domain.

68. Answers may vary. Because if a vertical line intersects the graph at more than one point, it means that for a particular x there is more than one y, and thus the graph is not the graph of a function.

69. Notice that if the units digit in the temperature reading is multiplied by 4, the result is the number of chirps per minute. Thus, the desired function is

$$c = f(x) = 4(x - 40), \text{ where } x \text{ is the}$$

temperature in degrees Fahrenheit.

70. Put $x = 80$ in the function $f(x) = 4(x - 40)$ to get $f(80) = 4(80 - 40) = 160$. Thus, when the temperature is $80°$F, there are 160 chirps per minute.

71. The table shows that the distance in feet is given by multiplying the square of the time (in sec) by 16. Thus, the desired function is $f(t) = 16t^2$.

72. Put $t = 10$ in the function $f(t) = 16t^2$ to get $f(t) = 16(10)^2 = 1600$. Thus, the height of the helicopter is 1600 ft.

73. For each table entry, the number of seconds is the square root of the number of units of length, so the suggested rule is $f(x) = \sqrt{x}$.

74. If $f(x) = \sqrt{x} = 6$, then, squaring both sides of $\sqrt{x} = 6$, we obtain $x = 6^2 = 36$. Thus, the length would be 36 units, or since 1 unit is about 25 cm, the length is about 900 cm.

75. If $f(x) = \sqrt{x} = 100$, then, squaring both sides of $\sqrt{x} = 100$, we obtain $x = 100^2 = 10,000$. Thus, the length would be 10,000 units, or since 1 unit is about 25 cm, the length is about 250,000 cm.

76. If $f(x) = \sqrt{x} = 7$, then, squaring both sides of $\sqrt{x} = 7$, we obtain $x = 7^2 = 49$. Thus, the length would be 49 units, or since 1 unit is about 25 cm, the length is about 1225 cm.

Collaborative Learning

1. Kitchen

2. Extend the axes and the lines and approximate the point of intersection. Yes, but since the points are not on a line, it

would not be a good approximation. The choice of points (both how many and which) would yield varying answers.

3. Answers will vary.   4. Answers will vary.

Section 7.2 Linear Functions, Relations, and Applications

1. According to the table, when $x = 3$,

$y = 2\dfrac{1}{4} = 2.25$ and $y = ax$. Thus, $2.25 = 3a$

and $a = 0.75 = \dfrac{3}{4}$. Now, $y = ax = \dfrac{3}{4}x$.

If $y = 3$, then $3 = \dfrac{3}{4}x$, so that $x = 4$.

2. According to the table, when $x = 1$,

$y = 2$ and $y = ax^2$. Thus, $2 = 1^2 a$

and $a = 2$. Now, $y = ax^2 = 2x^2$. If $y = 50$,

then $50 = 2x^2$, so that $x = 5$.

3. Since $f(x) = 3x + 6$, $f(0) = 6$ and

$f(-2) = 0$. Thus, (0, 6) and (-2, 0) are two

points on the line. Graph these points and draw the line through them, as shown on the graph:

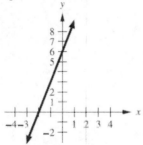

4. Since $f(x) = 2x + 5$, $f(0) = 5$ and

$f\left(-\dfrac{5}{2}\right) = 0$. Thus, (0, 5) and $\left(-\dfrac{5}{2}, 0\right)$ are

two points on the line. Graph these points and draw the line through them, as shown on the graph:

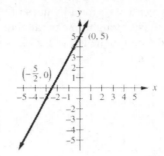

5. Since $f(x) = 3$ for all values of x, the

graph is a straight line parallel to the x-axis and 3 units above this axis as shown in the figure:

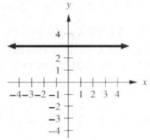

6. Since $f(x) = -2$ for all values of x, the graph is a straight line parallel to the x-axis and 2 units below this axis as shown in the figure:

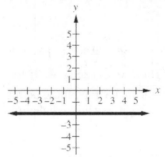

7. Here we are given $x = -1$ for all values of y. Thus, the graph is a straight line parallel to the y-axis and 1 unit to the left of this axis as shown in the figure:

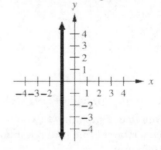

8. Here we are given $x = -1$ for all values of y.
    Thus, the graph is a straight line parallel to
    the y-axis and 1 unit to the left of this axis as
    shown in the figure:

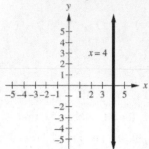

9. Since $f(x) = -x + 2$, then $f(0) = 2$ and
    $f(2) = 0$. Thus, (0, 2) and (2, 0) are two
    points on the line. Graph these points and
    draw the straight line through them as in the
    figure:

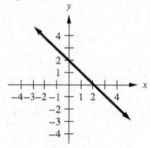

10. Since $f(x) = -2x - 4$, then $f(0) = -4$ and
    $f(-2) = 0$. Thus, (0, –4) and (–2, 0) are
    two points on the line. Graph these points
    and draw the straight line through them as in
    the figure:

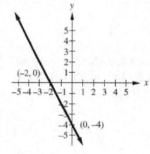

11. With $g(x) = -3x - 6$, we get $g(0) = -6$
    and $g(-2) = 0$. So (0, –6) and (–2, 0) are
    two points on the line. Graph these two
    points and draw a straight line through them
    as shown in the figure:

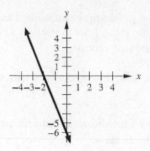

12. With $g(x) = -2x + 6$, we get $g(0) = 6$
    and $g(3) = 0$. So (0, 6) and (3, 0) are two
    points on the line. Graph these two points
    and draw a straight line through them
    as shown in the figure:

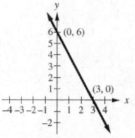

13. The equation $3x + 2y = 6$ is satisfied by the
    pairs (0, 3) and (2, 0), so these are two
    points on the line. Graph these points and
    draw the straight line through them as in the
    figure:

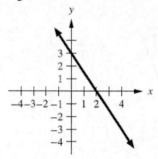

14. The equation $4x + 3y = 12$ is satisfied by the
    pairs (0, 4) and (3, 0), so these are two
    points on the line. Graph these points and
    draw the straight line through them as in the
    figure:

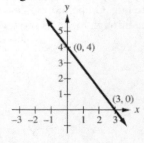

15. The equation $-2x + 3y = 6$ is satisfied by the pairs $(0, 2)$ and $(-3, 0)$, so these are two points on the line. Graph these points and draw the straight line through them as in the figure:

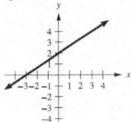

16. The equation $-3x + 2y = 12$ is satisfied by the pairs $(0, 6)$ and $(-4, 0)$, so these are two points on the line. Graph these points and draw the straight line through them as in the figure:

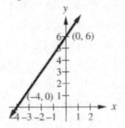

17. Two of the solutions of the equation $4x - 3y = 12$ are $(3, 0)$ and $(0, -4)$, and these are two points on the graph. Graph these two points and draw the straight line through them as shown in the figure:

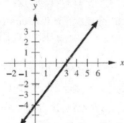

18. Two of the solutions of the equation $3x - 5y = 15$ are $(5, 0)$ and $(0, -3)$, and these are two points on the graph. Graph these two points and draw the straight line through them as shown in the figure:

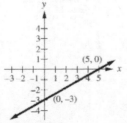

19. $d = \sqrt{(-1-2)^2 + (0-4)^2}$

   $= \sqrt{(-3)^2 + (-4)^2} = \sqrt{9 + 16} = \sqrt{25}$

   $= 5$ units

20. $= \sqrt{(-5)^2 + (-12)^2} = \sqrt{25 + 144} = \sqrt{169}$

   $= 13$ units

21. $d = \sqrt{(-1-(-4))^2 + (3-(-5))^2}$

   $= \sqrt{(3)^2 + (8)^2} = \sqrt{9 + 64} = \sqrt{73}$

   ≈ 8.54 units

22. $d = \sqrt{(5-(-2))^2 + (7-3)^2}$

   $= \sqrt{7^2 + 4^2} = \sqrt{49 + 16} = \sqrt{65}$

   ≈ 8.06 units

23. $d = \sqrt{(1-4)^2 + (-1-(-8))^2}$

   $= \sqrt{(-3)^2 + 7^2} = \sqrt{9 + 49} = \sqrt{58}$

   ≈ 7.62 units

24. $d = \sqrt{(-2-6)^2 + (-2-(-4))^2}$

   $= \sqrt{(-8)^2 + 2^2} = \sqrt{64 + 4} = \sqrt{68}$

   ≈ 8.25 units

25. These points are on a line parallel to the y-axis, so the distance is

   $d = |y_2 - y_1| = |-2 - 0| = 2$ units

26. These points are on a line parallel to the x-axis, so the distance is

   $d = |x_2 - x_1| = |4 - 6| = 2$ units

27. These points are on a line parallel to the y-axis, so the distance is

   $d = |y_2 - y_1| = |7 - 3| = 4$ units

28. These points are on a line parallel to the x-axis, so the distance is

   $d = |x_2 - x_1| = |1 - 8| = 7$ units

29. a. $E(x) = 500 + 25x;\ S(x) = 1000 + 20x$

b.

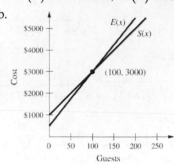

c. The two lines in the graph intersect at (100, 3000). This point checks in both equations. Thus, the cost is the same for 100 persons.

30. a.

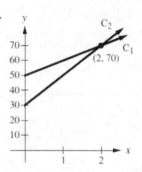

b. 2 hours

31. a. Refer to the table:
    $m(2) = \$30; m(5) = \$50$

b. The monthly access fee would be the base $m(2) = \$30$ and $d = 3$, 1 unit past the allowance for 2 GB, so fee of $10. Thus for $2 < d \le 3$,
    $m(d) = \$30 + \$10 = \$40.$

c. The monthly access fee would be the base $m(2) = \$30$ plus d = 4, 2 units past the allowance for 2 GB. For $3 < d \le 4$,
    $m(d) = \$30 + 2(\$10) = \$50.$

d. The monthly access fee would be the base $m(2) = \$30$ plus d = 5, 3 units past the allowance for 2 GB. For $4 < d < 5$,
    $m(d) = \$30 + 3(\$10) = \$60.$

    (The economical choice for this customer would have been to choose the 5GB plan.)

e.

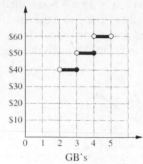

32. a. Refer to the table: $m(10) = \$80$

b. The monthly access fee would be the base $m(5) = \$50$ and $d = 6$, 1 unit past the allowance for 5 GB, so fee of $10. Thus for $5 < d \le 6$,
    $m(d) = \$50 + \$10 = \$60.$

c. The monthly access fee would be the base $m(5) = \$50$ and $d = 7$, 2 units past the allowance for 5 GB. Thus for $6 < d \le 7$, $m(d) = \$50 + 2(\$10) = \$70.$

d. The monthly access fee would be the base $m(5) = \$50$ and $d = 8$, 3 units past the allowance for 5 GB. Thus for $7 < d \le 8$, $m(d) = \$50 + 3(\$10) = \$80.$

e. The monthly access fee would be the base $m(5) = \$50$ and $d = 9$, 4 units past the allowance for 5 GB. Thus for $8 < d \le 9$, $m(d) = \$50 + 4(\$10) = \$90.$

   (The economical choice for this customer would have been to choose the 10 GB plan.)

f. The monthly access fee would be the base $m(5) = \$50$ and $d = 10$, 5 units past the allowance for 5 GB. Thus for $9 < d < 10$, $m(d) = \$50 + 5(\$10)$
    $= \$100.$ (The economical choice for this customer would have been to choose the 10 GB plan.)

g.

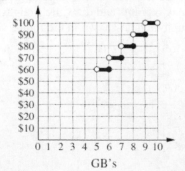

33. Yes. The distance d from $(2, -3)$ to $(-2, 3)$
    is: $\sqrt{(-2-2)^2 + (3-(-3))^2} = \sqrt{(-4)^2 + 6^2}$
    $= \sqrt{16+36} = \sqrt{52} < \sqrt{64} = 8 < 10$ mi

34. The distance d from $(-3, 5)$ to $(2, 7)$ is:
    $\sqrt{(-3-2)^2 + (5-7)^2} = \sqrt{(-5)^2 + (-2)^2}$
    $= \sqrt{25+4} = \sqrt{29} > \sqrt{25} = 5$ mi
    $\sqrt{29} > 5$, so you are not in the evacuation zone.

35. a. On the graph, find the year on the horizontal axis and move up to the red line representing Tobacco Products. The percent of users in 2002 is 30.4%. The percent of users in 2009 is 27.7%.
    b. For the year 2002, the number of years after 2002 is 0. So,
    $$P(0) = -0.3(0) + 30 = 30\%.$$
    For the year 2009, the number of years after 2002 is 7. So,
    $$P(7) = -0.3(7) + 30 = 27.9\%.$$
    c. For the year 2012, the number of years after 2002 is 10. So,
    $$P(10) = -0.3(10) + 30 = 27\%.$$
    d. Put $P(t) = 24$ in the equation
    $P(t) = -0.3t + 30$ to get
    $24 = -0.3t + 30$. Subtract 30, then divide by -0.3 to find $t = 20$. Thus, 20 years after 2002, the year 2022, is when the percent will reach 24%.

36. a. Put $a = 18$ in the equation
    $P(a) = 7a - 63$ to get
    $P(a) = 7(18) - 63 = 63$. The percent of 18-year-olds who use text messaging is 63%.
    b. Put $a = 19$ in the equation
    $P(a) = 7a - 63$ to get
    $P(a) = 7(19) - 63 = 70$. The percent of 19- year-olds who use text messaging is 70%.
    c. It increases by 7% per year.
    d. From the graph, about 13%. It does not fit the pattern for this age group.

37. a., c. The graph for the given data and for $y = V$ and $y = M$ are shown:

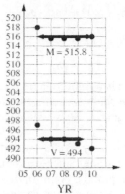

$y = M$ models the data very well; $y = V$ does not model the data as well, since the verbal is constantly decreasing but with one exception.

b. The average verbal score V is:
$$\frac{497 + 494 + 494 + 493 + 492}{5} = 494$$
The average math score M is:
$$\frac{518 + 515 + 515 + 515 + 516}{5} = 515.8$$

d. Yes, they are functions. You can tell by using the vertical line test (any vertical line touches the graph only once).

38. a., c.

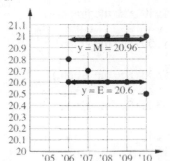

b. The average English score E is:
$$\frac{20.6 + 20.7 + 20.6 + 20.6 + 20.5}{5} = 20.6$$
The average math score M is:
$$\frac{20.8 + 21 + 21 + 21 + 21}{5} = 20.96$$

d. Yes, they are functions. You can tell by using the vertical line test (any vertical line touches the graph only once).

39. Answers may vary. Use the distance formula to find the square of the length of each side of the triangle:

$$(AB)^2 = (a_1 - b_1)^2 + (a_2 - b_2)^2$$

$$(AC)^2 = (a_1 - c_1)^2 + (a_2 - c_2)^2$$

$$(BC)^2 = (b_1 - c_1)^2 + (b_2 - c_2)^2$$

The triangle is a right triangle if and only if one of these squares equals the sum of the other two squares. So we can check this.

40. Answers may vary. We know that the graph is a horizontal line. Since $y = b$ for all values of x, we can plot the point $(0, b)$ and (a, b), where a is any convenient value of x. Then draw the straight line through $(0, b)$ and (a, b). The graph is a line parallel to the x-axis and b units from that axis.

41. Answers may vary. See the Problem Solving procedure following Example 1 and follow it step by step for $x = c$.

42. Answers may vary. Let $x = 0$ to get the point $(0, b)$. Then let $f(x) = 0$ to get the point $\left(-\dfrac{b}{a}, 0\right)$. Plot these two points and draw the straight line through them for the desired graph.

43. About \$940 (See the graph.)

44. About \$600 (See the graph.)

45. About \$800 (See the graph.)

46. About \$300 (See the graph.)

For problems 47–58, see the solutions to the corresponding exercises above.

Calculator Corner

1. Steps may vary due to type of calculator used to solve the problem.
Problem 19:

$\boxed{\sqrt{\ }}\ \boxed{(}\ \boxed{(}\ \boxed{-1}\ \boxed{-}\ \boxed{2}\ \boxed{)}\ \boxed{x^2}\ \boxed{+}\ \boxed{(}\ \boxed{0}\ \boxed{-}\ \boxed{4}\ \boxed{)}\ \boxed{x^2}\ \boxed{)}$

$\boxed{\text{ENTER}}$ Answer: 5

Problem 21:

$\boxed{\sqrt{\ }}\ \boxed{(}\ \boxed{(}\ \boxed{-1}\ \boxed{-}\ \boxed{(-)}\ \boxed{4}\ \boxed{)}\ \boxed{x^2}\ \boxed{+}\ \boxed{(}\ \boxed{3}\ \boxed{-}\ \boxed{(-)}\ \boxed{5}\ \boxed{x^2}\ \boxed{)}$

$\boxed{\text{ENTER}}$ Answer: 8.54

Problem 23:

$\boxed{\sqrt{\ }}\ \boxed{(}\ \boxed{(}\ \boxed{1}\ \boxed{-}\ \boxed{4}\ \boxed{)}\ \boxed{x^2}\ \boxed{+}\ \boxed{(}\ \boxed{-1}\ \boxed{-}\ \boxed{(-)}\ \boxed{8}\ \boxed{)}\ \boxed{x^2}$

$\boxed{\text{ENTER}}$ Answer: 7.62

Problem 25:

$\boxed{\sqrt{\ }}\ \boxed{(}\ \boxed{(}\ \boxed{3}\ \boxed{-}\ \boxed{3}\ \boxed{)}\ \boxed{x^2}\ \boxed{+}\ \boxed{(}\ \boxed{-2}\ \boxed{-}\ \boxed{0}\ \boxed{)}\ \boxed{x^2}\ \boxed{)}\ \boxed{\text{ENTER}}$

Answer: 2

Problem 27:

$\boxed{\sqrt{\ }}\ \boxed{(}\ \boxed{(}\ \boxed{-2}\ \boxed{-}\ \boxed{(-)}\ \boxed{2}\ \boxed{)}\ \boxed{x^2}\ \boxed{+}\ \boxed{(}\ \boxed{7}\ \boxed{-}\ \boxed{3}\ \boxed{)}\ \boxed{x^2}\ \boxed{)}$

$\boxed{\text{ENTER}}$ Answer: 4

Section 7.3 Slopes and Equations of a Line

1. $m = \dfrac{y_2 - y_1}{x_2 - x_1} = \dfrac{4 - 2}{3 - 1} = \dfrac{2}{2} = 1$

2. $m = \dfrac{y_2 - y_1}{x_2 - x_1} = \dfrac{-2 - (-4)}{1 - (-3)} = \dfrac{2}{4} = \dfrac{1}{2}$

3. $m = \dfrac{y_2 - y_1}{x_2 - x_1} = \dfrac{0 - 5}{5 - 0} = \dfrac{-5}{5} = -1$

4. $m = \dfrac{y_2 - y_1}{x_2 - x_1} = \dfrac{-6 - (-6)}{3 - 5} = \dfrac{0}{-2} = 0$

5. $m = \dfrac{y_2 - y_1}{x_2 - x_1} = \dfrac{-4 - (-3)}{7 - (-1)} = \dfrac{-1}{8} = -\dfrac{1}{8}$

6. $m = \dfrac{y_2 - y_1}{x_2 - x_1} = \dfrac{-5 - (-6)}{-2 - (-1)} = \dfrac{1}{-1} = -1$

7. $m = \dfrac{y_2 - y_1}{x_2 - x_1} = \dfrac{3 - 0}{12 - 0} = \dfrac{3}{12} = \dfrac{1}{4}$

8. $m = \dfrac{y_2 - y_1}{x_2 - x_1} = \dfrac{-1 - (-10)}{-1 - (-10)} = \dfrac{9}{9} = 1$

9. $m = \dfrac{y_2 - y_1}{x_2 - x_1} = \dfrac{5 - 5}{-2 - 3} = \dfrac{0}{-5} = 0$

10. $m = \dfrac{y_2 - y_1}{x_2 - x_1} = \dfrac{-3 - (-3)}{4 - 2} = \dfrac{0}{2} = 0$

11. Use the point-slope form $y - y_1 = m(x - x_1)$ to get:

$$y - 2 = \frac{1}{2}(x - 1)$$

$$y - 2 = \frac{1}{2}x - \frac{1}{2}$$

$$y = \frac{1}{2}x + \frac{3}{2}$$

12. Use the point-slope form $y - y_1 = m(x - x_1)$

to get: $y - (-2) = -2(x - (-1))$

$$y + 2 = -2x - 2$$

$$y = -2x - 4$$

13. Use the point-slope form $y - y_1 = m(x - x_1)$

to get: $y - 4 = -1(x - 2)$

$$y - 4 = -1x + 2$$

$$y = -x + 6$$

14. Use the point-slope form $y - y_1 = m(x - x_1)$

to get: $y - 1 = \frac{3}{2}(x - (-3))$

$$y - 1 = \frac{3}{2}x + \frac{9}{2}$$

$$y = \frac{3}{2}x + \frac{11}{2}$$

15. Use the point-slope form $y - y_1 = m(x - x_1)$ to get:

$$y - 5 = 0(x - 4)$$

$$y - 5 = 0$$

$$y = 5$$

16. Has no slope-intercept form. ($x = 3$ is the simplest form.)

17. By comparing $y = x + 2$ with the equation $y = mx + b$, where m is the slope and b the y-intercept we find that:
    a. $m = 1$ b. $b = 2$

18. Solve $2x + y = 3$ for y. Compare $y = -2x + 3$ with the equation $y = mx + b$, where m is the slope and b the y-intercept we find that:
    a. $m = -2$ b. $b = 3$

19. First solve $3y = 4x$ for y to get $y = \frac{4}{3}x$ then compare with $y = mx + b$, where m is the slope and b the y-intercept to find:
    a. $m = \frac{4}{3}$ b. $b = 0$

20. First solve $2y = x + 4$ for y to get $y = \frac{1}{2}x + 2$ then compare with $y = mx + b$, where m is the slope and b the y-intercept to find:
    a. $m = \frac{1}{2}$ b. $b = 2$

21. First solve $x + y = 14$ for y to get $y = -x + 14$ then compare with $y = mx + b$ to find:
    a. $m = -1$ b. $b = 14$

22. Solve $y - 4x = 8$ for y. Compare $y = 4x + 8$ with the equation $y = mx + b$, where m is the slope and b the y-intercept we find that:
    a. $m = 4$ b. $b = 8$

23. Compare the equation $y = 6$ with $y = mx + b$ to find:
    a. $m = 0$ b. $b = 6$

24. Solve $2y = 16$ for y. Compare $y = 8$ with the equation $y = mx + b$, where m is the slope and b the y-intercept we find that:
    a. $m = 0$ b. $b = 8$

25. The line whose equation is $x = 3$ is parallel to the y-axis. Thus,
    a. The slope is not defined.
    b. The line does not intersect the y-axis.

26. Solve $3x = -6y + 9$ for y. Compare $y = -\frac{1}{2}x + \frac{3}{2}$ with the equation $y = mx + b$, where m is the slope and b the y-intercept we find that:
    a. $m = -\frac{1}{2}$ b. $b = \frac{3}{2}$

27. For the line through the points $(1, -1)$ and $(2, 2)$, find the slope:

$$m = \frac{2 - (-1)}{2 - 1} = \frac{3}{1} = 3$$

Then use the point-slope form to get:

$$y - (-1) = 3(x - 1)$$
$$y + 1 = 3x - 3$$
$$3x - y = 4$$

28. For the line through the points (–3, –4) and (–2, 0), find the slope:
$$m = \frac{0 - (-4)}{-2 - (-3)} = \frac{4}{1} = 4$$
Then use the point-slope form to get:
$$y - (-4) = 4(x - (-3))$$
$$y + 4 = 4(x + 3)$$
$$4x - y = -8$$

29. For the line through the points (3, 2) and (2, 3), find the slope:
$$m = \frac{3 - 2}{2 - 3} = \frac{1}{-1} = -1$$
Then use the point-slope form to get:
$$y - 2 = -1(x - 3)$$
$$y - 2 = -x + 3$$
$$x + y = 5$$

30. For the line through the points (3, 0) and (0, 5), find the slope:
$$m = \frac{5 - 0}{0 - 3} = \frac{5}{-3} = -\frac{5}{3}$$
Then use the point-slope form to get:
$$y - 0 = -\frac{5}{3}(x - 3)$$
$$y = -\frac{5}{3}x + 5$$
$$5x + 3y = 15$$

31. For the line through the points (0, 0) and (1, 10), find the slope:
$$m = \frac{10 - 0}{1 - 0} = \frac{10}{1} = 10$$
Then use the point-slope form to get:
$$y - 0 = 10(x - 0)$$
$$y = 10x$$
$$10x - y = 0$$

32. For the line through the points (–4, –1) and (–4, 3), find the slope:

$$m = \frac{-1 + 3}{-4 - (-4)} = \frac{0}{0} \text{ undefined}$$
There is no slope, so use $x = c$: $x = -4$

33. Use the first two entries of the table: (62, 134) and (63,139) to find the slope m, then with h in place of x and w in place of y, substitute in the point-slope form for the line and solve for w:
$$m = \frac{139 - 134}{63 - 62} = \frac{5}{1} = 5$$
$$w - 134 = 5(h - 62)$$
$$w - 134 = 5h - 310$$
$$w = 5h - 176$$

34. Use the first two entries of the table: (62, 98) and (63, 102) to find the slope m, then with h in place of x and w in place of y, substitute in the point-slope form for the line and solve for w:
$$m = \frac{102 - 98}{63 - 62} = \frac{4}{1} = 4$$
$$w - 98 = 4(h - 62)$$
$$w - 98 = 4h - 248$$
$$w = 4h - 150$$

35. Use the first two entries of the table: (62, 123) and (63,128) to find the slope m, then with h in place of x and w in place of y, substitute in the point-slope form for the line and solve for w: $m = \frac{128 - 123}{63 - 62} = \frac{5}{1} = 5$
$$w - 123 = 5(h - 62)$$
$$w - 123 = 5h - 310$$
$$w = 5h - 187$$

36. Put h = 183 in the equation $w = 5h - 187$.
$$183 = 5h - 187$$
$$370 = 5h$$
$$h = 74$$
Divide 74 inches by 12 to get 6 ft 2 in.

37. The cost C is 2 dollars for the first mile and $1.70 for each additional mile. That is:
$$C = 2 + 1.70(m - 1) = 2 + 1.70m - 1.70$$
$$= 1.70m + 0.30$$
For $m = 30, C = 1.70(30) + 0.30 = \$51.30.$

38. The cost C is 3 dollars for the first mile and $1.50 for each additional mile. That is:

$$C = 3 + 1.50(m-1) = 3 + 1.50m - 1.50$$

$$= 1.50m + 1.50$$

For $m = 10, C = 1.50(10) + 1.50 = \$16.50$.

Compare the costs for this taxicab company and the company from problem 37. For problem 37 company, the cost would be

$m = 50, C = 1.70(50) + 0.30 = \$85.30$.

For this company, $m = 50$,

$$C = 1.50(50) + 1.50 = \$76.50.$$

This company would be cheaper if driving 50 miles.

39. From problem 37: $C = 1.70m + 0.30$
From problem 38: $C = 1.50m + 1.50$
If the cost C is the same:
$$1.70m + 0.30 = 1.50m + 1.50$$

$$0.20m + 0.30 = 1.50$$

$$0.20m = 1.20$$

$$m = 6 \text{ miles}$$

40. Find the cost of the initial mile a by putting $C = 32$ and $m = 20$ into the equation $C = a + 1.50m$.

$$32 = a + 1.50(20)$$

$$32 = a + 30$$

$$2 = a$$

Now, replace $a = 2.00$ in the equation $C = 1.5m + 2.00$.
For a 30-mi ride:

$$C = 1.5(30) + 2.00$$

$$C = 47$$

The cost of a 30-mi ride is $47.

41. a. The cost of the first mile is $2.
    b. After the first mile, you travel $m - 1$ miles.
    c. The cost per mile after the first mile is $1.70.
    d. The cost of the miles beyond the first is $C = 1.70(m-1)$.

    e. $C = 1.70(m-1) + 2$

    $= 1.70m - 1.70 + 2 = 1.70m + 0.30$
    Yes, this is the same as the answer to problem 37.

42. The cost of New York fares are $C = 1.50m + 2.00$. This is the same answer as in problem 40.

43. Since the cost C is equal to the rental fee R plus $2 for each minute m, we get:
$C = R + 2m$.
Knowing that cost was $C = \$175$ and $60 = m$ minutes were used, we get:
$$175 = R + 2 \cdot 60$$

$$175 = R + 120$$

$$55 = R$$
For $R = 55$, $C = R + 2m$ becomes
$C = 55 + 2m$ or $C = 2m + 55$.

44. a. The formula for long-distance calls to New York is $C = 7.8m$.
    b. Substitute the rental fee $175 from problem 43 to get $175 = 7.8m$.
    Solve for m: $7.8m = 175$
    $$m = \frac{175}{7.8} \approx 22$$
    Use about 22 min in order to have the same charges as in problem 43.

45. To find the slopes, compare with the slope-intercept form $y = mx + b$: For $y = 2x + 5$, $m = 2$. Solve $4x - 2y = 7$ for y to get

    $y = 2x - \dfrac{7}{2}$, which shows that $m = 2$ for the

    second line. Since the slopes are equal and the y-intercepts are different, the lines are parallel.

46. To find the slopes, compare with the slope-intercept form $y = mx + b$: For $y = 4 - 5x$, $m = -5$. Solve $15x + 3y = 3$ for y to get

    $y = -5x + 1$, which shows that $m = -5$ for the second line. Since the slopes are equal and the y-intercepts are different, the lines are parallel.

47. To find the slopes, compare with the slope-intercept form $y = mx + b$. Solve the first equation, $2x + 5y = 8$, for y to get

    $y = -\dfrac{2}{5}x + \dfrac{8}{5}$. This result shows that

    $m_1 = -\dfrac{2}{5}$. Solve the second equation,

$5x - 2y = -9$ for y to get $y = \dfrac{5}{2}x + \dfrac{9}{2}$, which

shows that $m_2 = \dfrac{5}{2}$ for the second line.
Since the slopes are not equal, the lines are not parallel.

48. To find the slopes, compare with the slope-intercept form $y = mx + b$. Solve the first equation, $3x + 4y = 4$, for y to get

$y = -\dfrac{3}{4}x + 1$. This result shows that

$m_1 = -\dfrac{3}{4}$. Solve the second equation,

$2x - 6y = 7$ for y to get $y = \dfrac{1}{3}x - \dfrac{7}{6}$, which

shows that $m_2 = \dfrac{1}{3}$ for the second line.
Since the slopes are not equal, the lines are not parallel.

49. To find the slopes, compare with the slope-intercept form $y = mx + b$. Solve the first equation, $x + 7y = 7$, for y to get

$y = -\dfrac{1}{7}x + 1$. This result shows that

$m_1 = -\dfrac{1}{7}$. Solve the second equation,

$2x + 14y = 21$ for y to get $y = -\dfrac{1}{7}x + \dfrac{3}{2}$,

which shows that $m_2 = -\dfrac{1}{7}$ for the second

line. Since $m_1 = m_2$, and the y-intercepts are different, the lines are parallel.

50. To find the slopes, compare with the slope-intercept form $y = mx + b$. The first equation is $y = 5x - 12$. This result shows that $m_1 = 5$. The second equation $y = 3x - 8$, which shows that $m_2 = 3$ for the second line. Since the slopes are not equal, the lines are not parallel.

51. Since the required line is to be parallel to the line $4x - y = 7$ or, equivalently, $y = 4x - 7$, the new line must have slope $m = 4$. Since the line passes through the point (1, –2), use

the point-slope formula $y - y_1 = m(x - x_1)$
with $m = 4$ and $(x_1, y_1) = (1, -2)$ to obtain
$y - (-2) = 4(x - 1)$. Solve for y to obtain
$y = 4x - 6$, which is an equation with slope 4, so is parallel to the given line and passes through (1, –2). In standard form, we have $4x - y = 6$.

52. Since the required line is to be parallel to the line $3x + 2y = 5$ or, equivalently,

$y = -\dfrac{3}{2}x + \dfrac{5}{2}$, the new line must have slope

$m = -\dfrac{3}{2}$. Since the line passes through the

point (2, 0), use the point-slope formula

$y - y_1 = m(x - x_1)$ with $m = -\dfrac{3}{2}$ and

$(x_1, y_1) = (2, 0)$ to obtain

$y - 0 = -\dfrac{3}{2}(x - 2)$. Solve for y to obtain

$y = -\dfrac{3}{2}x + 3$, which is an equation with

slope $-\dfrac{3}{2}$, so is parallel to the given line

and passes through (2, 0). In standard form, we have $3x + 2y = 6$.

53. a. In order to be perpendicular to the line $2x + 5y = 7$, the desired line must have an equation of the form $5x - 2y = c$, with c chosen so that the line goes through (2, 0). By substituting (2, 0) into the equation, we find that $5 \cdot 2 - 2 \cdot 0 = C$, so $C = 10$. Thus, the equation of the desired line is $5x - 2y = 10$.

b. The equation $y = 2x - 3$ can be written in the form $2x - y = 3$. In order to be perpendicular to the line $2x - y = 3$, the desired line must have an equation of the form $x + 2y = c$, with c chosen so that the line goes through (1, 1). By substituting (1, 1) into the equation, we find that $1 + 2 \cdot 1 = c$, so $c = 3$. Thus, an equation of the desired line is $x + 2y = 3$.

c. In order to be perpendicular to the line $x - 2y = 3$, the desired line must have an equation of the form $2x + y = c$, with c

chosen so that the line goes through
(2, –2). By substituting (2, –2) into the
equation, we find that $2 \cdot 2 + (-2) = c$,
so $c = 2$. Thus, an equation of the
desired line is $2x + y = 2$.

d. In order to be perpendicular to the line
$4x + 5y = 9$, the desired line must have
an equation of the form $5x - 4y = c$,
with c chosen so that the line goes
through (1, 1). By substituting (1, 1) into
the equation, we find that $5 \cdot 1 - 4 \cdot 1 = c$,
so $c = 1$. Thus, an equation of the
desired line is $5x - 4y = 1$.

54. If we write the equations in the general
form, we have $m_1 x - y = -b_1$ and
$m_2 x - y = -b_2$. The condition given in
problem 53 becomes $m_1 m_2 + 1 = 0$. Thus,
$m_2 = -\dfrac{1}{m_1}$. We need the condition $m_1 \neq 0$,
because we cannot divide by zero. Also, if
$m_1 = 0$, the first line is parallel to the x-axis
and the perpendicular line is parallel to the
y-axis, so its slope is not defined.

55. For the first line, $m_1 = \dfrac{200 - 0}{100 - 0} = \dfrac{200}{100} = 2$,
and for the second line,
$m_2 = \dfrac{-405 - 10}{790 - 0} = \dfrac{-415}{790} \neq -\dfrac{1}{2}$. Since
$m_2 \neq -\dfrac{1}{m_1}$, the two lines are not
perpendicular.

56. a. Let t be the number of years after 2000.
So 2009 would be $t = 9$. Use the points
(0, 9) and (9, 24) to find the slope:
$$m = \frac{24 - 9}{9 - 0} = \frac{15}{9} = \frac{5}{3}$$

b. Use the slope from part a, the point
(0, 9) and the point-slope form to get:
$$y - 9 = \frac{5}{3}(x - 0)$$
$$y - 9 = \frac{5}{3}x$$
$$y = \frac{5}{3}x + 9$$

c. $P(t) = \dfrac{5}{3}t + 9$

d. The slope represents the increase in
wireless subscribers per year.

e. For 2020 put $t = 20$ in $P(t) = \dfrac{5}{3}t + 9$.
$$P(20) = \frac{5}{3}(20) + 9$$
$$= \frac{100}{3} + 9 \approx 42.33$$
In 2020, there will be 42.33 million
wireless subscribers.

57. a. For (f, F), we have the points (0, 0)
and (1000, 1120) to find the slope:
$$m = \frac{1120 - 0}{1000 - 0} = \frac{1120}{1000} = \frac{28}{25} = 1.12$$
The slope is the number of friends F for
every follower f.

b. The point (0, 0) is on the line and so the
y-intercept is 0.

c. $F(f) = 1.12f$

d. Put $f = 12,000,000$ in the equation
$F(f) = 1.12f$.
$$F(12,000,000) = 1.12(12,000,000)$$
$$= 13,440,000$$
Lady Gaga has 13.44 million friends.

58. a. Compare $F = 190 + 0.8t$ with $y = mx + b$,
where m is the slope and b the y-intercept to
find that the slope is 0.8.

b. The slope represents the increase in the
number of grams of fat consumed per
year.

59. a. Compare $T = 3.87 - 0.13t$ with $y = mx + b$,
where m is the slope and b the y-intercept to
find that the slope is –0.13. Since the slope is
negative, the consumption of tuna is
decreasing.

b. Compare $F = -0.29t + 15.46$ wit
$y = mx + b$, where m is the slope and b the y-
intercept to find that the slope is –0.29. Since
the slope is negative, the consumption of fish
and shellfish is decreasing.

c. The steepest slope is –0.29, which means
that fish and shellfish consumption is
decreasing faster.

60. a. Compare $y = 0.16t + 79$ with $y = mx + b$,

where m is the slope and b the y-intercept to find that the slope is 0.16.

b. Since the slope is positive, the life span of American women is increasing.

c. The slope represents the annual increase in the life span for American women, which is 0.16 yr per year.

61. a. Compare $y = 0.19t + 74$ with $y = mx + b$, where m is the slope and b the y-intercept to find that the slope is 0.19.

b. Since the slope is positive, the life span of American men is increasing.

c. The slope represents the annual increase in life span for American men, which is 0.19 yr per year.

62. a. Compare $v = 15 - 5t$ with $y = mx + b$, where m is the slope and b the y-intercept to find that the slope is –5.

b. Since the slope is negative, the velocity of the ball is decreasing.

c. The slope represents the rate at which the velocity of the ball is decreasing, which is 5 m/sec.

63. a. Compare $f = 165 + 0.4t$ with $y = mx + b$, where m is the slope and b the y-intercept to find that the slope is 0.4.

b. Since the slope is positive, the consumption of fat is increasing .

c. The slope represents the annual increase in fat consumption by Americans, which is 0.4 gram more each year.

64. a. Compare $g = 24 - 0.2t$ with $y = mx + b$, where m is the slope and b the y-intercept to find that the slope is –0.2.

b. Since the slope is negative, the consumption of milk products is decreasing.

c. The slope represents the rate at which the consumption of milk by an average American is decreasing per year, which is 0.2 gal less milk products than the previous year.

65. a. Put $t = 2000 - 1970 = 30$ into the equation $g = 140 + 0.94t$ to get
$$g = 140 + 0.94(30) = 140 + 28.2 = 168.2$$
The daily fat available for consumption in 2000 was 168.2 grams.

b. For $t = 2010 - 1970 = 40$,
$$g = 140 + 0.94(40) = 177.6$$
The daily fat available for consumption In 2010 was 177.6 grams.

c. In 1970, t = 0 so $g = 140 + 0.94(0) = 140$.
The daily fat available for consumption In 1970 was 140 grams.

d. Since the slope 0.94 is positive, the daily fat available for consumption is increasing.

66. a. Put $t = 2008 - 1998 = 10$ into the equation $D = -9.8t + 260$ to get
$$D = -9.8(10) + 260 = -98 + 260 = 162$$
There are 162 deaths per 100,000 population in 2008.

b. Put $t = 2018 - 1998 = 20$ into the equation $D = -9.8t + 260$ to get
$$D = -9.8(20) + 260 = -196 + 260 = 64$$
There are 64 deaths per 100,000 population in 2018.

c. The slope is –9.8, which represents an annual decrease of 9.8 deaths per 100,000 from heart disease.

67. a. Compare $C = 2.5N + 175$ with $y = mx + b$, where m is the slope and b the y-intercept to find that the slope is 2.5.

b. The slope represents the annual population per square mile in coastal regions increase.

c. Put $N = 55$ into the equation $C = 2.5N + 175$ to get
$$C = 2.5(55) + 175 = 137.5 + 175 = 312.5$$
There are 312.5, or 313, persons per square mile in the year 2015.

d. Yes. From the graph, the persons per square mile in 2015 is approximately 300, which is close to 313 persons per square mile.

68. Answers may vary. The slope of a vertical line does not exist. (Let $x = a$ be the equation of the line. Then (a, b) and (a, c), $b \neq c$, are two distinct points on the line. The slope formula gives $\dfrac{b-c}{a-a} = \dfrac{b-c}{0}$, which is undefined.)

69. Answers may vary. If (x_1, y_1) and (x_2, y_2) are any two distinct points on a horizontal

line, $y_1 = y_2$ and $x_1 \neq x_2$. Thus, the slope is

$$m = \frac{y_2 - y_1}{x_2 - x_1} = \frac{0}{x_2 - x_1} = 0.$$

70. Answers may vary. The lines parallel to the y-axis. (The lines $y = b$ are parallel to the x-axis, so the perpendicular lines must be parallel to the y-axis.) The equations are of the form $x = a$.

71. a. $m = \dfrac{1}{1.266} \approx 0.79$

    b. No. The maximum allowed is 0.22.

72. a. $m = \dfrac{10}{31.7} \approx 0.32$

    b. No. The maximum allowed is 0.22.

73. a. $m = \dfrac{0.4}{1.6} = 0.25$

    b. Yes. The maximum allowed is 0.3. (With a maximum slope of 0.125 for wheelchairs, you would not want to take your wheelchair up this walking ramp!)

74. The slope (0.125) is equal to the ratio of height (8 ft) to run (x) of the ramp.

$$0.125 = \frac{8}{x}$$

$$0.125x = 8$$

$$x = 64$$

The shortest run of the ramp is 64 ft.

75. $m = \dfrac{20 - 16}{124 - 108} = \dfrac{4}{16} = 0.25$, which is not safe for parking (0.22 is the maximum allowed). The bottom of the driveway is

$(x, 16)$ so $0.22 = \dfrac{20 - 16}{124 - x}$

$$0.22(124 - x) = 4$$

$$27.28 - 0.22x = 4$$

$$-0.22x = -23.28$$

$$x \approx 105.8$$

If $x = 106$ ft, the slope would be too steep, so x should be approximately 105 ft so that the slope is the maximum allowable.

76. Let n be the number of persons and t be the total paid. Find the slope between the points to determine if it is a linear relationship. For

the point (n, t), use the points $(3, 13)$ and $(7, 25)$ to find the slope.

$$m = \frac{25 - 13}{7 - 3} = \frac{12}{4} = 3$$

Now use the points $(3, 13)$ and $(6, 22)$ to find the slope.

$$m = \frac{22 - 13}{6 - 3} = \frac{9}{3} = 3$$

Finally use the points $(7, 25)$ and $(6, 22)$ to find the slope.

$$m = \frac{25 - 22}{7 - 6} = \frac{3}{1} = 3$$

Since the slopes are equal, we have a linear relationship. Now find a model in the form $t = mn + b$. Use the slope $m = 3$, the point $(3, 13)$, and the point-slope form to get:

$$t - 13 = 3(n - 3)$$

$$t - 13 = 3n - 9$$

$$t = 3n + 4$$

The t-intercept represents the parking price with no admissions, so the parking is $4. The slope represents the admission price, so admission is $3.
(From the chart, students might figure that to go from 6 to 7 admissions, the price goes up $3; subtracting $18 for 6 admissions leaves a $4 parking fee. Therefore, the total cost is admissions + parking, or $t = 3n + 4$)

77. Let t be the total paid and h be the number of hours. Find the slope between the points to determine if it is a linear relationship. For the point (h, t), use the points $(3, 110)$ and $(1, 60)$ to find the slope.

$$m = \frac{110 - 60}{3 - 1} = \frac{50}{2} = 25$$

Now use the points $(3, 110)$ and $(5, 160)$ to find the slope.

$$m = \frac{160 - 110}{5 - 3} = \frac{50}{2} = 25$$

Finally use the points $(1, 60)$ and $(5, 160)$ to find the slope.

$$m = \frac{160 - 60}{5 - 1} = \frac{100}{4} = 25$$

Since the slopes are equal, we have a linear relationship. Now find a model in the form $t = mh + b$. Use the slope $m = 25$, the point $(1, 60)$, and the point-slope form to get:

$$t - 60 = 25(h - 1)$$

$$t - 60 = 25h - 25$$

$$t = 25h + 35$$

The t-intercept represents the service call with no hours, so the service call is $35. The slope represents the hourly rate, so the hourly rate is $25.

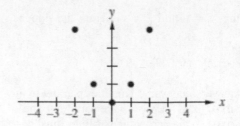

78. Let a be the air time fee and t be the total paid. Find the slope between the points to determine if it is a linear relationship. For the point (a, t), use the points (230, 87.50) and (90, 52.50) to find the slope.

$$m = \frac{87.50 - 52.50}{230 - 90} = \frac{35}{140} = \frac{1}{4}$$

Now use the points (230, 87.50) and (415, 133.75) to find the slope.

$$m = \frac{133.75 - 87.50}{415 - 230} = \frac{46.25}{185} = \frac{1}{4}$$

Finally use the points (90, 52.50) and (415, 133.75) to find the slope.

$$m = \frac{133.75 - 52.50}{415 - 90} = \frac{81.25}{325} = \frac{1}{4}$$

Since the slopes are equal, we have a linear relationship. Now find a model in the form $t = ma + b$. Use the slope $m = 3$, the point (3, 13), and the point-slope form to get:

$$t - 52.50 = 0.25(a - 90)$$

$$t - 52.50 = 0.25a - 22.5$$

$$t = 0.25a + 30$$

The t-intercept represents the monthly fee with no additional minutes, so the monthly fee is $30. The slope represents the additional amount for each minute of air time, so each additional minute is $0.25.

Skill Checker

1. $f(x) = x^2$

$$f(0) = 0^2 = 0$$

$$f(1) = 1^2 = 1$$

$$f(-1) = (-1)^2 = 1$$

$$f(2) = 2^2 = 4$$

$$f(-2) = (-2)^2 = 4$$

The corresponding ordered pairs are: (0, 0), (1, 1), (−1, 1), (2, 4) and (−2, 4). The graph of these five points is shown.

2. $f(x) = (x - 1)^2 - 2$

$$f(0) = (0 - 1)^2 - 2 = -1$$

$$f(1) = (1 - 1)^2 - 2 = -2$$

$$f(-1) = (-1 - 1)^2 - 2 = 2$$

$$f(2) = (2 - 1)^2 - 2 = -1$$

$$f(-2) = (-2 - 1)^2 - 2 = 7$$

The corresponding ordered pairs are: (0, −1), (1, −2), (−1, 2), (2, −1) and (−2, 7). The graph of these five points is shown.

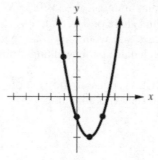

Section 7.4 Quadratic Functions and Their Graphs

1. a. $y = 2x^2$; $V(0,0)$ turns upward ($a > 0$). Select 3 values for x and get the corresponding y values:

x	0	1	−1
y	0	2	2

   Graph the corresponding points and join them with a curve as shown.

   b. To graph $y = 2x^2 + 2$, move the graph of $y = 2x^2$ two units up.

   c. To graph $y = 2x^2 - 2$, move the graph of $y = 2x^2$ two units down.

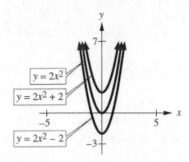

2. a. This graph has the same shape as
        $y = 3x^2$; $V(0,0)$; $a > 0$, so graph will
        turn upward. Select 3 values for x and
        get the corresponding y values:

x	0	1	-1
y	1	3	3

Graph the corresponding points and join
them with a curve. To graph
$y = 3x^2 + 1$, move the graph of $y = 3x^2$
one unit up.

    b. To graph $y = 3x^2 + 3$, move the graph of
        $y = 3x^2$ three units up.

    c. To graph $y = 3x^2 - 2$, move the graph
        of $y = 3x^2$ two units down.

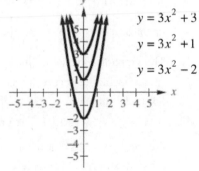

$y = 3x^2 + 3$

$y = 3x^2 + 1$

$y = 3x^2 - 2$

3. a. $y = -2x^2$; $V(0,0)$ turns downward
        $(a < 0)$. Select 3 values for x and get the
        corresponding y values:

x	0	1	-1
y	0	-2	-2

Graph the corresponding points and join
them with a curve as shown. The graph
looks exactly like that of $y = 2x^2$ but
"upside down," that is, it opens in the
opposite direction.

    b. To graph $y = -2x^2 + 1$, move the graph
        of $y = -2x^2$ one unit up.

c. To graph $y = -2x^2 - 1$, move the graph of
    $y = -2x^2$ one unit down.

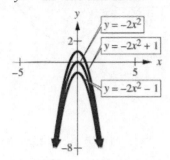

4. a. $y = -4x^2$; $V(0,0)$ turns downward
        $(a < 0)$. Select 3 values for x and get the
        corresponding y values:

x	0	1	-1
y	0	-4	-4

Graph the corresponding points and join
them with a curve as shown. The graph
looks exactly like that of $y = 4x^2$ but
"upside down," that is, it opens in the
opposite direction.

    b. To graph $y = -4x^2 + 1$, move the graph
        of $y = -4x^2$ one unit up.

    c. To graph $y = -4x^2 - 1$, move the graph
        of $y = -4x^2$ one unit down.

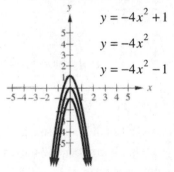

$y = -4x^2 + 1$

$y = -4x^2$

$y = -4x^2 - 1$

5. a. $y = \frac{1}{4}x^2$; $V(0,0)$ turns upward $(a > 0)$:

x	0	2	2
y	0	1	1

The graph has the same shape as that of
$y = x^2$ but it is wider.

    b. $y = -\frac{1}{4}x^2$; $V(0,0)$ looks exactly like
        the function in part a but opening in the
        opposite direction as shown in the
        graph:

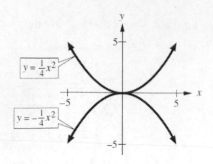

6. a. $y = \frac{1}{5}x^2$; $V(0,0)$ turns upward $(a > 0)$:

x	0	5	-5
y	0	5	5

    The graph has the same shape as that of $y = x^2$ but it is wider.

    b. $y = -\frac{1}{5}x^2$; $V(0,0)$ looks exactly like the function in part a but opening in the opposite direction as shown in the graph:

    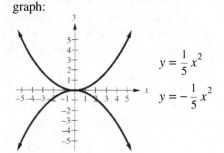

7. a. $y = \frac{1}{3}x^2 + 1$; $V(0,1)$ turns upward

    $(a > 0)$:
x	0	3	-3
y	1	4	4

    The graph has the same shape as that of $y = x^2$ but it is wider and moved up by one unit as shown.

    b. $y = -\frac{1}{3}x^2 + 1$; $V(0,1)$ looks exactly like the function in part a but opening in the opposite direction:

    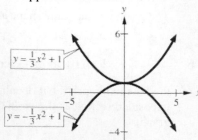

8. a. $y = \frac{1}{4}x^2 + 1$; $V(0,1)$ turns upward

    $(a > 0)$:
x	0	2	-2
y	1	2	2

    The graph has the same shape as that of $y = x^2$ but it is wider and moved up by one unit as shown.

    b. $y = -\frac{1}{4}x^2 + 1$; $V(0,1)$ looks exactly like the function in part a but opening in the opposite direction:

    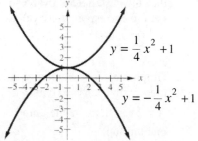

NOTE: Problems 9-16 are of the form $y = a(x - h)^2 + k$ and the vertex is at (h, k).

9. a. $y = (x + 2)^2 + 3$; $V(-2,3)$ turns

    upward $(a > 0)$:
x	-2	-1	-3
y	3	4	4

    The graph has the same shape as that of $y = x^2$ with the vertex moved 2 units left and 3 units up.

    b. $y = (x + 2)^2$; $V(-2,0)$ The graph has the same shape as that of $y = x^2$ with the vertex moved 2 units left.

    c. $y = (x + 2)^2 - 2$; $V(-2,-2)$ This time the vertex is moved 2 units left and two units down.

    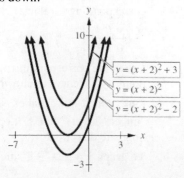

10. a. $y = (x-2)^2 + 2$; $V(2,2)$ turns upward

$(a > 0)$:

x	1	2	3
y	3	2	3

The graph has the same shape as that of $y = x^2$ with the vertex moved 2 units right and 3 units up.

b. $y = (x-2)^2$; $V(2,0)$ The graph has the same shape as that of $y = x^2$ with the vertex moved 2 units right.

c. $y = (x-2)^2 - 2$; $V(2,-2)$ This time the vertex is moved 2 units right and two units down.

$y = (x-2)^2 + 2$

$y = (x-2)^2$

$y = (x-2)^2 - 2$

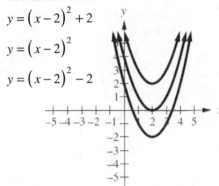

11. a. $y = -(x+2)^2 - 2$; $V(-2,-2)$ turns

downward $(a < 0)$:

x	-2	0	-4
y	-2	-6	-6

The graph has the same shape as that of $y = -x^2$ with the vertex moved 2 units left and 2 units down.

b. $y = -(x+2)^2$; $V(-2,0)$ The graph has the same shape as that of $y = -x^2$ with the vertex moved 2 units left.

c. $y = -(x+2)^2 - 4$; $V(-2,-4)$ This time the vertex is moved 2 units left and 4 units down.

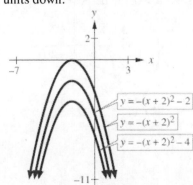

12. a. $y = -(x-1)^2 + 1$; $V(1,1)$ turns

downward $(a < 0)$:

x	0	1	2
y	0	1	0

The graph has the same shape as that of $y = -x^2$ with the vertex moved 1 unit right and 1 unit up.

b. $y = -(x-1)^2$; $V(1,0)$ The graph has the same shape as that of $y = -x^2$ with the vertex moved 1 unit right.

c. $y = -(x-1)^2 + 2$; $V(1,2)$ This time the vertex is moved 1 unit right and 2 units up.

$y = -(x-1)^2 + 2$

$y = -(x-1)^2 + 1$

$y = -(x-1)^2$

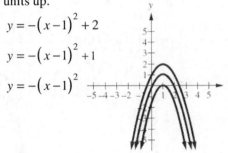

13. a. $y = -2(x+2)^2 - 2$; $V(-2,-2)$ turns

downward $(a < 0)$:

x	-2	-1	-3
y	-2	-4	-4

The graph has the same shape as that of $y = -x^2$ but narrower and with the vertex moved 2 units left and 2 units down.

b. $y = -2(x+2)^2$; $V(-2,0)$ The graph has the same shape as that of $y = -x^2$ but narrower and with the vertex moved 2 units left.

c. $y = -2(x+2)^2 - 4$; $V(-2,-4)$ This time the vertex is moved 2 units left and 4 units down.

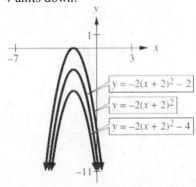

14. a. $y = -2(x-1)^2 + 1$; $V(1,1)$ turns downward ($a < 0$):

x	0	1	2
y	-1	1	-1

The graph has the same shape as that of $y = -x^2$ but narrower and with the vertex moved 1 unit right and 1 unit up.

b. $y = -2(x-1)^2$; $V(1,0)$ The graph has the same shape as that of $y = -x^2$ but narrower and with the vertex moved 1 unit right.

c. $y = -2(x-1)^2 + 2$; $V(1,2)$ This time the vertex is moved 1 unit right and 2 units up.

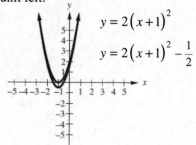

$$y = -2(x-1)^2 + 2$$
$$y = -2(x-1)^2 + 1$$
$$y = -2(x-1)^2$$

15. a. $y = 2(x+1)^2 + \dfrac{1}{2}$; $V\left(-1, \dfrac{1}{2}\right)$ turns upward ($a > 0$):

x	-1	0	-2
y	$\dfrac{1}{2}$	$\dfrac{5}{2}$	$\dfrac{5}{2}$

The graph has the same shape as that of $y = x^2$ but narrower and with the vertex moved 1 unit left and $\dfrac{1}{2}$ unit up.

b. $y = 2(x+1)^2$; $V(-1,0)$ The graph has the same shape as that of $y = x^2$ but narrower and with the vertex moved 1 unit left.

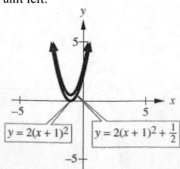

$y = 2(x+1)^2$ $y = 2(x+1)^2 + \dfrac{1}{2}$

16. a. $y = 2(x+1)^2 - \dfrac{1}{2}$; $V\left(-1, -\dfrac{1}{2}\right)$ turns upward ($a > 0$):

x	0	-1	-2
y	$\dfrac{3}{2}$	$-\dfrac{1}{2}$	$\dfrac{3}{2}$

The graph has the same shape as that of $y = x^2$ but narrower and with the vertex moved 1 unit left and $\dfrac{1}{2}$ unit down.

b. $y = 2(x+1)^2$; $V(-1,0)$ The graph has the same shape as that of $y = x^2$ but narrower and with the vertex moved 1 unit left.

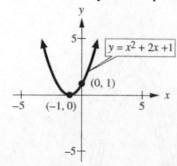

$$y = 2(x+1)^2$$
$$y = 2(x+1)^2 - \dfrac{1}{2}$$

17. $y = x^2 + 2x + 1$

1. Vertex: $x = \dfrac{-b}{2a} = \dfrac{-2}{2 \cdot 1} = \dfrac{-2}{2} = -1$

   Substitute $x = -1$ to find y
   $$y = (-1)^2 + 2(-1) + 1 = 1 - 2 + 1 = 0$$
   $V(-1, 0)$
2. If $x = 0$, $y = 1$; y-intercept: (0, 1)
3. By symmetry, (–2, 1) is on the graph.
4. If $y = 0$, $0 = x^2 + 2x + 1$
   $$0 = (x+1)(x+1)$$
   $$x = -1 \text{ (repeated)}$$
   x-intercept: (–1, 0)
5. Since $a > 0$, the parabola opens upward.

$y = x^2 + 2x + 1$

(0, 1)

(–1, 0)

18. $y = x^2 + 4x + 4$

   1. Vertex: $x = \dfrac{-b}{2a} = \dfrac{-4}{2 \cdot 1} = \dfrac{-4}{2} = -2$

      Substitute $x = -2$ to find y

      $y = (-2)^2 + 4(-2) + 4 = 4 - 8 + 4 = 0$

      $V(-2, 0)$

   2. If $x = 0$, $y = 4$; y-intercept: $(0, 4)$

   3. By symmetry, $(-4, 4)$ is on the graph.

   4. If $y = 0$, $0 = x^2 + 4x + 4$

         $0 = (x + 2)(x + 2)$

         $x = -2$ (repeated)

      x-intercept: $(-2, 0)$

   5. Since $a > 0$, the parabola opens upward.

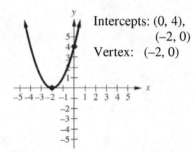

Intercepts: $(0, 4)$,
                 $(-2, 0)$
Vertex: $(-2, 0)$

19. $y = -x^2 + 2x + 1$

   1. Vertex: $x = \dfrac{-b}{2a} = \dfrac{-2}{2(-1)} = \dfrac{-2}{-2} = 1$

      Substitute $x = 1$ to find y

      $y = -1^2 + 2(1) + 1 = -1 + 2 + 1 = 2$

      $V(1, 2)$

   2. If $x = 0$, $y = 1$; y-intercept: $(0, 1)$

   3. By symmetry, $(2, 1)$ is on the graph.

   4. If $y = 0$, $0 = -x^2 + 2x + 1$

         $0 = x^2 - 2x - 1$

      $x = \dfrac{-(-2) \pm \sqrt{(-2)^2 - 4 \cdot 1(-1)}}{2 \cdot 1}$

      $= \dfrac{2 \pm \sqrt{4 + 4}}{2} = \dfrac{2 \pm 2\sqrt{2}}{2} = 1 \pm \sqrt{2}$

      x-intercept: $\left(1 + \sqrt{2}, 0\right), \left(1 - \sqrt{2}, 0\right)$

   5. Since $a < 0$, the parabola opens

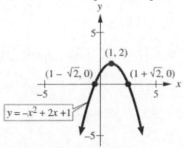

20. $y = -x^2 + 4x - 2$

   1. Vertex: $x = \dfrac{-b}{2a} = \dfrac{-4}{2(-1)} = \dfrac{-4}{-2} = 2$

      Substitute $x = 2$ to find y

      $y = -2^2 + 4(2) - 2 = -4 + 8 - 2 = 2$

      $V(2, 2)$

   2. If $x = 0$, $y = -2$; y-intercept: $(0, -2)$

   3. By symmetry, $(4, -2)$ is on the graph.

   4. If $y = 0$,

         $0 = -x^2 + 4x - 2$

         $0 = x^2 - 4x + 2$

      $x = \dfrac{-(-4) \pm \sqrt{(-4)^2 - 4 \cdot 1(2)}}{2 \cdot 1}$

      $= \dfrac{4 \pm \sqrt{16 - 8}}{2} = \dfrac{4 \pm 2\sqrt{2}}{2}$

      $= 2 \pm \sqrt{2} \approx 0.6, 3.4$

      x-intercept: $(0.6, 0), (3.4, 0)$

   5. Since $a < 0$, the parabola opens downward.

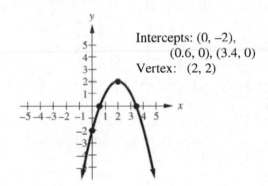

Intercepts: $(0, -2)$,
           $(0.6, 0)$, $(3.4, 0)$
Vertex: $(2, 2)$

21. $y = -x^2 + 4x - 5$

   1. Vertex: $x = \dfrac{-b}{2a} = \dfrac{-4}{2(-1)} = \dfrac{-4}{-2} = 2$

      Substitute $x = 2$ to find y

      $y = -2^2 + 4(2) - 5 = -4 + 8 - 5 = -1$

      $V(2, -1)$

   2. If $x = 0$, $y = -5$; y-intercept: $(0, -5)$

   3. By symmetry, $(4, -5)$ is on the graph.

   4. If $y = 0$,

         $0 = -x^2 + 4x - 5$

         $0 = x^2 - 4x + 5$

      $x^2 - 4x + 5$ is not factorable and the vertex is below the x-axis. This means that the equation has no solution and there are no x-intercepts; the graph does not cross the x-axis.

5. Since $a < 0$, the parabola opens downward.

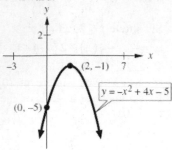

22. $y = -x^2 + 4x - 3$

1. Vertex: $x = \dfrac{-b}{2a} = \dfrac{-4}{2(-1)} = \dfrac{-4}{-2} = 2$

    Substitute $x = 2$ to find y

    $y = -2^2 + 4(2) - 3 = -4 + 8 - 3 = 1$

    $V(2, 1)$

2. If $x = 0$, $y = -3$; y-intercept: (0, –3)
3. By symmetry, (4, –3) is on the graph.
4. If $y = 0$, $0 = -x^2 + 4x - 3$

    $0 = x^2 - 4x + 3$

    $x = \dfrac{-(-4) \pm \sqrt{(-4)^2 - 4 \cdot 1(3)}}{2 \cdot 1}$

    $= \dfrac{4 \pm \sqrt{16 - 12}}{2} = \dfrac{4 \pm 2}{2} = 1, 3$

    x-intercept: $(1, 0), (3, 0)$

5. Since $a < 0$, the parabola opens downward.

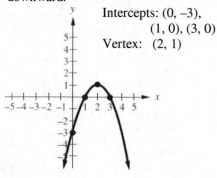

Intercepts: (0, –3),
(1, 0), (3, 0)
Vertex: (2, 1)

23. $y = 3 - 5x + 2x^2 = 2x^2 - 5x + 3$

1. Vertex: $x = \dfrac{-b}{2a} = \dfrac{-(-5)}{2 \cdot 2} = \dfrac{5}{4}$

    Substitute $x = \dfrac{5}{4}$ to find y

$y = 2\left(\dfrac{5}{4}\right)^2 - 5\left(\dfrac{5}{4}\right) + 3 = \dfrac{25}{8} - \dfrac{25}{4} + 3 = -\dfrac{1}{8}$

$V\left(\dfrac{5}{4}, -\dfrac{1}{8}\right)$

2. If $x = 0$, $y = 3$; y-intercept: (0, 3)

3. By symmetry, $\left(\dfrac{5}{2}, 3\right)$ is on the graph.

4. If $y = 0$, $0 = 2x^2 - 5x + 3$

    $0 = (2x - 3)(x - 1)$

    $x = \dfrac{3}{2},\ x = 1$

    x-intercepts: $\left(\dfrac{3}{2}, 0\right), (1, 0)$

5. Since $a > 0$, the parabola opens upward.

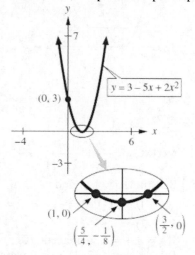

24. $y = 3 + 5x + 2x^2 = 2x^2 + 5x + 3$

1. Vertex: $x = \dfrac{-b}{2a} = \dfrac{-5}{2 \cdot 2} = -\dfrac{5}{4}$

    Substitute $x = -\dfrac{5}{4}$ to find y

$y = 2\left(-\dfrac{5}{4}\right)^2 + 5\left(-\dfrac{5}{4}\right) + 3 = \dfrac{25}{8} - \dfrac{25}{4} + 3$

$= -\dfrac{1}{8}$

$V\left(-\dfrac{5}{4}, -\dfrac{1}{8}\right)$

2. If $x = 0$, $y = 3$; y-intercept: (0, 3)

3. By symmetry, $\left(-\dfrac{5}{2}, 3\right)$ is on the graph.

4. If $y = 0$, $0 = 2x^2 + 5x + 3$
$$0 = (2x + 3)(x + 1)$$
$$x = -\frac{3}{2}, x = -1$$
x-intercepts: $\left(-\frac{3}{2}, 0\right), (-1, 0)$

5. Since $a > 0$, the parabola opens upward.
Intercepts: $(0, 3)$,
$$(-1, 0), \left(-\frac{3}{2}, 0\right)$$
Vertex: $\left(-\frac{5}{4}, -\frac{1}{8}\right)$

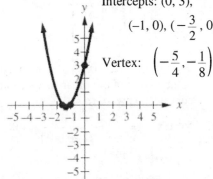

25. $y = 5 - 4x - 2x^2 = -2x^2 - 4x + 5$

1. Vertex: $x = \dfrac{-b}{2a} = \dfrac{-(-4)}{2(-2)} = \dfrac{4}{-4} = -1$

Substitute $x = -1$ to find y
$$y = -2(-1)^2 - 4(-1) + 5$$
$$= -2 + 4 + 5 = 7$$
$V(-1, 7)$

2. If $x = 0$, $y = 5$; y-intercept: $(0, 5)$
3. By symmetry, $(-2, 5)$ is on the graph.
4. If $y = 0$, $0 = -2x^2 - 4x + 5$
$$0 = 2x^2 + 4x - 5$$
$$x = \frac{-4 \pm \sqrt{4^2 - 4 \cdot 2(-5)}}{2 \cdot 2}$$
$$= \frac{-4 \pm \sqrt{16 + 40}}{4} = \frac{-4 \pm 2\sqrt{14}}{4}$$
$$= \frac{2 \pm \sqrt{14}}{2} \approx 0.9 \text{ or } -2.9$$
x-intercept: $(-2.9, 0), (0.9, 0)$

5. Since $a < 0$, the parabola opens downward.

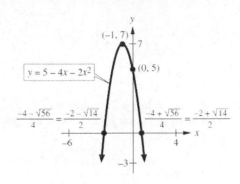

26. $y = 3 - 4x - 2x^2 = -2x^2 - 4x + 3$

1. Vertex: $x = \dfrac{-b}{2a} = \dfrac{-(-4)}{2(-2)} = \dfrac{4}{-4} = -1$

Substitute $x = -1$ to find y
$$y = -2(-1)^2 - 4(-1) + 3$$
$$= -2 + 4 + 3 = 5$$
$V(-1, 5)$

2. If $x = 0$, $y = 3$; y-intercept: $(0, 3)$
3. By symmetry, $(-2, 3)$ is on the graph.
4. If $y = 0$, $0 = -2x^2 - 4x + 3$
$$0 = 2x^2 + 4x - 3$$
$$x = \frac{-4 \pm \sqrt{4^2 - 4 \cdot 2(-3)}}{2 \cdot 2}$$
$$= \frac{-4 \pm \sqrt{16 + 24}}{4} = \frac{-4 \pm 2\sqrt{10}}{4}$$
$$= \frac{-2 \pm \sqrt{10}}{2} \approx -2.6 \text{ or } 0.6$$
x-intercept: $(-2.6, 0), (0.6, 0)$

5. Since $a < 0$, the parabola opens downward.
Intercepts: $(0, 3)$,
$(-2.6, 0), (0.6, 0)$
Vertex: $(-1, 5)$

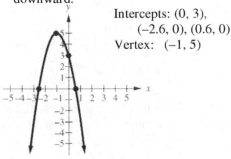

27. $y = -3x^2 + 3x + 2$

1. Vertex: $x = \dfrac{-b}{2a} = \dfrac{-3}{2(-3)} = \dfrac{-3}{-6} = \dfrac{1}{2}$

Substitute $x = \dfrac{1}{2}$ to find y

$$y = -3\left(\frac{1}{2}\right)^2 + 3\left(\frac{1}{2}\right) + 2 = -\frac{3}{4} + \frac{3}{2} + 2 = \frac{11}{4}$$

$$V\left(\frac{1}{2}, \frac{11}{4}\right)$$

2. If $x = 0$, $y = 2$; y-intercept: (0, 2)
3. By symmetry, (1, 2) is on the graph.
4. If $y = 0$, $0 = -3x^2 + 3x + 2$

$$x = \frac{-3 \pm \sqrt{3^2 - 4 \cdot (-3)(2)}}{2(-3)}$$

$$= \frac{-3 \pm \sqrt{9 + 24}}{-6} = \frac{-3 \pm \sqrt{33}}{-6}$$

$$\approx -0.5 \text{ or } 1.5$$

x-intercept: $(-0.5, 0), (1.5, 0)$

5. Since $a < 0$, the parabola opens downward.

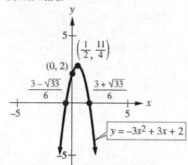

28. $y = -3x^2 + 3x + 1$

1. Vertex: $x = \frac{-b}{2a} = \frac{-3}{2(-3)} = \frac{-3}{-6} = \frac{1}{2}$

   Substitute $x = \frac{1}{2}$ to find y

   $$y = -3\left(\frac{1}{2}\right)^2 + 3\left(\frac{1}{2}\right) + 1 = -\frac{3}{4} + \frac{3}{2} + 1 = \frac{7}{4}$$

   $$V\left(\frac{1}{2}, \frac{7}{4}\right)$$

2. If $x = 0$, $y = 1$; y-intercept: (0, 1)
3. By symmetry, (1, 1) is on the graph.
4. If $y = 0$, $0 = -3x^2 + 3x + 12$

   $$x = \frac{-3 \pm \sqrt{3^2 - 4 \cdot (-3)(1)}}{2(-3)}$$

   $$= \frac{-3 \pm \sqrt{9 + 12}}{-6} = \frac{-3 \pm \sqrt{21}}{-6}$$

   $$\approx -0.3 \text{ or } 1.3$$

   x-intercept: $(-0.3, 0), (1.3, 0)$

5. Since $a < 0$, the parabola opens downward.

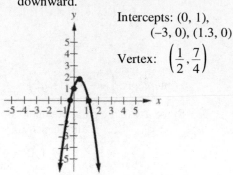

Intercepts: (0, 1), (−3, 0), (1.3, 0)

Vertex: $\left(\frac{1}{2}, \frac{7}{4}\right)$

29. $P = -5000 + 8x - 0.001x^2$ The maximum is at the vertex of the parabola since the graph curves downward ($a < 0$).

Vertex: $x = \frac{-b}{2a} = \frac{-8}{2(-0.001)} = 4000$

If $x = 4000$,

$$P = -5000 + 8(4000) - 0.001(4000)^2$$

$$= -5000 + 32,000 - 16,000 = 11,000$$

4000 items should be produced for maximum profit of $11,000.

30. $R = 1500p - 75p^2$ The maximum is at the vertex of the parabola since the graph curves downward ($a < 0$).

Vertex: $p = \frac{-b}{2a} = \frac{-1500}{2(-75)} = 10$

The price to maximize revenue is $10.

31. $N = 50x - x^2$ The maximum is at the vertex of the parabola since the graph curves downward ($a < 0$).

Vertex: $x = \frac{-b}{2a} = \frac{-50}{2(-1)} = 25$

Thus, $25 thousand ($25,000) should be spent to obtain maximum sales.

32. $N = 40x - x^2$ The maximum is at the vertex of the parabola since the graph curves downward ($a < 0$).

Vertex: $x = \frac{-b}{2a} = \frac{-40}{2(-1)} = 20$

Thus, $20 thousand ($20,000) should be spent to obtain maximum sales.

33. $h = -16t^2 + 160t$ The maximum height is at the vertex since $a < 0$.

Vertex: $t = \dfrac{-b}{2a} = \dfrac{-160}{2(-16)} = 5$

If $t = 5$,

$h = -16(5)^2 + 160 \cdot 5 = -400 + 800 = 400$

The maximum height is 400 ft.

34. $h = -16t^2 + 20t$ The maximum height is at the vertex since $a < 0$.

Vertex: $t = \dfrac{-b}{2a} = \dfrac{-20}{2(-16)} = \dfrac{5}{8}$

If $t = \dfrac{5}{8}$, $h = -16\left(\dfrac{5}{8}\right)^2 + 20 \cdot \dfrac{5}{8}$

$\qquad = -6.25 + 12.5 = 6.25$

The maximum height is $6\dfrac{1}{4}$ ft.

35. Let W = number of weeks to wait.
$600 + 100W$ is the number of bushels dug at the end of W weeks.
$1.00 - 0.10W$ = price per bushel at the end of W weeks.
If P is the price she'll be receiving, then

$P = (600 + 100W)(1.00 - 0.10W)$

$\quad = 600W + 100W - 60W - 10W^2$

$\quad = 600 + 40W - 10W^2$

The maximum she'll receive is at the vertex of the parabola since $a < 0$.

Vertex: $W = \dfrac{-b}{2a} = \dfrac{-40}{2(-10)} = 2$. The

maximum amount occurs when $W = 2$ weeks. At $W = 2$, we have

$P = 600 + 40 \cdot 2 - 10 \cdot 2^2 = 600 + 80 - 40 = 640$

Hence, she'll receive the maximum amount, $640, if she digs the potatoes at the end of 2 weeks.

36. Let the width $w = x$ and the length $l = 400 - 2x$. For area, use the formula $A = lw$. $A = (400 - 2x)x = 400x - 2x^2$

Vertex: $x = \dfrac{-b}{2a} = \dfrac{-400}{2(-2)} = 100$

The width is 100 ft, and the length is $400 - 2(100) = 200$ ft. The dimensions that will give the maximum area are 200 ft by 100 ft.

37. a. $R = -\dfrac{1}{98}x^2 + \dfrac{6}{7}x$ The vertex is at:

$x = \dfrac{-b}{2a} = \dfrac{-\dfrac{6}{7}}{2\left(-\dfrac{1}{98}\right)} = \dfrac{6}{7} \cdot \dfrac{49}{1} = 42$ in.

When $x = 42$,

$R = -\dfrac{1}{98}(42)^2 + \dfrac{6}{7}(42) = 18$

The vertex is (42, 18).

b. The maximum height is at the vertex of the parabola so $h = 18$ in.

c. Since the vertex is at $x = 42$, that's the midpoint of the parabola. The ending point will be 42 in. to the right of 42. Therefore the horizontal length is the distance from the beginning to the midpoint plus the distance from the midpoint to the end, that is, $42 + 42 = 84$ in.

d.

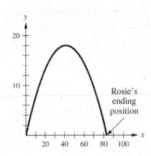

38. a. $S = -\dfrac{1}{200}x^2 + \dfrac{7}{10}x$ The vertex is at:

$x = \dfrac{-b}{2a} = \dfrac{-\dfrac{7}{10}}{2\left(-\dfrac{1}{200}\right)} = \dfrac{7}{10} \cdot \dfrac{100}{1} = 70$ in.

When $x = 70$,

$S = -\dfrac{1}{200}(70)^2 + \dfrac{7}{10}(70) = 24.5$

The vertex is (70, 24.5).

b. The maximum height is at the vertex of the parabola so $h = 24.5$ in.

c. Since the vertex is at $x = 70$, that's the midpoint of the parabola. The ending point will be 70 in. to the right of 70. Therefore the horizontal length is the distance from the beginning to the midpoint plus the distance from the midpoint to the end, that is, $70 + 70 = 140$ in.

d.

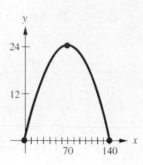

39. a. $d = -\dfrac{1}{400}x^2 + x$ The vertex is at:

$$x = \dfrac{-b}{2a} = \dfrac{-1}{2\left(-\dfrac{1}{400}\right)} = 1 \cdot \dfrac{200}{1} = 200 \text{ ft}$$

When $x = 200$,

$$d = -\dfrac{1}{400}(200)^2 + 200 = 100$$

The vertex is (200, 100).

b. The maximum height is at the vertex of the parabola so $h = 100$ ft.

c. The horizontal distance traveled is two times the x distance to the vertex or $2 \cdot 200 = 400$ ft.

d.

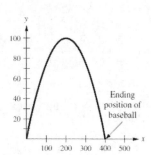

40. a. The lowest percent of low-birth-weight babies for mother who smoke is 10.5%, which occurs at about 22 years.

b. The highest percent of low-birth-weight babies for mother who smoke is 19.5%, which occurs at about 48–49 years.

c. $a > 0$

41. a. The lowest percent of low-birth-weight babies for mother who do not smoke is 6.3%, which occurs at the approximate age of 27 yr.

b. The highest percent of low-birth-weight babies for mother who do not smoke is 10.5%.

c. The approximate age of mothers who smoke that have the lowest percentage of low-birth-weight babies is 22 years.

d. The approximate age of mothers who do not smoke that have the highest percentage of low-birth-weight babies is 16 years.

42. Answers may vary. If $a > 0$, it opens up. If $a < 0$, it opens down.

43. Answers may vary. When $|a| > 1$, it is narrower. When $|a| < 1$, it is wider.

44. Answers may vary. For the function $y = ax^2 + k$, when k is positive, the graph of $y = ax^2$ is moved k units up; when k is negative, the graph of $y = ax^2$ is moved $|k|$ units down.

45. Answers may vary. It opens down. If it were to open up from (1, 1) it would have no x-intercept.

46. Answers may vary. Because if it had two y-intercepts it would not be a function (two y-values would occur at $x = 0$).

47. A parabola that would represent cardiovascular disease would open downward, so a is negative.

48. The maximum point on the curve is approximately (1962, 520). y-coordinate may vary, for instance, another possible answer might be (1962, 510).

49. The coordinates for the vertex is approximately (1962, 520).

50. The curve is going downward, so the number of deaths due to cardiovascular disease in the year 2010 is approximately 310.

51. The profit for an item costing $20 is expressed as $x - 20$. The profit for selling $60 - x$ items is

$$P = (60 - x)(x - 20) = -x^2 + 80x - 1200.$$

Find the x-value of the vertex:

$$x = \dfrac{-b}{2a} = \dfrac{-80}{2(-1)} = 40$$

The price to maximize profits is $40.

52.

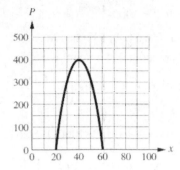

53. Let $x = 40$:

$$P = (60 - x)(x - 20)$$

$$= (60 - 40)(40 - 20)$$

$$= (20)(20) = 400$$

The maximum profit is $400.

Section 7.5 Exponential and Logarithmic Functions

1. Given 5^x:

   a. When $x = -1$, $5^{-1} = \dfrac{1}{5}$

   b. When $x = 0$, $5^0 = 1$

   c. When $x = 1$, $5^1 = 5$

2. Given 5^{-x}:

   a. When $x = -1$, $5^{-(-1)} = 5^1 = 5$

   b. When $x = 0$, $5^{-0} = 1$

   c. When $x = 1$, $5^{-1} = \dfrac{1}{5}$

3. Given 3^t:

   a. When $x = -2$, $3^{-2} = \dfrac{1}{3^2} = \dfrac{1}{9}$

   b. When $x = 0$, $3^0 = 1$

   c. When $x = 2$, $3^2 = 3 \cdot 3 = 9$

4. Given 3^{-t}:

   a. When $x = -2$, $3^{-(-2)} = 3^2 = 3 \cdot 3 = 9$

   b. When $x = 0$, $3^{-0} = 1$

   c. When $x = 2$, $3^{-2} = \dfrac{1}{3^2} = \dfrac{1}{9}$

5. Given $10^{t/2}$:

   a. When $x = -2$, $10^{-2/2} = 10^{-1} = \dfrac{1}{10}$

   b. When $x = 0$, $10^{0/2} = 10^0 = 1$

   c. When $x = 2$, $10^{2/2} = 10^1 = 10$

6. Given $10^{-t/2}$:

   a. When $x = -2$, $10^{-(-2/2)} = 10^1 = 10$

   b. When $x = 0$, $10^{-0/2} = 10^0 = 1$

   c. When $x = 2$, $10^{-2/2} = 10^{-1} = \dfrac{1}{10}$

7. a. Use the values found in problem 1 to graph $f(x) = 5^x$.

   b. Use the values found in problem 2 to graph $f(x) = 5^{-x}$.

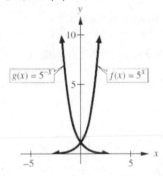

8. a. Use the values found in problem 3 to graph $f(x) = 3^t$.

   b. Use the values found in problem 4 to graph $f(x) = 3^{-t}$.

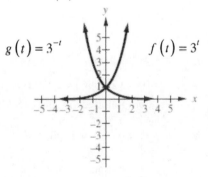

9. a. When $x = -1, 0$ and 1 the corresponding values are $10^{-1} = \dfrac{1}{10}$, 1 and 10 as shown in the graph.

b. When $x = -1, 0$ and 1 the corresponding values are $10^{-(-1)} = 10$, 1 and $10^{-1} = \dfrac{1}{10}$ as shown in the graph.

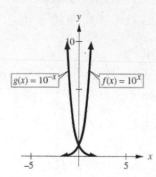

10. a. When $x = -2, 0$ and 2 the corresponding values are $10^{-2/2} = 10^{-1} = \dfrac{1}{10}$, 1 and 10 as shown in the graph.

b. When $x = -2, 0$ and 2 the corresponding values are $10^{-(-2/2)} = 10$, 1 and $10^{-(2/2)} = 10^{-1} = \dfrac{1}{10}$ as shown in the graph.

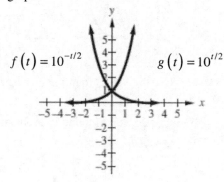

11. a. $A = Pe^{rt} = 1000e^{0.09(10)} = 1000e^{0.9}$

$= 1000(2.4596) = 2459.60$

The compounded amount is $2459.60.

b. $A = P\left(1 + \dfrac{r}{n}\right)^{nt} = 1000\left(1 + \dfrac{0.09}{4}\right)^{4(10)}$

$= 1000\left(\dfrac{4.09}{4}\right)^{40} = 1000(1.0225)^{40}$

$= 1000(2.43519) = 2435.19$

The amount compounded quarterly is $2435.19.

12. a. $A = Pe^{rt} = 1000e^{0.09(20)} = 1000e^{1.8}$

$= 1000(6.04965) = 6049.65$

The compounded amount is $6049.65.

b. $A = P\left(1 + \dfrac{r}{n}\right)^{nt} = 1000\left(1 + \dfrac{0.09}{4}\right)^{4(20)}$

$= 1000\left(\dfrac{4.09}{4}\right)^{80} = 1000(1.0225)^{80}$

$= 1000(5.93015) = 5930.15$

The amount compounded quarterly is $5930.15.

13. a. $A = Pe^{rt} = 1000e^{0.06(10)} = 1000e^{0.6}$

$= 1000(1.82212) = 1822.12$

The compounded amount is $1822.12.

b. $A = P\left(1 + \dfrac{r}{n}\right)^{nt} = 1000\left(1 + \dfrac{0.06}{4}\right)^{4(10)}$

$= 1000\left(\dfrac{4.06}{4}\right)^{40} = 1000(1.015)^{40}$

$= 1000(1.81402) = 1814.02$

The amount compounded quarterly is $1814.02.

14. a. $A = Pe^{rt} = 1000e^{0.06(20)} = 1000e^{1.2}$

$= 1000(3.32012) = 3320.12$

The compounded amount is $3320.12.

b. $A = P\left(1 + \dfrac{r}{n}\right)^{nt} = 1000\left(1 + \dfrac{0.06}{4}\right)^{4(20)}$

$= 1000\left(\dfrac{4.06}{4}\right)^{80} = 1000(1.015)^{80}$

$= 1000(3.29066) = 3290.66$

The amount compounded quarterly is $3290.66.

15. $P = 2000\left(2^{0.2t}\right)$ where t is the number of years after 2000.

a. In 2005, $t = 5$

$P = 2000\left(2^{0.2(5)}\right) = 2000\left(2^1\right) = 4000$

The population was 4000 in 2005.

b. In 2010, $t = 10$

$P = 2000\left(2^{0.2(10)}\right) = 2000\left(2^2\right) = 8000$

The population was 8000 in 2010.

c. In 2015, $t = 15$

$$P = 2000\left(2^{0.2(15)}\right) = 2000\left(2^3\right) = 16,000$$

The population was 16,000 in 2015.

16. $P = 1200\left(2^t\right)$ where t is in days.

   a. At the start, $t = 0$

$$P = 1200\left(2^0\right) = 1200\left(2^0\right) = 1200$$

The number of bacteria at the start is 1200.

   b. In 5 days, $t = 5$

$$P = 1200\left(2^5\right) = 1200\left(2^5\right) = 38,400$$

The number of bacteria in 5 days is 38,400.

   c. In 10 days, $t = 10$

$$P = 1200\left(2^{10}\right) = 1200\left(2^{10}\right) = 1,228,800$$

The number of bacteria in 10 days is 1,228,800.

17. $G = 2000e^{-1.05t}$ where t is in years.

   a. At the start, $t = 0$

$$G = 2000e^{-1.05(0)} = 2000e^0$$

$$= 2000 \cdot 1 = 2000$$

2000 grams are present at the start.

   b. In 1 year, $t = 1$

$$G = 2000e^{-1.05(1)} = 2000e^{-1.05}$$

$$= 2000(0.349938) - 699.876$$

699.9 grams are present in 1 year.

   c. In 2 years, $t = 2$

$$G = 2000e^{-1.05(2)} = 2000e^{-2.10}$$

$$= 2000(0.122456) = 244.912$$

244.9 grams are present in 2 years.

18. $G = 2000e^{-1.1t}$ where t is in years.

   a. At the start, $t = 0$

$$G = 2000e^{-1.1(0)} = 2000e^0$$

$$= 2000 \cdot 1 = 2000$$

2000 grams are present at the start.

   b. In 1 year, $t = 1$

$$G = 2000e^{-1.1(1)} = 2000e^{-1.1}$$

$$= 2000(0.332871) = 665.742$$

665.7 grams are present in 1 year.

   c. In 2 years, $t = 2$

$$G = 2000e^{-1.1(2)} = 2000e^{-2.2}$$

$$= 2000(0.110803) = 221.606$$

221.6 grams are present in 2 years.

19. $P = P_0 e^{kt}$ P is the population in t years

                P_0 is the initial population

                k the annual growth rate $(B - D)$

                t the number of years after 2000

Find k: $B - D = 0.0234 - 0.003 = 0.0204$

$P_0 = 50.5$ million, $t = 10$

$$P = 50.5e^{0.0204(10)} = 50.5e^{0.204} \approx 61.93$$

The number of Hispanics for the year 2020 is about 61.93 million.

20. $P = P_0 e^{kt}$ P is the population in t years

                P_0 is the initial population

                k the annual growth rate $(B - D)$

                t the number of years after 2000

Find k: $B - D = 0.017 - 0.0072 - 0.0098$

$P_0 = 39.6$ million, $t = 10$

$$P = 39.6e^{0.0098(10)} = 39.6e^{0.098} \approx 43.68$$

The number of African Americans for the year 2020 is about 43.68 million.

21. $C = 941e^{0.0053t}$ where t is in months.

   a. Total credit $= C = 1000$ billion

$$1000 = 941e^{0.0053t}$$

$$\frac{1000}{941} = e^{0.0053t}$$

$$\ln\left(\frac{1000}{941}\right) = \ln e^{0.0053t}$$

$$\ln\left(\frac{1000}{941}\right) = 0.0053t$$

$$t = \frac{\ln\left(\dfrac{1000}{941}\right)}{0.0053} \approx 11.5$$

The total credit will read one trillion dollars about 11.5 months later, or in December 2008.

   b. December 2007 total credit doubled is $2 \cdot 941 = 1882$.

$$1882 = 941e^{0.0053t}$$

$$2 = e^{0.0053t}$$

$$\ln 2 = \ln e^{0.0053t}$$

$$\ln 2 = 0.0053t$$

$$t = \frac{\ln 2}{0.0053} \approx 131$$

Twice the December 2007 total credit will be in 131 months, or in 2018.

22. $S(t) = 190e^{0.11t}$ million, where t is the

number of years after 2004.

a.   In the year 2011, $t = 7$.

$$S(7) = 190e^{0.11(7)} = 190e^{0.77}$$

$$= 190(2.159766) \approx 410.35556$$

The number of Smartphone sales in the year 2011 is approximately 410 million In the year 2015, $t = 11$.

$$S(11) = 190e^{0.11(11)} = 190e^{1.21}$$

$$= 190(3.3535) \approx 637.162$$

The number of Smartphone sales in the year 2015 is approximately 637 million.

b.   In the year 2011, Smartphones sales beat PC sales by 410 – 360 = 50 million.

23. a. $N(t) = 500,000\left(\dfrac{2}{3}\right)^{t}$

$$N(1) = 500,000\left(\dfrac{2}{3}\right)^{1} = 333,333$$

333,333 cans are still in use after 1 year.

b. $N(2) = 500,000\left(\dfrac{2}{3}\right)^{2} = 500,000 \cdot \dfrac{4}{9}$

$$= 222,222$$

After 2 years 222,222 cans are still in use.

c. $N(10) = 500,000\left(\dfrac{2}{3}\right)^{10}$

$$= 500,000\left(\dfrac{1024}{59049}\right) \approx 8671$$

8671 cans are still in use after 10 years.

24. $S(t) = C(0.6)^{t}$

a.   10 years after purchase, $t = 10$.

$$S(t) = 10,000(0.6)^{1} = 6000$$

After 1 year, the salvage value of the computer is $6000.

b.   10 years after purchase, $t = 10$.

$$S(t) = 10,000(0.6)^{10} \approx 60.47$$

After 10 years, the salvage value of the computer is $60.47.

25. $A(a) = 14.7(10)^{-0.000018a}$, where a is in feet.

a.   Let $a = 29,000$ ft.

$$A(29,000) = 14.7(10)^{-0.000018(29,000)}$$

$$= 14.7(10)^{-0.522} \approx 4.42$$

The atmospheric pressure at the top of Mt. Everest is 4.42 lb/in^2.

b.   Let $a = 20,000$ ft.

$$A(20,000) = 14.7(10)^{-0.000018(20,000)}$$

$$= 14.7(10)^{-0.36} \approx 6.42$$

The atmospheric pressure at the top of Mt. McKinley is 6.42 lb/in^2.

26. $A(a) = 14.7e^{-0.21a}$, where a is in miles.

a.   Let $a = 6$.

$$A(6) = 14.7e^{-0.21(6)} = 14.7e^{-1.26}$$

$$= 14.7(0.28365) \approx 4.17$$

The atmospheric pressure at the top of Mt. Everest is 4.17 lb/in^2.

b.   Let $a = 4$.

$$A(4) = 14.7e^{-0.21(4)} = 14.7e^{-0.84}$$

$$= 14.7(0.43171) \approx 6.35$$

The atmospheric pressure at the top of Mt. McKinley is 6.35 lb/in^2.

27. The graph of $f(x) = \log_5 x$ can be obtained by reflecting the graph of $y = 5^x$ along the line $y = x$ as shown below.

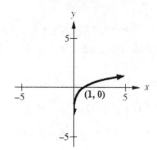

28. The graph of $f(x) = \log_6 x$ can be obtained by reflecting the graph of $y = 6^x$ along the line $y = x$ as shown below.

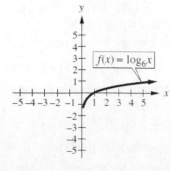

29. If A is double P and $r = 5\%$, find t:

$$2P = Pe^{0.05t}$$

$$2 = e^{0.05t}$$

$$\ln 2 = 0.05t\,(\ln e)$$

$$\ln 2 = 0.05t$$

$$t = \frac{\ln 2}{0.05} = \frac{0.693}{0.05} \approx 13.863$$

It takes about 13.86 years to double.

30. If A is double P and $r = 7\%$, find t:

$$2P = Pe^{0.07t}$$

$$2 = e^{0.07t}$$

$$\ln 2 = 0.07t\,(\ln e)$$

$$\ln 2 = 0.07t$$

$$t = \frac{\ln 2}{0.07} = \frac{0.693}{0.07} \approx 9.902$$

It takes about 9.9 years to double.

31. If A is double P and $r = 6.5\%$, find t:

$$2P = Pe^{0.065t}$$

$$2 = e^{0.065t}$$

$$\ln 2 = 0.065t\,(\ln e)$$

$$\ln 2 = 0.065t$$

$$t = \frac{\ln 2}{0.065} = \frac{0.693}{0.065} \approx 10.66$$

It takes about 10.66 years to double.

32. If A is double P and $r = 7.5\%$, find t:

$$2P = Pe^{0.075t}$$

$$2 = e^{0.075t}$$

$$\ln 2 = 0.075t\,(\ln e)$$

$$\ln 2 = 0.075t$$

$$t = \frac{\ln 2}{0.075} = \frac{0.693}{0.075} \approx 9.24$$

It takes about 9.24 years to double.

33. The population $P = 6.1e^{rt}$, P is in billions of people, t the number of years since 2000 and r is the rate of growth. If $r = 1.2\% = 0.012$ and the year is 2010, $t = 10$, then

$$P = 6.1e^{0.012(10)} = 6.1e^{0.12} \approx 6.88$$

The population in 2010 will be about 6.88 billion.

34. The population $P = 6.1e^{rt}$, P is in billions of people, t the number of years since 2000 and r is the rate of growth. If $r = 1.75\% = 0.0175$ and the year is 2010, $t = 10$, then

$$P = 6.1e^{0.0175(10)} = 6.1e^{0.175} \approx 7.27$$

The population in 2010 will be about 7.27 billion.

35. $$B = 1000e^{0.04t}$$

$$2000 = 1000e^{0.04t}$$

$$2 = e^{0.04t}$$

$$\ln 2 = 0.04t\,(\ln e)$$

$$\ln 2 = 0.04t$$

$$t = \frac{\ln 2}{0.04} \approx \frac{0.693147}{0.04} \approx 17.3287$$

It will take about 17.3 minutes.

36. $$B = 1000e^{0.04t}$$

$$5000 = 1000e^{0.04t}$$

$$5 = e^{0.04t}$$

$$\ln 5 = 0.04t\,(\ln e)$$

$$\ln 5 = 0.04t$$

$$t = \frac{\ln 5}{0.04} = \frac{1.6094}{0.04} \approx 40.2359$$

It will take about 40.2 minutes.

37. $$B = 1000e^{0.04t}$$

$$25{,}000 = 1000e^{0.04t}$$

$$25 = e^{0.04t}$$

$$\ln 25 = 0.04t\,(\ln e)$$

$$\ln 25 = 0.04t$$

$$t = \frac{\ln 25}{0.04} \approx \frac{3.218876}{0.04} \approx 80.4719$$

It will take about 80.5 minutes.

38. $$B = 1000e^{0.04t}$$

$$50{,}000 = 1000e^{0.04t}$$

$$50 = e^{0.04t}$$

$$\ln 50 = 0.04t\,(\ln e)$$

$$\ln 50 = 0.04t$$

$$t = \frac{\ln 50}{0.04} = \frac{3.921}{0.04} \approx 97.8$$

It will take about 97.8 minutes.

39. a. $B = 100,000e^{-0.2t}$, when $t = 0$,

$B = 100,000e^{-0.2(0)} = 100,000e^0$

$= 100,000 \cdot 1 = 100,000$

b. When $t = 2$,

$B = 100,000e^{-0.2(2)} = 100,000e^{-0.4}$

$= 100,000(0.67032) \approx 67,032$

c. When $t = 10$,

$B = 100,000e^{-0.2(10)} = 100,000e^{-2}$

$= 100,000(0.135335) \approx 13,534$

d. When $t = 20$,

$B = 100,000e^{-0.2(20)} = 100,000e^{-4}$

$= 100,000(0.018316) \approx 1832$

40. $N = N_0 e^{0.015t}$, where t is in days.

Let $N = 3N_0$.

$3N_0 = N_0 e^{0.015t}$

$3 = e^{0.015t}$

$\ln 3 = \ln e^{0.015t}$

$\ln 3 = 0.015t$

$t = \dfrac{\ln 3}{0.015} \approx 73.24$

The number of honey bees will triple in about 73 days.

41. If $A(t) = \dfrac{1}{2} A_0$ and $k = 0.003\% = 0.00003$,

find t:

$\dfrac{1}{2} A_0 = A_0 e^{-0.00003t}$

$\dfrac{1}{2} = e^{-0.00003t}$

$\ln\left(\dfrac{1}{2}\right) = -0.00003t (\ln e)$

$\ln(0.5) = -0.00003t$

$t = \dfrac{\ln(0.5)}{-0.00003} = \dfrac{-0.69315}{-0.00003}$

$\approx 23,105$

Plutonium's half-life is 23,105 years.

42. If $A(t) = \dfrac{1}{2} A_0$ and $k = 6.3\% = 0.063$, find t:

$\dfrac{1}{2} A_0 = A_0 e^{-0.063t}$

$\dfrac{1}{2} = e^{-0.063t}$

$\ln\left(\dfrac{1}{2}\right) = -0.063t (\ln e)$

$\ln(0.5) = -0.063t$

$t = \dfrac{\ln(0.5)}{-0.063} = \dfrac{-0.69315}{-0.063}$

≈ 11

Krypton's half-life is 11 years.

43. If $A(t) = \dfrac{1}{2} A_0$ and $k = 5.2\% = 0.052$, find t:

$\dfrac{1}{2} A_0 = A_0 e^{-0.052t}$

$\dfrac{1}{2} = e^{-0.052t}$

$\ln\left(\dfrac{1}{2}\right) = -0.052t (\ln e)$

$\ln(0.5) = -0.052t$

$t = \dfrac{\ln(0.5)}{-0.052} = \dfrac{-0.69315}{-0.052} \approx 13.3$

Its half-life is 13.3 years.

44. If $A(t) = \dfrac{1}{2} A_0$ and $k = 0.2\% = 0.002$, find t:

$\dfrac{1}{2} A_0 = A_0 e^{-0.002t}$

$\dfrac{1}{2} = e^{-0.002t}$

$\ln\left(\dfrac{1}{2}\right) = -0.002t (\ln e)$

$\ln(0.5) = -0.002t$

$t = \dfrac{\ln(0.5)}{-0.002} = \dfrac{-0.69315}{-0.002} \approx 346.6$

Its half-life is 346.6 years.

45. $P = 14.7e^{-0.00005h}$, h is the altitude in feet, P is the atmospheric pressure.

a.   If $h = 0$, $P = 14.7e^{-0.00005(0)} = 14.7e^{0}$

$= 14.7 \cdot 1 = 14.7 \text{ lb/in}^2$

b.   If $h = 5000$,

$P = 14.7e^{-0.00005(5000)} = 14.7e^{-0.25}$

$= 14.7(0.7788) \approx 11.4 \text{ lb/in}^2$

c.   If $h = 10,000$,

$P = 14.7e^{-0.00005(10,000)} = 14.7e^{-0.5}$

$= 14.7(0.606531) \approx 8.92 \text{ lb/in}^2$

46. $P = 30e^{-0.207h}$, h is the altitude in miles, P is the atmospheric pressure.

a.   At sea level, $h = 0$,

$P = 30e^{-0.207(0)} = 30e^{0}$

$= 30 \cdot 1 = 30 \text{ lb/in}^2$

b.   At 5 mi above seal leve, $h = 5$,

$P = 30e^{-0.207(5)} = 30e^{-1.035}$

$= 30(0.3552) \approx 10.66 \text{ lb/in}^2$

47. $S = 0.94e^{0.09h}$ million dollars, t is the number of years after 2000.

a.   If $S = 3$,

$3 = 0.94e^{0.09t}$

$\dfrac{3}{0.94} = 0.94e^{0.09t}$

$\ln\left(\dfrac{3}{0.94}\right) = \ln e^{0.09t}$

$\ln\left(\dfrac{3}{0.94}\right) = 0.09t$

$t = \dfrac{\ln\left(\dfrac{3}{0.94}\right)}{0.09} \approx \dfrac{1.1605}{0.09} \approx 12.89$

The players' average salaries will reach $3 million in about 13 years, or 2013.

b.   In year 1, the average salary was about 1.0 million, and in year 6 about 1.7 million. The difference is $1.7 - 1.0 = 0.7$. This is a percent increase of

$\dfrac{1.7 - 1.0}{1.0} = \dfrac{0.7}{1.0} = .70 = 70\%$.

c.   Owners revenues have a percent increase of

$\dfrac{8.88 - 6.49}{6.49} = \dfrac{2.39}{6.49} = 0.368 = 36.8\%$.

d.   The players have a higher increase but note that the years as well as the year intervals are different.

48. $N(t) = 500,000\left(\dfrac{2}{3}\right)^t$, t is in years

If $N = 100,000$,

$100,000 = 500,000\left(\dfrac{2}{3}\right)^t$

$0.2 = \left(\dfrac{2}{3}\right)^t$

$\ln 0.2 = \ln\left(\dfrac{2}{3}\right)^t$

$\ln 0.2 = t \ln\left(\dfrac{2}{3}\right)$

$t = \dfrac{\ln 0.2}{\ln\left(\dfrac{2}{3}\right)} = \dfrac{-1.6094}{-0.40546} \approx 4.0$

It will take about 4 years for the number of cans to reach 100,000.

49. $A = 5000e^{-0.04t}$ where t is the number of years after 1970.

a.   In 1970, $t = 0$

$A = 5000e^{-0.04(0)} = 5000e^{0} = 5000$

There were about 5000 aviation accidents in 1970.

b.   In 1990, $t = 20$

$A = 5000e^{-0.04(20)} = 5000e^{-0.8}$

$= 5000(0.4493) \approx 2247$

There were about 2247 aviation accidents in 1990.

c.   If $A = 1000$,

$1000 = 5000e^{-0.04t}$

$0.2 = e^{-0.04t}$

$\ln 0.2 = -0.04t(\ln e)$

$-1.6094 = -0.04t$

$t = \dfrac{-1.6094}{-0.04} \approx 40$

In 2010, 40 years after 1970, the number of aviation accidents is predicted to be 1000.

50. $P = 90e^{-0.5t}$, t is in minutes
    If $P = 80$,

$$80 = 90e^{-0.5t}$$

$$\frac{8}{9} = e^{-0.5t}$$

$$\ln\left(\frac{8}{9}\right) = \ln e^{-0.5t}$$

$$\ln\left(\frac{8}{9}\right) = -0.5t$$

$$t = \frac{\ln\left(\frac{8}{9}\right)}{-0.5} = \frac{-0.1178}{-0.5} \approx 0.24$$

It will take about 0.24 minute before the diastolic pressure decreases to 80.

51. $B = 50,000e^{0.2t}$ where t is the number of hours after 12 noon.
    a. At noon, $t = 0$

$$B = 50,000e^{0.2(0)} = 50,000e^0$$
$$= 50,000$$

There were 50,000 bacteria at noon.
    b. At 2 p.m., $t = 2$

$$B = 50,000e^{0.2(2)} = 50,000e^{0.4}$$
$$= 50,000(1.4918) \approx 74,591$$

There were about 74,591 bacteria at 2 p.m.
    c. At 6 p.m., $t = 6$

$$B = 50,000e^{0.2(6)} = 50,000e^{1.2}$$
$$= 50,000(3.3201) \approx 166,006$$

There were about 166,006 bacteria at 6 p.m.

52. $B = 50,000e^{-0.1t}$ where t in hours
    a. When $t = 0$

$$B = 50,000e^{-0.1(0)} = 50,000e^0 = 50,000$$

There were 50,000 bacteria when the bactericide is introduced.
    b. When $t = 1$

$$B = 50,000e^{-0.1(1)} = 50,000e^{-0.1}$$
$$= 50,000(0.9048) \approx 45,242$$

There were about 45,242 bacteria 1 hour after the bactericide is introduced.

c. When $t = 10$

$$B = 50,000e^{-0.1(10)} = 50,000e^{-1}$$
$$= 50,000(0.36788) \approx 18,394$$

There were about 18,394 bacteria 10 hours after the bactericide is introduced.

53. $S = 1000e^{-0.1d}$ where d is the number of days after the campaign.
    a. On the last day, $d = 0$

$$S = 1000e^{-0.1(0)} = 1000e^0 = 1000$$

There were 1000 sales on the last day of the campaign.
    b. 10 days after the campaign, $d = 10$

$$S = 1000e^{-0.1(10)} = 1000e^{-1}$$
$$= 1000(0.3679) \approx 368$$

There were about 368 sales 10 days after the campaign.

54. $p = 100e^{-q/2}$ where q is the number of units demanded at a price of p dollars per unit.
    a. For a 100-unit demand, $q = 100$

$$p = 100e^{-100/2}$$
$$= 100e^{-50} \approx 1.9 \times 10^{-20} \text{ dollar}$$

For a 100-unit demand, the price will be 1.9×10^{-20} dollar per unit.
    b. For no demand, $q = 0$

$$p = 100e^{-0/2}$$
$$= 100e^0 = 100 \text{ dollars}$$

For no demand, the price will be $100 per unit.

55. $C = 100\left(1 - e^{-0.5t}\right)$ where t is the number of hours.
    a. $t = 0$

$$C = 100\left(1 - e^{-0.5(0)}\right) = 100\left(1 - e^0\right)$$
$$= 100(1 - 1) = 100 \cdot 0 = 0$$

At $t = 0$ the concentration is 0.
    b. $t = 1$

$$C = 100\left(1 - e^{-0.5(1)}\right) = 100\left(1 - e^{-0.5}\right)$$
$$= 100(1 - 0.6065) = 100(0.3935) \approx 39.4$$

At $t = 1$ the concentration is 39.4.

56. $N(t) = \dfrac{5050}{1+100e^{-0.06t}}$ where t is time.

a. $N(0) = \dfrac{5050}{1+100e^{-0.06(0)}}$

$= \dfrac{5050}{1+100e^{0}} = \dfrac{5050}{101} = 50$

At $t = 0$, 50 people have been reached by a particular rumor.

b. $N(0) = \dfrac{5050}{1+100e^{-0.06(0)}}$

$= \dfrac{5050}{1+100e^{0}} = \dfrac{5050}{101} = 50$

At $t = 0$, 50 people have been reached by a particular rumor.

57. $M = -2.5\log\left(\dfrac{B}{B_0}\right)$ where B is the

brightness of the star and B_0 is the minimum of brightness.

a. $B = 2.1B_0$

$M = -2.5\log\left(\dfrac{2.1B_0}{B_0}\right)$

$= -2.5\log 2.1 \approx -0.8055$

The stellar magnitude of the North Star is –0.8055.

b. $B = 36.2B_0$

$M = -2.5\log\left(\dfrac{36.2B_0}{B_0}\right)$

$= -2.5\log 36.2 \approx -3.8968$

The stellar magnitude of Venus is –3.8968.

58. $P = 16.7\log(A-12) + 87$ where A the age of a male $13 \le A \le 18$.

a. For a 13-year-old male, $A = 13$

$P = 16.7\log(13-12) + 87$

$= 16.7\log(1) + 87$

$= 16.7(0) + 87 = 87$

The percent of adult height that a 13-year-old male has reached is 87%.

b. For an18-year-old male, $A = 18$

$P = 16.7\log(18-12) + 87$

$= 16.7\log(6) + 87$

$= 16.7(0.77815) + 87 \approx 99.995$

The percent of adult height that an 18-year-old male has reached is 99.995%.

59. For monthly compounding, use

$A = P\left(1+\dfrac{r}{n}\right)^{nt}$, where P is the principal, r the rate of interest, n the number of periods and t the number of years.

For continuous compounding, use $A = Pe^{rt}$ where P is the principal, r the rate of interest and t the time in years.

Monthly:

$A = 1000\left(1+\dfrac{0.06}{12}\right)^{12(10)} = 1000(1.005)^{120}$

$= 1000(1.8194) = 1819.40$

Compounded monthly, the amount is $1819.40.

Continuous:

$A = 1000e^{0.06(10)} = 1000e^{0.6}$

$= 1000(1.82212) = 1822.12$

Compounded continuously, the amount is $1822.12.

In 10 years, continuous compounding yields $2.72 more than monthly compounding.

60. For monthly compounding, use

$A = P\left(1+\dfrac{r}{n}\right)^{nt}$, where P is the principal, r the rate of interest, n the number of periods and t the number of years.

For continuous compounding, use $A = Pe^{rt}$ where P is the principal, r the rate of interest and t the time in years.

Monthly:

$A = 1000\left(1+\dfrac{0.06}{12}\right)^{12(20)}$

$= 1000(1.005)^{240}$

$= 1000(3.3102) = 3310.20$

Compounded monthly, the amount is $3310.20.

Continuous:

$A = 1000e^{0.06(20)} = 1000e^{1.2}$

$= 1000(3.32012) = 3320.12$

Compounded continuously, the amount is $3320.12.   In 20 years, continuous compounding yields $9.92 more than monthly compounding.

61. Answers may vary.

   a. $f(x) = 1^x = 1$, a horizontal line.

   b.   Yes, a horizontal line is a function.

62. Answers will vary. Some possibilities include: if $b = 0$, then we would have 0^0, which is undefined; if $b < 0$, for instance, $b = -2$, then we would have $(-2)^{\frac{1}{2}} = \sqrt{-2}$, neither are real numbers.

63. Answers may vary. The graphs are symmetric to the y-axis.

64. Answers will vary. The U.S. Census Bureau probably used a different annual growth rate.

Skill Checker

1. To graph $x + y = 4$, let $x = 0$, then $y = 4$. For $y = 0$, $x = 4$. Graph the points (0, 4) and (4, 0) and join them with a line as shown on the graph below.

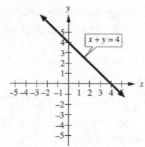

2. To graph $2x - y = 4$, let $x = 0$, then $y = -4$. For $y = 0$, $x = 2$. Graph the points (0, -4) and (2, 0) and join them with a line as shown on the graph below.

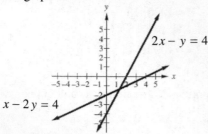

3. To graph $2x - y = 5$, let $x = 0$, then $y = -5$. For $y = 0$, $2x = 5$ which means that $x = 2.5$. Graph the points (0, -5) and (2.5, 0) and join them with a line as shown on the graph

below.

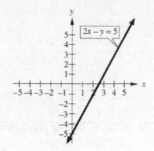

4. To graph $x - 2y = 4$, let $x = 0$, then $y = -2$. For $y = 0$, $x = 4$. Graph the points (0, -2) and (4, 0) and join them with a line as shown on the graph above in problem 2.

Section 7.6 Two Linear Equations in Two Variables

1. Two points on the line $x + y = 3$ are (0, 3) and (3, 0). Graph these points and draw a line through them. The line $2x - y = 0$ passes through the origin, (0, 0), and through the point (2, 4). Graph these points and draw a line through them. The graph shows that the lines intersect at (1, 2). Check that this point satisfies both equations: $1 + 2 = 3$ and $2 - 2 = 0$. Thus, the solution is (1, 2).

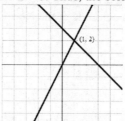

2. Two points on the line $x + y = 5$ are (0, 5) and (5, 0). Graph these points and draw a line through them. The line $x - 4y = 0$ passes through the origin, (0, 0), and through the point (8, 2). Graph these points and draw a line through them. The graph shows that the lines intersect at (4, 1). Check that this point satisfies both equations: $4 + 1 = 5$ and $4 - 4(1) = 0$. Thus, the solution is (4, 1).

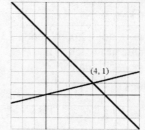

3. Two points on the line $2x - y = 10$ are
    (0, −10) and (5, 0). Graph these points and
    draw a line through them. Two points on the
    line $3x + 2y = 1$ are (1, −1) and (5, −7).
    Graph these two points and draw a line
    through them. The graph shows that the
    lines intersect at (3, −4). Check that this
    point satisfies both equations:
    $(2)(3) - (-4) = 6 + 4 = 10$ and
    $(3)(3) + (2)(-4) = 9 - 8 = 1$. Thus, the
    solution is (3, −4).

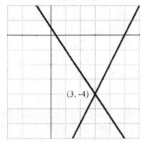

4. Two points on the line $2x - 3y = 1$ are
    (−1, −1) and (5, 3). Graph these points and
    draw a line through them. Two points on the
    line $x + 2y = 4$ are (0, 2) and (4, 0). Graph
    these two points and draw a line through
    them. The graph shows that the lines
    intersect at (2, 1). Check that this point
    satisfies both equations:
    $2(2) - 3(1) = 4 - 3 = 1$ and $2 + 2(1) = 2 + 2 = 4$
    Thus, the solution is (2, 1).

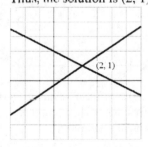

5. Two points on the line $3x + 4y = 4$ are
    (0, 1) and (4, −2). Graph these points
    and draw a line through them. Two
    points on the line $2x - 6y = 7$ are (7/2, 0)
    and (−1, −3/2). Graph these two points and
    draw a line through them. The graph
    shows that the two lines intersect at the
    point (2, −1/2). Check that this point
    satisfies both equations: $(3)(2) + (4)(-1/2) =$
    $6 - 2 = 4$ and $(2)(2) - (6)(-1/2) = 4 + 3 = 7$.
    Thus, the solution is (2, −1/2).

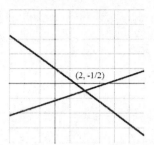

6. Two points on the line $y = 5x - 12$ are
    (0, −12) and (2, −2). Graph these points and
    draw a line through them. Two points on the
    line $y = 3x - 8$ are (0, −8) and (2, −2). Graph
    these two points and draw a line through
    them. The graph shows that the lines
    intersect at (2, −2). Check that this point
    satisfies both equations
    $5(2) - 12 = 10 - 12 = -2$ and
    $3(2) - 8 = 6 - 8 = -2$. Thus, the solution is
    (2, −2).

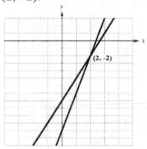

7. $x + y = 3$

    $\underline{2x - y = 0}$

    $3x \quad = 3$ Add the equations.

    $x = 1$ Divide by 3.

    $1 + y = 3$ Substitute into 1st eq.

    $y = 2$ Subtract 1.

    The solution is (1, 2). You can check this.

8. $x + y = 5$

    $\underline{x - 4y = 0}$

    $5y = 5$ Subtract the equations.

    $y = 1$ Divide by 5.

    $x + 1 = 5$ Substitute into 1st eq.

    $x = 4$ Subtract 1.

    The solution is (4, 1). You can check this.

9.　Multiply both sides of the first equation by 2 and add the equations:

$$x + y = 6 \rightarrow 2x + 2y = 12$$
$$\underline{3x - 2y = 8 \rightarrow 3x - 2y = 8}$$

Add:　　　　　$5x = 20$

Divide by 5:　　$x = 4$

Substitute into 1st eq:　$4 + y = 6$

Subtract 4:　　　　$y = 2$

The solution is (4, 2).

10.　Multiply both sides of the first equation by 3 and add the equations:

$$2x - y = 5 \rightarrow 6x - 3y = 15$$
$$\underline{5x + 3y = 18 \rightarrow 5x + 3y = 18}$$

Add:　　$11x\ \ \ = 33$

Divide by 11:　　$x = 3$

Substitute into 1st eq:　$2(3) - y = 5$

Simplify:　　　　　$6 - y = 5$

Add y, then subtract 5:　　$y = 1$

The solution is (3, 1).

11.　Multiply both sides of the first equation by 2 and add the equations:

$$2x - y = 10 \rightarrow 4x - 2y = 20$$
$$\underline{3x + 2y = 1 \rightarrow 3x + 2y = 1}$$

Add:　　　$7x\ \ \ = 21$

Divide by 7:　　$x = 3$

Substitute into 1st eq:　$6 - y = 10$

Solve:　　　　　$y = -4$

The solution is (3, −4).

12.　Multiply both sides of the second equation by −2 and add the equations:

$$2x - 3y = 1 \rightarrow 2x - 3y = 1$$
$$\underline{x + 2y = 4 \rightarrow -2x - 4y = -8}$$

Add:　　　　$-7y = -7$

Divide by − 7:　　$y = 1$

Substitute into 2nd eq:　$x + 2(1) = 4$

Solve:　　　　　$x = 2$

The solution is (2, 1).

13.　Multiply both sides of the first equation by −3 and add the equations:

$$5x + y = 4 \rightarrow -15x - 3y = -12$$
$$\underline{15x + 3y = 8 \rightarrow 15x + 3y = 8}$$

Add:　　　　　$0 = -4$

Since the last result is impossible, the two given equations have no common solution. (Note that the two lines corresponding to these equations are parallel.)

14.　Multiply both sides of the first equation by −2 and add the equations:

$$2x - y = -5 \rightarrow -4x + 2y = 10$$
$$\underline{4x - 2y = -10 \rightarrow 4x - 2y = -10}$$

Add:　　　　　$0 = 0$

The lines coincide; if a is any real number, both equations are satisfied by the solution $(a, 2a + 5)$.

15.　Multiply both sides of the first equation by 3, multiply both sides of the second equation by 5 and add the equations:

$$2x + 5y = 12 \rightarrow 6x + 15y = 36$$
$$\underline{5x - 3y = -1 \rightarrow 25x - 15y = -5}$$

Add:　　　$31x\ \ \ = 31$

Divide by 31:　　$x = 1$

Substitute into 1st eq:　$2 + 5y = 12$

Subtract 2:　　　　$5y = 10$

Divide by 5:　　　　$y = 2$

The solution is (1, 2).

16.　Multiply both sides of the first equation by 7, multiply both sides of the second equation by −3 and add the equations:

$$2x + 3y = 9 \rightarrow 14x + 21y = 63$$
$$\underline{11x + 7y = 2 \rightarrow -33x - 21y = -6}$$

Add:　　　$-19x\ \ \ = 57$

Divide by − 19:　　$x = -3$

Substitute into 1st eq:　$2(-3) + 3y = 9$

Simplify and add 6:　　$3y = 15$

Divide by 3:　　　　$y = 5$

The solution is (−3, 5).

17.　Multiply both sides of the first equation by 3, multiply both sides of the second equation by 2 and add the equations:

$3x + 4y = 4 \rightarrow 9x + 12y = 12$

$2x - 6y = 7 \rightarrow \underline{4x - 12y = 14}$

Add: $\qquad 13x \qquad = 26$

Divide by 13: $\qquad x = 2$

Substitute into 1st eq: $\quad 6 + 4y = 4$

Subtract 6: $\qquad\qquad 4y = -2$

Divide by 4: $\qquad\qquad y = -\dfrac{1}{2}$

The solution is $\left(2, -\dfrac{1}{2}\right)$.

18. Multiply both sides of the first equation by −1, and add the equations:

$y = 5x - 12 \rightarrow -y = -5x + 12$

$y = 3x - 8 \rightarrow \quad \underline{y = 3x - 8}$

Add: $\qquad\qquad 0 = -2x + 4$

Add 2x: $\qquad\quad 2x = 4$

Divide by 2: $\qquad x = 2$

Substitute into 1st eq: $\; y = 5(2) - 12$

Simplify: $\qquad\qquad y = 10 - 12 = -2$

The solution is (2, −2).

19. Write the first eqution in standard form. Multiply both sides of the first equation by 2, multiply both sides of the second equation by −3 and add the equations:

$11x + 3y = -3 \rightarrow \quad 22x + 6y = -6$

$5x + 2y = 5 \rightarrow \underline{-15x - 6y = -15}$

Add: $\qquad\qquad 7x \qquad = -21$

Divide by 7: $\qquad\qquad x = -3$

Substitute into 1st eq: $\; -33 + 3y = -3$

Add 33: $\qquad\qquad\qquad 3y = 30$

Divide by 3: $\qquad\qquad\quad y = 10$

The solution is (−3, 10).

20. Write the second eqution in standard form. Multiply both sides of the second equation by −2 and add the equations:

$10x + 6y = 1 \rightarrow \quad 10x + 6y = 1$

$5x + 3y = 9 \rightarrow \underline{-10x - 6y = -18}$

Add: $\qquad\qquad 0 = -17$

Since the last result is impossible, the two given equations have no common solution. (Note that the two lines corresponding

to these equations are parallel.)

21. $x = 2y - 3$

$\underline{x = -2y - 1}$

$2x = \quad -4 \qquad$ Add the equations.

$x = -2 \qquad$ Divide by 2.

$-2 = 2y - 3 \qquad$ Substitute into 1st eq.

$1 = 2y \qquad$ Add 3.

$y = \dfrac{1}{2} \qquad$ Divide by 2.

The solution is $\left(-2, \dfrac{1}{2}\right)$.

22. Write the first eqution in standard form. Multiply both sides of the first equation by 2, multiply both sides of the second equation by −3 and add the equations:

$4x - y = 2 \rightarrow -4x + y = -2$

$\qquad\qquad \underline{4x - 2y = 3}$

Add: $\qquad\qquad -y = 1$

Divide by −1: $\qquad y = -1$

Substitute into 1st eq: $\; 4x - (-1) = 2$

Simplify: $\qquad\qquad 4x + 1 = 2$

Subtract 1: $\qquad\qquad 4x = 1$

Divide by 4: $\qquad\qquad x = \dfrac{1}{4}$

The solution is $\left(\dfrac{1}{4}, -1\right)$.

23. Multiply both sides of the first equation by −2 and add the equations:

$2x + 3y + 11 = 0 \rightarrow -4x - 6y - 22 = 0$

$5x + 6y + 20 = 0 \rightarrow \underline{5x + 6y + 20 = 0}$

Add: $\qquad\qquad x - 2 = 0$

Add 2: $\qquad\qquad x = 2$

Substitute into 1st eq: $\; 4 + 3y + 11 = 0$

Subtract 15: $\qquad\qquad 3y = -15$

Divide by 3: $\qquad\qquad y = -5$

The solution is (2, −5).

24. Write the second equation in standard form. Multiply both sides of the first equation by 4 and add the equations:

$3x + y = 4 \rightarrow \quad 12x + 4y = 16$

$2x - 4y = -9 \rightarrow \underline{\quad 2x - 4y = -9}$

Add: $\qquad\qquad 14x \qquad = 7$

Divide by 14: $\qquad\qquad x = \dfrac{1}{2}$

Substitute into 2nd eq: $2\left(\dfrac{1}{2}\right) - 4y = -9$

Simplify: $\qquad\qquad\qquad 1 - 4y = -9$

Subtract 1, then divide by -4: $\quad y = \dfrac{5}{2}$

The solution is $\left(\dfrac{1}{2}, \dfrac{5}{2}\right)$.

25. Multiply both sides of the second equation by 6 and add the equations:

$3x - 12y = -8 \rightarrow 3x - 12y = -8$

$2x + 2y = 3 \rightarrow \underline{12x + 12y = 18}$

Add: $\qquad\qquad 15x \qquad = 10$

Divide by 15: $\qquad\qquad x = \dfrac{2}{3}$

Substitute into 1st eq: $2 - 12y = -8$

Subtract 2: $\qquad\qquad -12y = -10$

Divide by -12: $\qquad\qquad y = \dfrac{5}{6}$

The solution is $\left(\dfrac{2}{3}, \dfrac{5}{6}\right)$.

26. Multiply both sides of the second equation by -2 and add the equations:

$4x + 8y = 7 \rightarrow \quad 4x + 8y = 7$

$3x + 4y = 6 \rightarrow \underline{-6x - 8y = -12}$

Add: $\qquad\qquad -2x \qquad = -5$

Divide by -2: $\qquad\qquad x = \dfrac{5}{2}$

Substitute into 1st eq: $4\left(\dfrac{5}{2}\right) + 8y = 7$

Simplify: $\qquad\qquad\qquad 10 + 8y = 7$

Subtract 10: $\qquad\qquad\qquad 8y = -3$

Divide by 8: $\qquad\qquad\qquad y = -\dfrac{3}{8}$

The solution is $\left(\dfrac{5}{2}, -\dfrac{3}{8}\right)$.

27. Multiply both sides of the first equation by -2 and add the equations:

$r - 4s = -10 \rightarrow -2r + 8s = 20$

$2r - 8s = \ 13 \rightarrow \underline{\ 2r - 8s = 13}$

Add: $\qquad\qquad\qquad 0 = 33$

Since the last result is impossible, the two given equations have no common solution. (Note that the two lines corresponding to these equations are parallel.)

28. Multiply both sides of the second equation by 4 and add the equations:

$3r + 4s = 15 \rightarrow \ 3r + 4s = 15$

$4r - s = 20 \rightarrow \underline{16r - 4s = 80}$

Add: $\qquad\qquad\qquad 19s = 95$

Divide by 19: $\qquad\qquad s = 5$

Substitute into 2nd eq: $4(5) - s = 20$

Simplify: $\qquad\qquad\qquad 20 - s = 20$

Subtract 10, multiply by -1: $s = 0$

The solution is $r = 5$, $s = 0$.

29. Multiply both sides of the first equation by 3, multiply both sides of the second equation by 2 and add the equations:

$6u - 2v = -27 \rightarrow 18u - 6v = -81$

$4u + 3v = \ 8 \rightarrow \underline{\ 8u + 6v = \ 16}$

Add: $\qquad\qquad 26u \qquad = -65$

Divide by 26: $\qquad\qquad u = -\dfrac{5}{2}$

Substitute into 1st eq: $-15 - 2v = -27$

Add 15: $\qquad\qquad\qquad -2v = -12$

Divide by -2: $\qquad\qquad\qquad v = 6$

The solution is $u = -\dfrac{5}{2}$, $v = 6$; or $\left(-\dfrac{5}{2}, 6\right)$.

30. Write the equations in standard form. Multiply both sides of the first equation by 3, multiply both sides of the second equation by -2 and add the equations:

$8w - 16z = 4 \rightarrow \quad 24w - 48z = 12$

$12w - 18z = 3 \rightarrow \underline{-24w + 36z = -6}$

Add: $\qquad\qquad\qquad -12w = 6$

Divide by -12: $\qquad\qquad w = -\dfrac{1}{2}$

Substitute into 2nd eq: $12\left(-\dfrac{1}{2}\right) - 18z = 3$

Simplify: $\qquad\qquad -6 - 18z = 3$

Add 6: $\qquad\qquad\qquad -18z = 9$

Divide by -18: $\qquad\qquad z = -\dfrac{1}{2}$

The solution is $w = -\dfrac{1}{2}$, $z = -\dfrac{1}{2}$.

31. a.   Multiply both sides of the first equation by -1 and add the equations:

A: $y = 8x + 1000 \rightarrow -y = -8x - 1000$

B: $y = 10x + 800 \rightarrow \underline{\;y = 10x + 800\;}$

Add: $\qquad\qquad 0 = 2x - 200$

Add 200: $\qquad\quad 200 = 2x$

Divide by 2: $\qquad 100 = x$

The costs are equal for 100 guests.

b.   The first equation is satisfied by (0, 1000) and (200, 2600). The line through these points is the graph of the first equation. The second equation is satisfied by (0, 800) and by (200, 2800). The line through these points is the graph of the second equation. These lines are shown below.

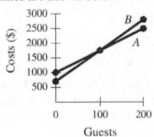

c.   The graph shows that company A is cheaper for more than 100 guests.

32. a.   Total cost of the solar heating system can be expressed as $y = 50x + 5400$.

b.   Total cost of the electric hot-water heating system can be expressed as $y = 600x + 1000$.

c.

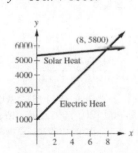

d.   Multiply both sides of the first equation by -1 and add the equations:

$y = 50x + 5400 \rightarrow -y = -50x - 5400$

$y = 600x + 1000 \rightarrow \underline{\;y = 600x + 1000\;}$

Add: $\qquad\qquad 0 = 550x - 4400$

Solve for x: $\qquad x = 8$

Substitute into 1st eq: $y = 50(8) + 5400$

Simplify: $\qquad\qquad y = 400 + 5400 = 5800$

The solution is $(8,\, 5800)$.

e.   It will take 8 years for the total cost of the solar heat to become less than the total cost of the electric heat.

33. a.   The amount of saturated fats when you eat one McDonald's and one family-style restaurant burger is $x + y = 22$.

b.   The amount of saturated fats for two Quarter Pounders is $P_Q = 2x$.

c.   The amount of saturated fats for one family-style restaurant burger is $P_F = y$.

d.   The total grams consumed in two Quarter Pounders and one family-style restaurant burger is $2x + y = 30$.

e.   The intersection of the two lines provides the answer. McDonald's has 8 grams saturated fat and the family-style restaurant has 14 grams.

34. a.   The amount of saturated fats when you eat one McDonald's and one Whopper Jr. is $x + y = 16$.

b.   The amount of saturated fats for two Quarter Pounders is $P_Q = 2x$.

c.   The amount of saturated fats for one Whopper Jr. is $P_W = y$.

d.   The total grams consumed in two Quarter Pounders and one Whopper Jr. is $2x + y = 24$.

e.   The intersection of the two lines provides the answer. McDonald's and the Whopper Jr. both have has 8 grams saturated fat.

35. a.   The amount of saturated fats when you eat one McDonald's and one Wendy's Jr. Bacon Cheeseburger is $x + y = 15$.

b. The amount of saturated fats for two Quarter Pounders is $P_Q = 2x$.

c. The amount of saturated fats for one Wendy's Jr. Bacon Cheeseburger is $P_B = y$.

d. The total grams consumed in two Quarter Pounders and one Wendy's Jr. Bacon Cheeseburger is $2x + y = 23$.

e. The intersection of the two lines provides the answer. McDonald's has 8 grams saturated fat and the Wendy's Jr. Bacon Cheeseburger has 7 grams.

36. a.

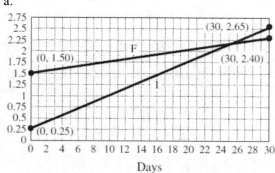

Days

b. The incandescent has the less expensive start-up.

c. The cost will be the same in 25 days.

37. a. $C = 20 + 35m$

b.

m	6	12	18
C	230	440	650

c.

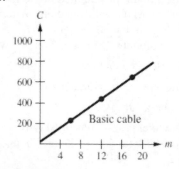

38. a. $C = 200 + 25m$

b.

m	6	12	18
C	350	500	650

c.

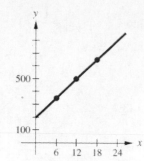

39. Use the table of values from problems 37 and 38 to plot the two graphs on the same coordinate axes.

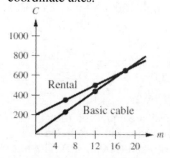

40. Cable service is cheaper if used less than 18 months.

41. DVD player and rental option is cheaper if used for more than 18 months.

42. a. $W = 80 + 5t$

b.

t	5	10	15	20
W	105	130	155	180

c. Plot the four points (5, 105), (10, 130), (15, 155) and (20, 160) and join them with a line as shown on the graph:

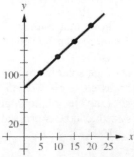

43. a. $W = 100 + 3t$

b.

t	5	10	15	20
W	115	130	145	160

c. Plot the four points (5, 115), (10, 130), (15, 145) and (20, 160) and join them with a line as shown on the graph:

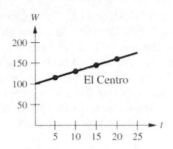

44. Lexmark: $y = 60 + 150x$

Cannon: $y = 100 + 80x$

Substitute $100 + 80x$ for y in the first equation and solve for x.

Substitute for y: $100 + 80x = 60 + 150x$

Simplify: $\qquad -70x = -40$

Divide by -70: $\qquad x = \dfrac{-40}{-70} = \dfrac{4}{7}$

Substitute into 1st eq: $y = 60 + 150\left(\dfrac{4}{7}\right)$

Simplify: $\qquad y \approx 145.71$

The solution is $\left(\dfrac{4}{7}, 145.71\right)$.

45. Cannon: $y = 100 + 80x$

Brother: $y = 130 + 70x$

Substitute $130 + 70x$ for y in the first equation and solve for x.

Substitute for y: $130 + 70x = 100 + 80x$

Simplify: $\qquad -10x = -30$

Divide by -10: $\qquad x = 3$

Substitute into 1st eq: $y = 100 + 80(3)$

Simplify: $\qquad y = 340$

The solution is $(3, 340)$.

46. Lexmark: $y = 60 + 150x$

Epson: $y = 150 + 70x$

Substitute $150 + 70x$ for y in the first equation and solve for x.

Substitute for y: $150 + 70x = 60 + 150x$

Simplify: $\qquad -80x = -90$

Divide by -80: $\qquad x = \dfrac{9}{8}$

Substitute into 1st eq: $y = 60 + 150\left(\dfrac{9}{8}\right)$

Simplify: $\qquad y = 228.75$

The solution is $\left(\dfrac{9}{8}, 228.75\right)$.

47. Total cost for Cannon (C): $y = 100 + 80x$

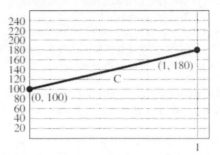

48. Total cost for Epson (E): $y = 150 + 70x$

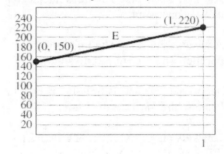

49. a. Cannon has the lower y-intercept and so has the less expensive start-up costs.
    b. The 1-year cost for Cannon is $180, and for Epson $220.
    c. If you use Cannon, your savings are $220 - 180 = \$40$.

50. Total cost for Brother (B): $y = 130 + 70x$

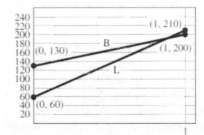

51. Total cost for Lexmark (L): $y = 60 + 150x$

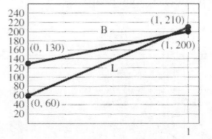

52. a. Lexmark has the lower y-intercept and so has the less expensive start-up costs.
    b. The 1-year cost for Brother is $200, and for Lexmark $210.
    c. If you use Brother, your savings are $210 - 200 = \$10$.

53. The Epson printer has the highest total cost for one-year. This cost is $220.

54. Answers may vary. The set of points that satisfy all the equations in the system.

55. Answers may vary. For a system of two linear equations, the lines will be parallel.

56. Answers may vary. The lines intersect at exactly one point.

57. Answers may vary. The lines will be parallel. The system has no solution.

58. Answers may vary. Infinitely many solution, because the lines are the same.

59. Answers may vary. Since the slopes are different, the lines will intersect. Thus, there will be one solution.

Collaborative Learning

1. The lines intersect at (66, 70.7).

2. The number of employed men and women is equal in the year 2021 at an employment rate of 70.7%.

Section 7.7 Linear Inequalities

1. $x + 2y \geq 2$: (0, 1) and (2, 0) are points on the line $x + 2y = 2$. Draw the line through these points. The point (0, 2) makes $x + 2y = 4 > 2$, so the required region is above the line as shown on the graph. Note that the line is drawn solid to show that all the points on it satisfy the given inequality.

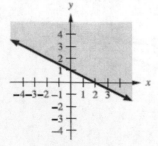

2. $x - 2y > 0$: (0, 0) and (2, 1) are points on the line $x - 2y = 0$. Draw the line through these points. The point (0, –2) makes $x - 2y = 4 > 0$, so the required region is on the same side of the line as the point (0, –2) as shown on the graph. Note that the line is drawn dashed since the points on this line are not in the solution set of the given inequality.

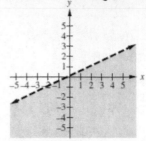

3. $x \leq 4$: Draw the line $x = 4$. Since (0, 0) satisfies the inequality, all the points in the region to the left of the line $x = 4$ also satisfy the inequality. Thus, the region to the left of this line is shaded. The solution set consists of all the points on the line and in the shaded region.

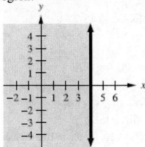

4. $y \leq 3$: Draw the line $y = 3$. Since (0, 0) satisfies the inequality, all the points in the region below the line $y = 3$ also satisfy the inequality. Thus, the region below this line is shaded. The solution set consists of all the points on the line and in the shaded region.

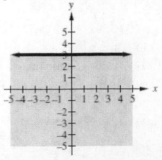

5. $3x - y < 6$: (2, 0) and (0, –6) are two points on the line $3x - y = 6$. Since the points on this line are not in the solution set of the

given inequality, draw a dashed line through these points. The point $(0, 0)$ satisfies the inequality, so all points on the same side of (above) the line as the origin form the required solution set. The shaded region in the figure is the graph of the solution set.

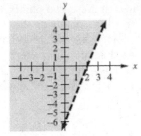

6. $3x + 4y \geq 12$: $(0, 3)$ and $(4, 0)$ are points on the line $3x + 4y = 12$. Draw the line through these points. The point $(0, 4)$ makes $3x + 4y = 16 \geq 12$, so the required region is above the line as shown on the graph. Note that the line is drawn solid to show that all the points on it satisfy the given inequality.

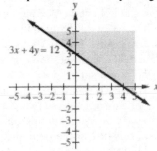

7. $2x + y \leq 4$: $(2, 0)$ and $(0, 4)$ are two points on the line $2x + y = 4$. Draw a solid line through these points. (All the points on this line are part of the solution set.) The point $(0, 0)$ satisfies the inequality $2x + y < 4$, so all points on the same side of (above) the line as the origin also satisfy this inequality. So the region to the left of $2x + y \leq 4$ is shaded. The solution set consists of all the points on the line and in the shaded region.

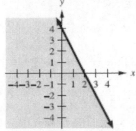

8. $2x - 3y < 0$: $(0, 0)$ and $(3, 2)$ are two points on the line $2x - 3y = 0$. Since the points on this line are not in the solution set of the

given inequality, draw a dashed line through these points. The point $(0, 1)$ satisfies the inequality, so all points on the same side of (above) the line as the point $(0, 1)$ form the required solution set. The shaded region in the figure is the graph of the solution set.

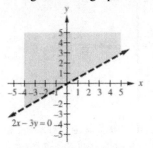

9. $4x + y > 8$: $(2, 0)$ and $(0, 8)$ are two points on the line $4x + y = 8$. Draw a dashed line through these two points, as the points on this line do not satisfy the given inequality. The point $(0, 0)$ does not satisfy the inequality, so the points on the side of the line opposite the origin (right of the line) do satisfy. Shade the region to the right of the line, the required solution set as shown in the figure.

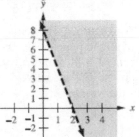

10. $x - 4y \leq 4$: $(4, 0)$ and $(0, -1)$ are two points on the line $x - 4y = 4$. Draw a solid line through these points. (All the points on this line are part of the solution set.) The point $(0, 0)$ satisfies the inequality $x - 4y \leq 4$, so all points on the same side of (above) the line as the origin also satisfy this inequality. So the region above $x - 4y \leq 4$ is shaded. The solution set consists of all the points on the line and in the shaded region.

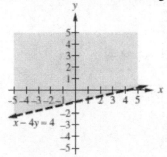

11. All the points that are on or to the right of the line $x = -4$ and also to the left of the line $x = 3$ satisfy this system. The shaded region in the graph shows the solution set.

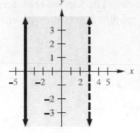

12. All the points that are on or above the line $y = 2$ and also on or below the line $y = 5$ satisfy this system. The shaded region in the graph shows the solution set.

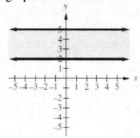

13. $x \leq -1$ or $x > 1$. The solution set of this system consist of all the points that are on or to the left of the line $x = -1$ or that are to the right of the line $x = 1$. The shaded regions in the graph shows the solution set.

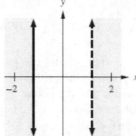

14. $y < 0$ or $y > 3$. The solution set of this system consist of all the points that are below the line $y = 0$ or that are above the line $y = 3$. The shaded regions in the graph shows the solution set.

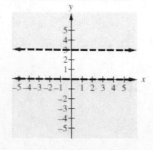

15. $x - y \geq 2$, $x + y \leq 6$. (2, 0) and (0, –2) are two points on the line $x - y = 2$. Draw a line through these two points. For (0, 0), $x - y < 2$, so all points on the side of the line opposite the origin satisfy $x - y \geq 2$. (6, 0) and (0, 6) are two points on the line $x + y = 6$. Draw a line through these two points. For (0, 0), $x + y < 6$ so all the points on the same sides of this line as the origin satisfy $x + y \leq 6$. Thus, the shaded region along with all points on the two lines below their point of intersection is the graph of the given system.

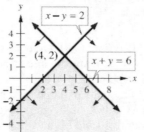

16. $x + 2y \leq 3$, $x \leq y$: (1, 1) and (–1, 2) are two points on the line $x + 2y = 3$. Draw a line through these two points. For (0, 0), $x + 2y = 0 \leq 3$, so all points on the same side of the line as the origin satisfy $x + 2y \leq 3$. (0, 0) and (3, 3) are two points on the line $x = y$. Draw a line through these two points. For (–2, 0), $x = -2 \leq y$ so all the points on the same side of this line as the point (–2, 0) satisfy $x \leq y$. Thus, the shaded region along with all points on the two lines to the left of their point of intersection is the graph of the given system.

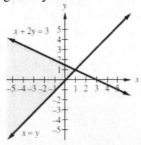

17. $2x - 3y \leq 6$, $4x - 3y \geq 12$. (3, 0) and (0, –2) are points on the line $2x - 3y = 6$. Draw a solid line through these points. Now, the point (0, 0) makes $2x - 3y = 0 < 6$, so all points on the same side of this line as the origin make $2x - 3y < 6$. (3, 0) and (0, –4) are points on the line $4x - 3y = 12$. Draw a solid line through these points. The point (0, 0) makes $4x - 3y = 0$, which is less than 12, so all points on the opposite side of this

line from the origin make $4x - 3y > 12$. The shaded region, along with its boundaries, is the graph of the solution set of the given system.

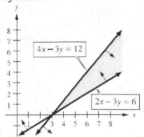

18. $2x - 5y \le 10$, $3x + 2y \le 6$. $(5, 0)$ and $(0, -2)$ are points on the line $2x - 5y = 10$. Draw a solid line through these points. $(2, 0)$ and $(0, 3)$ are points on the line $3x + 2y = 6$. Draw a solid line through these points. Now, the point $(0, 0)$ makes $2x - 5y = 0 \le 10$, so all points on the same side of this line as the origin make $2x - 5y \le 10$. The point $(0, 0)$ makes $3x + 2y = 0 \le 6$, so all points on the same side of this line as the origin make $3x + 2y \le 6$. The shaded region, along with its boundaries, is the graph of the solution set of the given system.

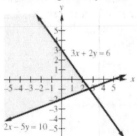

19. $2x - 3y \le 5$, $x \ge y$, $y \ge 0$. $(4, 1)$ and $(2.5, 0)$ are points on the line $2x - 3y = 5$. Draw a solid line through these points. $(0, 0)$ makes $2x - 3y = 0 < 5$, so the origin side of $2x - 3y = 5$ is the region where $2x - 3y < 5$. $(0, 0)$ and $(2, 2)$ are points on the line $x = y$. At the point $(1, 0)$, $x > y$, so the region below the line $x = y$ is where $x > y$. Draw a solid line a through these points. The line $y = 0$ is the x-axis. The region above the x-axis is where $y > 0$. The shaded region, along with its boundaries, is the graph of the solution set of this system.

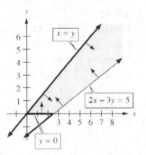

20. $x \le 2y$, $2x \ge y$, $x + y < 4$. $(0, 0)$ and $(2, 1)$ are points on the line $x = 2y$. Draw a solid line through these points. $(1, 2)$ makes $x \le 2y$ true, so the same side as that point is the region where $x \le 2y$. $(0, 0)$ and $(1, 2)$ are points on the line $2x = y$. Draw a solid line a through these points. $(2, 2)$ makes $2x \ge y$ true, so the same side as that point is the region where $2x \ge y$. $(0, 4)$ and $(2, 2)$ are points on the line $x + y = 4$. Draw a dashed line a through these points. $(0, 0)$ makes $x + y < 4$ true, so the same side as that point is the region where $x + y < 4$. The shaded region, along with its boundaries, is the graph of the solution set of this system.

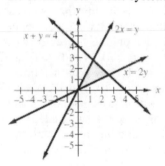

21. $x + 3y \le 6$, $x \ge 0$, $y \ge 0$. $(0, 2)$ and $(6, 0)$ are points on the line $x + 3y = 6$. Draw a solid line through these points. $(0, 0)$ makes $x + 3y = 0 < 6$, so the origin side of (below) this line is where $x + 3y < 6$. The system $x \ge 0$, $y \ge 0$ describes the first quadrant along with its boundaries. The shaded region, along with its boundaries, is the graph of the given system of inequalities.

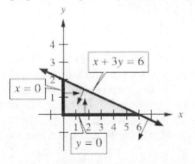

22. $2x - y \leq 2$, $y \geq 1$, $x \geq \frac{1}{2}$. $(0, -2)$ and $(1,0)$ are points on the line $2x - y = 2$. Draw a solid line through these points. $(0, 0)$ makes $2x - y \leq 2$ true, so the same side as that point is the region where $2x - y \leq 2$. For $y \geq 1$, draw a solid line through $y = 1$ and shade above the line. For $x \geq \frac{1}{2}$, draw a solid line through $x = \frac{1}{2}$ and shade to the right of the line. The shaded region, along with its boundaries, is the graph of the given system of inequalities.

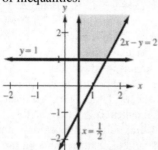

23. $x \geq 1$, $y \geq 1$, $x - y \leq 1$, $3y - x < 3$. The region to the right of the line $x = 1$ and above the line $y = 1$ and its boundaries is the graph of the solution set of the system $x \geq 1$ and $y \geq 1$. The points $(1, 0)$ and $(2, 1)$ are on the line $x - y = 1$. Draw a solid line through these points. $(0, 0)$ makes $x - y \leq 1$ true, so the same side as that point is the region where $x - y \leq 1$. The points $(0, 1)$ and $(3, 2)$ are on the line $3y - x = 3$. Draw a dashed line through these points. $(0, 0)$ makes $3y - x < 3$ true, so the same side as that point is the region where $3y - x < 3$. The shaded region, along with the solid line portions of the boundary, is the graph of the solution set of the given system of inequalities.

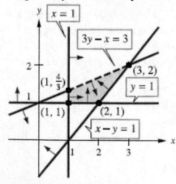

24. $x - y \geq -2$, $x + y \leq 6$, $x \geq 1$, $y \geq 1$. The points $(0, 2)$ and $(1, 3)$ are on the line $x - y = -2$. Draw a solid line through these points. $(0, 0)$ makes $x - y \leq 1$ true, so the same side as that point is the region where $x - y \leq 1$. The points $(2, 4)$ and $(4, 2)$ are on the line $x + y =$

6. Draw a solid line through these points. The region to the right of the line $x = 1$ and above the line $y = 1$ and its boundaries is the graph of the solution set of the system $x \geq 1$ and $y \geq 1$. The shaded region, along with the solid line portions of the boundary, is the graph of the solution set of the given system of inequalities.

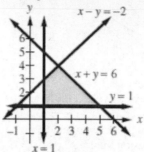

25. $x + y \geq 1$, $x \leq 2$, $y \geq 0$, $y \leq 1$. $(1, 0)$ and $(0, 1)$ are points on the line $x + y = 1$. $(0, 0)$ makes $x + y = 0 < 1$, so all points in the region opposite the origin make $x + y > 1$. All points in the region to the left of $x = 2$, above the x-axis, and below the line $y = 1$ are in the solution set of the system $x \leq 2$, $y \geq 0$, $y \leq 1$. The shaded region, including its boundaries is the graph of the solution set of the given system of inequalities.

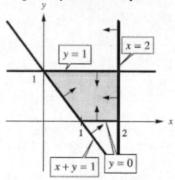

26. $1 < x + y < 8$, $x < 5$, $y < 5$. Consider $1 < x + y < 8$ as two inequalities, $x + y > 1$ and $x + y < 8$. The points $(0, 1)$ and $(1, 0)$ are on the line $x + y = 1$. Draw a dashed line through these points. $(1, 1)$ makes $x + y > 1$ true, so the same side as that point is the region where $x + y > 1$. The points $(4, 4)$ and $(3, 5)$ are on the line $x + y = 8$. Draw a dashed line through these points. $(0, 0)$ makes $x + y < 8$ true, so the same side as that point is the region where $x + y < 8$. The region to the left of the line $x = 5$ and below the line $y = 5$ is the graph of the solution set of the system $x < 5$ and $y < 5$.

The shaded region, along with the solid line portions of the boundary, is the graph of the solution set of the given system of inequalities.

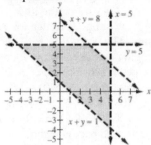

27. Conditions (b) are correct. x and y are to be greater than or equal to zero means that the points must be restricted to the first quadrant. The graph also shows all the points on and to the left of the line $3x + 2y = 6$. Condition (a) is incorrect. For example, the point $(-4, 0)$ meets the criteria but is not in the shaded area.

28. Conditions (b) are correct. x and y are to be greater than or equal to zero means that the points must be restricted to the first quadrant. The graph also shows all the points on and above the line $2x + 3y = 6$. Condition (a) is incorrect. For example, the point $(2, 3)$ is in the shaded area but does not meet the criteria.

29. Conditions (a) are correct. The point on or to the right of $x = 2$ or on or above the line $y = 1$. Conditions (b) are incorrect. For example, the point $(3, 0)$ is in the shaded area but does not meet the criteria.

30. Conditions (b) are the correct ones. The point on or to the left of $x = -1$ or on or above the line $y = 1$. Conditions (a) would allow only the points that are both above the line $y = 1$ and to the left of the line $x = -1$, as well as the boundaries of this region. For example, the point $(-2, 0)$ is in the shaded area but does not meet the criteria.

31. The line $x + y = 1$ goes through $(1, 0)$ and $(0, 1)$. The condition $x + y > 1$ is true only for the points to the right of this line. The line $x - y = 1$ goes through the points $(1, 0)$ and $(0, -1)$. The condition $x - y < 1$ is true only for the points to the left of this line. The shaded region that corresponds to this set of inequalities is (c). Test the point $(1,1)$,

which satisfies both inequalities, to see that it indeed is in the shaded region in (c).

32. The region is shaded above the line $x + y = 2$ and includes the boundary, so we have the inequality $x + y \geq 2$. x and y are to be greater than or equal to zero means that the points must be restricted to the first quadrant. Thus, the system is $x + y \geq 2$, $x \geq 0$, $y \geq 0$.

33. The yellow region is defined by points that satisfy $0 \leq x \leq 15$, $y \leq 13x + 1700$, and $y \geq 0$.

34. The blue region is defined by points that satisfy $0 \leq x \leq 15$, $y \geq 13x + 1700$, and $y \leq 30x + 180$.

35. a. and b.

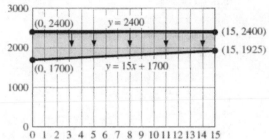

c. The region on and under the line $y = 2400$ and above and on the line $y = 15x - 1700$.

36.

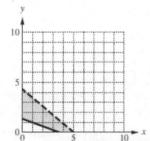

Answers may vary. Two ordered pairs that satisfy this system are $(1, 2)$ and $(2, 2)$.

37.

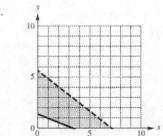

Answers may vary. Two ordered pairs that satisfy this system are (1, 3) and (2, 3).

38.

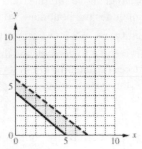

Answers may vary. Two ordered pairs that satisfy this system are (4, 2) and (5, 1).

39. $20n > 12n + 160,000$

$8n > 160,000$

$n > 20,000$

More than 20,000 units must be sold to make a profit.

40. $P = 0.45 + 0.20(x-1) < 6.00$

$0.45 + 0.20x - 0.20 < 6.00$

$0.20x + 0.25 < 6.00$

$0.20x < 5.75$

$x < 28.75$

The weight of the package must be less than 28.75 oz in order for the U.S. Postal Service to be cheaper.

41. $1 + 0.75(h-1) < 10$

$1 + 0.75h - 0.75 < 10$

$0.75h + 0.25 < 10$

$0.75h < 9.75$

$h < 13$

The cost is less than $10 when the number of hours parked is less than 13.

42. $N = 4200 + 70x < 1000$

$4200 + 70x < 1000$

$70x < -3200$

$x < -45.71 \approx -46$

According to this equation this occurred in $1960 - 46 = 1914$. Obviously, the number of cigarettes per person will not be less than 1000 after 1960.

43. The solution set of the inequality $62 \le h \le 76$ is the set of all points between

and on the lines $h = 62$ and $h = 76$. The points (62,108) and (76, 164) are on the line $w = 4h - 140$. In the figure a solid line is drawn joining these points. The points (62,134) and (76, 204) are on the line $w = 5h - 176$. A solid line is drawn joining these two points. The point (70, 150), which is inside the region enclosed by the four lines that have been drawn makes $w > 4h - 140$, since $150 > (4)(70) - 140 = 280 - 140 = 140$ and $w < 5h - 176$, since $150 < (5)(70) - 176 = 350 - 176 = 174$. This shows that the desired region is that enclosed by the four line segments drawn in the figure. Note that the boundaries are also included in the graph of the solution set of the given inequalities.

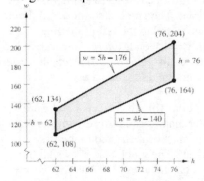

44. The solution set of the inequality $62 \le h \le 72$ is the set of all points between and on the lines $h = 62$ and $h = 72$. The points (62, 98) and (72, 138) are on the line $w = 4h - 150$. In the figure a solid line is drawn joining these points. The points (62,123) and (72, 173) are on the line $w = 5h - 187$. A solid line is drawn joining these two points. The point (70, 140), which is inside the region enclosed by the four lines that have been drawn makes $w > 4h - 150$, since $140 > (4)(70) - 150 = 280 - 150 = 130$ and $w < 5h - 187$, since $140 < (5)(70) - 187 = 350 - 187 = 163$. This shows that the desired region is that enclosed by the four line segments drawn in the figure. Note that the boundaries are also included in the graph of the solution set of the given inequalities.

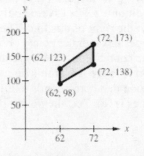

45. Answers may vary.
Suppose $c \neq 0$.
Step 1. Find the intercepts of the line
$ax + by = c$.
Step 2. Draw a dashed line through these intercepts.
Step 3. Substitute $(0, 0)$ into the equation. This gives zero for the left side.
Step 4. If $c > 0$, shade the region opposite the origin. If $c < 0$, shade the region on the origin side of the line.
Suppose $c = 0$.
Step 1. Draw the line $ax + by = 0$. This line goes through the origin and the point $(b, -a)$.
Step 2. Substitute (a, b) into the left side. This gives $a^2 + b^2 > 0$, so shade the region that is on the same side of the line as the point (a, b).

46. Answers may vary. Draw the line $y = mx + b$ dotted. On this line, the value of y is $mx + b$. If $y < mx + b$, the value of y must be less than its value on the line so the region below this line must be shaded.

47. Answers may vary. The graph would show $x = k$ as a solid line with the region to the right of this line as the shaded region.

48.

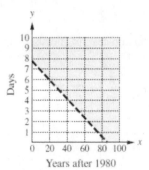

49.

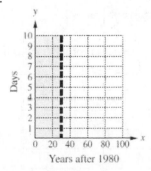

50.

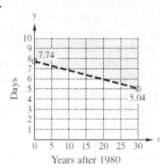

51. a. The cost for rental B is $C = 36 + 0.15m$ where m is the number of miles driven. If we want C to be \$41, we have to solve the equation
$$41 = 36 + 0.15m$$
$$5 = 0.15m$$
$$m = 33\frac{1}{3} \text{ or about 33 miles}$$

   b. If you are planning to drive 100 miles, the cost for rental A is \$41. For rental B the cost is $C = 36 + 0.15(100) = \$51$, so A is cheaper.

52. $36 + 0.15m = 42$
$$0.15m = 6$$
$$m = 40$$
You can drive a rental B car in 1 day 40 miles for \$42.

53. Rental B is cheaper (less than \$41) when you drive less than 33 miles. Rental A is cheaper when you drive more than 33 miles. If you drive exactly $33\frac{1}{3}$ miles, the cost is the same for both, \$41.

54. No. The closest you can get is when you drive 34 miles and the cost is $36 + 34(0.15) = \$41.10$. (This solution is based on rounding up $33\frac{1}{3}$ miles. To the nearest mile by rounding to 33, the cost would be $36 + 33(0.15) = \$40.95$.)

55. Answers will vary.

56. The first part of the flow chart graphs the line. If $c > 0$, then $(0, 0)$ is not in the desired region, so we shade the half-plane not containing the origin. If $c < 0$, then $(0, 0)$ is in the desired region, so we shade the half-plane containing the origin.

57. Leave everything as in the given flowchart except for interchanging the shading instructions at the end, so that if the answer to the question, "Is c > 0 ?" is "No" The half-plane not containing the origin will be shaded, and if the answer is "Yes", then the half-plane containing the origin will be shaded. You can check this by substituting (0, 0) in the inequality.

58.

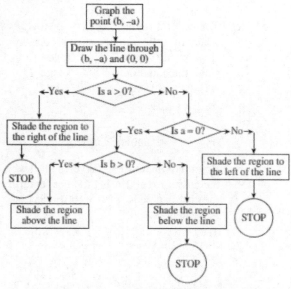

If the inequality is $ax + by < 0$, rewrite it as $-ax - by > 0$. Then use the $-a$ and the $-b$ for the a and the b in the flow chart.

Collaborative Learning

Team 1: $B = 0.0225D - 0.035$

$B > 0.0225D - 0.035$

Team 2: $m = 0.035$

$B = 0.035D - 0.04$

$B > 0.035D - 0.04$

Team 3: $0.00125W - 0.01875D > 0.1$

Section 7.8 Linear Programming

1. **Step 1**: Graph the constraints and shade the feasible region.

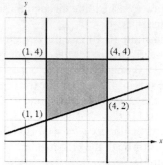

Step 2: Identify vertices (corner points) by inspection or solving a system.

Intersection of	Vertex
$x = 1$ and $y = 4$	(1, 4)
$x = 4$ and $y = 4$	(4, 4)
$x = 1$ and $x - 3y = -2$	(1, 1)
$x = 4$ and $x - 3y = -2$	(4, 2)

Step 3: Evaluate corner points in the objective function.

Vertex	$C = 2x + y$	Min/Max
(1, 4)	$2(1) + 4 = 6$	
(4, 4)	$2(4) + 4 = 12$	
(1, 1)	$2(1) + 1 = 3$	Minimum
(4, 2)	$2(4) + 2 = 10$	

The minimum value of $C = 2x + y$ is 3 at (1, 1).

2. **Step 1**: Graph the constraints and shade the feasible region.

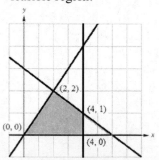

Step 2: Identify vertices (corner points) by inspection or solving a system.

Intersection of	Vertex
$y - x = 0$ and $y = 0$	(0, 0)
$y - x \leq 0$ and $x + 2y = 6$	(2, 2)
$x + 2y = 6$ and $x = 4$	(4, 1)
$y = 0$ and $x = 4$	(4, 0)

Step 3: Evaluate corner points in the objective function.

Vertex	$P = x + 4y$	Min/Max
(0, 0)	$0 + 4(0) = 0$	
(2, 2)	$2 + 4(2) = 10$	Maximum
(4, 1)	$4 + 4(1) = 8$	
(4, 0)	$4 + 4(0) = 4$	

The maximum value of $P = x + 4y$ is 10 at (2, 2).

3. **Step 1**: Graph the constraints and shade the feasible region.

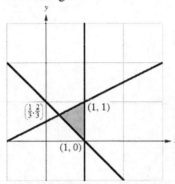

Step 2: Identify vertices (corner points) by inspection or solving a system.

Intersection of	Vertex
$x = 1$ and $x + y = 1$	$(1, 0)$
$x = 1$ and $2y - x = 1$	$(1, 1)$
$x + y = 1$ and $2y - x = 1$ $x + y = 1$ $-x + 2y = 1$ Add: $\qquad 3y = 2$ Divide by 3: $\; y = \dfrac{2}{3}$ Substitute into 1st eq: $\qquad x + \dfrac{2}{3} = 1$ Subtract $\dfrac{2}{3}$: $\quad x = \dfrac{1}{3}$	$\left(\dfrac{1}{3}, \dfrac{2}{3}\right)$

Step 3: Evaluate corner points in the objective function.

Vertex	$W = 4x + y$	Min/Max
(1, 0)	$4(1) + 0 = 4$	
(1, 1)	$4(1) + 1 = 5$	
$\left(\dfrac{1}{3}, \dfrac{2}{3}\right)$	$4\left(\dfrac{1}{3}\right) + \dfrac{2}{3} = 2$	Minimum

The minimum value of $W = 4x + y$ is 2 at (1/3, 2/3).

4. **Step 1**: Graph the constraints and shade the feasible region.

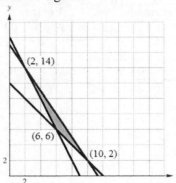

Step 2: Identify vertices (corner points) by inspection or solving a system.

Intersection of	Vertex
$2x + y = 18$ and $x + y = 12$	$(6, 6)$
$2x + y = 18$ and $3x + 2y = 34$	$(2, 14)$
$3x + 2y = 34$ and $x + y = 12$	$(10, 2)$

Step 3: Evaluate corner points in the objective function.

Vertex	$C = 2x + 3y$	Min/Max
(6, 6)	$2(6) + 3(6) = 30$	
(2, 14)	$2(2) + 3(14) = 46$	
(10, 2)	$2(10) + 3(2) = 26$	Minimum

The minimum value of $C = 2x + 3y$ is 26 at (10, 2).

5. **Step 1**: Graph the constraints and shade the feasible region.

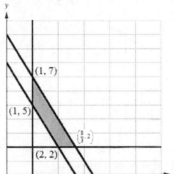

Step 2: Identify vertices (corner points) by inspection or solving a system.

Intersection of	Vertex
$3x + y = 10$ and $x = 1$	$(1, 7)$
$3x + y = 8$ and $x = 1$	$(1, 5)$
$3x + y = 8$ and $y = 2$	$(2, 2)$
$3x + y = 10$ and $y = 2$ Let $y = 2$: $\quad\quad\quad 3x + 2 = 10$ Subtract 2: $\quad 3x = 8$ Divide by 3: $\quad x = \dfrac{8}{3}$	$\left(\dfrac{8}{3}, 2\right)$

Step 3: Evaluate corner points in the objective function.

Vertex	$C = x + 2y$	Min/Max
$(1, 7)$	$1 + 2(7) = 15$	
$(1, 5)$	$1 + 2(5) = 11$	
$(2, 2)$	$2 + 2(2) = 6$	Minimum
$\left(\dfrac{8}{3}, 2\right)$	$\dfrac{8}{3} + 2(2) = \dfrac{20}{3}$	

The minimum value of $C = x + 2y$ is 6 at $(2, 2)$.

6. **Step 1**: Graph the constraints and shade the feasible region.

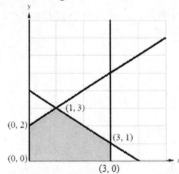

Step 2: Identify vertices (corner points) by inspection or solving a system.

Intersection of	Vertex
$y - x = 2$ and $x + y = 4$	$(1, 3)$
$y - x = 2$ and $x = 0$	$(0, 2)$
$y = 0$ and $x = 0$	$(0, 0)$
$x + y = 4$ and $x = 3$	$(3, 1)$
$y = 0$ and $x = 3$	$(3, 0)$

Step 3: Evaluate corner points in the objective function.

Vertex	$P = 2x + 3y$	Min/Max
$(1, 3)$	$2(1) + 3(3) = 11$	Maximum
$(0, 2)$	$2(0) + 3(2) = 6$	
$(0, 0)$	$2(0) + 3(0) = 0$	
$(3, 1)$	$2(3) + 3(1) = 9$	
$(3, 0)$	$2(3) + 3(0) = 6$	

The maximum value of $P = 2x + 3y$ is 11 at $(1, 3)$.

7. **Step 1**: Graph the constraints and shade the feasible region.

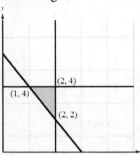

Step 2: Identify vertices (corner points) by inspection or solving a system.

Intersection of	Vertex
$2x + y = 6$ and $y = 4$	$(1, 4)$
$2x + y = 6$ and $x = 2$	$(2, 2)$
$x = 2$ and $y = 4$	$(2, 4)$

Step 3: Evaluate corner points in the objective function.

Vertex	$P = x + 2y$	Min/Max
$(1, 4)$	$1 + 2(4) = 9$	
$(2, 2)$	$2 + 2(2) = 6$	
$(2, 4)$	$2 + 2(4) = 10$	Maximum

The maximum value of $P = x + 2y$ is 10 at $(2, 4)$.

8. **Step 1**: Graph the constraints and shade the feasible region.

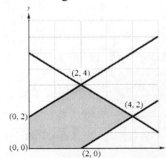

Step 2: Identify vertices (corner points) by inspection or solving a system.

Intersection of	Vertex
$y - x = 2$ and $x + y = 6$	(2, 4)
$y - x = 2$ and $y = 0$	(0, 2)
$x = 0$ and $y = 0$	(0, 0)
$x - y = 2$ and $x + y = 6$	(4, 2)
$x - y = 2$ and $y = 0$	(2, 0)

Step 3: Evaluate corner points in the objective function.

Vertex	$P = 4x + 5y$	Min/Max
(2, 4)	$4(2) + 5(4) = 28$	Maximum
(0, 2)	$4(0) + 5(2) = 10$	
(0, 0)	$4(0) + 5(0) = 0$	
(4, 2)	$4(4) + 5(2) = 26$	
(2, 0)	$4(2) + 5(0) = 8$	

The maximum value of $P = 4x + 5y$ is 28 at (2, 4).

9. **Step 1**: Identify the constraints.
   Let x = the number of cars
   y = the number of trucks

	Cars (x)	Trucks (y)
Space	$100x$	$200y$

$x + y \le 100$

$100x + 200y \le 12,000$

$x \ge 0, \ y \ge 0$

Step 2: Graph the constraints and shade the feasible region.

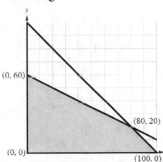

Step 3: Identify vertices (corner points) by inspection or solving a system.

Intersection of	Vertex
$x + y = 100$ and $100x + 200y = 12,000$	(80, 20)
$x + y = 100$ and $y = 0$	(100, 0)
$100x + 200y = 12,000$ and $x = 0$	(0, 60)
$x = 0$ and $y = 0$	(0, 0)

Step 4: Evaluate corner points in the objective function.

Vertex	$P = 20x + 35y$	Min/Max
(80, 20)	$20(80) + 35(20) = 2300$	Maximum
(100, 0)	$20(100) + 35(0) = 2000$	
(0, 60)	$20(0) + 35(60) = 2100$	
(0, 0)	$20(0) + 35(0) = 0$	

Store 80 cars and 20 trucks to provide the maximum revenue.

10. **Step 1**: Identify the constraints.
    Let x = the number of zigs
    y = the number of zags

Machine	Zigs (x)	Zags (y)
1	$4x$	$12y$
2	$8x$	$8y$
3	$6x$	$0y$

$4x + 12y \le 100$

$8x + 8y \le 120$

$6x \le 84 \rightarrow x \le 14$

$x \ge 0, \ y \ge 0$

Step 2: Graph the constraints and shade the feasible region.

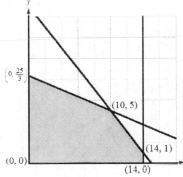

Step 3: Identify vertices (corner points) by inspection or solving a system.

Intersection of	Vertex
$4x + 12y = 100$ and $8x + 8y = 120$	(10, 5)
$x = 14$ and $y = 0$	(14, 0)
$4x + 12y = 100$ and $x = 0$	$\left(0, \dfrac{25}{3}\right)$
$x = 14$ and $8x + 8y = 120$	(14, 1)
$x = 0$ and $y = 0$	(0, 0)

Step 4: Evaluate corner points in the objective function.

Vertex	$P = 12x + 8y$	Min/Max
(10, 5)	$12(10) + 8(5) = 160$	
(14, 0)	$12(10) + 8(5) = 160$	
$\left(0, \dfrac{25}{3}\right)$	$12(0) + 8\left(\dfrac{25}{3}\right) = \dfrac{200}{3}$	
(14, 1)	$12(14) + 8(1) = 176$	Maximum
(0, 0)	$12(0) + 8(0) = 0$	

The company should make 14 Zigs and 1 Zag to maximize revenue.

11. **Step 1**: Identify the constraints.
Let x = the number of the first tablets
y = the number of the second tablets

	Tablet 1 (x)	Tablet 2 (y)
B_1	$1x$	$1y$
B_2	$1x$	$2y$

$x + y \leq 100$

$x + 2y \leq 150$

$x \geq 0, \; y \geq 0$

Step 2: Graph the constraints and shade the feasible region.

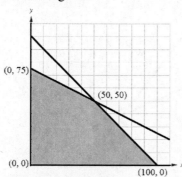

Step 3: Identify vertices (corner points) by inspection or solving a system.

Intersection of	Vertex
$x + y = 100$ and $x + 2y = 150$	(50, 50)
$x + y = 100$ and $y = 0$	(100, 0)
$x + 2y = 150$ and $x = 0$	(0, 75)
$x = 0$ and $y = 0$	(0, 0)

Step 4: Evaluate corner points in the objective function.

Vertex	$P = 2x + 3y$	Min/Max
(50, 50)	$2(50) + 3(50) = 250$	Maximum
(100, 0)	$2(100) + 3(0) = 200$	
(0, 75)	$2(0) + 3(75) = 225$	
(0, 0)	$2(0) + 3(0) = 0$	

The Kwik-Pep Vitamin Company should pack 50 tablets into each bottle in order to obtain the largest profit.

12. **Step 1**: Identify the constraints.
Let x = number 10-g portions of vegetable A
y = number 10-g portions of vegetable B

	A (x)	B (y)
Iron	$2x$	$1y$
B$_{12}$	$2x$	$5y$

$2x + y \geq 20$

$2x + 5y \geq 36$

$x \leq 10, \; y \leq 10 \qquad x \geq 0, \; y \geq 0$

Step 2: Graph the constraints and shade the feasible region.

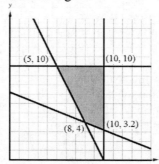

Step 3: Identify vertices (corner points) by inspection or solving a system.

Intersection of	Vertex
$2x + y = 20$ and $2x + 5y = 36$	(8, 4)
$2x + 5y = 36$ and $x = 10$ Let $x = 10$: $2(10) + 5y = 36$ Simplify: $20 + 5y = 36$ Subtract 20: $5y = 16$ Divide by 5: $y = 3.2$	(10, 3.2)
$2x + y = 20$ and $y = 10$ Let $y = 10$: $2x + 10 = 20$ Subtract 10: $2x = 10$ Divide by 2: $x = 5$	(5, 10)
$x = 10$ and $y = 10$	(10, 10)

Step 4: Evaluate corner points in the objective function.

Vertex	$C = 5x + 3y$	Min/Max
(8, 4)	$5(8) + 3(4) = 52$	Minimum
(10, 3.2)	$5(10) + 3(3.2) = 59.6$	
(5, 10)	$5(5) + 3(10) = 55$	
(10, 10)	$5(10) + 3(10) = 80$	

The nutritionist should include 8 10-g, or 80 g, of vegetable A and 4 10-g, or 40 g, of vegetable B in order to minimize calories.

13. **Step 1**: Identify the constraints.

Let x = number of ounces of additive X

y = number of ounces of additive Y

	X (x)	Y (y)
A	$16x$	$4y$
B	$2x$	$2y$
C	$4x$	$14y$

$x + y \le 10$

$16x + 4y \ge 32$

$2x + 2y \ge 10$

$4x + 14y \ge 40$ $x \ge 0, y \ge 0$

Step 2: Graph the constraints and shade the feasible region.

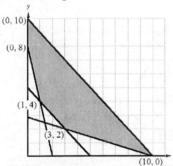

Step 3: Identify vertices (corner points) by inspection or solving a system.

Intersection of	Vertex
$x + y = 10$ and $y = 0$ or $4x + 14y = 40$ and $y = 0$	(10, 0)
$16x + 4y = 32$ and $x = 0$	(0, 8)
$16x + 4y = 32$ and $2x + 2y = 10$	(1, 4)
$2x + 2y = 10$ and $4x + 14y = 40$	(3, 2)
$x + y = 10$ and $x = 0$	(0, 10)

Step 4: Evaluate corner points in the objective function.

Vertex	$C = 20x + 40y$	Min/Max
(10, 0)	$20(10) + 40(0) = 200$	
(0, 8)	$20(0) + 40(8) = 320$	
(1, 4)	$20(1) + 40(4) = 180$	
(3, 2)	$20(3) + 40(2) = 140$	Minimum
(0, 10)	$20(0) + 40(10) = 400$	

The Jeri Tonic Company the company should put 3 oz of additive X and 2 oz of additive Y into each bottle in order to minimize cost.

14. **Step 1**: Identify the constraints.

Let x = number of days 1st factory operates

y = number of days 2nd factory operates

	1st (x)	2nd (y)
Low	$8x$	$2y$
Medium	$1x$	$1y$
High	$2x$	$7y$

$x + y \le 8$

$8x + 2y \ge 16$

$x + y \ge 5$

$2x + 7y \ge 20$

$x \ge 0, y \ge 0$

Step 2: Graph the constraints and shade the feasible region.

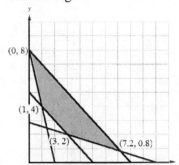

Step 3: Identify vertices (corner points) by inspection or solving a system.

Intersection of	Vertex
$x + y = 8$ and $x = 0$ or $8x + 2y = 16$ and $x = 0$	(0, 8)
$8x + 2y = 16$ and $x + y = 5$	(1, 4)
$2x + 7y = 20$ and $x + y = 5$	(3, 2)
$2x + 7y = 20$ and $x + y = 8$	(7.2, 0.8)

Multiply 2nd equation by -2:

$2x + 7y = 20 \rightarrow 2x + 7y = 20$

$x + y = 8 \rightarrow -2x - 2y = -16$

Add: $5y = 4$

Divide by 5: $y = 0.8$

Substitute into 2nd eq: $x + 0.8 = 8$

Subtract 0.8: $x = 7.2$

Step 4: Evaluate corner points in the objective function.

Vertex	$C = 1000x + 2000y$	Min/Max
(0, 8)	$1000(0) + 2000(8) = 16{,}000$	
(1, 4)	$1000(1) + 2000(4) = 9000$	
(3, 2)	$1000(3) + 2000(2) = 7000$	Minimum
(7.2, 0.8)	$1000(7.2) + 2000(0.8) = 8800$	

The Write-Right Paper Company should operate the 1st factory 3 days and the 2nd factory 2 days in order to minimize cost.

15. **Step 1**: Identify the constraints.

Let x = number of orders with Refinery I

y = number of orders with Refinery II

	Refinery I (x)	Refinery II (y)
A	$1x$	$1y$
B	$3x$	$4y$
C	$1x$	$5y$

$x + y \geq 100$

$3x + 4y \geq 340$

$x + 5y \geq 150$

$x \leq 100,\ y \leq 100$

$x \geq 0,\ y \geq 0$

Step 2: Graph the constraints and shade the feasible region.

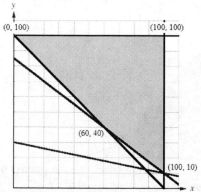

(0, 100)　　　(100, 100)

(60, 40)

(100, 10)

Step 3: Identify vertices (corner points) by inspection or solving a system.

Intersection of	Vertex
$x + y = 100$ and $x = 0$	(0, 100)
$x + y = 100$ and $3x + 4y = 340$	(60, 40)
$x + 5y = 150$ and $3x + 4y = 340$	(100, 10)
$x = 100$ and $y = 100$	(100, 100)

Step 4: Evaluate corner points in the objective function.

Vertex	$C = 300x + 500y$	Min/Max
(0, 100)	$300(0) + 500(100) = 50,000$	
(60, 40)	$300(60) + 500(40) = 38,000$	
(100, 10)	$300(100) + 500(0) = 35,000$	Minimum
(100, 100)	$300(100) + 500(100) = 80,000$	

The dealer should place 100 orders with Refinery I and 10 orders with Refinery II in order to minimize his cost.

16. **Step 1**: Identify the constraints.

Let x = number of times program A is run

y = number of times program B is run

	A (x)	B (y)
Music	$20x$	$10y$
Commercial	$1x$	$1y$

$x + y \geq 6$

$20x + 10y \leq 80$

$x \geq 0,\ y \geq 0$

Step 2: Graph the constraints and shade the feasible region.

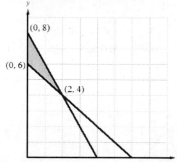

(0, 8)

(0, 6)

(2, 4)

Step 3: Identify vertices (corner points) by inspection or solving a system.

Intersection of	Vertex
$x + y = 6$ and $y = 0$	(0, 6)
$x + y = 6$ and $20x + 10y = 80$	(2, 4)
$20x + 10y = 80$ and $x = 0$	(0, 8)

Step 4: Evaluate corner points in the objective function.

Vertex	$V = 30,000x + 10,000y$	Min/Max
(0, 6)	$30,000(0) + 10,000(6)$ $= 60,000$	
(2, 4)	$30,000(2) + 10,000(4)$ $= 100,000$	Maximum
(0, 8)	$30,000(0) + 10,000(8)$ $= 80,000$	

The local television station should run Program A 2 times and Program B 4 times in order to obtain the maximum number of viewers.

17. **Step 1**: Identify the constraints.

Let x = number of boxes of oranges

y = number of boxes of grapefruit

z = number of boxes of tangerines

The total number of boxes is 800, so $x + y + z = 800$. Thus, $z = 800 - x - y$.

The constraints are

$x \geq 200$

$y \geq 100$　　　　$x \geq 0,\ y \geq 0$

$z \leq 200 \rightarrow 800 - x - y \leq 200 \rightarrow x + y \geq 600$

Step 2: Graph the constraints and shade the feasible region.

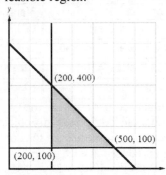

(200, 400)

(500, 100)

(200, 100)

Step 3: Identify vertices (corner points) by inspection or solving a system.

Intersection of	Vertex
$x + y = 600$ and $y = 100$	(500, 100)
$x + y = 600$ and $x = 200$	(200, 400)
$x = 200$ and $y = 100$	(200, 100)

Step 4: Evaluate corner points in the objective function $P = 20x + 10y + 30z$. Use $z = 800 - x - y$ to define z at each vertex.

Vertex	$P = 20x + 10y + 30z$	Min/Max
(500, 100) $z = 200$	20(500) + 10 (100) + 30(200) = 17,000	Maximum
(200, 400) $z = 200$	20(200) + 10 (400) + 30(200) = 14,000	
(200, 100) $z = 500$	Not possible, since $z \leq 200$	

The fruit dealer should ship 500 boxes of oranges, 100 boxes of grapefruit, and 200 boxes of tangerines in order to maximize her profit.

18. **Step 1**: Identify the constraints.
Let x = amount invested in bond A at 8%
y = amount invested in bond B at 10%
$x + y \leq 15,000$

$y - 0.4x \leq 1000$ $\qquad x \geq 0, y \geq 0$

Step 2: Graph the constraints and shade the feasible region.

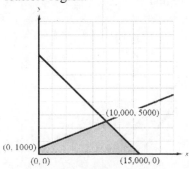

(10,000, 5000)

(0, 1000)

(0, 0)

(15,000, 0)

Step 3: Identify vertices (corner points) by inspection or solving a system.

Intersection of	Vertex
$x + y = 15,000$ and $y - 0.4x = 1000$	(10,000, 5000)
$x + y = 15,000$ and $y = 0$	(15,000, 0)
$y - 0.4x = 1000$ and $x = 0$	(0, 1000)
$x = 0$ and $y = 0$	(0, 0)

Step 4: Evaluate corner points in the objective function.

Vertex	$I = 0.08x + 0.1y$	Min/Max
(10,000, 5000)	0.08(10,000) + 0.1(5000) = 1300	Max
(15,000, 0)	0.08(15,000) + 0.1(0) = 1200	
(0, 1000)	0.08(0) + 0.1(1000) = 100	
(0, 0)	0.08(0) + 0.1(0) = 0	

Ms. Jones should invest \$10,000 in bond A at 8% and \$5000 in bond B at 10% in order to obtain the maximum number of dollars in interest per year.

19. **Step 1**: Identify the constraints.
Let x = number of imported fruit trees
y = number of oriental shrubs

	Fruit trees (x)	Shrubs (y)
Space	$2x$	$3y$
Prep	$2x$	$1y$

$2x + 3y \leq 12$

$2x + y \leq 8$ $\qquad x \geq 0, y \geq 0$

Step 2: Graph the constraints and shade the feasible region.

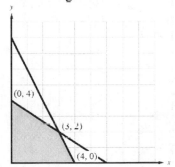

(0, 4)

(3, 2)

(4, 0)

Step 3: Identify vertices (corner points) by inspection or solving a system.

Intersection of	Vertex
$2x + 3y = 12$ and $y = 0$	(4, 0)
$2x + 3y = 12$ and $2x + y = 8$	(3, 2)
$2x + y = 8$ and $x = 0$	(0, 4)
$x = 0$ and $y = 0$	(0, 0)

Step 4: Evaluate corner points in the objective function.

Vertex	$P = 6x + 7y$	Min/Max
(4, 0)	$6(4) + 7(0) = 24$	
(3, 2)	$6(3) + 7(2) = 32$	Maximum
(0, 4)	$6(0) + 7(4) = 28$	
(0, 0)	$6(0) + 7(0) = 0$	

Growfast should display 3 imported fruit trees and 2 oriental shrubs in order to maximize its profit.

20. **Step 1**: Identify the constraints.
    Let x = number of days for EMC 1
    y = number of days for EMC 2

	EMC 1 (x)	EMC 2 (y)
Lead ore	$20x$	$15y$
Silver ore	$30x$	$35y$

$x + y \leq 20$

$30x + 35y \leq 630$

$x \geq 0, y \geq 0$

Note: Since x and y are nonnegative, $20x + 15y \geq 0$ necessarily is, and the inequality is neither implied nor needed based on the information which only states that there is no upper bound (it can sell all the lead ore it produces). Therefore, another equation (bounding) is not required.

Step 2: Graph the constraints and shade the feasible region.

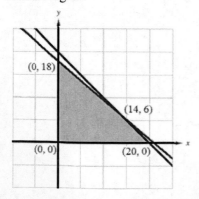

Step 3: Identify vertices (corner points) by inspection or solving a system.

Intersection of	Vertex
$x + y = 20$ and $y = 0$	(20, 0)
$x + y = 20$ and $30x + 35y = 630$	(14, 6)
$30x + 35y = 630$ and $x = 0$	(0, 18)
$x = 0$ and $y = 0$	(0, 0)

Step 4: Evaluate corner points in the objective function. To develop this objective function, consider the number of tons of lead or silver ore produced at each mine.
$P = 14(20x + 15y) + 34(30x + 35y)$
$= 1300x + 1400y$

Vertex	$P = 1300x + 1400y$	Min/Max
(20, 0)	$1300(20) + 1400(0)$ $= 26,000$	
(14, 6)	$1300(14) + 1400(6)$ $= 26,600$	Max
(0, 18)	$1300(0) + 1400(18)$ $= 25,200$	
(0, 0)	$1300(0) + 1400(0)$ $= 0$	

Excelsior should schedule 14 days for EMC 1 and 6 days for EMC 2 in order to maximize its income.

21. **Step 1**: Identify the constraints.
    Let x = number of ounces of orange juice
    y = number of ounces of grapefruit juice

	Orange (x)	Grapefruit (y)
A	$2x$	$3y$
C	$3x$	$2y$
D	$1x$	$1y$

$x + y \leq 15$

$2x + 3y \geq 26$

$3x + 2y \geq 30$

$x + y \geq 12 \qquad x \geq 0, y \geq 0$

Step 2: Graph the constraints and shade the feasible region.

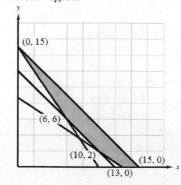

Step 3: Identify vertices (corner points) by inspection or solving a system.

Intersection of	Vertex
$x + y = 15$ and $x = 0$ or $3x + 2y = 30$ and $x = 0$	(0, 15)
$3x + 2y = 30$ and $x + y = 12$	(6, 6)
$x + y = 12$ and $2x + 3y = 26$	(10, 2)
$2x + 3y = 26$ and $y = 0$	(13, 0)
$x + y = 15$ and $y = 0$	(15, 0)

Step 4: Evaluate corner points in the objective function.

Vertex	$C = 4x + 3y$	Min/Max
(0, 15)	$4(0) + 3(15) = 45$	
(6, 6)	$4(6) + 3(6) = 42$	Minimum
(10, 2)	$4(10) + 3(2) = 46$	
(13, 0)	$4(13) + 3(0) = 52$	
(15, 0)	$4(15) + 3(0) = 60$	

a. The ABC Fruit Juice Company should put 6 oz of orange juice and 6 oz of grapefruit juice in each can to keep the total cost of the can as low as possible.
b. The minimum cost per can is 42¢.
c. The A vitamin content is $2(6) + 3(6) = 30$ units. The C vitamin content is $3(6) + 2(6) = 30$ units. The D vitamin content is $6 + 6 = 12$ units.

22. **Step 1**: Identify the constraints.
Let x = number of ounces of Grape-nuts
    y = number of ounces of Product 19
    z = number of ounces of Raisin Bran
The total number of ounces is 12, so $x + y + z = 12$. Thus, $z = 12 - x - y$.
The constraints written in terms of x and y are $100x + 110y + 90z \geq 1200 \rightarrow$

$100x + 110y + 90(12 - x - y) \geq 1200 \rightarrow$

$x + 2y \geq 12$

$100x + 110y + 90z \leq 1500 \rightarrow$

$100x + 110y + 90(12 - x - y) \leq 1500 \rightarrow$

$x + 2y \leq 42$

$x + z \leq 10 \rightarrow x + (12 - x - y) \leq 10 \rightarrow y \geq 2$

$x \geq 0, y \geq 0$

Step 2: Graph the constraints and shade the feasible region.

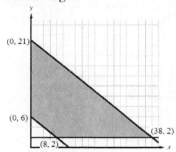

Step 3: Identify vertices (corner points) by inspection or solving a system.

Intersection of	Vertex
$x + 2y = 12$ and $x = 0$	(0, 6)
$x + 2y = 42$ and $x = 0$	(0, 21)
$x + 2y = 12$ and $y = 2$	(8, 2)
$x + 2y = 42$ and $y = 2$	(38, 2)

Step 4: Evaluate corner points in the objective function $S = 195x + 325y + 170z$.
Use $z = 12 - x - y$ to define z at each vertex.

Vertex	$S = 195x + 325y + 170z$	Min/Max
(0, 6) $z = 6$	$195(0) + 325(6) + 170(6) = 2970$	
(0, 21) $z = -9$	Not possible since z is negative.	
(8, 2) $z = 2$	$195(8) + 325(2) + 170(2) = 2550$	Min
(38, 2) $z = -28$	Not possible since z is negative.	

Joey should mix 8 oz Grape-nuts, 2 oz Product 19, and 2 oz Raisin Bran to minimize the sodium content. The mixture is 12 oz. So, there are $8 \cdot 100 + 2 \cdot 110 + 2 \cdot 90 = 1200$ calories in the mixture, or $\dfrac{1200 \, \text{cal}}{12 \, \text{oz}} = 100$ cal/oz .

Total fat is $8 \cdot 1 + 2 \cdot 0 + 2 \cdot 1 = 10$ g, or $\dfrac{10 \, \text{g}}{12 \, \text{oz}} = \dfrac{5}{6}$ g/oz . Total sodium is $8 \cdot 195 + 2 \cdot 325 + 2 \cdot 170 = 2550$ mg, or $\dfrac{2550 \, \text{mg}}{12 \, \text{oz}} = 212.5$ mg/oz .

23. **Step 1**: Identify the constraints.
Let x = number of McDonald's FOF
    y = number of Burger King TGC

	FOF (x)	TGC (y)
Sugar	$5x$	$7y$
Protein	$15x$	$55y$

$5x + 7y < 40$

$15x + 55y \geq 50$

$x \geq 0, y \geq 0$

Step 2: Graph the constraints and shade the feasible region.

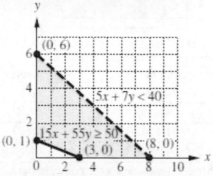

Step 3: Identify vertices (corner points) by inspection or solving a system.

Intersection of	Vertex
$5x + 7y = 40$ and $y = 0$	$(8, 0)$
$5x + 7y = 40$ and $x = 0$	$(0, 6)$
$15x + 55y = 50$ and $y = 0$	$(3, 0)$
$15x + 55y = 50$ and $x = 0$	$(0, 1)$

Step 4: Evaluate corner points in the objective function.

Vertex	$C = 3x + 4y$	Min/Max
$(8, 0)$	$3(8) + 4(0) = 24$	
$(0, 6)$	$3(0) + 4(6) = 24$	
$(3, 0)$	$3(3) + 4(0) = 9$	
$(0, 1)$	$3(0) + 4(1) = 4$	Minimum

You should each no McDonald's FOF sandwiches and only 1 Burger King TGC sandwich in order to minimize cost at $4.

24. **Step 1**: Identify the constraints.
Let x = number of McDonald's FOF
y = number of Burger King TGC

	FOF (x)	TGC (y)
Carbohydrates	$38x$	$40y$
Protein	$15x$	$55y$

$38x + 40y < 300$

$15x + 55y \geq 50$

$x \geq 0, y \geq 0$

Step 2: Graph the constraints and shade the feasible region.

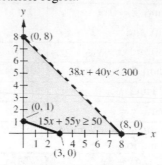

Step 3: Identify vertices (corner points) by inspection or solving a system.

Intersection of	Vertex
$38x + 40y = 300$ and $y = 0$	$(8, 0)$
$38x + 40y = 300$ and $x = 0$	$(0, 8)$
$15x + 55y = 50$ and $y = 0$	$(3, 0)$
$15x + 55y = 50$ and $x = 0$	$(0, 1)$

Step 4: Evaluate corner points in the objective function.

Vertex	$C = 3x + 4y$	Min/Max
$(8, 0)$	$3(8) + 4(0) = 24$	
$(0, 8)$	$3(0) + 4(8) = 32$	Maximum
$(3, 0)$	$3(3) + 4(0) = 9$	
$(0, 1)$	$3(0) + 4(1) = 4$	

You should order no McDonald's FOF sandwiches and 8 Burger King TGC sandwiches in order to maximize cost at $32.

25. **Step 1**: Identify the constraints.
Let x = number of McDonald's FOF
y = number of Burger King TGC

	FOF (x)	TGC (y)
Carbohydrates	$38x$	$40y$
Protein	$5x$	$7y$

$38x + 40y \leq 300$

$5x + 7y \geq 40$ $\qquad x \geq 0, y \geq 0$

Step 2: Graph the constraints and shade the feasible region.

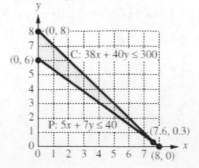

Step 3: Identify vertices (corner points) by inspection or solving a system.

Intersection of	Vertex
$38x + 40y = 300$ and $5x + 7y = 40$	(7.6, 0.3)
$38x + 40y = 300$ and $x = 0$	(0, 8)
$5x + 7y = 40$ and $y = 0$	(8, 0)
$5x + 7y = 40$ and $x = 0$	(0, 6)

Step 4: Evaluate corner points in the objective function.

Vertex	$C = 3x + 4y$	Min/Max
(7.6, 0.3)	$3(7.6) + 4(0.3) = 24$	
(0, 8)	$3(0) + 4(8) = 32$	Max
(8, 0)	$3(8) + 4(0) = 24$	
(0, 6)	$3(0) + 4(6) = 24$	

You should order no McDonald's FOF Sandwiches and 8 Burger King TGC sandwiches in order to maximize cost at $32.

26. Answers may vary.
   a. The specified conditions in a linear programming problem, usually defined by a set of linear inequalities.
   b. The solution of the inequalities given in the constraints.

27. Answers may vary.
   a. The requirement that the variables of the objective function be nonnegative.
   b. A polygon such that the points of the line segment joining any two points on the boundary lie entirely inside the region.

28. Answers may vary. A function specifying the quantities to be maximized or minimized.

29. c. **Step 1**: Identify the constraints.
   Let x = dollars to be placed on the champion to win with A
   y = dollars to be placed on the challenger to win with B
   $$\frac{3}{5}x - y \geq 100$$
   $$-x + 2y \geq 100$$
   $$x \geq 0, \ y \geq 0$$

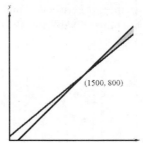

The least amount that Gary can bet for a net gain of $100 is $1500 on the champion to win and $800 on the challenger to win, for a total of $2300.

30.

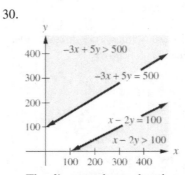

The diagram shows that there is no region where all four inequalities are true. Therefore, there is no feasible region.

Chapter 7 Practice Test

1. The domain is the set of x values: $\{0, 2, 3, 5\}$ the range is the set of y values: $\{-1, 2, 3, 4\}$.

2. The domain is the set of x values, which for this relation is the set of all real numbers; the range is also the set of all real numbers.

3. The relations in (b) and (c) are both functions. In each of these there is just one y value for each value of x in the domain.

4. Since $f(x) = x^2 - x$,
   a. $f(0) = 0^2 - 0 = 0$
   b. $f(1) = 1^2 - 1 = 1 - 1 = 0$
   c. $f(-2) = (-2)^2 - (-2) = 4 + 2 = 6$

5. Solve: $\qquad 35.30 = 15 + 0.10m$
   Subtract 15: $\qquad 20.30 = 0.10m$
   Divide by 0.10: $\qquad 203 = m$
   Thus, the person drove 203 mi.

6. Since x is an integer between -1 and 3 inclusive, the table of values is as follows:

x	y
-1	-3
0	0
1	3
2	6
3	9

The corresponding points are the heavy dots shown in the graph.

7. Since x and y are nonnegative integers, the table of values is as follows:

x	y
0	0
0	1
0	2
1	0
1	1
2	0

The corresponding points are the heavy dots shown in the graph.

8. x is an integer between -2 and 2, inclusive, so the table of values is as follows:

x	$g(x)$
-2	7
-1	1
0	-1
1	1
2	7

The corresponding points are the heavy dots shown in the graph.

9. The function defined by $f(x) = 2x - 6$ is a linear function, so we need to find two points on the graph and draw the line through them for the graph of the function. We find $f(0) = -6$ and $f(3) = 0$, so the graph is the straight line through the points $(0, -6)$ and $(3, 0)$.

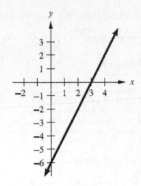

10. $3x - 2y = 5$ is the equation of a straight line. Two points that satisfy the equation are $(1, -1)$ and $(3, 2)$. These points are plotted on the graph and the line through them is the graph of the equation.

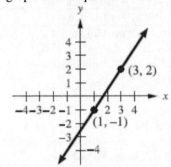

11. a. $d = \sqrt{(x_2 - x_1)^2 + (y_2 - y_1)^2}$
    $= \sqrt{(7 - 4)^2 + (3 - 7)^2}$
    $= \sqrt{9 + 16} = \sqrt{25} = 5$ units

    b. The two points have the same x coordinate, so are on the same vertical line. Thus,
    $d = |y_2 - y_1| = |-2 - 8| = |-10| = 10$ units

12. $m = \dfrac{y_2 - y_1}{x_2 - x_1} = \dfrac{-2 - (-3)}{9 - (-1)} = \dfrac{1}{10}$

13. a. Use the point-slope form and simplify:
    $y - (-1) = -2(x - 3)$
    $y + 1 = -2x + 6$
    $y = -2x + 5$

    b. Solve the equation $2y = 4 - 8x$ for y to get $y = -4x + 2$ as the slope-intercept form of the equation. Now, compare $y = mx + b$ with $y = -4x + 2$ and we obtain $m = -4$ and $b = 2$.

14. Use the point-slope form $y - y_1 = m(x - x_1)$

   where $m = \dfrac{1}{10}$ (see problem 12) to get

   $$y - (-3) = \frac{1}{10}(x - (-1))$$

   Simplify: $\qquad y + 3 = \dfrac{1}{10}x + \dfrac{1}{10}$

   Multiply by 10: $10y + 30 = x + 1$

   General form: $\quad x - 10y = 29$

15. a. Solve each equation for y:

   $$y = -2x + 1; \; y = -4x + \frac{4}{3}.$$

   This shows that the slope of the first line is –2 and the slope of the second line is –4, so the lines are not parallel. By equating the two expressions for y, we get the equation:

   $$-2x + 1 = -4x + \frac{4}{3}$$

   Add $4x$ and -1: $\; 2x = \dfrac{1}{3}$

   Divide by 2: $\qquad x = \dfrac{1}{6}$

   Substitute: $y = -2\left(\dfrac{1}{6}\right) + 1 = \dfrac{2}{3}$

   Thus, the lines intersect at $\left(\dfrac{1}{6}, \dfrac{2}{3}\right)$.

   b. The slope of the line $y = 2x - 5$ is $m = 2$. Solving the second equation for y, we get $y = 2x - \dfrac{7}{2}$, so the slope of the second line is also $m = 2$. Since the slopes are the same and the y-intercepts are different, the two lines are parallel.

16. Since the required line is to be parallel to the line $2x - 3y = 5$, its equation must be of the form $2x - 3y = C$, where C is to be determined so that the line passes through the point $(1, -2)$. So, we substitute into the equation to get $(2)(1) - (3)(-2) = C$, which gives $C = 8$. Thus, the answer is $2x - 3y = 8$.

17. The graph is like that of $y = x^2$ but opening downward and then lowered 3 units as shown. The vertex is at $V(0, -3)$.

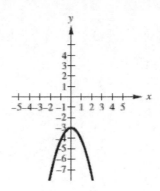

18. As you recall, the graph of $y = a(x - h)^2 + k$ has its vertex at (h, k).

   Since $y = (x + 2)^2 - 1$, the vertex is at $(-2, -1)$. Because $a = 1 > 0$, the graph opens upward.

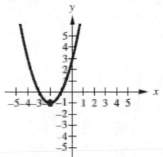

19. The graph of $y = ax^2 + bx + c$ has its vertex at $x = \dfrac{-b}{2a}$. In this case, $a = 1$ and $b = 6$, so

   $x = \dfrac{-6}{2 \cdot 1} = -3$. To find y substitute $x = -3$ in

   the original equation $y = x^2 + 6x + 8$:

   $$y = (-3)^2 + 6(-3) + 8 = 9 - 18 + 8 = -1$$

   So the vertex is at $(-3, -1)$. Since $a > 0$, the graph opens up.

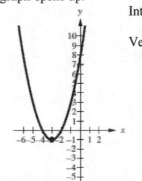

   Intercepts: (–4, 0), (–2, 0), (7, 0)
   Vertex: (–3, –1)

20. To graph $f(x) = 3^x$ and $g(x) = \left(\dfrac{1}{3}\right)^x$ let
$x = -1, 0,$ and 1.

$f(-1) = 3^{-1} = \dfrac{1}{3} \qquad \left(-1, \dfrac{1}{3}\right)$

$f(0) = 3^0 = 1 \qquad (0, 1)$

$f(1) = 3^1 = 3 \qquad (1, 3)$

$g(-1) = \left(\dfrac{1}{3}\right)^{-1} = 3 \quad (-1, 3)$

$g(0) = \left(\dfrac{1}{3}\right)^0 = 1 \qquad (0, 1)$

$g(1) = \left(\dfrac{1}{3}\right)^1 = \dfrac{1}{3} \qquad \left(1, \dfrac{1}{3}\right)$

Both graphs are shown.

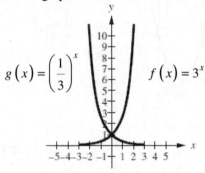

21. For convenience, use $x = -2, 0$ and 2 in
$f(x) = e^{x/2}$.

$f(-2) = e^{-2/2} = e^{-1} = \dfrac{1}{e}$ (about $\tfrac{1}{3}$)

$f(0) = e^{0/2} = e^0 = 1$

$f(2) = e^{2/2} = e^1$ (about 2.7)

Graph the points $(-2, 1/3)$, $(0, 1)$ and $(2, 2.7)$ and join them with a curve.

For $g(x) = \ln\left(\dfrac{x}{2}\right)$:

$g(x) = \ln\left(\dfrac{-2}{2}\right) = \ln(-1)$ is not defined.

$g(0) = \ln\left(\dfrac{0}{2}\right) = \ln 0$ is not defined.

$g(2) = \ln\left(\dfrac{2}{2}\right) = \ln 1 = 0$

The graph of both functions is shown.

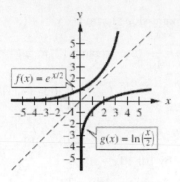

22. Set $2P = Pe^{rt}$ or $2 = e^{rt}$, then take the natural log of both sides:

$\ln 2 = \ln\left(e^{rt}\right) = rt(\ln e) = rt$

$t = \dfrac{\ln 2}{r} = \dfrac{\ln 2}{0.08} = \dfrac{0.6931471}{0.08} \approx 8.66$ years

23. Multiply both sides of the first equation by 3, multiply both sides of the second equation by 2 and add the equations:

$3x + 2y = 9 \rightarrow 9x + 6y = 27$

$2x - 3y = 19 \rightarrow \underline{4x - 6y = 38}$

Add: $\qquad\qquad 13x \qquad = 65$

Divide by 13: $\qquad\qquad x = 5$

Substitute into 1st eq: $15 + 2y = 9$

Subtract 15: $\qquad\qquad 2y = -6$

Divide by 2: $\qquad\qquad y = -3$

The solution is $(5, -3)$. (You should check this answer in the second equation.)

24. The first equation can be written in the form $2x - y = 3$. If both sides of this equation are multiplied by 3, the result is $6x - 3y = 9$, which is exactly the second equation. This means that the two lines corresponding to these equations are coincident, so that any solution of one equation is also a solution of the other equation. A general solution can be obtained by letting $x = a$, where a is any real number. Then, the first equation gives $y = 2a - 3$. The solution set can be written as: $\{(a, 2a - 3) \mid a$ is any real number$\}$.

25. To graph the solution set of $4x - 3y \le 12$, first graph the line $4x - 3y = 12$, as in the figure. The point $(0, 0)$ makes the left side of $4x - 3y = 0$ and satisfies the inequality $4x - 3y \le 12$. Thus, all points on the origin side (above) the line are in the solution set. This region is shaded in the figure. Note that

the line is drawn solid to show that it belongs in the graph of the solution set.

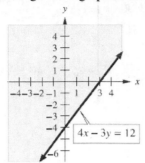

26. To graph the solution set of $x + 3y \leq 6$ and $x - y \geq 2$ draw the lines $x + 3y = 6$ and $x - y = 2$, as in the figure. The point $(0, 0)$ satisfies $x + 3y \leq 6$ so the desired region is under the line $x + 3y = 6$. $(0, 0)$ does not satisfy $x - y \geq 2$, so the desired region is under the line $x - y = 2$. Thus, the solution set is the darker region under both lines as well as the boundaries shown.

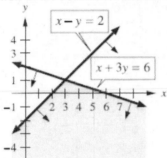

27. To graph the solution set of the system $x + 2y \leq 3$, $x \leq y$, and $x \geq 0$, draw the lines $x + 2y = 3$, $x = y$, and $x = 0$. The point $(0, 0)$ satisfies $x + 2y \leq 3$, so the desired region is on the origin side of (under) the line $x + 2y = 3$. The point $(1, 2)$ satisfies $x \leq y$, so the region is on the side above the line $x = y$. All points to the right of the y-axis satisfy $x \geq 0$. The shaded region along with its boundaries satisfies all inequalities and is the graph of the solution set of the given system.

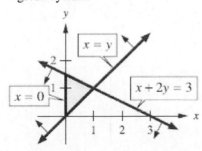

28. **Step 1**: Graph the constraints and shade the feasible region.

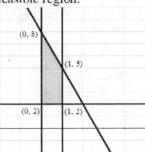

Step 2: Identify vertices (corner points) by inspection or solving a system.

Intersection of	Vertex
$3x + y = 8$ and $x = 0$	$(0, 8)$
$3x + y = 8$ and $x = 1$	$(1, 5)$
$y = 2$ and $x = 1$	$(1, 2)$
$y = 2$ and $x = 0$	$(0, 2)$

Step 3: Evaluate corner points in the objective function.

Vertex	$C = x + 2y$	Min/Max
$(0, 8)$	$0 + 2(8) = 16$	Maximum
$(1, 5)$	$1 + 2(5) = 11$	
$(1, 2)$	$1 + 2(2) = 5$	
$(0, 2)$	$0 + 2(2) = 4$	

The maximum value of $C = x + 2y$ is 16 at $(0, 8)$.

29. **Step 1**: Graph the constraints and shade the feasible region.

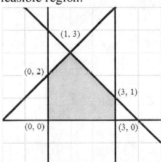

Step 2: Identify vertices (corner points) by inspection or solving a system.

Intersection of	Vertex
$y = 0$ and $x = 0$	$(0, 0)$
$x = 0$ and $y - x = 2$	$(0, 2)$
$y - x = 2$ and $x + y = 4$	$(1, 3)$
$x = 3$ and $x + y = 4$	$(3, 1)$
$x = 3$ and $y = 0$	$(3, 0)$

Step 3: Evaluate corner points in the objective function.

Vertex	$P = 3y - 2x$	Min/Max
(0, 0)	$3(0) - 2(0) = 0$	
(0, 2)	$3(2) - 2(0) = 6$	
(1, 3)	$3(3) - 2(1) = 7$	
(3, 1)	$3(1) - 2(3) = -3$	
(3, 0)	$3(0) - 2(3) = -6$	Minimum

The minimum value of $P = 3y - 2x$ is -6 at (3, 0).

30. **Step 1**: Identify the constraints.
    Let x = the number of hours for Machine A
    y = the number of hours for Machine B

Machine	Items produced per hour
A (x)	10
B (y)	12

$10x + 12y \geq 420$

$x + y \leq 40$

$x \geq 0, y \geq 0$

Step 2: Graph the constraints and shade the feasible region.

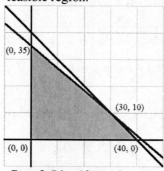

Step 3: Identify vertices (corner points) by inspection or solving a system.

Intersection of	Vertex
$x = 0$ and $y = 0$	(0, 0)
$x = 0$ and $10x + 12y = 420$	(0, 35)
$10x + 12y = 420$ and $x + y = 40$	(30, 10)
$x + y = 40$ and $y = 0$	(40, 0)

Step 4: Evaluate corner points in the objective function.

Vertex	$C = 20x + 25y$	Min/Max
(0, 0)	$20(0) + 25(0) = 0$	
(0, 35)	$20(0) + 25(35) = 875$	
(30, 10)	$20(30) + 25(10) = 850$	Minimum
(40, 0)	$20(40) + 25(0) = 800$	*

Machine A should run 30 hr and Machine B should run 10 hr in order to minimize the machine cost at $850.

If only Machine A operates for 40 hr, only

400 items could be produced, which is below the requirement of at least 420 items produced each 40-hr week.

Chapter 8 Geometry

Section 8.1 Points, Lines, Planes, and Angles

1. a.
    b.
    c.

2. a.
    b.
    c.

3. The segment $\overline{BC}$ 4. The segment $\overline{BC}$

5. The ray $\overrightarrow{AD}$ (or $\overrightarrow{AC}$ or $\overrightarrow{AB}$)

6. The ray $\overrightarrow{DA}$ or $\overrightarrow{DB}$ or $\overrightarrow{DC}$

7. The segment $\overline{AD}$ 8. The segment $\overline{BD}$

9. The line $\overleftrightarrow{AD}$ 10. The line $\overleftrightarrow{AD}$

11. ∅   12. ∅

13. The point C   14. The point B

15. a. $\overline{AB}, \overline{AC}, \overline{AD}, \overline{BC}, \overline{BD},$ and $\overline{CD}$
     b. $\overline{AB}$ and $\overline{CD}$; $\overline{AC}$ and $\overline{BD}$; $\overline{AD}$ and $\overline{BC}$
     c. None of the edges determine parallel lines.

16. a. $\overline{AB}, \overline{BC}, \overline{CD}, \overline{DA}, \overline{EA}, \overline{EB}, \overline{EC}, \overline{ED}$
     b. Parallel: $\overline{AB}$ and $\overline{CD}$, $\overline{AD}$ and $\overline{BC}$
     c. Skew: $\overline{AB}$ and $\overline{EC}$, $\overline{AB}$ and $\overline{ED}$,
         $\overline{BC}$ and $\overline{EA}$, $\overline{BC}$ and $\overline{ED}$, $\overline{CD}$ and $\overline{EA}$,
         $\overline{CD}$ and $\overline{EB}$, $\overline{DA}$ and $\overline{EB}$, and
         $\overline{DA}$ and $\overline{EC}$
     d. Intersecting: $\overline{EA}, \overline{EB}, \overline{EC}$ and $\overline{ED}$;
         $\overline{EB}, \overline{AB},$ and $\overline{CB}$; $\overline{EC}, \overline{BC},$ and $\overline{DC}$; and
         $\overline{AD}, \overline{CD},$ and $\overline{ED}$; $\overline{BA}, \overline{DA},$ and $\overline{EA}$

17. True   18. False   19. True

20. True   21. True   22. False

23. False (They can be skew lines.)

24. True

25. If a plane, say *EFG*, contains line *m*, it must contain the point where line *m* intersects plane *ABC*. So plane *EFG* must intersect plane *ABC*, and the given statement is false.

26. True

27. a. $\angle BAC$ (or $\angle CAB$) is the same as $\angle \alpha$.
     b. $\angle \beta$ (or $\angle FAE$) is the same as $\angle EAF$.

28. a. $\angle CAB$ is the same as $\angle \alpha$ (or $\angle BAC$).
     b. $\angle \beta$ is the same as $\angle EAF$ (or $\angle FAE$).

29. $\angle BAC, \angle CAD, \angle DAE, \angle EAF$

30. $\angle BAD, \angle DAF$

31. $\angle BAE, \angle CAE, \angle CAF$

32. a. $\angle CAD$ b. $\angle DAE$

33. a. $\angle DAE$ b. $\angle CAD$

34. a. $\angle CAF$ b. $\angle BAE$

35. a. $\angle DAF$ b. $\angle BAE$

36. $m\angle CAD = 90° - 15° = 75°$

37. $m\angle DAE = 90° - 55° = 35°$

38. $m\angle DAE = 90° - 35° = 55°$

39. $m\angle \alpha = 90° - 75° = 15°$

40. $m\angle CAE = 180° - 15° - 55° = 110°$

41. $\angle B$ is vertical to the 70° angle.

42. $\angle A$ and $\angle C$ are supplementary to the 70° angle.

43. $m\angle A = 180° - 70° = 110°$

44. $m\angle B = m\angle D = 70°$

45. $90° - 70° = 20°$

46. $m\angle A + m\angle B + m\angle C = 110° + 70° + 110°$
$$= 290°$$

47. $m\angle A = m\angle C = 180° - 70° = 110°$, so
$$m\angle A + m\angle C = 110° + 110° = 220°$$

48. $m\angle A = (180 - x)°$

49. a. $m\angle A = 180° - 30° = 150°$
   b. $m\angle B = 30°$
   c. $m\angle C = m\angle A = 150°$

50. a. $m\angle D = 30°$
   b. $m\angle E = 180° - 30° = 150°$
   c. $m\angle F = 30°$

51. $\angle A, \angle C, \angle E, \angle G$ are all supplementary to $\angle B$.

52. a. $m\angle BOC = m\angle AOC - m\angle AOB$
$$= 70° - 30° = 40°$$
   b. $m\angle AOB = m\angle COD$ and
$m\angle AOD = m\angle AOB + m\angle COD + m\angle BOC$,
   thus $m\angle AOD = 2(m\angle COD) + m\angle BOC$.
$$100° = 2(m\angle COD) + 2x°$$
$$50° = m\angle COD + x°$$
$$m\angle COD = (50 - x)°$$

53. a. $m\angle B = 90° - 41° = 49°$
   b. $m\angle B = 180° - 41° = 139°$

54. a. $m\angle B = 90° - 19° = 71°$
   b. $m\angle B = 180° - 19° = 161°$

55. Since the two angles are complementary, the sum of their measures is 90°. Thus,
$$(3x + 15) + (2x - 5) = 90$$
Simplify: $5x + 10 = 90$
Subtract 10: $5x = 80$
Divide by 5: $x = 16$

56. Since the two angles are supplementary, the sum of their measures is 180°. Thus,
$$(3x + 15) + (2x - 5) = 180$$
Simplify: $5x + 10 = 180$
Subtract 10: $5x = 170$
Divide by 5: $x = 34$

57. The angles are supplementary, so their measures must add to 180°. Thus, we have the equation: $(10x - 5) + (2x + 5) = 180$
Simplify: $12x = 180$
Divide by 12: $x = 15$
Evaluate: $2x + 5 = 35$
$$10x - 5 = 145$$
This shows that $x = 15$ and one angle measures 35°; the other measures 145°.

58. The angles are complementary, so their measures must add to 90°. Thus, we have the equation: $4x + 2x = 90$
Simplify: $6x = 90$
Divide by 6: $x = 15$
Evaluate: $4x = 60$
$$2x = 30$$
This shows that $x = 15$ and one angle measures 30°; the other measures 60°.

59. The two angles are complementary, so their measures must add to 90°. Thus we have the equation: $(2x + 10) + (5x + 10) = 90$
Simplify: $7x + 20 = 90$
Subtract 20: $7x = 70$
Divide by 7: $x = 10$
Thus, $2x + 10 = 30$, $5x + 10 = 60$, so that one angle measures 30° and the other measures 60°.

60. The two angles are supplementary, so their measures must add to 180°. Thus we have the equation: $(8x - 14) + (6x - 2) = 180$
Simplify: $14x - 16 = 180$
Add 16: $14x = 196$
Divide by 14: $x = 14$
Thus, $6x - 2 = 87$, $8x - 14 = 98$, so that one angle measures 82° and the other measures 98°.

61. a.   It moves through 1/12th of 360°, that is, through 30°.
   b.   It moves through 6/12ths of 360°, that is, through 180°.

62. a.   It moves through 7/12th of 360°, that is, through 210°.
   b.   It moves through 12/12ths of 360°, that is, through 360°.

63. $m\angle A + m\angle B + m\angle C = 180°$. Thus, if the number of degrees in $\angle B$ is x, then $37 + x + 53 = 180$. This gives $x = 90$, so $m\angle B = 90°$.

64. $m\angle A + m\angle B + m\angle C = 180°$. Thus, if the number of degrees in $\angle A$ is x, then $x + 67 + 105 = 180$. This gives $x = 8$, so $m\angle A = 8°$.

65. The total number of degrees in the three angles is 180°, so we have the equation:
$$(x+10)+(2x+10)+(3x+10)=180$$

Simplify: $\qquad 6x + 30 = 180$

Subtract 30: $\qquad 6x = 150$

Divide by 6: $\qquad x = 25$

66. $m\angle A = (x-10)°, m\angle B = x°$, and $m\angle C = (x+40)°$. The total number of degrees in the three angles is 180°, so we have the equation:
$$(x-10)+x+(x+40)=180$$

Simplify: $\qquad 3x + 30 = 180$

Subtract 30: $\qquad 3x = 150$

Divide by 3: $\qquad x = 50$

Thus, $m\angle A = 40°, m\angle B = 50°, m\angle C = 90°$.

67. a. $m\angle A + m\angle B = 180°$ Angles A and B form a straight angle.
    b. $m\angle C + m\angle B = 180°$ Angles C and B form a straight angle.
    c. $m\angle A + m\angle B = m\angle C + m\angle B$ Both equal $180°$. (Substitution)
    d. $m\angle A = m\angle C$ Subtract $m\angle B$ from both sides.

68. $\angle \alpha$ is an acute angle.

69. $\angle \beta$ is an acute angle.

70. $\angle \gamma$ is a right angle.

71. $\angle \delta$ is a right angle.

72. The two types of angles are acute and right angles.

73. The angle is an obtuse angle.

74. The angle shown is about 150°.

75. With the phone closed, the angle would be 0°.

76. $m\angle \alpha = 180° - 43° - 92° = 45°$

77. $m\angle \theta = 180° - 40° - 40° = 100°$

78. Technically speaking, a straight line has no distance. The distance between two points on a straight line is the measure of the segment between these points.

79. Point, line, and plane are all undefined.

80. Answers will vary.

81. The ray may have its endpoint only in common with the plane, or it may have some other single point in common with the plane, or it may lie entirely in the plane.

82. The ray can have its endpoint on the line or some other point of the ray can be a point on the line or the ray can be on the line.

83. a. One of the usual meanings of <u>acute</u> is "sharp" or "intense." Thus "an acute pain" means "a sharp or intense pain."
    b. One of the ordinary meanings of <u>obtuse</u> is "dull." Thus, "obtuse intelligence" means "dull intelligence" or "stupidity."

84. Answers will vary.
    a.

    b.

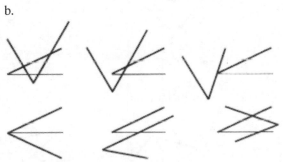

85. $\angle \alpha$ is an obtuse angle; $\angle \beta$ is an acute angle.

86. $\angle \delta$ is a right angle; $\angle \varepsilon$ is an obtuse angle.

87. The triangle is isosceles and right.

88. The total number of degrees in the three angles is 180°, so we have the equation:

$$62° + 62° + m\angle\beta = 180°$$

$$124° + m\angle\beta = 180°$$

$$m\angle\beta = 56°$$

89. Both angles are acute angles.

90. $\angle\gamma$ is an acute angle; $\angle\beta$ is an acute angle; $\angle\delta$ is a right angle.

91. a. $\angle\alpha$ is an straight angle; $m\angle\alpha = 180°$
    b. $\angle\beta$ is an acute angle;
       $m\angle\beta = 0.22 \cdot 360° = 79.2°$
    c. $\angle\delta$ is an acute angle;
       $m\angle\delta = 0.19 \cdot 360° = 68.4°$
    d. $\angle\gamma$ is an acute angle;
       $m\angle\gamma = 0.09 \cdot 360° = 32.4°$

92. a. $\angle\delta$ is an straight angle; $m\angle\delta = 180°$
    b. $\angle\beta$ is an acute angle;
       $m\angle\beta = 0.08 \cdot 360° = 28.8°$
    c. $\angle\alpha$ is an acute angle;
       $m\angle\alpha = 0.09 \cdot 360° = 32.4°$
    d. $\angle\varepsilon$ is an acute angle;
       $m\angle\varepsilon = 0.13 \cdot 360° = 46.8°$
    e. $\angle\gamma$ is an acute angle;
       $m\angle\gamma = 0.20 \cdot 360° = 72°$

Section 8.2 Triangles and Other Polygons

1. Answers may vary.
   a.   b.

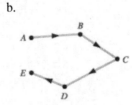

2. Answers may vary.
   a.   b.

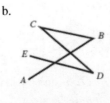

3. a. C, D, I, J, L, M, N, O, P, S, U, V, W, Z

   b. B, D, O

4. a. B   b. C, I, J, L, M, N, P, S, U, V, W, Z

5. a. D, O
   b. A, E, F, G, H, K, Q, R, T, X, Y

6. Concave   7. Convex

8. a. Rectangle   b. Triangle

9. Parallelogram   10. Parallelogram

11. Rectangle   12. Square

13. Trapezoid   14. Trapezoid

15. Parallelogram   16. Trapezoid

17. A scalene, right triangle

18. An isosceles, right triangle

19. A scalene, acute triangle

20. An isosceles, obtuse triangle

21. An isosceles, acute triangle

22. A scalene, right triangle

23. A scalene, obtuse triangle

24. An isosceles, right triangle

25. Triangles (a) and (c) are similar because
    $$\frac{4/3}{4} = \frac{1}{3} = \frac{2/3}{2}.$$

26. Triangles (a) and (c) are similar because
    $\frac{4}{5} = \frac{4.8}{6}$. Note: triangles (a) and (c) also have two corresponding angles; since the sum of angles is 180°, the third angles are equal, so the triangles are similar.

27. Because the triangles are similar, corresponding sides are proportional. Thus,
    $\frac{x}{4} = \frac{y}{5} = \frac{4}{3}$ so that $x = \frac{16}{3} = 5\frac{1}{3}$ and
    $y = \frac{20}{3} = 6\frac{2}{3}$.

28. Because the parallelograms are similar,

corresponding sides are proportional. Thus,
$\dfrac{\overline{PR}}{10} = \dfrac{10}{8}$ so that $\overline{PR} = \dfrac{100}{8} = 12\dfrac{1}{2}$.

29. PQ is parallel to AB, so triangle PQC is similar to triangle ABC. Thus, corresponding sides of these triangles are proportional.

This gives the proportion $\dfrac{AC}{PC} = \dfrac{BC}{QC}$. Let x be the length of BC, so that $x - 6$ is the length of QC. Since AP is of length 3 and PC is of length 4, AC is of length 7. With these lengths, our proportion gives the equation $\dfrac{7}{4} = \dfrac{x}{x-6}$.

By cross-multiplication, we get:
$7x - 42 = 4x$

$3x = 42$

$x = 14$

30. PQ is parallel to AB, so triangle PQC is similar to triangle ABC. Thus, corresponding sides of these triangles are proportional.

This gives the proportion $\dfrac{AC}{AP} = \dfrac{BC}{BQ}$. Let x be the length of BQ and BC is of length 6. Since AP is of length 5 and PC is of length 4, AC is of length 9. With these lengths, our proportion gives the equation $\dfrac{9}{5} = \dfrac{6}{x}$.

By cross-multiplication, we get:
$9x = 30$

$x = \dfrac{10}{3} = 3\dfrac{1}{3}$

31. Let x be the length of PC. Then, since the length of AP is 2, the length of AC is $x + 2$. Using the same proportion as in problem 29, we get the equation:
$\dfrac{x+2}{x} = \dfrac{5}{2}$.

By cross-multiplication, we get:
$2x + 4 = 5x$

$4 = 3x$

$x = \dfrac{4}{3} = 1\dfrac{1}{3}$

32. Let x be the length of AP. Then, since the length of PC is 4, the length of AC is

$x + 4$. Using the same proportion as in problem 30, we get the equation:
$\dfrac{x+4}{x} = \dfrac{8}{4}$

By cross-multiplication, we get:
$4x + 16 = 8x$

$16 = 4x$

$x = 4$

33. Let x be the length of the side of the smaller triangle that corresponds to the 6 cm side of the larger triangle, and let y be the length of the side of the smaller triangle that corresponds to the 9 cm side of the larger triangle. Then, since the triangles are similar, $\dfrac{x}{6} = \dfrac{y}{9} = \dfrac{7}{12}$.

This proportion gives
$x = \dfrac{6 \cdot 7}{12} = \dfrac{7}{2} = 3\dfrac{1}{2}$ cm and

$y = \dfrac{9 \cdot 7}{12} = \dfrac{21}{4} = 5\dfrac{1}{4}$ cm.

34. Let x be the length of the side of the smaller triangle that corresponds to the 12 cm side of the larger triangle, and let y be the length of the side of the smaller triangle that corresponds to the 9 cm side of the larger triangle. Then, since the triangles are similar, $\dfrac{x}{12} = \dfrac{y}{9} = \dfrac{5}{6}$.

This proportion gives
$x = \dfrac{5 \cdot 12}{6} = \dfrac{60}{6} = 10$ cm and

$y = \dfrac{5 \cdot 9}{6} = \dfrac{45}{6} = 7\dfrac{1}{2}$ cm

35. Let the sides of the second triangle be x, y, and z in. long, respectively. Since the triangles are similar, the perimeters are also similar. Thus, $\dfrac{x}{2} = \dfrac{y}{3} = \dfrac{z}{4} = \dfrac{36}{9} = 4$.

$\dfrac{x}{2} = 4$ or $x = 8$; $\dfrac{y}{3} = 4$ or $y = 12$; $\dfrac{z}{4} = 4$.

or $z = 16$. The sides of the second triangle are 8 in., 12 in., and 16 in. long.
For an algebraic approach, if the sides of the second triangle are x, y and z in long respectively, we have: $x + y + z = 36$.

Since the triangles are similar, $\dfrac{x}{2} = \dfrac{y}{3} = \dfrac{z}{4}$

This gives $x = \dfrac{1}{2}z$ and $y = \dfrac{3}{4}z$. Substituting into the first equation, we get:

$$\frac{1}{2}z + \frac{3}{4}z + z = 36$$

Multiply by 4: $2z + 3z + 4z = 144$

Add: $9z = 144$

Divide by 9: $z = 16$

$$x = \frac{1}{2}z = 8$$

$$y = \frac{3}{4}z = 12$$

The respective sides of the second triangle are 8 in., 12 in., and 16 in. long as before.

36. Let the sides of the second triangle be x, y, and z in. long, respectively. Since the triangles are similar, the perimeters are also similar. Thus, $\dfrac{x}{3} = \dfrac{y}{4} = \dfrac{z}{5} = \dfrac{18}{12} = \dfrac{3}{2}$.

$\dfrac{x}{3} = \dfrac{3}{2}$ or $x = \dfrac{9}{2} = 4\dfrac{1}{2}; \dfrac{y}{4} = \dfrac{3}{2}$ or $y = 6;$

$\dfrac{z}{5} = \dfrac{3}{2}$ or $z = \dfrac{15}{2} = 7\dfrac{1}{2}$. The sides of the

second triangle are $4\dfrac{1}{2}$ in., 6 in., and $7\dfrac{1}{2}$

in. long.
For an algebraic approach, if the sides of the second triangle are x, y and z in long respectively, we have: $x + y + z = 18$.

Since the triangles are similar, $\dfrac{x}{3} = \dfrac{y}{4} = \dfrac{z}{5}$

This gives $x = \dfrac{3}{5}z$ and $y = \dfrac{4}{5}z$. Substituting into the first equation, we get:

$$\frac{3}{5}z + \frac{4}{5}z + z = 18$$

Multiply by 5: $3z + 4z + 5z = 90$

Add: $12z = 90$

Divide by 12: $z = 7\dfrac{1}{2}$

$$x = \frac{3}{5}z = 4\frac{1}{2}$$

$$y = \frac{4}{5}z = 6$$

The respective sides of the second triangle are $4\dfrac{1}{2}$ in., 6 in., and $7\dfrac{1}{2}$ in. long as before.

37. Let the telephone pole be x ft high. Then the similar right triangles in the figure give the proportion: $\dfrac{x}{5} = \dfrac{30}{8}$.

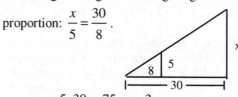

Thus, $x = \dfrac{5 \cdot 30}{8} = \dfrac{75}{4} = 18\dfrac{3}{4}$, so the pole is

$18\dfrac{3}{4}$ ft high.

38. Make similar triangles by drawing a horizontal line at the height of 4 ft. Let the flagpole be $h = (x + 4)$ ft high. Then the similar triangles in the figure give the proportion:

$$\frac{x}{32 + 116} = \frac{4}{32}$$

$32x = 4 \cdot 148$

$x = \dfrac{592}{32} = 18.5$

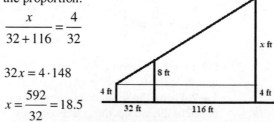

So the flagpole is $(18.5 + 4)$ ft, or 22.5 ft high.

39. Assume that both the tree and 5-ft stake make a right angle with the ground and the angle of the tip of each shadow to the top of the respective object made by the sun's position in the sky will be the same. Therefore, the third angles will be equal, and the triangles similar. Let the height of the tree be h ft. Then the two similar right

triangles give the proportion $\dfrac{h}{5} = \dfrac{40}{8}$. Thus, $h = 5 \cdot 5 = 25$, so the tree is 25 ft high.

40. Let the distance AB across a small lake be x m. Then the similar right triangles give the proportion $\dfrac{x}{240} = \dfrac{60}{80}$. Thus,

$$x = \dfrac{240 \cdot 60}{80} = \dfrac{14,400}{80} = 180,$$

so the distance AB across a small lake is 180 m.

41. The marked angles are equal and the vertical angles in the figure are equal, so the two triangles are similar. If the tunnel is t meters long, then we have the proportion:

$$\dfrac{t}{20} = \dfrac{540}{18} = 30.$$ We have $t = 20 \cdot 30 = 600$, that is, the tunnel is 600 m long.

42. Two corresponding angles are equal, so the two triangles are similar. AB measures 10 cm and CB 18 cm. Convert 100 m to 10,000 cm. We have the proportion $\dfrac{10,000}{PQ} = \dfrac{AB}{BC} = \dfrac{10}{18}$.

$$PQ = \dfrac{10,000 \cdot 18}{10} = 18,000. \text{ Thus, } \overline{PQ} \text{ is 180 m.}$$

43. Recall that an isosceles triangle is one that has two equal sides. By the SAS Theorem, $\triangle ABD \cong \triangle CBD$. This implies that $AB \cong BC$. that is, two of the sides are equal, so $\triangle ABC$ is isosceles.

44. Note that $\overline{BD}$ is the included side of $\angle D$ and $\angle B$ in both triangles, so we can apply ASA to get $\triangle ABD \cong \triangle BCD$.

45. It is given that $\triangle ACD$ and $\triangle BCE$ have two pairs of sides with equal length ($AD = BC$ and $AC = BD$). They also share the side CD. Thus, by the SSS theorem $\triangle ACD \cong \triangle BCD$.

46. The two triangular plots have three pairs of sides with equal length. According to SSS, these plots are congruent and therefore, must have the same area. In other words, Old McBello is telling the truth.

47. a. $\angle C$ is supplementary to the 100° angle, so $m\angle C = 80°$. $AC = BC$ means that

$\angle A \cong \angle B$. Since $m\angle A + m\angle B = 180 - m\angle C$, we have that $2 \cdot m\angle A = 100°$. Thus, $m\angle A = m\angle B = 50°$.

b. $\angle B$ is supplementary to the 140° angle, so $m\angle B = 40°$. As in part a, $\angle A \cong \angle B$. Hence, $m\angle A = 40°$. $m\angle A + m\angle B + m\angle C = 180°$. Therefore, $80° + m\angle C = 180°$. Consequently, $m\angle C = 100°$.

48. $ABCD$ is a parallelogram with diagonal $\overline{DB}$. The sum of the measures of the angles of triangle BDC is 180°, $m\angle DCB = 180° - 70° - 35° = 75°$. $\overline{AD}$ is parallel to $\overline{BC}$ so that alternate angles are equal: $m\angle DBA = m\angle BDC = 35°$ and $m\angle ADB = m\angle CBD = 70°$. Since $\overline{BD} = \overline{DB}$, $\triangle BDA \cong \triangle DBC$ by ASA. Therefore, $m\angle DCB = m\angle BAD = 75°$.

49. AE and BD are parallel, so $\angle ABD$ equals the 120° angle. $\angle CBD$ is supplementary to $\angle ABD$, which makes $m\angle CBD = 60°$. Because CE is perpendicular to BD, $m\angle CDB = 90°$. Since the sum of the measures of the angles of triangle BCD is $180° \ m\angle BCD = 180° - 60° - 90° = 30°$.

50. The sum of angles in a triangle is 180°. $m\angle C = 180° - 75° - 30° = 75°$. The sides opposite these two equal angles are equal. Thus, this is an isosceles triangle.

51. The sum of the measures of the angles of a regular n-sided polygon is $S = (n-2)180°$, where $n = 14$: $(14-2)180° = 12 \cdot 180° = 2160°$.

52. The sum of the measures of the angles of a regular 20-sided polygon is $S = (n-2)180°$, where $n = 20$: $(20-2)180° - 18 \cdot 180° = 3240°$.

53. The sum of the measures of the angles of a regular pentagon is $S = (n-2)180°$, where $n = 5$: $(5-2)180° = 3 \cdot 180° = 540°$. Since there are five angles, the measure of each must be $\dfrac{540}{5} = 108°$.

54. The sum of the measures of the angles of a regular hexagon is $S = (n-2)180°$, where $n = 6$: $(6-2)180° = 4 \cdot 180° = 720°$. Since there are six angles, the measure of each must be $\dfrac{720}{6} = 120°$.

55. The sum of the measures of the angles of a regular octagon is $S = (n-2)180°$, where $n = 8$: $(8-2)180° = 6 \cdot 180° = 1080°$. Since there are eight angles, the measure of each must be $\dfrac{1080}{8} = 135°$.

56. The sum of the measures of the angles of a regular nonagon is $S = (n-2)180°$, where $n = 9$: $(9-2)180° = 7 \cdot 180° = 1260°$. Since there are nine angles, the measure of each must be $\dfrac{1260}{9} = 140°$.

57. The sum of the measures of the angles of a regular decagon is $S = (n-2)180°$, where $n = 10$: $(10-2)180° = 8 \cdot 180° = 1440°$. Since there are ten angles, the measure of each must be $\dfrac{1440}{10} = 144°$.

58. The sum of the measures of the angles of a regular dodecagon is $S = (n-2)180°$, where $n = 12$: $(12-2)180° = 10 \cdot 180° = 1800°$. Since there are twelve angles, the measure of each must be $\dfrac{1800}{12} = 150°$.

59. a. $(E \cup I \cup S) = T \subset P$

    b.

    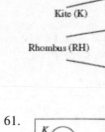

60.

Quadrilateral (Q)

Kite (K)   Parallelogram (P)   Trapezoid (T)

Rhombus (RH)   Rectangle (R)

Square (S)

61.

62. They are similar (same shape but different size).

63. Answers will vary.

64. $\dfrac{8}{4} = \dfrac{10}{5} \neq \dfrac{12}{7}$. Corresponding sides are not proportional so the triangles are not similar.

65. a.   b.   c.

66. a.   b.   c. Impossible

67. a.   b.   c. Impossible

68. Triangles ER and EO are impossible.

Section 8.3 Perimeter and Circumference

1. $10 + 25 + 30 = 65$; perimeter is 65 cm.

2. $2 \cdot 10 + 2 \cdot 20 = 60$; perimeter is 60 ft.

3. $2 + 5 + 1.6 + 4 = 12.6$; perimeter is 12.6 yd.

4. $4 \cdot 7.2 = 28.8$; perimeter is 28.8 in.

5. $2(61.2 + 31.1) = 184.6$; perimeter is 184.6 m.

6. $1.6 + 4.7 + 2 + 5.8 = 14.1$; perimeter is 14.1 m.

7. $2(19.4 + 9.2) = 57.2$; perimeter is 57.2 m.

8. $2 \cdot 3 + 2 \cdot 9.2 = 24.4$; perimeter is 24.4 km.

9. $5 \cdot 6 = 30$; perimeter is 30 cm.

10. $8 \cdot 6 = 48$; perimeter is 48 in.

11. If the width was x ft, then $2x + 2 \cdot 30 = 80$, so that $2x + 60 = 80$. By subtracting 60 from both sides and dividing both sides by 2, we obtain $x = 10$. Therefore, the width was 10 ft.

12. If the width is x m, then $2x + 2 \cdot 480 = 1110$, so that $2x + 960 = 1110$. By subtracting 960 from both sides and dividing both sides by 2, we obtain $x = 75$. Therefore, the width is 75 m.

13. This distance is 1/4th of the perimeter, that is, $\dfrac{360}{4} = 90$ ft.

14. If the width is x yd, then $2x + 2 \cdot 120 = 346$, so that $2x + 240 = 346$. By subtracting 240 from both sides and dividing both sides by 2, we obtain $x = 53$. Therefore, the width is 53 yd.

15. Let x ft be the width. Then, the length is $(x + 198)$ ft, and, in terms of x, the perimeter is $[2x + 2(x + 198)]$ ft. Thus, we have the equation:
$$2x + 2(x + 198) = 2468$$
Simplify: $\qquad 4x + 396 = 2468$

Subtract 396: $\qquad 4x = 2072$

Divide by 4: $\qquad x = 518$
$$x + 198 = 716$$
Thus, the dimensions are 716 ft by 518 ft.

16. The perimeter of a regular hexagon with side length 5 in. is $6 \cdot 5 = 30$ in. The circumference of a circle with radius 5 in. is

$2 \cdot \pi \cdot 5 = 10\pi \approx 31.4$ in. The perimeter of the hexagon is $31.4 - 30 = 1.4$ in. shorter than that circumference of the circle.

17. $C = \pi d = \pi \cdot 7 = 7\pi \approx 7 \cdot 3.14 \approx 22.0$ m.

18. $C = \pi d = \pi \cdot 8 = 8\pi \approx 8 \cdot 3.14 \approx 25.1$ ft.

19. $C = 2\pi r = 2\pi \cdot 10 = 20\pi \approx 20 \cdot 3.14$
≈ 62.8 ft.

20. $C = 2\pi r = 2\pi \cdot 4.4 = 8.8\pi$
$\approx 8.8 \cdot 3.14 \approx 27.6$ m

21. $C = \pi d = \pi \cdot 3 = 3\pi \approx 3 \cdot 3.14 \approx 9.42$ cm

22. $C = \pi d = \pi \cdot 6 = 6\pi \approx 6 \cdot 3.14 \approx 18.8$ in.

23. $C = 2\pi r = 2\pi \cdot 4.5 = 9\pi$
$\approx 9 \cdot 3.14 \approx 28.3$ yd

24. $C = 2\pi r = 2\pi \cdot 5.5 = 11\pi$
$\approx 11 \cdot 3.14 \approx 34.6$ m

25. $C = \pi d = \pi \cdot 61 = 61\pi \approx 61 \cdot 3.14 \approx 192$
When the wheel makes one complete turn, the bicycle goes a distance of 192 cm.

26. $C = \pi d = \pi \cdot 17 = 17\pi \approx 17 \cdot 3.14 \approx 53.4$
The length of the circumference of the lid is 53.4 in.

27. $C = 2\pi r = 2\pi \cdot 8 = 16\pi \approx 16 \cdot 3.14 \approx 50.2$
The tip of the minute hand travels 50.2 cm in 1 hr.

28. $\dfrac{3}{4}C = \dfrac{3}{4}\pi d = \dfrac{3}{4}\pi \cdot 4 = 3\pi \approx 3 \cdot 3.14 \approx 9.42$
A point on the rim of a CD travels 9.42 in. in three-fourths of a complete revolution.

29. $C = 2\pi r = 2\pi \cdot 4 = 8\pi \approx 8 \cdot 3.14 \approx 25.1$
The border should be 25.1 ft long.

30. $C = 2\pi r = 2\pi \cdot 6 = 12\pi \approx 12 \cdot 3.14 \approx 37.7$
The point on the rim moves 37.7 in. when the record goes around once.

31. $\pi d = 15\pi$, so $d = 15$ cm and $r = 7.5$ cm.

32. $C = 8$ ft. is 96 in. and $C = 2\pi r = 96$, so

$r = \dfrac{48}{\pi} \approx 15.3$. The radius of this hoop is 15.3 in.

33. $C = \pi d = 7$, so $d = \dfrac{7}{\pi} \approx \dfrac{7}{3.14} \approx 2.23$

The diameter of the ring is 2.23 cm.

34. $C = \pi d = 251.2$, so

$d = \dfrac{251.2}{\pi} \approx \dfrac{251.2}{3.14} \approx 80.0$.

The diameter of the pizza is 80.0 ft.

35. $\pi d = 4\dfrac{1}{8}$, so $d = \dfrac{4.125}{3.14} \approx 1.31$.

The diameter of this tiny record is 1.31 in.

36. One mile is 5280 ft., or 63,360 in. A point would travel 26π in. in one revelution. Thus, the wheel will make $\dfrac{63,360}{26\pi} \approx 776$ rev/mi.

37. The answer to problem 36 is approximately 776 revolutions. Thus, 20,000 mi would be approximately (20,000)(776) or 15,500,000 (rounded from 15,520,000) revolutions.

38. $C = \pi d = 70$, so $d = \dfrac{70}{\pi} \approx \dfrac{70}{3.14} \approx 22.3$.

We would need a pan with a 23 ft. diameter. The diameter of the ring is 2.23 cm.

39. The diameter of the pool is $20 - 4 = 16$ yd. Thus, the circumference of the pool is $\pi d = 16\pi \approx 16 \cdot 3.14 \approx 50.2$ yd.

40. It takes 15 minutes to walk $C = \pi d$. So, to walk the diameter would take $d = \dfrac{15}{\pi}$ min ≈ 4.8 min.

41. $d = 154 + 156 + 180 = 490$ mi

42. $d = 237 + 235 + 197 = 669$ mi

43. $d = 190 + 151 + 223 = 564$ mi

44. $114 + 200 + d = 555$ mi and solve for d. The distance from Oklahoma City to Fort Smith is 241 mi.

45. The amount of mesh needed is equal to the

perimeter of the rectangular compost bin: $P = 2 \cdot 60 + 2 \cdot 70 = 260$ in. Thus, you would need 260 in. of the 48-in. high wire mesh.

46. The amount of mesh needed is equal to the perimeter of the rectangular compost bin: $P = 2 \cdot 50 + 2 \cdot 60 = 220$ in. Thus, you would need 220 in. of the 30-in. high wire mesh.

47. The amount of mesh needed is equal to the circumference of the circular compost bin: $C = \pi d = 3.14 \cdot 30 = 94.20$. Thus, you would need 94.20 in. of the 36-in. high wire mesh.

48. The amount of mesh needed is equal to the circumference of the circular compost bin: $C = \pi d = 3.14 \cdot 48 = 150.72$. Thus, you would need 150.72 in. of the 36-in. high wire mesh.

49. A bicycle tire because, as a circle, it is made up of 'points' that are the same distance from the center.

50. Find the circumference of the finger where the ring is to fit. Substitute this number of inches for C in the formula and solve for s.

51. The worn tire has a smaller circumference, so will turn more times per mile.

52. Answers will vary, but to the nearest tenth, the rounded answers should agree.

53. This is one fourth of the large circumference: $\dfrac{3}{4}$ in.

54. Point b has traveled 1 in. relative to circle B.

55. Point b travels $\dfrac{3}{4}$ in.

56. $\dfrac{3}{4}$ in. = one revolution of circle B. It takes four revolutions for circle B to go around circle A.

Calculator Corner

1. Problem 25:

    $\boxed{61}\boxed{\pi}\boxed{\text{ENTER}}\,191.6371519$

    Problem 26:

    $\boxed{17}\boxed{\pi}\boxed{\text{ENTER}}\,53.40707511$

    Problem 30:

    $\boxed{2}\boxed{\times}\boxed{6}\boxed{\pi}\boxed{\text{ENTER}}\,37.69911184$

    Problem 32:

    $\boxed{8}\boxed{\div}\boxed{(}\boxed{2}\boxed{\times}\boxed{\pi}\boxed{)}\boxed{\text{ENTER}}\,1.273239545$

    Problem 34:

    $\boxed{251.2}\boxed{\div}\boxed{\pi}\boxed{\text{ENTER}}\,79.95944341$

Section 8.4 Area Measure and the Pythagorean Theorem

1. This is the area of a triangle with base 6 in. and height 5 in.: $A = \frac{1}{2}bh = \frac{1}{2}\cdot 5 \cdot 6 = 15 \text{ in}^2$

2. The required area can be calculated as the sum of the area of the square and the triangle. The base of the triangle is $5 - 3 = 2$ in. Thus:

    $$A = 3\cdot 3 + \frac{1}{2}\cdot 2 \cdot 3 = 9 + 3 = 12 \text{ in}^2$$

3. This is the area of a parallelogram with base 5 cm and height 3 cm:

    $$A = bh = 5 \cdot 3 = 15 \text{ cm}^2$$

4. This is the area of a trapezoid with $b_1 = 6$ m, $b_2 = 2$ m, and height 4 m:

    $$A = \frac{1}{2}\left(b_1 + b_2\right)h = \frac{1}{2}(6+2)\cdot 4 = 16 \text{ cm}^2$$

5. The required area can be calculated as the area of the outside rectangle minus the area of the triangle to be taken out. Thus:

    $$A = 10\cdot 3 - \frac{1}{2}\cdot 6 \cdot 2 = 30 - 6 = 24 \text{ ft}^2$$

6. The required area can be calculated as the area of the rectangle minus the area of the square to be taken out. Thus:

    $$A = 8\cdot 4 - 2\cdot 2 = 32 - 4 = 28 \text{ ft}^2$$

7. This area can be calculated as the sum of the area of the rectangle and the triangle on the left end. Thus:

    $$A = 6\cdot 4 + \frac{1}{2}\cdot 4 \cdot 3 = 24 + 6 = 30 \text{ ft}^2$$

8. The required area can be calculated as the area of the outside rectangle minus the areas of the two rectangles to be taken out. The height of the outside rectangle is

    $\frac{1}{2} + 2 + \frac{1}{2} = 3$ in. Thus,

    $$A = 3\cdot 3 - 2\left(1\cdot 2\right) = 9 - 4 = 5 \text{ in}^2.$$

9. This area can be calculated as the sum of the area of the rectangle and the semicircle on the left end. Thus:

    $$A = 40\cdot 20 + \frac{1}{2}\pi \cdot 10^2 = 800 + 50\pi$$

    $$\approx 800 + 50\cdot 3.14 = 957 \text{ cm}^2$$

10. This area can be calculated as the sum of the area of the triangle, base $10 + 10 = 20$ m and height 25 m, and the semicircle ($r = 5$) on the right end. Thus:

    $$A = \frac{1}{2}\cdot 20 \cdot 25 + \frac{1}{2}\pi \cdot 10^2 = 250 + 50\pi$$

    $$\approx 250 + 50\cdot 3.14 = 407 \text{ m}^2$$

11. This area can be calculated as the area of the square plus the area of the four semicircles. Thus,

    $$A = 8^2 + 2\pi \cdot 4^2 = 64 + 32\pi$$

    $$\approx 64 + 32\cdot 3.14 = 164 \text{ cm}^2$$

12. This area can be calculated as the area of the outer semicircle ($r = 10$ in.) minus the area of the inner semicircle ($r = 5$ in.). Thus,

    $$A = \frac{1}{2}\pi \cdot 10^2 - \frac{1}{2}\pi \cdot 5^2 = 50\pi - \frac{25}{2}\pi = 37.5\pi$$

    $$\approx 37.5\cdot 3.14 = 118 \text{ in}^2$$

13. The shaded area is the area of the rectangle minus the area of the inscribed semicircle. Thus,

    $$A = 6\cdot 3 - \frac{1}{2}\pi \cdot 3^2 = 18 - 4.5\pi$$

    $$\approx 18 - 4.5\cdot 3.14 = 3.87 \text{ cm}^2$$

14. The shaded area is the area of the outer circle ($r = 6$ in.) minus the area of the inner circle ($r = 4$ in.). Thus,

$A = \pi \cdot 6^2 - \pi \cdot 4^2 = 36\pi - 16\pi = 20\pi$

$\approx 20 \cdot 3.14 = 62.8 \text{ in}^2$

15. The shaded area is the area of the large semicircle minus the area of the two smaller semicircles. Thus,

$$A = \frac{1}{2}\pi \cdot 5^2 - 2 \cdot \frac{1}{2}\pi\left(\frac{5}{2}\right)^2 = \frac{25}{2}\pi - \frac{25}{4}\pi$$

$$= \frac{25}{4}\pi \approx 6.25(3.14) = 19.6 \text{ ft}^2$$

16. The shaded area is the area of the rectangle minus the area of the trapezoid. Thus,

$$A = 8 \cdot 6 - \frac{1}{2}(6+4) \cdot 3 = 48 - 15 = 33 \text{ in}^2$$

17. Since the displays are rectangles, the diagonal is the hypotenuse of two right triangles. Thus if x ft. is the length of the diagonal of the HD video display, then $x^2 = 72^2 + 160^2$. This equation gives $x^2 = 5184 + 25,600 = 30,784$ so that $x \approx 175$. The diagonal measurement of each video display is about 175 ft.

18. Since the displays are rectangles, the diagonal is the hypotenuse of two right triangles. Thus if x ft. is the length of the diagonal of the HD video display, then $x^2 = 51^2 + 29^2$. This equation gives $x^2 = 2601 + 840 = 3442$ so that $x \approx 59$. The diagonal measurement of each of the smaller video displays is about 59 ft.

19. Refer to the diagram in the text, where we have a right triangle with a hypotenuse measuring 720 ft and one leg 650 ft. Thus if h ft is the height of the pole, then $h^2 + 650^2 = 720^2$. This equation gives $h^2 = 720^2 - 650^2 = 518,400 - 422,500 = 95,900$ so that $h \approx 310$. The height of the pole is 310 ft tall.

20. Refer to the diagram in the text, where we have a right triangle with a hypotenuse measuring 700 ft. and one leg 650 ft. Thus if h ft. is the height of the pole, then $h^2 + 650^2 = 700^2$. This equation gives $h^2 = 700^2 - 650^2 = 490,000 - 422,500$

$= 67,500$ so that $h \approx 260$. The height of the pole is 260 ft. tall.

21. Since the DVD case is a rectangle, the diagonal is the hypotenuse of two right triangles. Thus if x cm is the length of the diagonal of the DVD case, then $x^2 = 14^2 + 11^2$. This equation gives $x^2 = 196 + 121 = 317$ so that $x \approx 17.804$. The diagonal measurement of the DVD case is about 17.804 cm.

22. Refer to the diagram in the text, where we have a right triangle with one leg measuring 40 ft. and the other leg 120 ft. Thus if x ft. is the length of the conveyor belt, then $x^2 = 40^2 + 120^2$. This equation gives $x^2 = 40^2 + 120^2 = 1600 + 14,400 = 16,000$ so that $x \approx 126$. The length of the conveyor belt is about 126 ft. long.

23. Refer to the diagram in the text, where we have a right triangle with one leg measuring 45 ft and the other leg 118 ft. Thus if x ft is the length of the conveyor belt, then $x^2 = 45^2 + 118^2$. This equation gives $x^2 = 45^2 + 118^2 = 2025 + 13,924 = 15,949$ so that $x \approx 126$. The materials need to travel about 126 ft to get to the top of the conveyor belt.

24. Refer to the diagram in the text, where we have a right triangle with one leg measuring 40 ft. and the other leg 220 ft. Thus if x ft. is the number of feet that the plane has traveled, then $x^2 = 40^2 + 220^2$. This equation gives $x^2 = 40^2 + 220^2 = 1600 + 48,400 = 50,000$ so that $x \approx 224$. The plane has traveled about 224 ft.

25. $A = 120 \cdot 53\frac{1}{3} = 120 \cdot \frac{160}{3} = 6400$. Thus, 6400 yd^2 of turf are needed.

26. a. Sum of the areas of the three rooms:
    $9 \cdot 10 + 12 \cdot 12 + 15 \cdot 15 = 459 \text{ ft}^2$

    Divide by 9 to convert to yd^2: $\frac{459}{9} = 51 \text{ yd}^2$

b. $51 \text{ yd}^2 \cdot \dfrac{\$14}{\text{yd}^2} = \$714$

27. Let w ft be the width. Then, $16w = 288$, so that $w = \dfrac{288}{16} = 18$. The room must be 18 ft wide.

28. Let r ft. be the radius. Then, $\pi r^2 = 363,000$, so that $r = \sqrt{\dfrac{363,000}{\pi}} \approx \sqrt{\dfrac{363,000}{3.14}} = 340$ ft. The diameter of the Superdome is $340 \cdot 2 = 680$ ft.

29. Let w be the width. Then, $70w = 6,720$, so that $w = \dfrac{6720}{70} = 96$. The screen is 96 ft wide.

30. Let r ft. be the radius. Then, $\pi r^2 = 5024$, so that $r = \sqrt{\dfrac{5024}{\pi}} \approx \sqrt{\dfrac{5024}{3.14}} = 40$ ft. The diameter of the pizza is $40 \cdot 2 = 80$ ft.

31. $A = \pi r^2 = \pi \cdot 4^2 = 16\pi \text{ cm}^2$

32. $A = \dfrac{1}{2}bh$ so $70 = \dfrac{1}{2} \cdot 20 \cdot h = 10h$ such that $h = 7$ in.

33. Since the cost of the glass is $4.50 at $3/ft^2, the area of the glass is $4.50 \div 3 = 1.50 \text{ ft}^2$. Let x ft be the width of the frame, so that $1.5x$ ft is the length. The area of the glass in terms of x is $(1.5x)(x) = 1.5x^2$. Hence, we have the equation $1.5x^2 = 1.5$. Thus, $x^2 = 1$ and $x = 1$. Thus, the dimensions are 1 ft by 1.5 ft, that is, 12 in. by 18 in.

34. Since one ounce covers 125 ft^2, 32 oz would cover $32 \cdot 125 = 4000 \text{ ft}^2$. Let x ft be the length and since the width is 16 ft., we have the equation $16x = 4000$. Thus, $x = 250$. The median strip of a highway is 250 ft. long.

35. $A = \pi r^2 = \pi \cdot 70^2 = 4900\pi$
$\approx 4900 \cdot 3.14 = 15,386 \text{ ft}^2$

36. $A = \pi r^2 = \pi \cdot 6^2 = 36\pi$
$\approx 36 \cdot 3.14 = 113.04 \text{ m}^2$

37. $A = \pi r^2 = \pi \cdot 16^2 = 256\pi$
$\approx 256 \cdot 3.14 = 803.84 \text{ mi}^2$

38. $A = \pi r^2 = \pi \cdot 120^2 = 14,400\pi$
$\approx 14,400 \cdot 3.14 = 45,216 \text{ mi}^2$

39. $A = \pi r^2 = \pi \cdot 5^2 = 25\pi$
$\approx 25 \cdot 3.14 = 78.5 \text{ mi}^2$
Difference $= 803.84 - 78.5 = 7252.34 \text{ mi}^2$

40. $A = \pi r^2 = \pi \cdot 20^2 = 400\pi$
$\approx 400 \cdot 3.14 = 1256 \text{ ft}^2$

41. $A = \dfrac{1}{2}\pi r^2 = \dfrac{1}{2}\pi \cdot 3^2 = 4.5\pi$
$\approx 4.5(3.14) = 13.345 \text{ ft}^2$

42. $A = \pi r^2 = \pi \cdot 27^2 = 729\pi$
$\approx 729 \cdot 3.14 = 2289.06 \text{ ft}^2$

43. Subtract the inner area from the outer area:
$A = \pi r_o^2 - \pi r_i^2 - = \pi(2.25)^2 - \pi(0.75)^2$
$= 5.0625\pi - 0.5625\pi = 4.5\pi$
$\approx 4.5(3.14) = 14.13 \text{ in}^2$

44. For a triangle to be a right triangle, the square of one of the sides must equal the sum of the squares of the other two sides.
a.   Not a right triangle, $3^2 + 5^2 \neq 6^2$.
b.   A right triangle, $5^2 + 12^2 = 13^2$.
c.   A right triangle, $7^2 + 24^2 = 25^2$.
d.   Not a right triangle, $9^2 + 10^2 \neq 15^2$.

45. a. in^2 and cm^2 b. mi^2 and km^2
c. yd^2 and m^2 d. yd^2 and m^2

46. A 2-in. square is a square that is 2 in. on a side; its area is 4 in^2. 2 in^2 is an area of 2 in^2.

47. The perimeter of the first room is $20 + 24 = 44$ ft, of the second room is $28 + 30 = 58$ ft, and of the third room is $24 + 24 = 48$ ft. Hence, the sum of the perimeters is $44 + 58 + 48 = 150$ ft. The ceiling is 8 ft high, so the total wall area to be painted is $8 \cdot 150 = 1200 \text{ ft}^2$.

    a. Since a gallon of paint covers 450 ft^2, the number of gallons needed is
    $$\frac{1200}{450} = \frac{8}{3} = 2\frac{2}{3} \text{ gal.}$$

    b. The paint is sold only by the gallon, so 3 gallons will have to be bought at a cost of $3 \cdot 14 = \$42$.

48. The area to be painted is the area of the triangle region plus the area of the rectangular front minus the area of the door. The area of the triangle region is $\frac{1}{2} \cdot 50 \cdot 6 = 150 \text{ ft}^2$. The area of the front minus the area of the door is $50 \cdot 12 - 3 \cdot 7 = 579 \text{ ft}^2$. The total area to be painted is $150 + 579 = 729 \text{ ft}^2$.

    a. Each gallon covers 400 ft2, so you would need $729 \div 400 = 1.8225$. You would need to buy 2 gal.

    b. The cost to paint the front of the house is $\$17 / \text{gal} \cdot 2 \text{gal} = \$34$.

49. The entire lot area is $100 \cdot 200 = 20,000 \text{ ft}^2$. The area occupied by the shed is $10 \cdot 10 = 100 \text{ ft}^2$; the area occupied by the house is $30 \cdot 50 = 1500 \text{ ft}^2$; the area occupied by the drive is $10 \cdot 50 = 500 \text{ ft}^2$. Thus, the lawn area is:
    $$20,000 - 100 - 1500 - 500 = 17,900 \text{ ft}^2$$

    a. A bag of fertilizer covers 1200 ft^2, so it will take $\frac{17,900}{1200} \approx 14.9^+$ bags. Thus, 15 bags are needed.

    b. The cost will be $4 \cdot 15 = \$60$.

50. a. The radius of an 11-in. diameter pizza is 5.5 in. So, the area of the small pizza is $\pi \cdot 5.5^2 = 30.25\pi \approx 30.25 \cdot 3.14 \approx 95 \text{ in}^2$.

    b. The radius of a 15-in. diameter pizza is

7.5 in. So, the area of the large pizza is $\pi \cdot 7.5^2 = 56.25\pi \approx 56.25 \cdot 3.14 \approx 177 \text{ in}^2$.

    c. Two small pizzas would cost $2(\$10) = \$10$ for $2(95 \text{ in}^2) = 190 \text{ in}^2$. This would be a price of $\frac{\$10}{190 \text{in}^2} = \$0.0526$ per oz. One large pizza would cost $\frac{\$8}{177 \text{in}^2} = \$0.0452$ per oz. One large pizza would be the better deal.

51. a. For the 8-in. pie, $A = \pi r^2 = \pi \cdot 4^2 = 16\pi \approx 16 \cdot 3.14 \approx 50.24 \text{ in}^2$. Thus, the unit price is $\frac{125}{50.24} \approx 2.49$ cents/in^2.

    b. For the 10-in. pie, $A = \pi r^2 = \pi \cdot 5^2 = 25\pi \approx 25 \cdot 3.14 \approx 78.5 \text{ in}^2$. Thus, the unit price is $\frac{185}{78.5} \approx 2.36$ cents/in^2.

    c. On the basis of the unit price, the 10-in. pie is the better buy.

52. The Golden Ratio is the ratio of the longer side to the shorter side. Refer to the diagram in the text to see that the ratio will be the length of $\overline{AF}$ to the length of $\overline{AB}$. To find the length of $\overline{AF}$: If a side of the square ABCD is 2a, then $\overline{CD} = 2a$. Line segment $\overline{ED}$ is the midpoint of $\overline{AD}$, so it's length is a. Use the Pythagorean theorem with hypotenuse $\overline{EC}$. Thus,
$$\left(\overline{EC}\right)^2 = a^2 + (2a)^2$$
$$\left(\overline{EC}\right)^2 = a^2 + 4a^2 = 5a^2$$
$$\overline{EC} = \sqrt{5}a$$
Since the length of $\overline{EC}$ is equal to the length of $\overline{EF}$, we have that $\overline{AF} = \overline{AE} + \overline{EF} = 1a + \sqrt{5}a$. Therefore, we have the ratio
$$\frac{1a + \sqrt{5}a}{2a} = \frac{a\left(1 + \sqrt{5}\right)}{2a} = \frac{1 + \sqrt{5}}{2}.$$

53. The area of the rectangle taken away is Wx, and the area of the rectangle added on is hy.

Since $\frac{y}{W} = \frac{x}{h}$, it follows that $hy = Wx$.

Thus, the area of the new rectangle is equal to the area of the original rectangle.

54. The construction should look like that in problem 53.

Collaborative Learning

Group 1:
1. $\sqrt{2}\,r$
2. $2r^2$

Group 2:
1. $h = \dfrac{\sqrt{3}}{2}r$
2. $\dfrac{3\sqrt{3}}{2}r^2$

Group 3:
1. The perimeter of the polygon.
2. $nb = 2\pi h$ (the circumference)
3. $A = \dfrac{1}{2}(nb)h = \dfrac{1}{2}(2\pi h)h = \pi h^2$

Section 8.5 Volume and Surface Area

1. a. A, B, C, D, E
   b. $\overline{AB}, \overline{AC}, \overline{AD}, \overline{AE}, \overline{BC}, \overline{BE}, \overline{CD}, \overline{CE}, \overline{DE}$

2. a. A, B, C, D, E, F
   b. $\overline{AB}, \overline{BC}, \overline{CA}, \overline{DE}, \overline{EF}, \overline{FD}, \overline{AD}, \overline{BE}, \overline{CF}$

3. $ABCD$

4. $ADHE$

5.

6.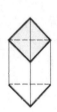

7.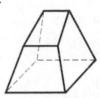

8.

9. a. If the original edge is of length a, then $V = a^3$. The new edge is of length $2a$, so the volume is $(2a)^3 = 8a^3$. Thus, the volume is multiplied by 8.
   b. If the length of the edge is tripled, the new volume is $(3a)^3 = 27a^3$. Thus, the volume is multiplied by 27.

10. $V = \dfrac{4}{3}\pi r^3 = \dfrac{4}{3}\pi \cdot 24^3 = 18{,}432\pi$
    $\approx 18{,}432 \cdot 3.14 = 57{,}876.48$ ft^3
    $\dfrac{7.5\,\text{gal}}{1\text{ft}^3} \cdot 57{,}876.48 \text{ ft}^3 = 434{,}073.6$ gal

11. $S = 4\pi r^2 = 4\pi \cdot 24^2 = 2304\pi$
    $\approx 2304 \cdot 3.14 = 7234.6$ ft^2

12. $V = \dfrac{4}{3}\pi r^3 = \dfrac{4}{3}\pi \cdot 7.2^3 = 497.664\pi$
    $\approx 497.664 \cdot 3.14 = 1562.66496$ m^3
    $\dfrac{1000\text{ L}}{1\text{ m}^3} \cdot 1562.66496 \text{ m}^3 = 1{,}562{,}665.0$ L

13. $S = 4\pi r^2 = 4\pi \cdot 7.2^2 = 207.36\pi$
    $\approx 207.36 \cdot 3.14 = 651.1$ m^2

14. $V = \dfrac{4}{3}\pi r^3 = \dfrac{4}{3}\pi \cdot 1^3 = \dfrac{4}{3}\pi$
    $\approx \dfrac{4}{3} \cdot 3.14 \approx 4.2$ in^3

15. $V = Bh = 10 \cdot 5 = 50$ in^3

16. $V = Bh = \left(\dfrac{1}{2} \cdot 3 \cdot 4\right) \cdot 5 = 30$ ft^3

17. $V = \dfrac{1}{3}Bh = \dfrac{1}{3} \cdot 492^2 \cdot 138 = 11{,}134{,}944$ ft^3

18. The area of the base is $A = bh$, where h is
    $h^2 = 3^2 - \left(\dfrac{3}{2}\right)^2$ so that $h = \sqrt{\dfrac{27}{4}} = \dfrac{3\sqrt{3}}{2}$.
    Thus $A = \dfrac{1}{2} \cdot \sqrt{\dfrac{27}{4}} \cdot 3 = \dfrac{1}{2} \cdot \dfrac{3\sqrt{3}}{2} \cdot 3 = \dfrac{9\sqrt{3}}{4}$.
    The volume of the first pyramid is
    $V_1 = \dfrac{1}{3}Bh = \dfrac{1}{3} \cdot \dfrac{9\sqrt{3}}{4} \cdot 2 = \dfrac{3\sqrt{3}}{2}$ in^3.
    The volume of the second period is

$V_2 = \frac{1}{3}Bh = \frac{1}{3} \cdot \frac{9\sqrt{3}}{4} \cdot 4 = 3\sqrt{3} \text{ in}^3$. The convex

polyhedron is $V_1 + V_2 = \frac{3\sqrt{3}}{2} + 3\sqrt{3} = \frac{9\sqrt{3}}{2} \text{ in}^3$.

19. The volume of the cube is $V = 10^3$

    $= 1000 \text{ cm}^3$; the volume of the pyramid is

    $V_P = \frac{1}{3}Bh = \frac{1}{3} \cdot 10^2 \cdot 15 = 500 \text{ cm}^3$. Thus,

    the total volume is 1500 cm^3, or 1.5 liters.

20. $V = \frac{1}{3}Bh = \frac{1}{3} \cdot 227^2 \cdot 137 = 2,353,158 \text{ m}^3$

21. a. $V = \pi r^2 h = \pi \cdot 5^2 \cdot 9 = 225\pi$

    $\approx 225(3.14) \approx 707 \text{ in}^3$

    $S = 2\pi rh + 2\pi r^2 = 2\pi \cdot 5 \cdot 9 + 2\pi \cdot 5^2$

    $= 90\pi + 50\pi = 140\pi \approx 140(3.14)$

    $\approx 440 \text{ in}^2$

    b. $V = \frac{1}{3}\pi r^2 h = \frac{1}{3}\pi \cdot 5^2 \cdot 9 = 75\pi$

       $\approx 75(3.14) \approx 236 \text{ in}^3$

       $S = \pi r^2 + \pi rs = \pi \cdot 5^2 + \pi \cdot 5\sqrt{106}$

       $= (25 + 5\sqrt{106})\pi \approx 76.5(3.14)$

       $\approx 240 \text{ in}^2$
       (Use the Pythagorean theorem to find
       the slant height. $s^2 = 5^2 + 9^2$.)

22. a. $V = 600\pi \approx 1880 \text{ cm}^3$

       $S = 320\pi \approx 1000 \text{ cm}^2$

    b. $V = 200\pi \approx 628 \text{ cm}^3$

       $S = (100 + 20\sqrt{34})\pi \approx 680 \text{ cm}^2$

23. a. $V = \pi r^2 h = \pi \cdot 3^2 \cdot 4 = 36\pi$

       $\approx 36(3.14) \approx 113 \text{ ft}^3$

       $S = 2\pi rh + 2\pi r^2 = 2\pi \cdot 3 \cdot 4 + 2\pi \cdot 3^2$

       $= 24\pi + 18\pi = 42\pi \approx 42(3.14)$

       $\approx 132 \text{ ft}^2$

    b. $V = \frac{1}{3}\pi r^2 h = \frac{1}{3}\pi \cdot 3^2 \cdot 4 = 12\pi$

$\approx 12(3.14) \approx 37.7 \text{ ft}^3$

$S = \pi r^2 + \pi rs = \pi \cdot 3^2 + \pi \cdot 3 \cdot 5$

$= (9 + 15)\pi \approx 24(3.14) \approx 75.4 \text{ ft}^2$

24. a. $V = 432\pi \approx 1360 \text{ cm}^3$

       $S = 216\pi \approx 678 \text{ cm}^2$

    b. $V = 144\pi \approx 452 \text{ cm}^3$

       $S = (36 + 36\sqrt{5})\pi \approx 366 \text{ cm}^2$

25. $V = \frac{4}{3}\pi r^3 = \frac{4}{3}\pi \cdot 6^3 = 288\pi$

    $\approx 288(3.14) \approx 904 \text{ in}^3$

26. $V = \frac{4}{3}\pi r^3 = \frac{4}{3}\pi \cdot 12^3 = 2304\pi$

    $\approx 2304(3.14) \approx 7235 \text{ cm}^3$

27. $V = \pi r^2 h = \pi \cdot 58^2 \cdot 754 = 2,536,456\pi$

    $\approx 2,536,456(3.14) \approx 7,960,000 \text{ ft}^3$

28. $V = \frac{1}{3}\pi r^2 h = \frac{1}{3}\pi \cdot 4^2 \cdot 7 = \frac{112}{3}\pi$

    $\approx \frac{112}{3}\pi(3.14) \approx 117.2 \text{ cm}^3$

29. $V = \frac{1}{3}\pi r^2 h = \frac{1}{3}\pi \cdot 500^2 \cdot 2000 = 166,666,666.7\pi$

    $\approx 166,666,666.7(3.14) \approx 523,333,333.3 \text{ ft}^3$

30. $V = \frac{4}{3}\pi r^3 = \frac{4}{3}\pi \cdot 60^3 = 288,000\pi$

    $\approx 288,000(3.14) = 904,320 \text{ ft}^3$
    The fuel tank can hold about
    $904,320 \cdot 7.5 = 6,782,400 \text{ gal}$.

31. $r = 1.5(2.54) \text{ cm}$ and $h = 4(2.54) \text{ cm}$.

    $V = \pi r^2 h = \pi[1.5(2.54)]^2 (4)(2.54)$

    $= \pi(9)(2.54)^3 \approx (3.14)(147.5)$

    $\approx 463 \text{ cm}^3$

    Thus, the can will hold about 463 g.

32. $V_{Cone} = \dfrac{1}{3}\pi r^2 h = \dfrac{1}{3}\pi \cdot 3.5^2 \cdot 10 = \dfrac{245}{6}\pi$

$\approx \dfrac{245}{6}(3.14) \approx 128.22 \text{ cm}^3$

$V_{Hemisphere} = \dfrac{1}{2}\left(\dfrac{4}{3}\pi r^3\right) = \dfrac{2}{3}\pi \cdot 3.5^3 = \dfrac{343}{12}\pi$

$\approx \dfrac{343}{12}(3.14) \approx 89.75 \text{ cm}^3$

$V_{Cone} + V_{Hemisphere} = 128.22 + 89.75 = 217.97 \text{ cm}^3$

The ice cream weights about

$217.97 \text{ cm}^3 \cdot \dfrac{1}{2}\text{ g/cm}^3 \approx 109 \text{ g}.$

33. a. Baseball: $r = \dfrac{9}{2\pi}$, so

$S_1 = 4\pi r^2 = 4\pi\left(\dfrac{9}{2\pi}\right)^2 = \dfrac{81}{\pi}$

$\approx 25.8 \text{ in}^2$

$V_1 = \dfrac{4}{3}\pi r^3 = \dfrac{4}{3}\pi\left(\dfrac{9}{2\pi}\right)^3 = \dfrac{243}{2\pi^2}$

$\approx 12.3 \text{ in}^3$

Soccer Ball: $r = \dfrac{27}{2\pi}$, so

$S_2 = 4\pi r^2 = 4\pi\left(\dfrac{27}{2\pi}\right)^2 = \dfrac{729}{\pi}$

$\approx 232 \text{ in}^2$

$V_2 = \dfrac{4}{3}\pi r^3 = \dfrac{4}{3}\pi\left(\dfrac{27}{2\pi}\right)^3 = \dfrac{6561}{2\pi^2}$

$\approx 333 \text{ in}^3$

Basketball: $r = \dfrac{30}{2\pi}$, so

$S_3 = 4\pi r^2 = 4\pi\left(\dfrac{30}{2\pi}\right)^2 = \dfrac{900}{\pi}$

$\approx 287 \text{ in}^2$

$V_3 = \dfrac{4}{3}\pi r^3 = \dfrac{4}{3}\pi\left(\dfrac{30}{2\pi}\right)^3 = \dfrac{4500}{\pi^2}$

$\approx 456 \text{ in}^3$

b. $\dfrac{S_1}{S_3} = \dfrac{81/\pi}{900/\pi} = \dfrac{81}{\pi}\cdot\dfrac{\pi}{900} = \dfrac{9}{100}$

c. $\dfrac{V_1}{V_2} = \dfrac{243/(2\pi^2)}{6561/(2\pi^2)} = \dfrac{243}{2\pi^2}\cdot\dfrac{2\pi^2}{6561} = \dfrac{1}{27}$

34. a. $V = \pi r^2 h = \pi \cdot 150^2 \cdot 200 = 4,500,000\pi$

$\approx 4,500,000(3.14) = 14,130,000 \text{ ft}^3$

The storage tank can hold
14,130,000 · 7.5 = 105,975,000 gal , or
about 106 million gallons.

b. $S = 2\pi rh + \pi r^2 = 2\pi \cdot 150 \cdot 200 + \pi \cdot 150^2$

$= 60,000\pi + 22,500\pi = 82,500\pi$

$\approx 82,500 \cdot 3.14 = 259,050 \text{ ft}^2$

To paint the exterior and top of the tank,

you would need $\dfrac{259,050 \text{ ft}^2}{400 \text{ ft}^2} = 647.625$ gal,

so for two coats, about 1300 gallons of paint
are needed.

35. a. $V = \dfrac{4}{3}\pi r^3 = \dfrac{4}{3}\pi\left(\dfrac{27}{2\pi}\right)^3 = \dfrac{6561}{2\pi^2}$

$\approx 333 \text{ in}^3$

b. The volumes drilled out are
approximately cylinders of radii 5/8 and
1/2 in., respectively, and height 5/2 in.
This volume is:

$\pi\left(\dfrac{5}{8}\right)^2\cdot\dfrac{5}{2} + \pi\left(\dfrac{1}{2}\right)^2\cdot\dfrac{5}{2} + \pi\left(\dfrac{1}{2}\right)^2\cdot\dfrac{5}{2}$

$=\left(\dfrac{125}{128} + \dfrac{5}{8} + \dfrac{5}{8}\right)\pi = \dfrac{285}{128}\pi \approx 6.99 \text{ in}^3$

Thus, the volume remaining is about
$333 - 7 = 326 \text{ in}^3$ so that the final

weight is about $\dfrac{326}{333}\cdot 16 \approx 15.66$ lb.

36. a. Basketball: $r = \dfrac{30}{2\pi} = \dfrac{15}{\pi}$, so

$V = \dfrac{4}{3}\pi r^3 = \dfrac{4}{3}\pi\left(\dfrac{15}{\pi}\right)^3 = \dfrac{4500}{\pi^2}$

$\approx \dfrac{4500}{(3.14)^2} \approx 456 \text{ in}^3$

b. For cubical box, the length of the side s

must be $2r$, or $2\cdot\dfrac{15}{\pi} = \dfrac{30}{\pi}$ so that volume is $V = lwh = s^3 = \left(\dfrac{30}{\pi}\right)^3 \approx 872 \text{ in}^3$.

c. $\dfrac{456 \text{ in}^3}{872 \text{ in}^3} \approx 0.5229 \approx 52\%$

37. a. $V = Bh = 7 \cdot 12 \cdot 17 = 1428 \text{ in}^3$
   b. $S = $ area of base $+$ area of four sides
        $= 7 \cdot 12 + 2 \cdot 7 \cdot 17 + 2 \cdot 12 \cdot 17 = 730 \text{ in}^2$
   c.   Two tons of recycled paper are needed
        in order to save 34 trees. One ton is
        equal to 2000 lb, and one pound is equal
        to 16 oz. So, for two tons of recycled

        paper, we have $\dfrac{2 \cdot 2000 \cdot 16}{2} = 32,000$

        bags have to be recycled to save 34
        trees.

38. $V = lwh = 26 \cdot 16 \cdot 19 = 7904 \text{ in}^3$

39. $V = lwh = 16 \cdot 11 \cdot 10 = 1760 \text{ in}^3$

40. $V = lwh = 8 \cdot 11 \cdot 5 = 440 \text{ in}^3$

41. $V = lwh = 16 \cdot 11 \cdot 13 = 2288 \text{ in}^3$

42. $V = \pi r^2 h = \pi \cdot \left(\dfrac{1}{2}\right)^2 \cdot 4 = \pi \approx 3.14 \text{ ft}^3$

43. $V = \pi r^2 h = \pi (1.5)^2 (5) = 11.25\pi$
      $\approx 11.25 \cdot 3.14 \approx 35.33 \text{ in}^3$

44. $V = \pi r^2 h = \pi \cdot \left(\dfrac{1}{2}\right)^2 \cdot 2 = \dfrac{1}{2}\pi$
      $\approx \dfrac{1}{2} \cdot 3.14 = 1.57 \text{ ft}^3$

45. $2.5(35.33) = 88 \text{ in}^3$

46. a. $V = lwh = 16 \cdot 12 \cdot 12 = 2304 \text{ in}^3$
        $V = 2304 \text{ in}^3 \cdot \dfrac{1 \text{ ft}^3}{12^3 \text{ in}^3} \approx 1.33 \text{ ft}^3$
   b. $V = lwh = 18 \cdot 18 \cdot 16 = 5184 \text{ in}^3$
        $V = 5184 \text{ in}^3 \cdot \dfrac{1 \text{ ft}^3}{12^3 \text{ in}^3} = 3 \text{ ft}^3$

c. $V = lwh = 18 \cdot 18 \cdot 24 = 7776 \text{ in}^3$
     $V = 7776 \text{ in}^3 \cdot \dfrac{1 \text{ ft}^3}{12^3 \text{ in}^3} = 4.5 \text{ ft}^3$

d.   b and c

47. a. $V = lwh = 22 \cdot 7 \cdot 8 = 1232 \text{ ft}^3$
   b. $V = lwh = 3 \cdot 7 \cdot 3 = 63 \text{ ft}^3$
   c.   Truck volume: $1232 + 63 = 1295 \text{ ft}^3$
        No. $1300 > 1295$.

48. a. $V = lwh = 20 \cdot 7 \cdot 8 = 1120 \text{ ft}^3$
   b. $V = lwh = 3 \cdot 7 \cdot 3 = 63 \text{ ft}^3$
   c.   No. You have only 1183 ft^3.

49. $V = \pi r^2 h = \pi \left(\dfrac{1.5}{2}\right)^2 (2.5) = 1.41\pi$
      $\approx 1.41 \cdot 3.14 \approx 4.43 \text{ ft}^3$

50. $V = \dfrac{1}{2}\left(\dfrac{4}{3}\pi r^3\right) = \dfrac{2}{3}\pi \left(\dfrac{1.5}{2}\right)^3 = 0.28125\pi$
      $\approx 0.28125 \cdot 3.14 \approx 0.88 \text{ ft}^3$

51. $V_{Bottom} = \pi r^2 h = \pi \left(\dfrac{1.5}{2}\right)^2 (2.5) = 1.41\pi$
      $\approx 1.41 \cdot 3.14 \approx 4.43 \text{ ft}^3$
      $V_{Top} = \dfrac{1}{2}\left(\dfrac{4}{3}\pi r^3\right) = \dfrac{1}{2} \cdot \dfrac{4}{3}\pi \left(\dfrac{1.5}{2}\right)^3$
      $\approx 0.88 \text{ ft}^3$
      $V_{Total} = 4.43 + 0.88 \approx 5.31 \text{ ft}^3$

52. $V_{Total} = 3 \cdot 4 \cdot \left(1.41\pi + \dfrac{2}{3}\pi\left(\dfrac{1.5}{2}\right)^3\right) \approx 63.6 \text{ ft}^3$

53. $\dfrac{500 \text{ ft}^3}{5.31 \text{ ft}^3} \approx 94.16 \approx 94$ cans of trash

54. $\dfrac{500 \text{ ft}^3}{63.6 \text{ ft}^3} \approx 7.86$ buildings, so about 7 buildings

55.   Answers will vary.

56. The volume. The circumference and area can be made very large by flattening the burger.

57. $C_M = 2\pi r = 2\pi \cdot 1 = 2\pi$

$C_B = 2\pi r = 2\pi \cdot (1.75) = 3.50\pi$

The ratio of the circumferences is

$\dfrac{3.50\pi}{2\pi} = 1.75$, so the Burger King burger is 75% larger than the McDonald burger.

58. For the McDonald burger, $C = 2\pi$. For the Burger King burger, $C = 3.5\pi$. The ratio of Burger King to McDonald is

$\dfrac{3.5\pi}{2\pi} = 1.75 = 175\%$, so you can claim

(erroneously) that the Burger King burger has 75% more meat than the McDonald burger.

59. Answers will vary. Length is one dimensional, area is two dimensional, and volume is three dimensional.

60. For a sphere, if the diameter is doubled, the volume is 8 times as large and the surface area is 4 times as large.

61. No. This is true only if the radius is more

than three units long. (Compare $\dfrac{4}{3}\pi r^3$ and

$4\pi r^2$.)

62. The volume is doubled.

63. Since the sum of the face angles at a vertex must be less than 360°, three, four or five equilateral triangles, three squares or three pentagons can be put together at any vertex. There are no other possibilities, so only the five regular polyhedrons listed are possible.

64. Make the icosahedron.

65.

Figure	F	V	E	F + V
8.68B	6	8	12	14 = E + 2
8.69C	6	5	9	11 = E + 2
8.69D	7	10	15	17 = E + 2
8.70	5	6	9	11 = E + 2
8.71	6	6	10	12 = E + 2

Thus, Euler's formula is $F + V = E + 2$.

66. $F = 20, V = 12, E = 30$.

Thus, $F + V = 32 = E + 2$.

Calculator Corner

1. $\boxed{4}\boxed{\times}\boxed{\pi}\boxed{\times}\boxed{6}\boxed{y^x}\boxed{3}\boxed{\div}\boxed{3}\boxed{\text{ENTER}}$

$904.78 \approx 905$

Section 8.6 Networks, Non-Euclidean Geometry, and Topology

1. a. 3 b. 0
    c. This network is traversable; all three vertices are possible starting points.

2. a. 2 (A, C) b. 2 (B, D)
    c. This network is traversable; start at B or D.

3. a. 3 (B, D, and E) b. 2 (A and C)
    c. This network is traversable; start at either A or C.

4. a. 3 (D, G, E) b. 4 (A, B, C, F)
    c. This network is not traversable; it has more than 2 odd vertices.

5. a. 1 (A only) b. 4 (B, C, D, E)
    c. This network is not traversable; it has more than 2 odd vertices.

6. a. 2 (A, B) b. 2 (C, D)
    c. This network is traversable; start at C or D.

7. a. 5 (A, C, D, E, G) b. 2 (B, F)
    c. This network is traversable; start at B or F.

8. a. 3 (B, D, F) b. 4 (A, C, E, G)
    c. This network is not traversable; it has more than 2 odd vertices.

9. a. 1 (The vertex of the pyramid)
    b. 4 (The vertices of the base)
    c. This network is not traversable; it has more than 2 odd vertices.

10. a. 0 b. 8
    c. This network is not traversable; it has more than 2 odd vertices.

11. Think of each region as a vertex with the individual line segments in its boundary as the number of paths to the vertex. The boundary of region A has four segments, so

the corresponding network point would be even. The boundary of region *B* has five segments, so the corresponding network point would be odd. The boundary of region *C* has four segments, so the corresponding network point would be even. The boundary of region *D* has five segments, so the corresponding network point would be odd. The boundary of region *E* has 10 segments, so the corresponding network point would be even. Thus, the network would have two odd vertices (*B* and *D*). By starting in region *B* or *D*, it is possible to draw a simple connected broken line that crosses each line segment exactly once.

12. Think of each region as a vertex with the individual line segments in its boundary as the number of paths to the vertex. The boundary of region *A* has five segments, so the corresponding network point would be odd. The boundary of region *B* has five segments, so the corresponding network point would be odd. The boundary of region *C* has four segments, so the corresponding network point would be even. The boundary of region *D* has five segments, so the corresponding network point would be odd. The boundary of region *E* has four segments, so the corresponding network point would be even. The boundary of the region outside has nine segments, so the corresponding network point would be odd. It is not possible to draw a simple connected broken line that crosses each line segment exactly once because the corresponding network has four odd vertices.

13. Region *A* has three doorways, so the corresponding vertex would be odd. Regions *B*, *C*, *D* and *E* each have two doorways, so the corresponding vertices would be even. Region *F* has three doorways, so the corresponding vertex would be odd. (Two doorways lead to the outside region, so the outside region is also an even vertex.) Thus, the network would have two odd vertices, *A* and *F*. By starting in *A* and ending in *F* (or vice versa), it is possible to take a walk and pass through each doorway exactly once. It is not possible to start and end outside, because the walk must start in one of the regions corresponding to one odd vertex and end in the region corresponding to the other odd vertex.

14. Regions *A*, *B*, *C*, *D*, *E* and *F* each have two doorways, so the corresponding vertices would be even. (Two doorways lead to the outside region, so the outside region is also an even vertex.) Thus, the network has no odd vertices. By starting in any room and end in that same room, it is possible to take a walk and pass through each doorway exactly once. It is possible to start and end outside, because the outside region is also even.

15. *A* and *D* each have three doorways and all the other rooms have an even number of doorways. Thus, the corresponding network would have two odd vertices, *A* and *D*. By starting in either *A* or *D* and ending in the other, it is possible for a walk to pass through each doorway exactly once. It is not possible to start and end outside.

16. *C, D, E,* and the outside each have three doorways and all the other rooms have an even number of doorways. Thus, the corresponding network would have four odd vertices so it is not possible for a walk to pass through each doorway exactly once. It is not possible to start and end outside.

17. All the rooms and the outside have an even number of doorways, so the corresponding network would have no odd vertices. The walk can start in any room or outside and end in the same place and pass through each doorway exactly once.

18. *A* and *F* each have three doorways and all the other rooms and the outside have an even number of doorways. Thus, the corresponding network would have two odd vertices, *A* and *D*. By starting in either *A* or *D* and ending in the other, it is possible for a walk to pass through each doorway exactly once. It is not possible to start and end outside.

19. Rooms *B* and *D* each have three doorways and all the other rooms have an even number of doorways (two doorways lead to the outside region, so the outside region is also an even vertex), so the corresponding network would have two odd vertices. The walk can start in either *B* or *D* and end in the other, passing through each doorway exactly once. It is not possible to start and end outside.

20. *C, D, F*, and the outside each have three doorways and all the other rooms have an even number of doorways. Thus, the corresponding network would have four odd vertices so it is not possible for a walk to pass through each doorway exactly once. It is not possible to start and end outside.

21. Room *A* and the outside *D* each have three doorways and *B* and *C* each have an even number of doorways, so the corresponding network would have two odd vertices. By starting in *A* and ending in *D* (or vice versa), a walk could pass through each doorway exactly once. It is not possible to start and end outside.

22. *A* and *D* each have three doorways and all the other rooms and the outside have an even number of doorways. Thus, the corresponding network would have two odd vertices, *A* and *D*. By starting in either *A* or *D* and ending in the other, it is possible for a walk to pass through each doorway exactly once. It is not possible to start and end outside.

23. Given a line and any point not on that line, there is one and only one line through that point and parallel to the given line.

24. Given a line and a point not on the line, there is more than one line through the given point parallel to the given line.

25. Given a line and any point not on that line, there is no line through that point that is parallel to the given line.

26. Euclidean

27. In hyperbolic geometry

28. Elliptic or Riemannian

29. The surface of a rectangular box

30. A pseudosphere

31. The surface of a sphere

32. Riemannian

33. (a) - (e) are topologically equivalent

34. a. True   b. False   c. False

d. True   e. True

35. (a) - (e) are of genus 2. (f) is of genus 1.

36. a. Zero   b. Three

37. Topo is correct. If you cut through a loop of the left-hand figure, you can unwind it into a single strip as you can with the circular cord.

38. Yes. It takes only one cut to give two pieces of either clip.

39. a. 6 points are marked on the network.
    b. Each point has 2 edges.
    c. Yes, because there are no odd vertices.
    d. 10,471 km   e. 108 hr
    f. $\dfrac{10,471 \text{ km}}{108 \text{ hr}} \approx 97 \text{ km/hr}$

    $\dfrac{97 \text{ km}}{\text{hr}} \cdot \dfrac{1 \text{ mi}}{1.609 \text{ km}} \approx 60 \text{ mi/hr}$

40. a.

b. Vertex 1: 3 edges   Vertex 2: 3 edges
    Vertex 3: 4 edges   Vertex 4: 2 edges
    Vertex 5: 2 edges   Vertex 6: 4 edges
    Vertex 7: 2 edges
c. Yes, as there are only two odd vertices it is traversable.
d. Answers will vary.

41. a. Yes. Removing any bridge will reduce by one the edges at two vertices (making them even) leaving only two odd vertices. So, for instance, close bridge *f*.
    b. You have to start at one of the odd vertices.
    c. You will end at the other odd vertex.

42. a. Yes.
    b. No. Adding a bridge joining any two of the vertices makes it traversable.

43. Since each arc has two endpoints, the total number of endpoints must be even. An odd

vertex accounts for an odd number of endpoints, while an even vertex accounts for an even number of endpoints. Thus, there must be an even number of odd vertices.

44. Use the stops as vertices and plan the route so that there are no more than two odd vertices.

Exercises 45 – 52, refer to the table.

Figure	Vertices (V)	Regions (R)	Arcs (A)
45	3	2	3
46	4	3	5
47	5	2	5
48	4	3	5
49	2	3	3
50	5	3	6
51	6	3	7
52	9	4	11

You can check that the results in problems 45 – 52 all fit the formula $V + R = A + 2$.

Section 8.7 Right Triangle Trigonometry

1. Substitute the known values into $c^2 = a^2 + b^2$
$$c^2 = 3^2 + 4^2 = 9 + 16 = 25$$
$$c = 5$$

2. Substitute the known values into $c^2 = a^2 + b^2$
$$c^2 = 5^2 + 12^2 = 25 + 144 = 169$$
$$c = 13$$

3. Substitute the known values into $c^2 = a^2 + b^2$
$$c^2 = 8^2 + 15^2 = 64 + 225 = 289$$
$$c = 17$$

4. Substitute the known values into $c^2 = a^2 + b^2$
$$c^2 = 6^2 + 8^2 = 36 + 64 = 100$$
$$c = 10$$

5. Substitute the known values into $b^2 = c^2 - a^2$
$$b^2 = 15^2 - 9^2 = 225 - 81 = 144$$
$$b = 12$$

6. Substitute the known values into $b^2 = c^2 - a^2$

$$b^2 = 20^2 - 12^2 = 400 - 144 = 256$$
$$b = 16$$

7. Substitute the known values into $a^2 = c^2 - b^2$
$$a^2 = 26^2 - 24^2 = 676 - 576 = 100$$
$$a = 10$$

8. Substitute the known values into $a^2 = c^2 - b^2$
$$a^2 = 25^2 - 20^2 = 625 - 400 = 225$$
$$a = 15$$

9. a. $\cos A = \dfrac{b}{c} = \dfrac{3}{5}$ b. $\sin A = \dfrac{a}{c} = \dfrac{4}{5}$

   c. $\tan A = \dfrac{a}{b} = \dfrac{4}{3}$

10. a. $\cos A = \dfrac{b}{c} = \dfrac{5}{13}$ b. $\sin A = \dfrac{a}{c} = \dfrac{12}{13}$

    c. $\tan A = \dfrac{a}{b} = \dfrac{12}{5}$

11. a. $\cos A = \dfrac{b}{c} = \dfrac{16}{34} = \dfrac{8}{17}$

    b. $\sin A = \dfrac{a}{c} = \dfrac{30}{34} = \dfrac{15}{17}$

    c. $\tan A = \dfrac{a}{b} = \dfrac{30}{16} = \dfrac{15}{8}$

12. a. $\cos A = \dfrac{b}{c} = \dfrac{10}{26} = \dfrac{5}{13}$

    b. $\sin A = \dfrac{a}{c} = \dfrac{24}{26} = \dfrac{12}{13}$

    c. $\tan A = \dfrac{a}{b} = \dfrac{24}{10} = \dfrac{12}{5}$

13. a. Substitute the known values into
$$c^2 = a^2 + b^2$$
$$c^2 = 9^2 + 12^2 = 81 + 144 = 225$$
$$c = 15$$

    b. $\cos A = \dfrac{9}{15} = \dfrac{3}{5}$; $\sin A = \dfrac{12}{15} = \dfrac{4}{5}$

$$\tan A = \frac{12}{9} = \frac{4}{3}$$

14. a. Substitute the known values into
$$c^2 = a^2 + b^2$$
$$c^2 = 9^2 + 40^2 = 81 + 1600 = 1681$$
$$c = 41$$

  b. $\cos A = \dfrac{9}{41}$; $\sin A = \dfrac{40}{41}$

$$\tan A = \frac{40}{9}$$

15. a. Substitute the known values into
$$c^2 = a^2 + b^2$$
$$c^2 = 12^2 + 35^2 = 144 + 1225 = 1369$$
$$c = 37$$

  b. $\cos A = \dfrac{12}{37}$; $\sin A = \dfrac{35}{37}$

$$\tan A = \frac{35}{12}$$

16. a. Substitute the known values into
$$c^2 = a^2 + b^2$$
$$c^2 = 21^2 + 28^2 = 441 + 784 = 1225$$
$$c = 35$$

  b. $\cos A = \dfrac{21}{35} = \dfrac{3}{5}$; $\sin A = \dfrac{28}{35} = \dfrac{4}{5}$

$$\tan A = \frac{28}{21} = \frac{4}{3}$$

17. a. $\tan A = \dfrac{a}{16} = 1.43$, then solve for a.

$$a = 16 \cdot 1.43 \approx 23 \text{ in.}$$

  b. Substitute the known values into
$$c^2 = a^2 + b^2$$
$$c^2 = 23^2 + 16^2 = 529 + 256 = 785$$
$$c \approx 28 \text{ in.}$$

18. a. $\tan A = \dfrac{25}{b} = 1.43$, then solve for b.

$$b = \frac{25}{1.43} \approx 17 \text{ ft}$$

  b. Substitute the known values into
$$c^2 = a^2 + b^2$$
$$c^2 = 25^2 + 17^2 = 625 + 289 = 914$$
$$c \approx 30 \text{ ft.}$$

19. a. $\tan A = \dfrac{24}{b} = 0.36$, then solve for b.

$$b = \frac{24}{0.36} \approx 67 \text{ in.}$$

  b. Substitute the known values into
$$c^2 = a^2 + b^2$$
$$c^2 = 24^2 + 67^2 = 576 + 4489 = 5065$$
$$c \approx 71 \text{ in.}$$

20. a. $\tan A = \dfrac{a}{40} = 0.36$, then solve for a.

$$a = 40 \cdot 0.36 \approx 14 \text{ ft}$$

  b. Substitute the known values into
$$c^2 = a^2 + b^2$$
$$c^2 = 14^2 + 40^2 = 196 + 1600 = 1796$$
$$c \approx 43 \text{ in.}$$

(Using non-rounded value for a)

21. Let h be the height of the tree.
$$\tan 72° = \frac{\text{opposite}}{\text{adjacent}} = \frac{h}{32}$$

$$3 = \frac{h}{32}$$

$$h = 3 \cdot 32 = 96$$
The tree is 96 ft high.

22. Let s be the length of the shadow.
$$\tan 27° = \frac{\text{opposite}}{\text{adjacent}} = \frac{s}{555}$$

$$0.5 = \frac{s}{555}$$

$$s = 0.5 \cdot 555 \approx 278$$
The shadow is about 278 ft long.

23. Let a be altitude of the plane. The trajectory of the plane is
$$d = r \cdot t = 5 \cdot 5 = 25 \text{ mi}.$$

$$\sin 30° = \frac{\text{opposite}}{\text{hypotenuse}} = \frac{a}{25}$$

$$0.5 = \frac{a}{25}$$

$$a = 0.5 \cdot 25 \approx 13$$

The altitude of the plane is 13 mi.

24. Let a be altitude of the rocket. The trajectory of the rocket is $d = r \cdot t = 25 \cdot 10 = 250 \text{ mi}$.

$$\sin 67° = \frac{\text{opposite}}{\text{hypotenuse}} = \frac{a}{250}$$

$$0.92 = \frac{a}{250}$$

$$a = 0.92 \cdot 250 \approx 230$$

The altitude of the rocket is 230 mi.

25. Let h be the height of the bird. The trajectory of the bird is $d = r \cdot t = 200 \cdot 7 = 1400 \text{ ft}$.

$$\sin 12° = \frac{\text{opposite}}{\text{hypotenuse}} = \frac{a}{1400}$$

$$0.21 = \frac{a}{1400}$$

$$a = 0.21 \cdot 1400 \approx 294$$

The height of the bird is 294 ft.

26. Let a be the altitude of the helicopter. The trajectory of the helicopter is

$$d = r \cdot t = 40 \cdot \frac{1}{4} = 10 \text{ mi}.$$

$$\sin 45° = \frac{\text{opposite}}{\text{hypotenuse}} = \frac{a}{10}$$

$$0.7 = \frac{a}{10}$$

$$a = 0.7 \cdot 10 \approx 7$$

The altitude of the helicopter is 7 mi.

27. Let x be the length of the runway. The altitude of the plane is 40 ft.

$$\tan 10° = \frac{\text{opposite}}{\text{adjacent}} = \frac{40}{x}$$

$$0.18 = \frac{40}{x}$$

$$x = \frac{40}{0.18} \approx 222$$

The length of the runway is 222 ft.

28. Let h be the height of the pole. The

length of the cable is 720 ft.

$$\sin 25° = \frac{\text{opposite}}{\text{hypotenuse}} = \frac{h}{720}$$

$$0.42 = \frac{h}{720}$$

$$h = 0.42 \cdot 720 \approx 302$$

The height of the pole is 302 ft.

29. Let x be the distance the materials travel. The height of the belt at the end is 40 ft.

$$\sin 20° = \frac{\text{opposite}}{\text{hypotenuse}} = \frac{40}{x}$$

$$0.34 = \frac{40}{x}$$

$$x = \frac{40}{0.34} \approx 118$$

The distance the materials travel is 118 ft. The length of the conveyor belt is $118 \cdot 2 = 236$ ft.

30. Let x be the distance the materials travel. The height of the belt at the end is 45 ft.

$$\sin 18° = \frac{\text{opposite}}{\text{hypotenuse}} = \frac{45}{x}$$

$$0.31 = \frac{45}{x}$$

$$x = \frac{45}{0.31} \approx 145$$

The distance the materials travel is 145 ft. The length of the conveyor belt is $145 \cdot 2 = 290$ ft.

31. Answers will vary.

32. Answers may vary. Find the missing sides and angles of the triangle.

33. Answers may vary. The tangent of the angle gets infinitely large.

34. Answers may vary. The angle of elevation is an angle above the horizon; the angle of depression is an angle below the horizon.

35. If $c = 2$, then $\cos 30° = \frac{a}{2}$. Solve for a:

$$\frac{\sqrt{3}}{2} = \frac{a}{2}; \ a = 2 \cdot \frac{\sqrt{3}}{2} = \sqrt{3}$$

If $c = 2$, then $\sin 30° = \dfrac{b}{2}$. Solve for b:

$$\frac{1}{2} = \frac{b}{2}; \ b = 2 \cdot \frac{1}{2} = 1$$

Alternatively, since c and a are known, we can use $b^2 = c^2 - a^2$ to find b.

$$b^2 = 2^2 - \left(\sqrt{3}\right)^2 = 4 - 3 = 1$$

$$b = 1$$

36. If $b = 4$, then $\sin 30° = \dfrac{4}{c}$. Solve for c:

$$\frac{1}{2} = \frac{4}{c}; \ c = 2 \cdot 4 = 8$$

If $b = 4$, then $\cos 30° = \dfrac{a}{8}$. Solve for a:

$$\frac{\sqrt{3}}{2} = \frac{a}{8}; \ a = 8 \cdot \frac{\sqrt{3}}{2} = 4\sqrt{3}$$

Alternatively, since c and b are known, we can use $a^2 = c^2 - b^2$ to find a.

$$a^2 = 8^2 - 4^2 = 64 - 16 = 48$$

$$b = 4\sqrt{3}$$

37. If $a = \sqrt{3}$, then $\sin 60° = \dfrac{\sqrt{3}}{c}$. Solve for c:

$$\frac{\sqrt{3}}{2} = \frac{\sqrt{3}}{c}; \ c = \frac{2}{\sqrt{3}} \cdot \sqrt{3} = 2$$

If $a = \sqrt{3}$, then $\cos 60° = \dfrac{b}{2}$. Solve for b:

$$\frac{1}{2} = \frac{b}{2}; \ b = 2 \cdot \frac{1}{2} = 1$$

Alternatively, since c and a are known, we can use $b^2 = c^2 - a^2$ to find b.

$$b^2 = 2^2 - \left(\sqrt{3}\right)^2 = 4 - 3 = 1$$

$$b = 1$$

38. If $c = 5$, then $\cos 30° = \dfrac{a}{5}$. Solve for a:

$$\frac{\sqrt{3}}{2} = \frac{a}{5}; \ a = 5 \cdot \frac{\sqrt{3}}{2} = \frac{5\sqrt{3}}{2}$$

If $c = 5$, then $\sin 30° = \dfrac{b}{5}$. Solve for b:

$$\frac{1}{2} = \frac{b}{5}; \ b = 5 \cdot \frac{1}{2} = \frac{5}{2}$$

Alternatively, since c and a are known, we can use $b^2 = c^2 - a^2$ to find b.

$$b^2 = 5^2 - \left(\frac{5\sqrt{3}}{2}\right)^2 = 25 - \frac{75}{4} = \frac{25}{4}$$

$$b = \frac{5}{2}$$

39. $\sin 30° = \dfrac{b}{c}$ so that $b = c \sin 30°$ and

$\cos 30° = \dfrac{a}{c}$ so that $a = c \cos 30°$

$$\tan 30° = \frac{b}{a} = \frac{c \sin 30°}{c \cos 30°} = \frac{\sin 30°}{\cos 30°}$$

$$= \frac{\frac{1}{2}}{\frac{\sqrt{3}}{2}} = \frac{1}{2} \cdot \frac{2}{\sqrt{3}} = \frac{1}{\sqrt{3}} = \frac{1}{\sqrt{3}} \cdot \frac{\sqrt{3}}{\sqrt{3}} = \frac{\sqrt{3}}{3}$$

40. $\sin 60° = \dfrac{a}{c}$ so that $a = c \sin 60°$ and

$\cos 60° = \dfrac{b}{c}$ so that $b = c \cos 60°$

$$\tan 60° = \frac{a}{b} = \frac{c \sin 60°}{c \cos 60°} = \frac{\sin 60°}{\cos 60°}$$

$$= \frac{\frac{\sqrt{3}}{2}}{\frac{1}{2}} = \frac{\sqrt{3}}{2} \cdot 2 = \sqrt{3}$$

41. Given $(\sin A)^2 + (\cos A)^2 = 1$, then

$(\sin 30°)^2 + (\cos 30°)^2 = 1$ and with the

Pythagorean theorem $a^2 + b^2 = c^2$, we have

$a = \sin 30°$ and $b = \cos 30°$. We also know

that $\tan A = \dfrac{\text{opposite}}{\text{hypotenuse}} = \dfrac{a}{b}$, so

$\tan 30° = \dfrac{\sin 30°}{\cos 30°}$. Substitute the values for

$\sin 30°$ and $\cos 30°$:

$$\tan 30° = \frac{\dfrac{1}{2}}{\dfrac{\sqrt{3}}{2}} = \frac{1}{2} \cdot \frac{2}{\sqrt{3}} = \frac{1}{\sqrt{3}} \cdot \frac{\sqrt{3}}{\sqrt{3}} = \frac{\sqrt{3}}{3}$$

This answer is identical to the answer for problem 39.

42. Given $(\sin A)^2 + (\cos A)^2 = 1$, then
$(\sin 45°)^2 + (\cos 45°)^2 = 1$. Substitute $\cos 45°$ value and solve for $\sin 45°$.

$$(\sin 45°)^2 + \left(\frac{\sqrt{2}}{2}\right)^2 = 1$$

$$(\sin 45°)^2 = 1 - \left(\frac{\sqrt{2}}{2}\right)^2 = 1 - \frac{2}{4} = \frac{1}{2}$$

$$\sin 45° = \frac{1}{\sqrt{2}} \cdot \frac{\sqrt{2}}{\sqrt{2}} = \frac{\sqrt{2}}{2}$$

$\tan 45° = \dfrac{\sin 45°}{\cos 45°}$. Substitute the values for $\sin 45°$ and $\cos 45°$.

$$\tan 45° = \frac{\dfrac{\sqrt{2}}{2}}{\dfrac{\sqrt{2}}{2}} = \frac{\sqrt{2}}{2} \cdot \frac{2}{\sqrt{2}} = 1$$

43. Given $(\sin A)^2 + (\cos A)^2 = 1$, then
$(\sin 15°)^2 + (\cos 15°)^2 = 1$. Substitute $\cos 15°$ value and solve for $\sin 15°$.
$(\sin 15°)^2 + (0.97)^2 = 1$
$(\sin 15°)^2 = 1 - (0.97)^2 = 1 - 0.9409 = 0.0591$
$\sin 15° = \sqrt{0.0591} \approx 0.24$
$\tan 15° = \dfrac{\sin 15°}{\cos 15°}$. Substitute the values for $\sin 15°$ and $\cos 15°$:

$$\tan 15° = \frac{0.24}{0.97} \approx 0.25$$

44. Given $(\sin A)^2 + (\cos A)^2 = 1$, then
$(\sin 23°)^2 + (\cos 23°)^2 = 1$. Substitute $\sin 23°$ value and solve for $\cos 23°$.

$(0.39)^2 + (\cos 23°)^2 = 1$
$(\cos 23°)^2 = 1 - (0.39)^2 = 1 - 0.1521 = 0.8479$
$\cos 23° = \sqrt{0.8479} \approx 0.92$
$\tan 23° = \dfrac{\sin 23°}{\cos 23°}$. Substitute the values for $\sin 23°$ and $\cos 23°$.

$$\tan 23° = \frac{0.39}{0.92} \approx 0.42$$

Section 8.8 Chaos and Fractals

Note: Answers may vary because of rounding.

1.

x	0.200	0.862	0.850	0.865	0.846
y	0.560	0.416	0.446	0.409	0.456

x	0.868	0.841	0.871	0.835	0.874
y	0.402	0.468	0.393	0.482	0.385

x	0.829	**0.875**	**0.827**	**0.875**	**0.827**
y	0.496	**0.383**	**0.501**	**0.383**	**0.501**

There are four attractors: **0.383**, **0.501**, **0.827**, and **0.875**

2.

x	0.700	0.682	0.640	0.547	0.404
y	0.735	0.759	0.806	0.867	0.843

x	0.463	0.396	0.478	continue…	
y	0.870	0.837	0.873	continue…	

After about 20 steps you will find the first attractor: **0.383**
Note: If you continue, you will find 0.501, 0.827, and 0.875.

3.

x	0.400	0.605	0.609	0.613	0.615
y	0.720	0.717	0.714	0.712	0.710

x	0.618	0.620	0.621	0.623	0.624
y	0.708	0.707	0.706	0.705	0.704

x	0.625	0.626	0.628	0.629	0.630
y	0.703	0.702	0.701	0.700	**0.699**

x	0.631	0.631
y	0.699	0.699

There are two attractors: **0.631** and **0.699**

4.

x	0.800	0.435	**0.500**
y	0.320	0.492	**0.500**

After about 4 steps you will find one attractor: **0.500**

5. Take s as the length of one side of the original triangle, thus the original perimeter is $3s$. For each iteration, the length of each piece of the broken line will decrease by $\frac{1}{3}$, and the number of pieces in the broken line will increase by a factor of 4.
   a. The perimeter of the third step (Step C in Figure 8.94) would be $3\left(\frac{1}{3^1}s \cdot 4^1\right) = 4s$
   b. The perimeter of the fourth step (Step D in Figure 8.94) would be
   $$3\left(\frac{1}{3^2}s \cdot 4^2\right) = \frac{16}{3}s$$

6.

7. On completing the second step, the fractal appears like this.

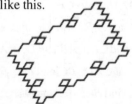

8.

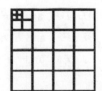

9. For each step, each small square is divided into fourths. Thus, the area will decrease by

$\frac{1}{4}$. So for the first step the area of first small square is $\frac{1}{4}$ in^2, the second step $\frac{1}{16}$ in^2, the third step $\frac{1}{64}$ in^2, and the fourth step $\frac{1}{256}$ in^2.
Then for the fifth step the area of the small square will be $\frac{1}{1024}$ in^2.

10. a.

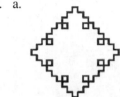

   b. No. since the length increases indefinitely, the perimeter will not be finite.
   c. Yes, if the side of the original square is S, the figure will always be inside a square of side $2S$.

11. On completing the second step, the fractal appears like this.

12. Take s as the length of one side of the original square. After the first step, the area removed is $\frac{1}{3}s \cdot \frac{1}{3}s = \frac{1}{9}s^2$ from each side.
   We have 4 sides, so the area of the square after the first step would be
   $$s^2 - 4 \cdot \frac{1}{9}s^2 = \frac{5}{9}s^2.$$

13. After the second step, the area will decrease by a factor of $\frac{5}{9}$ (see problem 12).
   Thus, the area after the second step would be $\frac{5}{9} \cdot \frac{5}{9}s^2 = \frac{25}{81}s^2$.

14. The perimeter becomes longer and longer. It does have infinite length.

15. The remaining area approaches zero.

16.

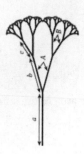

17. a.

b. The initial segment is about $\dfrac{1}{2}$ in., the segment from that is about $\dfrac{1}{4}$ in. Their

ratio is $\dfrac{\frac{1}{2}}{\frac{1}{4}} = \dfrac{1}{2} \cdot 4 = 2$.

c. The length of the next segment would

be $\dfrac{1}{8}$ in. This ratio is $\dfrac{\frac{1}{4}}{\frac{1}{8}} = \dfrac{1}{4} \cdot 8 = 2$.

Yes, the ratio is maintained.

d. The measure of the angle is about 165°.

e. Yes, the angle measure is maintained.

18. It should resemble the figure in the text.

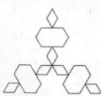

19. In the first step of problem 18, three triangles will be removed, for a total area of

$$3\left(\frac{1}{2} \cdot \frac{1}{3} s \cdot \frac{\sqrt{3}}{6} s\right) = 3\left(\frac{\sqrt{3}}{36} s^2\right) = \frac{\sqrt{3}}{12} s^2.$$

Subtract from the original area to obtain the

new area $\dfrac{\sqrt{3}}{4} s^2 - \dfrac{\sqrt{3}}{12} s^2 = \dfrac{\sqrt{3}}{6} s^2$.

20. In the second step of problem 18, twelve triangles will be removed, for a total area of

$$12\left(\frac{1}{2} \cdot \frac{1}{9} s \cdot \frac{\sqrt{3}}{18} s\right) = 12\left(\frac{\sqrt{3}}{324} s^2\right) = \frac{\sqrt{3}}{27} s^2.$$

Subtract from the area found in problem 19 To obtain the new area

$\dfrac{\sqrt{3}}{6} s^2 - \dfrac{\sqrt{3}}{27} s^2 = \dfrac{7\sqrt{3}}{54} s^2$.

21. The perimeter will increase without limit.

22. The area tends to zero as more and more triangles are taken away.

Chapter 8 Practice Test

1. a. $\overline{XY}$ b. Point Y

    c. The ray $\overrightarrow{WZ}$

2.

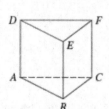

a. $\overline{AD}, \overline{BE},$ and $\overline{CF}$; $\overline{BC}$ and $\overline{EF}$;

   $\overline{DE}$ and $\overline{AB}$; and $\overline{DF}$ and $\overline{AC}$

b. $\overline{AB}$ and $\overline{CF}$; $\overline{AB}$ and $\overline{DF}$; $\overline{AB}$ and $\overline{EF}$;

   $\overline{BC}$ and $\overline{AD}$; $\overline{BC}$ and $\overline{DE}$; $\overline{BC}$ and $\overline{DF}$;

   $\overline{AC}$ and $\overline{BE}$; $\overline{AC}$ and $\overline{DE}$; $\overline{AC}$ and $\overline{EF}$;

   $\overline{DE}$ and $\overline{CF}$; $\overline{EF}$ and $\overline{AD}$; $\overline{DF}$ and $\overline{BE}$

c. $\overline{AB}, \overline{AC},$ and $\overline{AD}$; $\overline{AD}, \overline{DE},$ and $\overline{DF}$;

   $\overline{BE}, \overline{AB},$ and $\overline{BC}$; $\overline{BE}, \overline{EF},$ and $\overline{ED}$;

   $\overline{CF}, \overline{AC},$ and $\overline{BC}$; $\overline{CF}, \overline{EF},$ and $\overline{DF}$

3. a. $\dfrac{4}{12} \cdot 360° = 120°$ b. $\dfrac{2}{12} \cdot 360° = 60°$

4. Let $m\angle B = x°$. Then $m\angle A = 3x°$. Since the
    two angles are supplementary,
    $$x + 3x = 180$$
    $$4x = 180$$
    $$x = 45$$
    Therefore, $m\angle B = 45°$ and $m\angle A = 135°$.

5. a. $\angle C$ and the 50° angle are
        supplementary, so $m\angle C = 130°$.
    b. $\angle E$ and the 50° angle are equal, so
        $m\angle E = 50°$.
    c. $\angle D$ and $\angle C$ are equal, so
        $m\angle D = 130°$.

6. a. $m\angle C = 180° - 38° - 43° = 99°$
    b. Let $m\angle C = x°$, so that
        $m\angle A = m\angle B = 2x°$. Then,
        $$x + 2x + 2x = 180$$
        $$5x = 180$$
        $$x = 36$$
        Thus, $m\angle C = 36°$ and
        $m\angle A = m\angle B = 72°$.

7. a.   b.

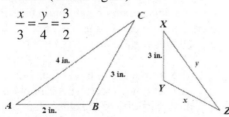

8. Since the triangles are similar, the
    corresponding sides are proportional. Thus,
    we have (see the figure)
    $$\frac{x}{3} = \frac{y}{4} = \frac{3}{2}$$

    Therefore, $x = \frac{9}{2} = 4\frac{1}{2}$ in. and

    $y = \frac{12}{2} = 6$ in.

9. a. The sum of the measures of the 9 angles
        is $(9-2)180°$, so the measure of one

        angle is $\dfrac{(9-2)180°}{9} = 140°$.

    b. The sum of the measures of the 10
        angles is $(10-2)180°$, so the measure

        of one angle is $\dfrac{(10-2)180°}{10} = 144°$.

10. If w is the width, then the length is $2w$.
    Hence, the perimeter is $6w$, and this is to be
    120 yd. Thus, $6w = 120$, so that $w = 20$. This
    means that the width is 20 yd and the length
    is 40 yd.

11. The figure shows that d is the hypotenuse of
    a right triangle whose legs are each 2 cm
    long.

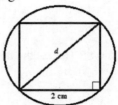

    Thus, $d^2 = 2^2 + 2^2 = 8$, so $d = \sqrt{8} = 2\sqrt{2}$
    cm, and the circumference of the circle is
    $C = \pi d = 2\sqrt{2}\pi$ cm.

12. The circumference of the cylinder would be
    11 in. Hence, if the diameter is d, then

    $\pi d = 11$, so that $d = \dfrac{11}{\pi}$ in.

13. The area that is inside the circle and outside
    the square is $\pi r^2 - s^2$, where r is the radius
    of the circle and s is the side of the square.
    Thus, this area is

    $$\pi\left(\sqrt{2}\right)^2 - 2^2 = (2\pi - 4) \text{ cm}^2.$$

14. As the figure shows, we need to find the
    area of a rectangle of base 3 ft and height
    4 ft, and the area of a semicircle of radius
    3/2 ft.

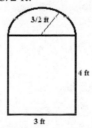

    Thus, $A = bh + \dfrac{1}{2}\pi r^2 = 3 \cdot 4 + \dfrac{1}{2}\pi\left(\dfrac{3}{2}\right)^2$

$$= 12 + \frac{9}{8}\pi \approx 12 + 1.125(3.14)$$

$$\approx 15.5 \text{ ft}^2$$

15. The area that is outside the circle and inside the square is $s^2 - \pi r^2$, where r is the radius of the circle and s is the side of the square. Thus, this area is

$$2^2 - \pi \cdot 1^2 = (4 - \pi) \approx 4 - 3.14 \approx 0.86 \text{ in}^2.$$

16. The diagonal of a rectangle is the hypotenuse of a right triangle whose legs are the sides of the rectangle. Thus,

$$d^2 = b^2 + h^2 = 84^2 + 13^2$$

$$= 7056 + 169 = 7225$$

so that $d = \sqrt{7225} = 85$. Hence, the diagonal is 85 ft long.

17. $S = 2(lw + lh + wh)$

$$= 2(5 \cdot 3 + 5 \cdot 2 + 3 \cdot 2) = 62 \text{ ft}^2$$

18. The volume of a pyramid is given by the formula $V = \frac{1}{3}BH$ where B is the area of the base and H is the height of the pyramid.

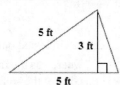

The given triangle is the base of the pyramid, and its area is $\frac{1}{2}bh$, where b is the length of the base and h is the height of the triangle. The figure shows that $b = 5$ ft and $h = 3$ ft, so the area of the triangle is

$\frac{1}{2} \cdot 5 \cdot 3 = \frac{15}{2}$ ft^2. The volume of the

pyramid is $V = \frac{1}{3} \cdot \frac{15}{2} \cdot 4 = 10 \text{ ft}^3$.

19. The volume of the hemisphere is

$$\frac{1}{2}\left(\frac{4}{3}\pi r^3\right) = \frac{2}{3}\pi \cdot 2^3 = \frac{16}{3}\pi \text{ in}^3.$$

The volume of the cone is

$\frac{1}{3}\pi r^2 h = \frac{1}{3}\pi \cdot 2^2 \cdot h = \frac{4}{3}\pi h \text{ in}^3$, where h is

the number of inches in the height of the cone. Since the volumes are equal, we have the equation $\frac{4}{3}\pi h = \frac{16}{3}\pi$. Dividing both

sides by $\frac{4}{3}\pi$, we get $h = 4$. Thus, the cone is 4 in. high.

20. The surface area of the sphere is $4\pi r^2$ and of the cylinder is $2\pi rh + 2\pi r^2$. Since these areas are to be equal, we have

$$2\pi rh + 2\pi r^2 = 4\pi r^2$$

Subtract $2\pi r^2$:　　　$2\pi rh = 2\pi r^2$

Divide by $2\pi r$:　　　$h = r$

The height of the cylinder is equal to the given radius, 10 in.

21. The figure shows a traversable network; it has no odd vertices.

The figure shows a non-traversable network; it has four odd vertices: $A, B, D,$ and E.

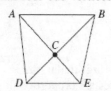

22. Given a line and any point not on that line, there is one and only one line through that point that is parallel to the given line.

23. a. The button. It can be cut four times and still be in one piece. This cannot be done with any of the other objects.
    b. Zero (No holes)
    c. Four (Four holes)
    d. Zero

24. a. Substitute the known values into
    $c^2 = a^2 + b^2$.
    $$c^2 = 20^2 + 21^2 = 400 + 441 = 841$$
    $$c = 29$$

    b. $\cos A = \dfrac{20}{29}$; $\sin A = \dfrac{21}{29}$

$$\tan A = \frac{21}{20}$$

25. $\tan 40° = \dfrac{26}{b} = 0.84$, then solve for b.

$$b = \frac{26}{0.84} \approx 31 \text{ in.}$$

26. $\cos 15° = \dfrac{16}{c} = 0.97$, then solve for c.

$$c = \frac{16}{0.97} \approx 16 \text{ in.}$$

27. Let x be the height of the Statue of Liberty. The length of the cable is 337 ft.

$$\sin 65° = \frac{\text{opposite}}{\text{hypotenuse}} = \frac{x}{337}$$

$$0.9063 = \frac{x}{337}$$

$$x = 0.9063 \cdot 337 \approx 305 \text{ ft}$$

The height of the Statue of Liberty is 305 ft.

28. Let a be altitude of the plane. The trajectory of the plane is $d = r \cdot t = 3 \cdot 5 = 15 \text{ mi}$.

$$\sin 15° = \frac{\text{opposite}}{\text{hypotenuse}} = \frac{a}{15}$$

$$0.21 = \frac{a}{15}$$

$$a = 0.21 \cdot 15 \approx 3 \text{ mi}$$

The altitude of the plane is 3 mi.

29. $y_4 = 1.455$

x	0.100	0.4248	1.455
y	−0.18	−0.4887	

30.

Chapter 9 Mathematical Systems

Section 9.1 Clock and Modular Arithmetic

1. $9 \oplus 7$ means 7 hours after 9 o'clock, so the answer is 4.

2. $2 \oplus 8$ means 8 hours after 2 o'clock, so the answer is 10.

3. $8 \oplus 3$ means 3 hours after 8 o'clock, so the answer is 11.

4. $5 \oplus 7$ means 7 hours after 5 o'clock, so the answer is 12.

5. $7 \oplus 8$ means 8 hours after 7 o'clock, so the answer is 3.

6. $9 \oplus 9$ means 9 hours after 9 o'clock so the answer is 6.

7. $8 \oplus 11$ means 11 hours after 8 o'clock so the answer is 7.

8. $12 \oplus 3$ means 3 hours after 12 o'clock so the answer is 3.

9. $8 \ominus 3$ means 3 hours before 8 o'clock, so the answer is 5.

10. $5 \ominus 8$ means 8 hours before 5 o'clock, so the answer is 9.

11. $9 \ominus 12$ means 12 hours before 9 o'clock, so the answer is 9.

12. $6 \ominus 9$ means 9 hours before 6 o'clock, so the answer is 9.

13. $8 \ominus 7$ means 7 hours before 8 o'clock, so the answer is 1.

14. $1 \ominus 12$ means 12 hours before 1 o'clock, so the answer is 1.

15. $n \oplus 7 = 9$ is true if $n = 9 \ominus 7 = 2$.

16. $n \oplus 8 = 2$ is true if $n = 2 \ominus 8 = 6$.

17. $2 \oplus n = 1$ is true if $n = 1 \ominus 2 = 11$.

18. $7 \oplus n = 3$ is true if $n = 3 \ominus 7 = 8$.

19. $3 \ominus 5 = n$ means 5 hours before 3 o'clock, so the answer is 10.

20. $2 \ominus 4 = n$ means 4 hours before 2 o'clock, so the answer is 10.

21. $1 \ominus n = 12$ is true if $1 = n \oplus 12$, so $n = 1$.

22. $3 \ominus 7 = n$ means 7 hours before 3 o'clock, so the answer is 8.

23. $4 \otimes 3 = 3 \oplus 3 \oplus 3 \oplus 3 = 12$

24. $3 \otimes 8 = 12$ because in ordinary arithmetic $3 \cdot 8 = 24$, which divided by 12, leaves a remainder of 0.

25. $9 \otimes 2 = 6$ because in ordinary arithmetic $9 \cdot 2 = 18$, which divided by 12, leaves a remainder of 6.

26. $3 \otimes 9 = 3$ because in ordinary arithmetic $3 \cdot 9 = 27$, which divided by 12, leaves a remainder of 3.

27. $2 \otimes 8 = 4$ because in ordinary arithmetic $2 \cdot 8 = 16$, which divided by 12, leaves a remainder of 4.

28. $12 \otimes 3 = 12$ because in ordinary arithmetic $12 \cdot 3 = 36$, which divided by 12, leaves a remainder of 0.

29.

$\otimes$	1	2	3	4	5	6	7	8	9	10	11	12
1	1	2	3	4	5	6	7	8	9	10	11	12
2	2	4	6	8	10	12	2	4	6	8	10	12
3	3	6	9	12	3	6	9	12	3	6	9	12
4	4	8	12	4	8	12	4	8	12	4	8	12
5	5	10	3	8	1	6	11	4	9	2	7	12
6	6	12	6	12	6	12	6	12	6	12	6	12
7	7	2	9	4	11	6	1	8	3	10	5	12
8	8	4	12	8	4	12	8	4	12	8	4	12
9	9	6	3	12	9	6	3	12	9	6	3	12
10	10	8	6	4	2	12	10	8	6	4	2	12
11	11	10	9	8	7	6	5	4	3	2	1	12
12	12	12	12	12	12	12	12	12	12	12	12	12

30. $\dfrac{9}{7} = n$ only if $9 = 7 \otimes n$. Problem 29 table shows that $7 \otimes 3 = 3$, so $n = 3$.

31. $\dfrac{3}{5} = n$ only if $3 = 5 \otimes n$. Problem 29 table

shows that $5 \otimes 3 = 3$, so $n = 3$.

32. $\dfrac{3}{9} = n$ only if $3 = 9 \otimes n$. Problem 29 table
shows that $9 \otimes 3 = 3$, so $n = 3$;
$9 \otimes 7 = 3$, so $n = 7$; and $9 \otimes 11 = 3$, so $n = 11$.

33. $\dfrac{1}{11} = n$ only if $1 = 11 \otimes n$. Problem 29
table shows that $11 \otimes 11 = 1$, so $n = 11$.

34. $\dfrac{1}{12} = n$ only if $1 = 12 \otimes n$. This is impossible
as every multiply of 12 will equal 12.

35. $\dfrac{n}{5} = 8$ is true if $n = 5 \otimes 8 = 4$.
(See problem 29 table.)

36. $\dfrac{n}{2} = 4$ is true if $n = 2 \otimes 4 = 8$.
(See problem 29 table.)

37. $\dfrac{n}{2} \oplus 4 = 8$ is true if $\dfrac{n}{2} = 8 \ominus 4 = 4$, and

$\dfrac{n}{2} = 4$ if $n = 2 \otimes 4 = 8$.
(See problem 29 table.)

38. $\dfrac{n}{7} = 9$ is true if $n = 9 \otimes 7 = 3$.
(See problem 29 table.)

39. $\dfrac{2}{n} = 3$ is true only if $2 = 3 \otimes n$. Problem
29 table shows no entry of 2 in the row for
3. Therefore, there is no solution.

40. $\dfrac{12}{12} = n$ is true only if $12 = 12 \otimes n$, where $n = 1, 2,$
3, 4, 5, 6, 7, 8, 9, 10, 11, 12. (See problem 29
table. This condition is the same as 0/0,
usually specified as 'indeterminate,' since
every value can be considered a solution.)

41. False; $4 - 2 = 2$ is not a multiple of 3.

42. True; $5 - 2 = 3$ is a multiple of 3.

43. False; $7 - 6 = 1$ is not a multiple of 5.

44. True; $5 - 3 = 2$ is a multiple of 2.

45. False; $9 - 8 = 1$ is not a multiple of 10.

46. True; $12 - 8 = 4$ is a multiple of 4.

47. $3 + 4 = 7 \equiv 2 \,(\text{mod } 5)$

48. $2 + 9 = 11 \equiv 1 \,(\text{mod } 10)$

49. $3 + 1 \equiv 4 \,(\text{mod } 5)$

50. $3 + 6 = 9 \equiv 2 \,(\text{mod } 7)$

51. $4 \times 2 = 8 \equiv 3 \,(\text{mod } 5)$

52. $4 \times 3 = 12 \equiv 2 \,(\text{mod } 5)$

53. $2 \times 3 = 6 \equiv 1 \,(\text{mod } 5)$

54. $3 \times 3 = 9 \equiv 4 \,(\text{mod } 5)$

55. $2 - 4 = -2 = 5 - 2 \equiv 3 \,(\text{mod } 5)$

56. $3 - 4 = -1 = 5 - 1 \equiv 4 \,(\text{mod } 5)$

57. $1 - 3 = -2 = 5 - 2 \equiv 3 \,(\text{mod } 5)$

58. $0 - 2 = -2 = 5 - 2 \equiv 3 \,(\text{mod } 5)$

59. By the distributive property,
$4 \times (3 + 0) \equiv \big[(4 \times 3) + (4 \times 0)\big] (\text{mod } 5)$.
Thus, $n = 0$ will make the sentence
$4 \times (3 + 0) \equiv \big[(4 \times 3) + (4 \times n)\big] (\text{mod } 5)$ true.

60. By the distributive property,
$2 \times (1 + 3) \equiv \big[(2 \times 1) + (2 \times 3)\big] (\text{mod } 5)$.
Thus, $n = 2$ will make the sentence
$2 \times (1 + 3) \equiv \big[(2 \times 1) + (n \times 3)\big] (\text{mod } 5)$ true.

61. By the distributive property,
$2 \times (0 + 3) \equiv \big[(2 \times 0) + (2 \times 3)\big] (\text{mod } 5)$.
Thus, $n = 0$ will make the sentence
$2 \times (0 + 3) \equiv \big[(2 \times n) + (2 \times 3)\big] (\text{mod } 5)$ true.

62. By the distributive property,
$4 \times (1 + 2) \equiv \big[(4 \times 1) + (4 \times 2)\big] (\text{mod } 5)$.

Thus, $n = 2$ will make the sentence
$$4 \times (1 + n) \equiv \left[(4 \times 1) + (4 \times 2) \right] (\mathrm{mod}\, 5)$$
true.

63. By inspection of Table 9.2 (or 9.4), we see that $2 + 1 \equiv 3 (\mathrm{mod}\, 5)$. Thus $n = 1$ will make the sentence $2 + n \equiv 3 (\mathrm{mod}\, 5)$ true.

64. By inspection of Table 9.2 (or 9.4), we see that $3 + 3 \equiv 1 (\mathrm{mod}\, 5)$. Thus $n = 3$ will make the sentence $n + 3 \equiv 1 (\mathrm{mod}\, 5)$ true.

65. By inspection of Table 9.3, we see that $2 \times 2 \equiv 4 (\mathrm{mod}\, 5)$. Thus $n = 2$ will make the sentence $2 \times n \equiv 4 (\mathrm{mod}\, 5)$ true.

66. By inspection of Table 9.3, we see that $3 \equiv 2 \times 4 (\mathrm{mod}\, 5)$. Thus $n = 4$ will make the sentence $3 \equiv 2 \times n (\mathrm{mod}\, 5)$ true.

67. $n - 3 \equiv 4 (\mathrm{mod}\, 5)$ if and only if $n \equiv (3 + 4)(\mathrm{mod}\, 5)$. From Table 9.2 (or 9.4), we see that $3 + 4 \equiv 2 (\mathrm{mod}\, 5)$. Thus $2 - 3 \equiv 4 (\mathrm{mod}\, 5)$, so $n = 2$.

68. $2 \equiv n - 1 (\mathrm{mod}\, 5)$ if and only if $2 + 1 \equiv n (\mathrm{mod}\, 5)$. From Table 9.2 (or 9.4), we see that $2 + 1 \equiv 3 (\mathrm{mod}\, 5)$. Thus $2 \equiv 3 - 1 (\mathrm{mod}\, 5)$, so $n = 3$.

69. $3 \equiv (n - 4)(\mathrm{mod}\, 5)$ if and only if $3 + 4 \equiv n (\mathrm{mod}\, 5)$. From Table 9.2 (or 9.4), we see that $3 + 4 \equiv 2 (\mathrm{mod}\, 5)$. Thus $3 \equiv (2 - 4)(\mathrm{mod}\, 5)$, so $n = 2$.

70. $n - 2 \equiv 1 (\mathrm{mod}\, 5)$ if and only if $n \equiv (2 + 1)(\mathrm{mod}\, 5)$. From Table 9.2 (or 9.4), we see that $3 \equiv (2 + 1)(\mathrm{mod}\, 5)$. Thus $n - 2 \equiv 1 (\mathrm{mod}\, 5)$, so $n = 3$.

71. $\dfrac{n}{2} \equiv 4 (\mathrm{mod}\, 5)$ is true if and only if $n \equiv (2 \times 4)(\mathrm{mod}\, 5)$. From Table 9.3, we see that $3 \equiv (2 \times 4)(\mathrm{mod}\, 5)$. Thus

$\dfrac{3}{2} \equiv 4 (\mathrm{mod}\, 5)$, so $n = 3$.

72. $\dfrac{n}{3} \equiv 2 (\mathrm{mod}\, 5)$ is true if and only if $n \equiv (2 \times 3)(\mathrm{mod}\, 5)$. From Table 9.3, we see that $1 \equiv (2 \times 3)(\mathrm{mod}\, 5)$. Thus $\dfrac{1}{3} \equiv 2 (\mathrm{mod}\, 5)$ so $n = 1$.

73. $\dfrac{3}{4} \equiv n (\mathrm{mod}\, 5)$ is true if and only if $3 \equiv (4 \times n)(\mathrm{mod}\, 5)$ From Table 9.3, we see that $3 \equiv (4 \times 2)(\mathrm{mod}\, 5)$. Thus $\dfrac{3}{4} \equiv 2 (\mathrm{mod}\, 5)$, so $n = 2$.

74. $\dfrac{1}{2} \equiv n (\mathrm{mod}\, 5)$ is true if and only if $1 \equiv (2 \times n)(\mathrm{mod}\, 5)$ From Table 9.3, we see that $1 \equiv (2 \times 3)(\mathrm{mod}\, 5)$. Thus $\dfrac{1}{2} \equiv 3 (\mathrm{mod}\, 5)$, so $n = 3$.

75. Yes, all the entries in the table are elements of S.

76. Yes, $(n \times m)(\mathrm{mod}\, 5) = (m \times n)(\mathrm{mod}\, 5)$ in the table.

77. Yes. The identity is 1 because, if a is an element of S, then $1 \times a = a \times 1 \equiv a (\mathrm{mod}\, 5)$

78. a. No inverse   b. 1   c. 3
    d. 2   e. 4

79. $\dfrac{1985}{12} = 165$ with a remainder of 5, which corresponds to the Ox.

80. $\dfrac{2000}{12} = 166$ with a remainder of 8, which corresponds to the Dragon.

81. No. There are many numbers that can be divided by 12 and leave a remainder of 5. For example 1949 and 1961.
Yes. If the year is, say 2009, they were born in

the 80's. $\dfrac{1980}{12} = 164$ with a no remainder, so $1980 + 5 = 1985$ will leave a remainder of 5 when divided by 12.

82. Answers will vary. For a person who is in their 30's, if the year is say 2015, they were born between 1976 and 1985.
$\dfrac{1976}{12} = 164$ has a remainder of 8. The goat sign is associated with the number 11, so $1976 + 3 = 1979$ will leave a remainder of 11 when divided by 12.

83. What decade they were born in or if they are in their 20's, 30's, and so on.

84. Yes. Since she was born in the 1960s, we have
$\dfrac{1960}{12} = 163$ with a remainder of 4. The snake sign is associated with the number 9, so $1960 + 5 = 1965$ will leave a remainder of 9 when divided by 12.

85. The year of the Rat occurs when the remainder is 4. Multiply a sufficiently large number by 12, say 165, and add 4. We obtain $165 \cdot 12 + 4 = 1984$. So 1984 and all other years obtained by subtracting 12 or adding 12 successively will be years of the Rat. Thus, $1984 - 12 = 1972$ and $1984 + 12 = 1996$ are years of the Rat. Similarly, 1948, 1960, 1972, 1984, 1996, 2008, and so on are years of the Rat.

86. The year of the Tiger occurs when the remainder is 6. Divide 1950 by 12 to see that it will have a remainder of 6. So, 1950 has the sign of the Tiger. To obtain future years, add multiples of 12 to 1950. Thus, $1950 + 12 = 1962$ is the year of the Tiger. Similarly, 1974, 1986, 1998, 2010, and so on are years of the Tiger.

87. A military clock has a 24-hour cycle. One of the advantages is that there is no confusion over a.m. (day) and p.m. (night) time.

88. Since Tuesday is be numbered 3, $3 + 15 = 18 \equiv 4 \pmod 7$. Thus, 15 days from Tuesday would be Wednesday.

89. Answers will vary.

90. The 0005234983 is correct as $523498 \div 7 = 3$, which agrees with the check number 3. Divide 523498 by 7 and have a remainder of 3, not 1.

91. Write the digits in the ISBN under the numbers 10, 9, 8, . . ., 2 as shown in the text. Multiply the two numbers in a vertical line and add the results as below:

10	9	8	7	6	5	4	3	2
0	0	6	0	4	0	6	1	3

$0 + 0 + 48 + 0 + 24 + 0 + 24 + 3 + 6 = 105$
Then solve the congruence
$105 + c \equiv 0 \pmod{11}$.

Since 110 is the multiple of 11 that is just greater than 105, and $105 + 5 = 110$, we have $c = 5$. You can also divide 105 by 11 and get a remainder of 6. Since the check number c is the solution of $c + 6 \equiv 0 \pmod{11}$, we still get $c = 5$.

92. Write the digits in the ISBN under the numbers 10, 9, 8, . . ., 2 as shown in the text. Multiply the two numbers in a vertical line and add the results as below:

10	9	8	7	6	5	4	3	2
0	5	1	7	5	3	0	5	2

$0 + 45 + 8 + 49 + 30 + 15 + 0 + 15 + 4 = 166$
Then solve the congruence
$166 + c \equiv 0 \pmod{11}$.

Since 176 is the multiple of 11 that is just greater than 166, and $166 + 10 = 176$, we have $c = 10$. You can also divide 166 by 11 and get a remainder of 1. Since the check number c is the solution of $c + 1 \equiv 0 \pmod{11}$, we still get $c = 10$. This would be written as the Roman numeral X.

93. Follow the same procedure as in problem 91:

10	9	8	7	6	5	4	3	2
0	3	1	2	8	7	8	6	7

$0 + 27 + 8 + 14 + 48 + 35 + 32 + 18 + 14 = 196$
Now solve the congruence
$196 + c \equiv 0 \pmod{11}$.

Since 198 is the multiple of 11 that is just greater then 196, and $196 + 2 = 198$, we have $c = 2$. You can also divide 196 by 11 obtaining a remainder of 9 and then solving $c + 9 \equiv 0 \pmod{11}$, which yields $c = 2$.

94. Let x be the blurred digit and proceed as in problems 91 – 93.

10	9	8	7	6	5	4	3	2
0	0	6	0	4	0	9	8	x

$0 + 0 + 48 + 0 + 24 + 0 + 36 + 24 + 2x$
$= 132 + 2x$
Since the check number is $c = 3$, we must have $132 + 2x + 3 \equiv 0 \pmod{11}$ or
$135 + 2x \equiv 0 \pmod{11}$. Now, 143 is the multiple of 11 that is just greater than 135, and $143 = 135 + 8$. Therefore, we must have $2x = 8$, so $x = 4$.

95. Let x be the blurred digit and proceed as in problems 91 and 93:

10	9	8	7	6	5	4	3	2
0	0	3	0	5	8	9	x	4

$0 + 0 + 24 + 0 + 30 + 40 + 36 + 3x + 8$
$= 138 + 3x$
Since the check number is $c = 2$, we must have $138 + 3x + 2 \equiv 0 \pmod{11}$ or
$140 + 3x \equiv 0 \pmod{11}$. Now, 143 is the multiple of 11 that is just greater than 140, and $143 = 140 + 3$. Therefore, we must have $3x = 3$, so $x = 1$.

96. Let x be the blurred digit and proceed as in Problems 91 – 93.

10	9	8	7	6	5	4	3	2
0	7	1	6	x	0	4	5	6

$0 + 63 + 8 + 42 + 6x + 0 + 16 + 15 + 12$
$= 156 + 6x$
Since the check number is $c = 0$, we must have $156 + 6x + 0 \equiv 0 \pmod{11}$ or
$156 + 6x \equiv 0 \pmod{11}$. Now, 165 is the multiple of 11 that is just greater than 156, however, solving would give a value of $x = 1.5$. Therefore, choose a larger multiple of 11. Let's use 198, so that $198 = 156 + 42$. Therefore, we must have $6x = 42$, so $x = 7$.

97. Following the procedure of Example 10, we have

$3n_1 + n_2 + 3n_3 + n_4 + 3n_5 + n_6 + 3n_7 + n_8$
$\quad + 3n_9 + n_{10} + 3n_{11} + c \equiv 0 \pmod{10}$

$3 \cdot 0 + 4 + 3 \cdot 3 + 1 + 3 \cdot 6 + 8 + 3 \cdot 3 + 8$
$\quad + 3 \cdot 5 + 4 + 3 \cdot 0 + c \equiv 0 \pmod{10}$

$76 + c \equiv 0 \pmod{10}$
Since $76 + c$ must be a multiple of 10, we make $c = 4$.

98. Following the procedure of Example 10, we have

$3n_1 + n_2 + 3n_3 + n_4 + 3n_5 + n_6 + 3n_7 + n_8$
$\quad + 3n_9 + n_{10} + 3n_{11} + c \equiv 0 \pmod{10}$

$3 \cdot 0 + 5 + 3 \cdot 1 + 0 + 3 \cdot 0 + 0 + 3 \cdot 0 + 2$
$\quad + 3 \cdot 9 + 5 + 3 \cdot 2 + c \equiv 0 \pmod{10}$

$48 + c \equiv 0 \pmod{10}$
Since $48 + c$ must be a multiple of 10, we make $c = 2$.

99. Following the procedure of Example 10, we have
$3 \cdot 0 + 2 + 3 \cdot 4 + 0 + 3 \cdot 0 + 0 + 3 \cdot 0 + 2$
$\quad + 3 \cdot 1 + 4 + 3 \cdot 0 + c \equiv 0 \pmod{10}$

$23 + c \equiv 0 \pmod{10}$
Since $23 + c$ must be a multiple of 10, we make $c = 7$.

100. Following the procedure of Example 10, we have
$3 \cdot 0 + 7 + 3 \cdot 0 + 7 + 3 \cdot 3 + 4 + 3 \cdot 0 + 0$
$\quad + 3 \cdot 5 + 0 + 3 \cdot 1 + c \equiv 0 \pmod{10}$

$45 + c \equiv 0 \pmod{10}$
Since $45 + c$ must be a multiple of 10, we make $c = 5$.

101. Following the procedure of Example 10, we have
$3 \cdot 0 + 7 + 3 \cdot 4 + 1 + 3 \cdot 0 + 1 + 3 \cdot 7 + 4$
$\quad + 3 \cdot 0 + 1 + 3 \cdot 0 + c \equiv 0 \pmod{10}$

$47 + c \equiv 0 \pmod{10}$
Since $47 + c$ must be a multiple of 10, we make $c = 3$.

102. Following the procedure of Example 10, we have
$3 \cdot 3 + 0 + 3 \cdot 0 + 4 + 3 \cdot 5 + 0 + 3 \cdot 1 + 7$
$\quad + 3 \cdot 6 + 1 + 3 \cdot 5 + c \equiv 0 \pmod{10}$

$72 + c \equiv 0 \pmod{10}$
Since $72 + c$ must be a multiple of 10, we make $c = 8$.

103. Let x be the missing digit.
$3 \cdot 0 + 4 + 3 \cdot 1 + 3 + 3 \cdot 3 + x + 3 \cdot 0 + 3$
$\quad + 3 \cdot 1 + 8 + 3 \cdot 3 + 7 \equiv 0 \pmod{10}$

$49 + x \equiv 0 \pmod{10}$
Since $49 + x$ must be a multiple of 10, we make $x = 1$.

104. Let x be the missing digit.
$3 \cdot 0 + 4 + 3 \cdot 0 + 0 + 3 \cdot 0 + 0 + 3 \cdot 1 + 2$
$\quad + 3 \cdot 1 + 3 + 3 \cdot x + 9 \equiv 0 \pmod{10}$

$$24 + 3x \equiv 0 \,(\mathrm{mod}\,10)$$

Since $24 + 3x$ must be a multiple of 10, we make $x = 2$.

105. Let x be the missing digit.

$$3 \cdot 0 + x + 3 \cdot 0 + 4 + 3 \cdot 0 + 4 + 3 \cdot 0 + 0$$
$$+ 3 \cdot 1 + 0 + 3 \cdot 0 + 2 \equiv 0 \,(\mathrm{mod}\,10)$$

$$13 + x \equiv 0 \,(\mathrm{mod}\,10)$$

Since $13 + x$ must be a multiple of 10, we make $x = 7$.

106. $1 + 4 + 8 + 3 + 7 + 0 + 4 + 8 = 35$

$1 + 3 + 5 + 7 + 9 + 1 + 3 + 5 = 34$

$35 + 34 = 69$
69 is not a multiple of 10 so the card is not valid. The check digit should be 6.

107. $1 + 0 + 0 + 0 + 2 + 5 + 0 + 0 = 8$

$5 + 0 + 1 + 0 + 4 + 9 + 0 + 3 = 22$

$8 + 22 = 30$
30 is a multiple of 10 so the card is valid.

108. $8 + 2 + 2 + 2 + 2 + 6 + 0 + 4 = 26$

$1 + 1 + 1 + 1 + 2 + 4 + 0 + 3 = 13$

$26 + 13 = 39$
39 is not a multiple of 10 so the card is not valid. The check digit should be 4.

109. $6 + 3 + 6 + 4 + 5 + 0 + 8 + 5 = 37$

$4 + 5 + 4 + 1 + 9 + 2 + 6 + 9 = 40$

$40 + 37 = 77$
77 is not a multiple of 10 so the card is not valid. The check digit should be 2.

110. $6 + 4 + 1 + 9 + 5 + 8 + 7 + 6 = 46$

$7 + 8 + 2 + 0 + 3 + 2 + 2 + 7 = 31$

$46 + 31 = 77$
77 is not a multiple of 10 so the card is not valid. The check digit should be 0.

111. $6 + 0 + 8 + 1 + 4 + 8 + 8 = 35$

$0 + 2 + 4 + 6 + 9 + 0 + 1 = 22$

$35 + 22 = 57$
57 is not a multiple of 10 so the card is not valid. The check digit should be 4.

112. $6 + 0 + 0 + 6 + 0 + 0 + 0 = 12$
$0 + 0 + 0 + 0 + 1 + 0 + 4 = 5$
$12 + 5 = 17$

17 is not a multiple of 10 so the card is not valid. The check digit should be 7.

113. $6 + 3 + 9 + 4 + 6 + 6 + 8 = 42$

$6 + 3 + 0 + 3 + 9 + 8 + 9 = 38$

$42 + 38 = 80$
80 is a multiple of 10 so the card is valid.

114. $6 + 4 + 8 + 3 + 4 + 9 + 6 = 40$

$8 + 3 + 4 + 7 + 3 + 0 + 8 = 33$

$40 + 33 = 73$
73 is not a multiple of 10 so the card is not valid. The check digit should be 5.

115. $3 + 2 + 0 + 6 + 0 + 0 + 2 + 6 = 19$

$0 + 1 + 0 + 0 + 5 + 7 + 0 + 1 = 14$

$19 + 14 = 33$
33 is not a multiple of 10 so the card is not valid. The check digit should be 8.

116. $7 \cdot 0 + 3 \cdot 0 + 9 \cdot 1 + 7 \cdot 2 + 3 \cdot 3 + 9 \cdot 4$

$+ 7 \cdot 5 + 3 \cdot 6 + 9 \cdot 7 = 184$

$= 4 \,(\mathrm{mod}\,10) \neq 0 \,(\mathrm{mod}\,10)$
The routing number is not valid.

117. $7 \cdot 0 + 3 \cdot 3 + 9 \cdot 1 + 7 \cdot 3 + 3 \cdot 1 + 9 \cdot 3 + 7 \cdot 5$

$+ 3 \cdot 6 + 9 \cdot 2 = 140 \equiv 0 \,(\mathrm{mod}\,10)$
The routing number is valid.

118. $7 \cdot 0 + 3 \cdot 6 + 9 \cdot 3 + 7 \cdot 1 + 3 \cdot 0 + 9 \cdot 7$

$+ 7 \cdot 5 + 3 \cdot 1 + 9 \cdot 3 = 180 \equiv 0 \,(\mathrm{mod}\,10)$
The routing number is valid.

119. $7 \cdot 0 + 3 \cdot 6 + 9 \cdot 3 + 7 \cdot 1 + 3 \cdot 0 + 9 \cdot 7$

$+ 7 \cdot 5 + 3 \cdot 1 + 9 \cdot 4 = 189$

$\equiv 9 \,(\mathrm{mod}\,10) \neq 0 \,(\mathrm{mod}\,10)$
There is an error in the routing number.

120. $7 \cdot 1 + 3 \cdot 1 + 9 \cdot 1 + 7 \cdot 0 + 3 \cdot 3 + 9 \cdot 6$

$+ 7 \cdot 0 + 3 \cdot 0 + 9 \cdot 2 = 100 \equiv 0 \,(\mathrm{mod}\,10)$
The routing number is valid.

To read a project concerning checking numbers under different schemes, go to:
**http://www.missioncollege.org/depts/math/
sanitate/lynn.htm**

Collaborative Learning

1.
```
            1
          1   1
        1   2   1
      1   3   3   1
    1   4   6   4   1
  1   5   10   10   5   1
1   6   15   20   15   6   1
```

2.
```
            1
          1   1
        1   0   1
      1   1   1   1
    1   0   0   0   1
  1   1   0   0   1   1
1   0   1   0   1   0   1
```

3.   Here are the first 8 rows:

**Section 9.2 Abstract Mathematical Systems:
        Groups and Fields**

1. a. $a @ b = a$ b. $b @ c = c$

    c. $c @ a = b$

2. a. $a @ (b @ c) = a @ c = b$

    b. $(a @ b) @ c = a @ c = b$ c. Yes

3. a. $b @ (a @ b) = b @ a = a$

    b. $(b @ a) @ b = a @ b = a$ c. Yes

4. a. $(a @ b) @ a = a @ a = c$

    b. $a @ (b @ a) = a @ a = c$ c. Yes

5. a. $b @ c = c$ b. $c @ b = c$

    c. Yes

6. Yes. The table is symmetric with respect
    to the diagonal from upper left to lower
    right.

7. Yes; if $x \in S$ and $y \in S$, then $x @ y \in S$,
    that is, all the entries in the table are
    elements of S.

8. a.

F	1	2	3
1	1	1	1
2	2	2	2
3	3	3	3

    b. Yes, A is closed under the operation F.
    c. No, the operation F is not
        commutative.

    d. $a F (b F c) = a F b = a$

        $(a F b) F c = a F c = a$

        Therefore, $a F (b F c) = (a F b) F c$

9. a. Yes; if a and b are natural numbers, then a
        F $b = a$, which is a natural number.
    b. Yes. a F $(b$ F $c) = a$ F $b = a$, and
        $(a$ F $b)$ F $c = a$ F $c = a$. Thus,
        a F $(b$ F $c) = (a$ F $b)$ F c.
    c. No. a F $b = a$, and b F $a = b$, so if
        $a \neq b$, then a F $b \neq b$ F a.

10. a. Yes. The product of two multiples of 5 is
        a multiple of 5.
    b. Yes. This is a property of ordinary
        multiplication of numbers.
    c. Yes. This is a property of ordinary
        multiplication of numbers.

11. a. No. For example, $1 + 3 = 4$, which is not
        an odd number.
    b. Yes; the product of two odd numbers is an
        odd number.
    c. Yes; the sum of two even numbers is an
        even number.
    d. Yes; the product of two even numbers is
        an even number.

12. a. Ordinary addition. $1 + 1 = 2 \notin S$
    b. Subtraction: $1 - (0 - 1) = 2$ but
        $(1 - 0) - 1 = 0$.
    c. Subtraction: $1 - 0 \neq 0 - 1$

13.

∩	∅	$\{a\}$	$\{b\}$	$\{a,b\}$
∅	∅	∅	∅	∅
$\{a\}$	∅	$\{a\}$	∅	$\{a\}$
$\{b\}$	∅	∅	$\{b\}$	$\{b\}$
$\{a,b\}$	∅	$\{a\}$	$\{b\}$	$\{a,b\}$

14. a. $(\{a\} \cap \{b\}) \cap \{a,b\} = \emptyset \cap \{a,b\} = \emptyset$

    b. $\{a\} \cap (\{b\} \cap \{a,b\}) = \{a\} \cap \{b\} = \emptyset$

    c. Yes

15. a. $\left(\{b\}\cap\{a,b\}\right)\cap\{a\}=\{b\}\cap\{a\}=\varnothing$

b. $\{b\}\cap\left(\{a,b\}\cap\{a\}\right)=\{b\}\cap\{a\}=\varnothing$

c. Yes

16. Yes

17. Yes; all the entries in the table from problem 13 are elements of S.

18. Yes. The table is symmetric across the diagonal from upper left to lower right.

19. a.

L	1	2	3	4
1	1	2	3	4
2	2	2	3	4
3	3	3	3	4
4	4	4	4	4

b. The first row is the same as the L row, and the first column is the same as the L column, so the identity element is 1.

20. Yes, the fourth row is the same as the S row, and the fourth column is the same as the S column, so the identity element is 4.

21. The table given for this problem shows that 4 is the identity element. This information is needed here.

a. There is no 4 in the first row of the table, so 1 has no inverse.

b. There is no 4 in the second row of the table, so 2 has no inverse.

c. There is no 4 in the third row of the table, so 3 has no inverse.

d. Since 4 S 4 = 4, the element 4 is its own inverse.

22.

×	−1	0	1
−1	1	0	−1
0	0	0	0
1	−1	0	1

23. Yes; $1\times a=a\times1=a$ for each element a of the set S, so 1 is the identity element.

24. a. The inverse of 1 is 1 because $1\times1=1=1\times1$.

b. The inverse of −1 is −1 because $-1\times-1=1=-1\times-1$.

c. Since 1 is not in the second row, there is no inverse for 0.

25. a. A is the identity element because if B is any subset of A, then $A\cap B=B\cap A=B$.

b. No; there is only the one identity element.

26. Yes. All elements in the table are elements of S.

27. Yes. The 0 row of the table is the same as the @ row, and the 0 column is the same as the @ column, so 0 is the identity element.

28. a. The inverse of 0 is 0 because $0\times0=0=0\times0$.

b. The inverse of 1 is 3 because $1\times3=0=3\times1$.

c. The inverse of 2 is 2 because $2\times2=0=2\times2$.

d. The inverse of 3 is 1 because $3\times1=0=1\times3$.

29. a. 3 F (4 L 5) = 3 F 5 = 3, because 3 is the first of the numbers 3 and (4 L 5).

b. 4 F (5 L 6) = 4 F 6 = 4, because 4 is the first of the numbers 4 and (5 L 6).

30. a. 4 L (4 F 5) = 4 L 4 = 4, because 4 is the larger of the numbers 4 and (4 F 5).

b. 5 L (6 F 7) = 5 L 6 = 6, because 6 is the larger of the numbers 5 and (6 F 7).

31. Suppose a, b, c are real numbers. Then a F (b L c) = a and (a F b) L (a F c) = a L a = a. This shows that the distributive property of F over L holds for all real numbers. (Keep in mind that F means to select the first of the numbers in the expression a F b.)

32. If a, b, c are real numbers, then a L (b F c) = a L b and (a L b) F (a L c) = a L b. Therefore, this distributive property holds.

33. Yes. If a, b, c are real numbers, we may replace $b-c$ by $b+(-c)$. Then, since the distributive property of multiplication over addition holds, we have $a(b-c)$

$=a\left[b+(-c)\right]=ab+a(-c)=ab-ac$. This shows that multiplication is distributive over subtraction.

34. First, $a \div (b - c) \neq (a \div b) - (a \div c)$. For

    example, $20 \div (4 - 2) = 20 \div 2 = 10$, but

    $(20 \div 4) - (20 \div 2) = 5 - 10 = -5$.

    However, $(a - b) \div c = (a - b) \cdot \dfrac{1}{c} = \dfrac{a - b}{c}$

    $= \dfrac{a}{c} - \dfrac{b}{c} = (a \div c) - (b \div c)$. Thus, one of

    the distributive laws holds for division:

    $(a - b) \div c = (a \div c) - (b \div c)$

35. Yes; fractions are real numbers and multiplication is distributive over addition for the set of real numbers.

36. No; fractions are real numbers and addition is not distributive over multiplication for the set of real numbers.

37. Yes. We check the four requirements as follows:
    1. The set S is closed under the operation $*$ because every entry in the table is an element of S.
    2. For all x, y, z that are elements of S: $x * (y * z) = (x * y) * z$. This can be checked for all possibilities. For instance, $a * (b * c) = a * b = c$ and $(a * b) * c = c * c = c$. Thus, the set S has the associative property under the operation $*$.
    3. The bottom row is the same as the $*$ row, and the last column is the same as the $*$ column, so c is the identity element.
    4. The identity element c occurs once in each row and column of the table, so every element has an inverse. For instance, $a * b = b * a = c$, so a and b are inverses of each other.

    This shows that the set S under the operation $*$ meets the four requirements and is thus a group. (Note that it is a commutative group.)

38. No. The set of odd integers under addition fails the condition of the closure property. The set of odd integers under addition is not closed because odd + odd = even.

39. No. The set of odd integers under

multiplication is not a group because, except for the number 1, no number in this set has an inverse that is an element of the set. (The fractions are not in this set.)

40. Yes. We check the four requirements as follows:
    1. If a and b are even integers, then $a + b$ is an even number, so the set of even numbers is closed under addition.
    2. If a, b, c are even integers then $(a + b) + c = a + (b + c)$, so the set of even integers has the associative property under addition.
    3. The number 0 can be considered an even integer and $0 + a = a + 0 = a$ for every even integer a. Thus, 0 is the identity element for the set of even integers under addition.
    4. If a is an even integer, then $-a$ is also an even integer and $a + (-a) = (-a) + a = 0$. Thus, every even integer has an inverse under addition.

    Since the set of even integers under addition meets all four requirements, the system is a group. (Note that it is a commutative group because $a + b = b + a$.)

41. No. The set of even integers under multiplication is not a group because it has no identity element. (The number 1 is not in this set.)

42. No. The set of positive integers under addition is not a group because it has no identity element. (The number 0 is not in this set.)

43. No. The set of positive integers under multiplication is not a group because, except for the number 1, no number in this set has an inverse that is an element of the set. (The fractions are not in this set.)

44. Yes. We check the four requirements as follows:
    1. If a and b are integers, then $a + b$ is an integers, so the set of integers is closed under addition.
    2. If a, b, c are integers then $(a + b) + c = a + (b + c)$, so the set of integers has the associative property under addition.
    3. The number 0 is an integer and $0 + a = a + 0 = a$ for every integer a.

Thus, 0 is the identity element for the set of integers under addition.

4. If a is an integer, then $-a$ is also an integer and $a + (-a) = (-a) + a = 0$.

Thus, every integer has an inverse under addition.

Since the set of integers under addition meets all four requirements, the system is a group. (Note that it is a commutative group because $a + b = b + a$.)

45. No. The set of integers under multiplication is not a group because, except for the numbers 1 and –1, no number in this set has a multiplicative inverse that is an element of the set. (The fractions are not in this set.)

46. No. The set of real numbers under multiplication is not a group because 0 has no multiplicative inverse. (You can't divide by zero.)

47. Yes. We check the four requirements as follows:

1. If a and b are real numbers, then $a + b$ is a real number, so the set of real numbers is closed under addition.

2. If a, b, c are real numbers then $(a+b)+c = a+(b+c)$, so the set of real numbers has the associative property under addition.

3. The number 0 is a real number and $0 + a = a + 0 = a$ for every real number a. Thus, 0 is the identity element for the set of real numbers under addition.

4. If a is a real number, then $-a$ is also a real number and $a + (-a) = (-a) + a = 0$. Thus, every real number has an inverse under addition.

Since the set of real numbers under addition meets all four requirements, the system is a group. (Note that it is a commutative group because $a + b = b + a$.)

48. No. The set $\{-1, 0, 1\}$ under addition fails the condition of the closure property, so this set is not a group. The set $\{-1, 0, 1\}$ is not closed because $1 + 1 = 2$, which is not an element of the set.

49. No. The set $\{-1, 0, 1\}$ under multiplication is not a group because the number 0 has no multiplicative inverse under multiplication.

50.

#	a	b	c
a	c	a	b
b	a	b	c
c	b	c	a

51. No. The set $\{a, b, c, d, e\}$ under the operation # defined by the table is not a group because there is no identity element. (There is no column of the table that reads a, b, c, d, e in that order.)

52. No. The set of positive odd integers has no multiplicative inverses that are elements of the set, so this system is not a field.

53. No. The set of positive even integers has no multiplicative inverses that are elements of the set, so this system is not a field.

54. No. The set of integral multiples of 5 is the set $\{\ldots -10, -5, 0, 5, 10, \ldots\}$. This set has no multiplicative inverses that are elements of the set, so this system is not a field.

55. No. The set of integral multiples of 2 is the set of even integers. This set has no multiplicative inverses that are elements of the set, so this system is not a field.

56. Yes. The set of real numbers holds to the definition of a field.

57. Check to see that $a \blacklozenge b$ is always an element of S, that is, every entry in the table is a member of S.

58. Check to see if the table is symmetric to the diagonal from upper left to lower right. If it is, then the operation has the commutative property, otherwise, it does not have this property.

59. Check the table to see if there is an element e in S such that the column under e is identical to the column at the far left and the row opposite e is identical to the top row. If there is, then e is the identity element. If there is no such element, then there is no identity element.

60. If there is an identity element, say e, check to see if $a \blacklozenge b = b \blacklozenge a = e$.

61. You have to check that
$x * (y * z) = (x * y) * z$ for all possible values of x, y, z from the set $\{a, b, c\}$. If you had to check all possible cases, there would be 27 of these because each of the 3 places has three possible values. However, since the operation has the commutative property, the number of cases to be checked is greatly reduced. Think about it. (You would need to check only 10 cases.)

62. The operation $\cdot$ is associative and the identity element is e. To use the theorem, we only have to check that a and b have inverses. The table shows that $a \cdot b = c$ and $b \cdot a = c$. This completes the check.

63.

$\oplus$	1	2	3	4	5	6	7
1	1	1	1	1	1	1	1
2	1	2	2	2	2	2	2
3	1	2	3	3	3	3	3
4	1	2	3	4	4	4	4
5	1	2	3	4	5	5	5
6	1	2	3	4	5	6	6
7	1	2	3	4	5	6	7

a. Yes, all elements in the table are elements of $\{1, 2, 3, 4, 5, 6, 7\}$.
b. Yes, it is commutative because $a \oplus b = b \oplus a$, where a and b are in the set $\{1, 2, 3, 4, 5, 6, 7\}$.
c. Yes, it is associative because $(a \oplus b) \oplus c = a \oplus (b \oplus c)$, where a, b and c are in the set $\{1, 2, 3, 4, 5, 6, 7\}$.
d. The identity element is 7 because $7 \oplus b = b \oplus 7 = b$, where b are in the set $\{1, 2, 3, 4, 5, 6, 7\}$.

64.

$\otimes$	0	1	2	3	4	5	6
0	0	1	2	3	4	5	6
1	1	2	3	4	5	6	7
2	2	3	4	5	6	7	8
3	3	4	5	6	7	8	9
4	4	5	6	7	8	9	10
5	5	6	7	8	9	10	11
6	6	7	8	9	10	11	12

a. No, there are elements in the table that are not in the set $\{0, 1, 2, 3, 4, 5, 6\}$.
b. Yes, it is commutative because $a \oplus b = b \oplus a$, where a and b are in the set $\{0, 1, 2, 3, 4, 5, 6\}$.
c. Yes, it is associative because $(a \oplus b) \oplus c = a \oplus (b \oplus c)$, where a, b and c are in the set $\{0, 1, 2, 3, 4, 5, 6\}$.
d. The identity element is 0 because $0 \oplus b = b \oplus 0 = b$, where b are in the set $\{0, 1, 2, 3, 4, 5, 6\}$.

65. Yes, $3 \otimes (4 \oplus 5) = 3 \otimes 4 = 3 + 4 = 7$ and $(3 \otimes 4) \oplus (3 \otimes 5) = 7 \oplus 3 = 7$. Thus, $3 \otimes (4 \oplus 5) = (3 \otimes 4) \oplus (3 \otimes 5)$.
Note: You are comparing $a + \min\{b, c\}$ to $\min\{a + b, a + c\}$.

66. a. The definition of $e \oplus x = \min\{e, x\} = x$.
b. If $\min\{e, x\} = x$ then $x \leq e$.
c. $3 \oplus \infty = 3$
d. $(-5) \oplus \infty = -5$
e. $x \oplus \infty = x$

67. $6 \times 9999 = 6(10,000 - 1) = 60,000 - 6$
$= 59,994$

68. $8 \cdot 99 = 8(100 - 1) = 800 - 8 = 792$

69. $7 \times 59 = 7(60 - 1) = 420 - 7 = 413$

70. $8 \cdot 999 = 8(1000 - 1) = 8000 - 8 = 7992$

71. $4 \times 9995 = 4(10,000 - 5) = 40,000 - 20$
$= 39,980$

72. $3 \cdot 9998 = 3(10,000 - 2) = 30,000 - 6$
$$= 29,994$$

73. Let x be the number you select, then the following steps show why the puzzle works:

Think of a number: x
Add 3 to it: $x + 3$
Triple the result: $3x + 9$
Subtract 9: $3x$
Divide by the number

with which you started: $\dfrac{3x}{x} = 3$

It does not matter what value of x is used, the left side will always be 3.

74. Let x be the number you select, then the following steps show why the puzzle works:

Think of a number: x
Add 2 to it: $x + 2$
Double the result: $2x + 4$
Subtract 4: $2x$
Divide by the number

with which you started: $\dfrac{2x}{x} = 2$

It does not matter what value of x is used, the left side will always be 2.

Collaborative Learning

FB	At	R	L	A
At	At	R	L	A
R	R	A	At	L
L	L	At	A	R
A	A	L	R	At

1. Yes. Answers are elements of C.

2. *At*   3. *At*   4. *L*

5. *R*   6. *A*   7. Yes

8. Yes. Satisfies Definition 8.18.

9. Yes. The reflection of the bottom half of the table along the diagonal is identical to the top half.

Section 9.3 Game Theory

1. The 4 in the first row is the smallest element in its row and the largest in its column. The game is strictly determined. Optimum strategy: Row player should play row 1; column player should play column 1. Value of the game is 4.

2. The 1 in the first row is the smallest element in its row and the largest in its column. The game is strictly determined. Optimum strategy: Row player should play row 1, column player column 2. Value of the game is 1.

3. There is no element that is the smallest in its row and the largest in its column. Hence, the game is not strictly determined.

4. There is no element that is the smallest in its row and the largest in its column. Hence, the game is not strictly determined.

5. The 4 in the first row is the smallest element in its row and the largest in its column. The game is strictly determined. Optimum strategy: Row player should play row 1; column player should play column 3. Value of the game is 4.

6. The 0 in the third row is the smallest element in its row and the largest in its column. The game is strictly determined. Optimum strategy: Row player should play row 3, column player column 2. Value of the game is 0.

7. Either 4 in the third row is the smallest element in its row and the largest in its column. The game is strictly determined. Optimum strategy: Row player should play row 3; column player should play column 3 (or column 1). The value of the game is 4.

8. Either 1 in the second column is the smallest element in its row and the largest in its column. The game is strictly determined. Optimum strategy: Row player should play row 1 or row 3, column player column 2. Value of the game is 1.

9. a. There is no element that is the smallest in its row and the largest in its column, so there is no saddle point.

   b. Row player's expected value is given by
   $E_R =$
   $$p \cdot 2 + (1 - p)(-1) = p \cdot 1 + (1 - p) \cdot 4$$

$$2p - 1 + p = p + 4 - 4p$$
$$3p - 1 = 4 - 3p$$
$$6p = 5$$
$$p = \frac{5}{6}$$

This means that the row player should play row 1 five-sixths of the time and row 2 one-sixth of the time. (The row player's expected value is

$$E_R = 3\left(\frac{5}{6}\right) - 1 = \frac{5}{2} - 1 = \frac{3}{2} = 1.5 .)$$

10. a.   There is no element that is the smallest in its row and the largest in its column, so there is no saddle point.

b.   Row player's expected value is given by $E_R =$

$$p \cdot 3 + (1 - p) \cdot 2 = p \cdot 2 + (1 - p) \cdot 4$$
$$3p + 2 - 2p = 2p + 4 - 4p$$
$$3p + 2 = 4$$
$$3p = 2$$
$$p = \frac{2}{3}$$

This means that the row player should play row 1 two-thirds of the time and row 2 one-third of the time. (The row player's expected value is

$$E_R = \left(\frac{2}{3}\right) \cdot 3 + \left(1 - \frac{2}{3}\right) \cdot 2 = 2 + \frac{2}{3} = \frac{8}{3} .)$$

11. a.   There is no element that is the smallest in its row and the largest in its column, so there is no saddle point.

b.   Row player's expected value is given by $E_R =$

$$p \cdot 3 + (1 - p)(-1) = p(-2) + (1 - p) \cdot 0$$
$$3p - 1 + p = -2p$$
$$4p - 1 = -2p$$
$$6p = 1$$
$$p = \frac{1}{6}$$

This means that the row player should play row 1 one-sixth of the time and row 2 five-sixths of the time. The row player's expected value is:

$$E_R = 4\left(\frac{1}{6}\right) - 1 = \frac{2}{3} - 1 = -\frac{1}{3} .$$

12. a.   There is no element that is the smallest in its row and the largest in its column, so there is no saddle point.

b.   Row player's expected value is given by
$$E_R =$$
$$p \cdot 10 + (1 - p) \cdot 6 = p \cdot 5 + (1 - p) \cdot 12$$
$$10p + 6 - 6p = 5p + 12 - 12p$$
$$4p + 6 = -7p + 12$$
$$11p = 6$$
$$p = \frac{6}{11}$$

This means that the row player should play row 1 six-elevenths of the time and row 2 five-elevenths of the time. The row player's expected value is:

$$E_R = 4\left(\frac{6}{11}\right) + 6 = \frac{24}{11} + \frac{66}{11} = \frac{90}{11} .$$

NOTE: In Exercises 13 – 23 and 29, there is no saddle point.

13.   Since row 2 dominates row 3, row 3 may be discarded and we may use rows 1 and 2 for the payoff matrix. The row player's expected value is given by

$$E_R = p \cdot 6 + (1 - p) \cdot 2 = p \cdot 0 + (1 - p) \cdot 4$$
$$6p + 2 - 2p = 4 - 4p$$
$$4p + 2 = 4 - 4p$$
$$8p = 2$$
$$p = \frac{1}{4}$$

This means that the row player should play row 1 one-fourth of the time and row 2 three-fourths of the time. The row player's expected

value is $E_R = 4\left(\frac{1}{4}\right) + 2 = 1 + 2 = 3$.

14.   Since row 1 dominates row 2, row 2 may be discarded and we may use rows 1 and 3 for the payoff matrix. The row player's expected value is given by

$$E_R = p \cdot 5 + (1 - p) \cdot 25 = p \cdot 30 + (1 - p) \cdot 15$$
$$5p + 25 - 25p = 30p + 15 - 15p$$
$$-20p + 25 = 15p + 15$$

$$-35p = -10$$

$$p = \frac{10}{35} = \frac{2}{7}$$

Row player should select row 1 two-sevenths of the time and row 3 five-sevenths of the time. He should not select row 2. The row player's expected value is

$$-20\left(\frac{2}{7}\right) + 25 = -\frac{40}{7} + 25 = \frac{135}{7} = 19\frac{2}{7}.$$

15. The expected row value is $E_R =$

$$p \cdot 70 + (1-p) \cdot 85 = p \cdot 80 + (1-p) \cdot 75$$

$$70p + 85 - 85p = 80p + 75 - 75p$$

$$85 - 15p = 5p + 75$$

$$10 = 20p$$

$$p = \frac{1}{2}$$

This means that you should study 2 hr half the time and 4 hr the other half the time. (Your expected score is

$$E_R = 85 - 15\left(\frac{1}{2}\right) = 85 - 7.5 = 77.5 .)$$

16. The expected row value is

$$E_R = p \cdot 80 + (1-p) \cdot 90 = p \cdot 85 + (1-p) \cdot 75$$

$$80p + 90 - 90p = 85p + 75 - 75p$$

$$90 - 10p = 10p + 75$$

$$15 = 20p$$

$$p = \frac{3}{4}$$

Study English 2 hr, Math 3 hr three-fourths of the time and English 3 hr, Math 2 hr one-fourth of the time.
(John's expected score is

$$E_R = 90 - 10\left(\frac{3}{4}\right) = 90 - 7.5 = 82.5 .)$$

17. Since the first row is dominated by both the other rows, Ann should not use the first row. This leaves a 2-by-2 matrix for which Ann's expected value is

$$E_R = p \cdot 10 + (1-p) \cdot 15 = p \cdot 12 + (1-p) \cdot 10$$

$$10p + 15 - 15p = 12p + 10 - 10p$$

$$15 - 5p = 2p + 10$$

$$5 = 7p$$

$$p = \frac{5}{7}$$

This means that Ann should buy no bonds, buy stocks with five-sevenths and money market funds with two-sevenths of her investment. Ann's expected return is found from

$$E_R = 15 - 5\left(\frac{5}{7}\right) = 15 - \frac{25}{7} = \frac{80}{7} = 11\frac{3}{7}$$

that is, her expected return would be $11\frac{3}{7}\%$.

18. The expected row value is

$$E_R = p \cdot 0.2 + (1-p) \cdot 0.6 = p \cdot 0.8 + (1-p) \cdot 0.4$$

$$0.2p + 0.6 - 0.6p = 0.8p + 0.4 - 0.4p$$

$$0.6 - 0.4p = 0.4p + 0.4$$

$$0.8p = 0.2$$

$$p = \frac{1}{4}$$

In the long run, the stock increase in price will occur $\frac{1}{4}$ of the time.

19. The expected row value is

$$E_R = p \cdot 60 + (1-p) \cdot 30 = p \cdot 50 + (1-p) \cdot 70$$

$$60p + 30 - 30p = 50p + 70 - 70p$$

$$30p + 30 = 70 - 20p$$

$$50p = 40$$

$$p = \frac{4}{5}$$

This means that station R should price its gasoline at $1.00 four-fifths of the time and at $1.10 the other fifth of the time. (The expected row value would be

$$E_R = 30\left(\frac{4}{5}\right) + 30 = 24 + 30 = 54 , \text{ that is,}$$

with this strategy, station R would expect to get 54% of the business.)

20. Since row 1 dominates row 3, row 3 may be discarded and column 1 dominates column 3, so column 3 may be discarded. We may use rows 1 and 2 and columns 1 and 2 for the payoff matrix. The expected row value is

$$E_R =$$

$$p \cdot 0.5 + (1-p) \cdot 0.3 = p \cdot 0.4 + (1-p) \cdot 0.6$$

$$0.5p + 0.3 - 0.3p = 0.4p + 0.6 - 0.6p$$

$$0.2p + 0.3 = -0.2p + 0.6$$

$$0.4p = 0.3$$

$$p = \frac{3}{4}$$

The expected percent going from upper Manhattan to a different sector would be

$$E_R = 0.2\left(\frac{3}{4}\right) + 0.3 = 0.15 + 0.3 = 0.45 = 45\%$$

21. a. The payoff matrix can be written as follows:

$$\begin{array}{c} \\ \text{Performance} \\ \text{Safety} \end{array} \begin{array}{cc} \text{Young} & \text{Old} \\ \begin{bmatrix} 70\% & 20\% \\ 40\% & 80\% \end{bmatrix} \end{array}$$

   b. The expected row value is

$$E_R = p \cdot 70 + (1-p) \cdot 40 = p \cdot 20 + (1-p) \cdot 80$$

$$70p + 40 - 40p = 20p + 80 - 80p$$

$$30p + 40 = 80 - 60p$$

$$90p = 40$$

$$p = \frac{4}{9}$$

This means that 4/9 of the ads should be based on performance and 5/9 should be based on safety. (With this strategy, the expected row value would

be $E_R = 30\left(\frac{4}{9}\right) + 40 = \frac{40}{3} + 40 = \frac{160}{3}$,

that is, the ads would be effective on

$53\frac{1}{3}\%$ of the buyers.)

22.

$$\begin{array}{c} \\ \text{You} \quad P \\ N \end{array} \begin{array}{cc} \text{Friend} \\ P \quad N \\ \begin{bmatrix} +1 & -1 \\ -5 & +5 \end{bmatrix} \end{array}$$

$$E_R = p \cdot 1 + (1-p) \cdot (-5) = p \cdot (-1) + (1-p) \cdot 5$$

$$p - 5 + 5p = -1p + 5 - 5p$$

$$6p - 5 = -6p + 5$$

$$12p = 10$$

$$p = \frac{5}{6}$$

Your optimal strategy is to put down your penny five-sixths of the time and your nickel one-sixth of the time.

$$E_R = 6\left(\frac{5}{6}\right) - 5 = 5 - 5 = 0, \text{ thus the}$$

expected value of the game is 0.

23. With the numbers in dollars, the required matrix can be written as

$$\begin{array}{c} \\ \\ \text{Water?} \quad \begin{array}{c} \text{Yes} \\ \text{No} \end{array} \end{array} \begin{array}{c} \text{Freeze?} \\ \begin{array}{cc} \text{Yes} & \text{No} \end{array} \\ \begin{bmatrix} 6000 & -400 \\ -4000 & 4000 \end{bmatrix} \end{array}$$

The expected row value is $E_R =$

$$p \cdot 6000 + (1-p)(-4000)$$

$$= p(-400) + (1-p) \cdot 4000$$

$$6000p - 4000 + 4000p$$

$$= -400p + 4000 - 4000p$$

$$10,000p - 4000 = 4000 - 4400p$$

$$14,400p = 8000$$

$$p = \frac{5}{9}$$

This means that the farmer's optimal strategy would be to water five-ninths of the time and not to water four-ninths of the time. The corresponding expected payoff is

$$E_R = 10,000\left(\frac{5}{9}\right) - 4000$$

$$= \frac{50,000 - 36,000}{9} = \frac{14,000}{9}$$

So the farmer's expected payoff is $\dfrac{14,000}{9}$ or about \$1556.

24. Because it is a minimum in its row and a maximum in its column.

25. If row i dominates row j, this means that, in the long run, playing row i is more profitable than playing row j. Thus, row j may be eliminated from the row player's options.

26. Because in the long run, column i is more profitable than column j for the column player and therefore the column player would never choose it.

27. Both entries in row 1 are less than the corresponding entries in row 2. Therefore, row 1 is dominated by row 2.

28. Since row 1 is dominated by row 2, row 1 can be eliminated.

29. With row 1 eliminated, the payoff matrix is:

$$\begin{array}{cc} & \text{Allergic} \quad \text{On a Diet} \\ \begin{array}{c} \text{Poems} \\ \text{Candy} \end{array} & \begin{bmatrix} 2 & 5 \\ 3 & -2 \end{bmatrix} \end{array}$$

The expected row value is

$$E_R = p \cdot 2 + (1-p) \cdot 3 = p \cdot 5 + (1-p)(-2)$$
$$2p + 3 - 3p = 5p - 2 + 2p$$
$$3 - p = 7p - 2$$
$$5 = 8p$$
$$p = \frac{5}{8}$$

Hence, the student's optimal strategy is to send poems five-eighths of the time and candies three-eighths of the time. He should not send flowers.

30. The expected payoff is

$$E_R = 3 - \frac{5}{8} = \frac{24}{8} - \frac{5}{8} = \frac{19}{8} = 2\frac{3}{8}$$

Collaborative Learning

1.

$$\begin{array}{cc} & \text{Clyde} \\ & \text{Confess} \quad \text{Don't} \\ \text{Bonnie} \begin{array}{c} \text{Confess} \\ \text{Don't} \end{array} & \begin{bmatrix} (10,10) & (0,20) \\ (20,0) & (1,1) \end{bmatrix} \end{array}$$

2. Bonnie should confess since only two things can happen:
Clyde can confess or not.
If Clyde confesses, Bonnie gets 20 years if she doesn't, 10 years if she does, so she should confess.
If Clyde does not confess, Bonnie goes free if she confesses or gets 1 year if she doesn't, so she should confess.

3. Same strategy as Bonnie: confess.

4. Each gets 10 years.

5. Each gets 1 year.

6. The "dilemma" is that when they both confess each goes to prison for 10 years but if they both had kept silent (not confess) each would have gotten only 1 year.

For more reading on Prisoner's Dilemma try:
http://william-king.www.drexel.edu/top/eco/game/ dilemma.html
http://www.saddleback.cc.ca.us/div/la/neh/ prisoner.htm
http://www.saddleback.cc.ca.us/div/la/neh/ neutral.htm (the "neutral" case)
http://www.constitution.org/pd/pd.htm

For many variations of the problem, in alphabetical order, try: **http://plato.stanford.edu/entries/prisoner-dilemma/**

Chapter 9 Practice Test

1. a. $3 \oplus 11 = 2$ (11 hours after 3 o'clock is 2 o'clock.)
   b. $8 \oplus 9 = 5$ (9 hours after 8 o'clock is 5 o'clock.)
   c. $3 \ominus 9 = 6$ (9 hours before 3 o'clock is 6 o'clock.)
   d. $5 \ominus 12 = 5$ (12 hours before 5 o'clock is 5 o'clock.)

2. a. $3 \otimes 5 = 3$ ($3 \cdot 5 = 15$ and $15 - 12 = 3$)
   b. $6 \otimes 8 = 12$ ($6 \cdot 8 = 48$, a multiple of 12)
   c. Look at the clock arithmetic multiplication table and go along the row for 11 until you come to 3. The number in the top line is 9. Thus, in clock arithmetic, $\dfrac{3}{11} = 9$. You can check this by noting that $11 \cdot 9 = 99$, which leaves a remainder of 3 when divided by 12.
   d. There is no solution. If you look at the multiplication table and go along the row for 6, you will see that there is no 5 in this row.

3. a. True. $5 - 2$ is a multiple of 3.
   b. True. $9 - 5$ is a multiple of 4.
   c. False. $9 - 2 = 7$ is not a multiple of 6.

4. a. By inspection of Table 9.2, we see that $3 + 2 \equiv 0 (\text{mod} 5)$. Thus $n = 0$ will make the sentence $3 + 2 \equiv n (\text{mod} 5)$ true.
   b. By inspection of Table 9.3, we see that $4 \times 3 \equiv 2 (\text{mod} 5)$. Thus $n = 2$ will make the sentence $4 \times 3 \equiv n (\text{mod} 5)$ true.
   c. $2 - 4 \equiv n (\text{mod} 5)$ if and only if $2 \equiv 4 + n (\text{mod } 5)$. From Table 9.2 (or

9.4), we see that $2 \equiv 4 + 3 \pmod 5$.

Thus $2 - 4 \equiv 3 \pmod 5$, so $n = 3$.

d. $\dfrac{3}{2} \equiv n \pmod 5$ is true if and only if

$3 \equiv 2n \pmod 5$. From Table 9.3, we

see that $3 \equiv 2 \times 4 \pmod 5$. Thus

$\dfrac{3}{2} \equiv 4 \pmod 5$, so $n = 4$.

5.   a. $6 + n \equiv 1 \pmod 7$ is true if $6 + n = 8$
that is, if $n = 2$. Since any multiple of
7 may be added to this solution, the
general solution is $n = 2 + 7k$, k any
integer.

b. $3 - n \equiv 4 \pmod 7$ is true if

$3 \equiv n + 4 \pmod 7$, which is true if

$n + 4 = 10$, that is, if $n = 6$. Since any
multiple of 7 may be added to this
solution, the general solution is

$n = 6 + 7k$, k any integer.

6.   a. $2n \equiv 1 \pmod 3$ is true if $2n = 4 + 3k$,

k any integer. Thus, the general

solution is $n = 2 + \dfrac{3k}{2}$, k any integer.

b. $\dfrac{n}{2} \equiv 2 \pmod 3$ is true if $n \equiv 4 \pmod 3$

$= 1 \pmod 3$, so the general solution is

$n = 1 + 3k$, k any integer.

7.   a. $(\$ * \cent) * \# = \# * \# = \#$
b. $\$ * (\cent * \#) = \$ * \cent = \#$
c. $(\$ * \#) * (\% * \cent) = \$ * \$ = \%$

8.   Yes. The set S is closed with respect to the
operation $*$ because all the entries in the
table are elements of S.

9.   Yes. The operation is commutative
because the table is symmetric with
respect to the main diagonal from upper
left to lower right. This means that if a
and b are any two elements of S, then $a *$
$b = b * a$.

10.   The identity element is # because the #
column is the same as the column under $*$
and the # row is the same as the top row
of the table. This means that if a is any

element of S, then $a * \# = \# * a = a$.

11.   a.   The inverse of # is itself because # is the
identity element.
b.   Because $\$ * \cent = \#$, the inverse of $\$$ is $\cent$.
c.   Because $\% * \% = \#$, the inverse of % is
%.
d.   Because $\cent * \$ = \#$, the inverse of $\cent$ is $\$$.

12.   a.   There is no identity element because no
column reads exactly the same as the
column under @.
b.   Since there is no identity element, no
element has an inverse.
c.   No. The table is not symmetric to the
diagonal from upper left to lower right.

13.   a.   Yes. Since the operation S selects the
second of the two numbers in $a\,S\,b$,
$a\,S\,(b\,L\,c) = b\,L\,c$. Also, $a\,S\,b = b$ and a
$S\,c = c$, so that $(a\,S\,b)\,L\,(a\,S\,c) = b\,L\,c$.
Thus, it is true that
$a\,S\,(b\,L\,c) = (a\,S\,b)\,L\,(a\,S\,c)$.
Therefore, S is distributive over L.
b.   Yes. Since $b\,S\,c = c$, it follows that
$a\,L\,(b\,S\,c) = a\,L\,c$. Also, it is true that $(a$
$L\,b)\,S\,(a\,L\,c) = a\,L\,c$, because
$a\,L\,c$ is the second number. Thus,
$a\,L\,(b\,S\,c) = (a\,L\,b)\,S\,(a\,L\,c)$, so L is
distributive over S.

14.   Yes. With the operation of addition mod 3, the
set $S = \{0, 1, 2\}$ has the five properties
required to make it a commutative group
1. S has the closure property because the
sum (mod 3) of any two elements of S is
an element of S.
2. S has the associative property because
ordinary addition does.
3.   0 is the identity element.
4.   Every element of S has an inverse. The
inverse of 0 is 0 and the elements 1 and 2
are inverses of each other.
$[1 + 2 = 2 + 1 = 3$ and $3 \equiv 0 \pmod 3.]$
5. S has the commutative property because
ordinary addition does.

15.   Yes. With the operation of multiplication mod
3, the set $T = \{1, 2\}$ has the five properties
required to make it a commutative group.
1. T has the closure property because the
product of any two elements (mod 3) is an
element of T.
2. T has the associative property because
ordinary multiplication does.

3. The identity element is 1.
4. Since $1 \cdot 1 \equiv 1 \pmod 3$ and
   $2 \cdot 2 \equiv 1 \pmod 3$, the elements 1 and 2
   are their own inverses.
5. T has the commutative property
   because ordinary multiplication does.

16. Yes. The system has the six required
   properties (closure, associative,
   commutative, identity, distributive of
   multiplication over addition, and inverses,
   except there is no inverse for zero with
   respect to multiplication), so the system is
   a field.

17. Yes, all the requirements of the definition
   of a group are satisfied. Let $S = \{0, 1\}$.
   We check the requirements for S to be a
   group under the operation $\oplus$.
   1. S has the closure property because all
      the entries in the table are elements of
      S.
   2. You can check that the operation $\oplus$
      corresponds to addition (mod 2), so S
      has the associative property under
      this operation.
   3. The identity element is 0 because
      $0 \oplus 0 = 0$, and $0 \oplus 1 = 1 \oplus 0 = 1$.
   4. Each row and column of the table has
      an identity element, so each element
      of S has an inverse. The table shows
      that 0 and 1 are both their own
      inverses.
   Therefore, the set S with the operation $\oplus$
   is a group.

18. No. You can check as in problem 17 that
   the set S under the operation $\otimes$ has the
   closure and associative properties. The
   identity element is 1. However, the
   element 0 has no inverse, so the system is
   not a group.

19. Yes. In problems 17 and 18, we have
   checked all the requirements for a field
   except the distributive property of $\otimes$ over
   $\oplus$. Since the operation $\oplus$ corresponds to
   addition (mod 2) and the operation $\otimes$
   corresponds to multiplication (mod 2), the
   system does have this distributive
   property. Thus, the system is a field.

20. a. There is no element that is both the least in
      its row and the greatest in its column, so
      there is no saddle point and the game is
      not strictly determined.
    b. The 1 in the third row, third column is the
      least in its row and the greatest in its
      column, so this is a saddle point. The game
      is strictly determined and its value is 1.
    c. The 2's in the bottom row are the least in
      the row and the greatest in their respective
      columns, so these are saddle points. The
      game is strictly determined and its value is
      2.

21. The –6 in the first row is the saddle point. The
   row player should play row 1 and the column
   player should play column 2. The payoff for
   the row player is –6.

22. a. With the given percents written as decimals,
      the payoff matrix is:

      $$\begin{array}{cc} & \begin{array}{cc} \text{H} & \text{C} \end{array} \\ \begin{array}{c} \text{This Year} \\ \text{Next Year} \end{array} & \begin{bmatrix} 0.6 & 0.4 \\ 0.3 & 0.7 \end{bmatrix} \end{array}$$

    b. There is no saddle point, so this is not a
      strictly determined game. If E_R is the
      expected value for HART and p is the
      probability that the first row is what will
      happen, then $E_R =$

      $$p \cdot 0.6 + (1 - p) \cdot 0.3 = p \cdot 0.4 + (1 - p) \cdot 0.7$$
      $$0.6p + 0.3 - 0.3p = 0.4p + 0.7 - 0.7p$$
      $$0.3p + 0.3 = 0.7 - 0.3p$$
      $$0.6p = 0.4$$
      $$p = \frac{2}{3}$$

      Hence,

      $$E_R = 0.3\left(\frac{2}{3}\right) + 0.3 = 0.2 + 0.3 = 0.5\text{, so}$$

      that the expected percentage of persons
      using HART next year is 50%.

Chapter 10 Counting Techniques

Section 10.1 The Sequential Counting Principle (SCP): A Problem-Solving Tool

1. 8 different outfits

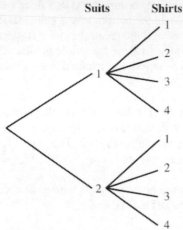

2. 10 different choices

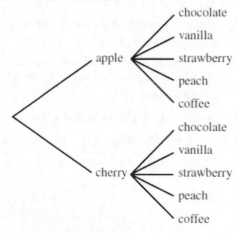

3. $4 \times 3 = 12$ outcomes

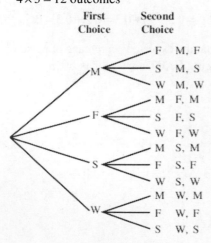

4. a. $5 + 5^2 + 5^3 + 5^4 + 5^5 = 3905$ letters would have your name on the list.

   b. You would receive $5^5 \cdot \$0.10 = \$312.50$.

5. a. $1 \cdot 3 \cdot 3 = 9$ ways to get 3 bells.

   b. $3 \cdot 6 \cdot 7 = 126$ ways to get 3 oranges.

   c. $5 \cdot 1 \cdot 5 = 25$ ways to get 3 plums.

6. a. $26 \cdot 25 = 650$ ways for both cards to be red.

   b. $26 \cdot 25 = 650$ ways for both cards to be black.

   c. $2 \cdot 26 \cdot 26 = 1352$ ways for one card to be black and the other is red. (The first card could be black, the other red or the first card could be red, the other black)

7. a. $4 \cdot 3 = 12$ ways to get a pair of aces.

   b. $4 \cdot 3 \cdot 4 \cdot 3 = 144$ ways to get a pair of aces, then a pair of eights.

8. a. $5 \cdot 4 = 20$ ways they could miss each other.

   b. $5 \cdot 1 = 5$ ways they could meet.

9. $5 \cdot 6 = 30$ ways to select 1 man and 1 woman from 5 men and 6 women.

10. $26 \cdot 26 = 676$ different sets of 2 intials from the English alphabet.

11. $26 \cdot 26 \cdot 26 = 26^3 = 17,576$ different sets of 3 initials from the English alphabet.

12. $2 \cdot 3 = 6$ ring choices.

13. $7 \cdot 6 \cdot 9 = 378$ meal choices.

14. Each person can rank the waters $4 \cdot 3 \cdot 2 \cdot 1 = 24$ ways. (For all three to rank the waters would be $24 \cdot 24 \cdot 24 = 24^3 = 13,824$ ways.)

15. a. $6 \cdot 5 \cdot 4 \cdot 3 \cdot 2 \cdot 1 = 720$ ways to list the possible treatments.

    b. $4 \cdot 3 \cdot 2 \cdot 1 = 24$ ways to rank the four top-ranked treatements.

16. a. $26 \cdot 26 \cdot 26 = 17,576$ arrangements for the 3 letters.

    b. $10 \cdot 10 \cdot 10 = 1000$ arrangements for the 3 numbers.

    c. $10 \cdot 10 \cdot 10 \cdot 26 \cdot 26 \cdot 26 = 17,576,000$ possible license plates.

17. $9 \cdot 10 = 90$ 2-digit numbers in the set of

natural numbers.

18. $9 \cdot 10 \cdot 10 = 900$ 3-digit numbers in the set of natural numbers.

19. a. $9 \cdot 10^8 = 900,000,000$ possible Social Security numbers.
     b. $10^9 = 1,000,000,000$ possible Social Security numbers.

20. $8 \cdot 10^6 = 8,000,000$ possible local telephone numbers.

21. a. $40 \cdot 39 \cdot 38 = 59,280$ combinations if no number is used twice.
     b. $40^3 = 64,000$ combinations if repetition of numbers is allowed.

22. $6 \cdot 5 = 30$ dinner choices.

23. a. Billy has 10 choices from group A.
     b. Billy has 2 choices for soup.
     c. Billy has 4 choices for dessert.
     d. Billy has $10 \cdot 2 \cdot 4 = 80$ choices for an item from group A, soup, and dessert.

24. a. Sue has 9 choices from group B.
     b. Sue has $9 \cdot 2 \cdot 4 = 72$ choices for an item from group B, soup, and dessert.

25. a. Pedro has 19 choices from group A or group B.
     b. Pedro has $19 \cdot 2 \cdot 4 = 152$ choices for an item from group A or B, soup, and dessert.

26. a. Bob and Sue have $10 \cdot 9 = 90$ choices with one item from group A and one from group B.
     b. The family dinner has $10 \cdot 9 \cdot 2 \cdot 4 = 720$ choices.

27. Sam and Sally have $10 \cdot 9 \cdot 2 \cdot 4 = 720$ choices.

28. Sam and Sally have $10 \cdot 7 \cdot 2 \cdot 4 = 560$ choices.

29. Sam and Sally have $10 \cdot 6 \cdot 2 \cdot 4 = 480$ choices.

30. Sam and Sally have $10 \cdot 7 \cdot 1 \cdot 4 = 280$ choices.

31. $(a, @), (a, \&), (a, \%), (b, @), (b, \&).$
     $(b, \%), (c, @), (c, \&), (c, \%), (@, a),$
     $(\&, a), (\%, a), (@, b), (\&, b), (\%, b),$
     $(@, c), (\&, c), (\%, c)$

32. $120 \cdot 210 = 25,200$ different couples.

33. $2 \cdot 2 = 4$ choices as to when and what to buy.

34. $2 \cdot 2 = 4$ possibilities.

35. $3 \cdot 2 = 6$ investment possibilities.

36. $3 \cdot 3 = 9$ choices in bring a new product to market.

37. The first step indicates that the product can be developed (D) or abandoned (A). Second, if the product is developed (D) they can decide to get a patent (P) or not (N). Third, if they get a patent (P) they can license the product (Li) or sell it (S). Finally, if they decide to sell it (S) the sales can be high (H), low (L) or medium (M).

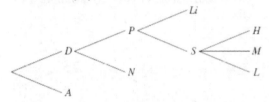

38. The first step indicates the forecast that the hurricane will make landfall (L) or will not (NL). Second, need to make a decision whether to evacuate (E) or not (NE) regardless of whether the hurricane made landfall or not. Finally, the hurricane makes landfall (L) or not (NL).

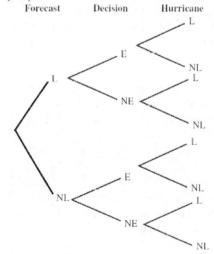

39. The first decision is to treat (T) or not to treat (~T). If the person is treated, there may be some side effect (S) or not (~S). If the person is not treated (~T) the person may get HIV (H)

or not (~H). Regardless of side effects, the person may get HIV (H) or not (~H). Note: The tilde (~) is used to mean NOT.

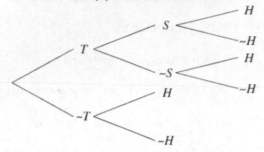

40. The first step involves a company considering two projects (P₁ and P₂). Each project must be approved (A) or rejected (R). If the project is approved, it will either be a market success (S) or failure (F).

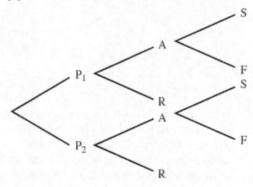

41. If a single event can occur in m ways or in n ways, then the total number of ways in which the event can occur is $m + n$. (This assumes that the m ways and the n ways are all distinct.)

42. There are 26 different letters available so the number of different plates available is much greater than with the use of digits.

43. $4 \cdot 3 \cdot 2 \cdot 1 = 24$ 44. $4 \cdot 3 \cdot 2 = 24$

45. Yes. Only 17,576 different sets of initials are possible. Thus, if there are 27,000 people, at least two people must have the same set of initials.

46. There are 12 ways in which the front air value could come to rest.

47. $12 \cdot 12 = 144$ ways in which the front and rear air valves could come to rest.

48. There are $12 \cdot 12 \cdot 12 \cdot 12 = 20,736$ positions in which the 4 air valves could come to rest.

49. It will point to 3 if no slippage occurs.

50. There are 12 possible positions for the 2 wheels on the curb side of the car if the owner did move it and return later.

Collaborative Learning

1. Conventional Therapy ($250)

2. New drug with side effects ($600)

3. Answers may vary. You can only choose from two treatments. One might or might not have side effects. That is why there is room for discussion. A possible choice is new drug, no side effects.

4. Answers may vary. You can only choose from two treatments. One might or might not have side effects. That is why there is room for discussion. A possible choice is new drug with side effects.

5. Make improvements, rent for $2100, start lease Sept 1 ($24,000)

6. Make improvements, rent for $1950, start lease Nov 1 ($18,300)

Section 10.2 Permutations

1. $4 \cdot 3 \cdot 2 \cdot 1 = 24$ different orders can be written with the letters in the set $\{a, b, c, d\}$.

2. $4 \cdot 3 \cdot 2 \cdot 1 = 24$ different ways 4 people can be seated in a row.

3. $6 \cdot 5 \cdot 4 \cdot 3 \cdot 2 \cdot 1 = 720$ different ways that the horses can finish the race.

4. $7 \cdot 6 \cdot 5 \cdot 4 \cdot 3 \cdot 2 \cdot 1 = 5040$ different ways that 7 people can be lined up at the checkout counter in a supermarket.

5. $5 \cdot 4 \cdot 3 \cdot 2 \cdot 1 = 120$ different ways to list the 5 top reasons people hate scanning their own groceries.

6. $5 \cdot 4 \cdot 3 \cdot 2 \cdot 1 = 120$ different ways that the

agent can telephone the prospects.

7. $8! = 8 \cdot 7 \cdot 6 \cdot 5 \cdot 4 \cdot 3 \cdot 2 \cdot 1 = 40{,}320$

8. $10! = 10 \cdot 9 \cdot 8 \cdot 7 \cdot 6 \cdot 5 \cdot 4 \cdot 3 \cdot 2 \cdot 1 = 3{,}628{,}800$

9. $9! = 9 \cdot 8 \cdot 7 \cdot 6 \cdot 5 \cdot 4 \cdot 3 \cdot 2 \cdot 1 = 362{,}880$

10. $\dfrac{10!}{7!} = \dfrac{10 \cdot 9 \cdot 8 \cdot 7!}{7!} = 720$

11. $\dfrac{11!}{8!} = \dfrac{11 \cdot 10 \cdot 9 \cdot 8!}{8!} = 990$

12. $\dfrac{8!}{2!6!} = \dfrac{8 \cdot 7 \cdot 6!}{2 \cdot 1 \cdot 6!} = 4 \cdot 7 = 28$

13. $\dfrac{9!}{5!4!} = \dfrac{9 \cdot 8 \cdot 7 \cdot 6 \cdot 5!}{5! \cdot 4 \cdot 3 \cdot 2 \cdot 1} = 9 \cdot 7 \cdot 2 = 126$

14. $P(9,4) = 9 \cdot 8 \cdot 7 \cdot 6 = 3024$

15. $P(10,2) = 10 \cdot 9 = 90$

16. $\dfrac{P(6,3)}{4!} = \dfrac{6 \cdot 5 \cdot 4}{4 \cdot 3 \cdot 2 \cdot 1} = 5$

17. $\dfrac{P(5,2)}{2!} = \dfrac{5 \cdot 4}{2 \cdot 1} = 10$

18. $2 \cdot P(8,3) = 2 \cdot 8 \cdot 7 \cdot 6 = 672$

19. $3 \cdot P(8,5) = 3 \cdot 8 \cdot 7 \cdot 6 \cdot 5 \cdot 4 = 20{,}160$

20. $4 \cdot P(3,3) = 4 \cdot 3 \cdot 2 \cdot 1 = 24$

21. $5! = 5 \cdot 4 \cdot 3 \cdot 2 \cdot 1 = 120$ ways to stack the 5 books she must carry.

22. $P(10,3) = 10 \cdot 9 \cdot 8 = 720$ different ways that the first 3 places can come out.

23. a. $5! = 5 \cdot 4 \cdot 3 \cdot 2 \cdot 1 = 120$ permutations of the 5 qualities.

    b. $P(5,3) = 5 \cdot 4 \cdot 3 = 60$ different buildings.

    c. Yes, 7,601,445 is divisible by 3:
    $7{,}601{,}445 \div 3 = 2{,}533{,}815$

Yes, 7,601,445 is divisible by 5:
$7{,}601{,}445 \div 5 = 1{,}520{,}289$

24. $P(10,5) = 10 \cdot 9 \cdot 8 \cdot 7 \cdot 6 = 30{,}240$ different ways to fill the basketball positions.

25. $P(13,3) = 13 \cdot 12 \cdot 11 = 1716$ different ways to draw 3 hearts without replacement.

26. $P(4,2) = 4 \cdot 3 = 12$ different ways to draw 2 kings without replacement.

27. $P(26,2) = 26 \cdot 25 = 650$ different ways to draw 2 red cards without replacement.

28. $P(13,4) = 13 \cdot 12 \cdot 11 \cdot 10 = 17{,}160$ different ways to draw 4 diamonds without replacement.

29. $P(5,3) = 5 \cdot 4 \cdot 3 = 60$ different 3-digit numbers with no repetitions from the digits, 1, 3, 5, 7, and 9.

30. $4 \cdot 3 \cdot 2 = 24$ different even 3-digit numbers with no repetitions with from the digits 2, 4, 5, 7, and 9.

31. $3 \cdot 3 = 9$ different ways for both dice to come up even numbers.

32. $2 \cdot 3 \cdot 3 = 18$ different ways for one dice to come up an odd number and the other to come up an even number (distinguish between the 2 dice).

33. There is just one way to have no boys. Therefore, there are $2^5 - 1 = 32 - 1 = 31$ ways to have at least one boy.

34. There are $5 \cdot 5 = 25$ ways to have no 6s. Therefore, there are $6^2 - 25 = 36 - 25 = 11$ ways to have at least one 6.

35. There is just one way to have no tails. All the coins must come up heads.

36. The number of ways in which the six coins can fall is $2^6 = 64$. The number of ways of getting no heads is 1. Thus, the number of ways of getting at least 1 tail is $64 - 1 = 63$.

37. The number of ways in which the six coins can fall is $2^6 = 64$. The number of ways of getting no heads is 1 and the number of ways of getting exactly one head is 6. Thus, the number of ways of getting at least 2 heads is $64 - 1 - 6 = 57$.

38. The number of ways of getting no heads is 1 and the number of ways of getting exactly one head is 6. Thus, the number of ways of getting at most one head is $1 + 6 = 7$.

39. There are 50 multiples of 2; there are 20 multiples of 5; and there are 10 multiples of $2 \cdot 5$. Use the equation
$$n(A \cup B) = n(A) + n(B) - n(A \cap B)$$
with $n(A) = 50, n(B) = 20$, and $n(A \cap B) = 10$. Then,
$$n(A \cup B) = 50 + 20 - 10 = 60.$$

40. There are 50 multiples of 2; there are 33 multiples of 3; and there are 16 multiples of $2 \cdot 3$. Use the equation
$$n(A \cup B) = n(A) + n(B) - n(A \cap B)$$
with $n(A) = 50, n(B) = 33$, and $n(A \cap B) = 16$. Then,
$$n(A \cup B) = 50 + 33 - 16 = 67.$$

41. a. $10^6 = 1,000,000$

   b. $P(10,6) = 10 \cdot 9 \cdot 8 \cdot 7 \cdot 6 \cdot 5 = 151,200$

   c. There will only be 151,200 license plate numbers available, which is not enough for a population of 608,827.

42. a. $10 \cdot 26 \cdot 26 \cdot 26 \cdot 10 \cdot 10 \cdot 10 = 175,760,000$

   b. $10 \cdot 26 \cdot 25 \cdot 24 \cdot 9 \cdot 8 \cdot 7 = 78,624,000$

43. There are two events involved: pick the first letter (2 choices, K or W) and then pick 3 other letters with no repetitions $P(25, 3)$, since there are 25 letters left in the alphabet to choose the 3 letters from. The total number of possibilities is
$$2 \cdot P(25,3) = 2 \cdot 25 \cdot 24 \cdot 23 = 27,600.$$

44. a. 10^9 Social Security numbers are possible.

   b. $P(10,9) = 10 \cdot 9 \cdot 8 \cdot 7 \cdot 6 \cdot 5 \cdot 4 \cdot 3 \cdot 2 = 3,628,800$

   c. $10! - 9(8!) = 3,265,920$

45. (1) $n! = n(n-1)!$ for $n > 1$. This formula holds for $n = 1$ only if 0! is defined to be 1.

   (2) The formula $P(n,r) = \dfrac{n!}{(n-r)!}$ holds for $n = r$ only if 0! is defined to be 1.

46. $P(n,0) = 1$. $P(n,0) = \dfrac{n!}{(n-0)!} = \dfrac{n!}{n!} = 1$

47. The number of elements in the union of two sets is found by finding the sum of the number of elements in each of the sets, then subtracting the number of elements that have been counted twice (that is, the number of elements common to the two sets).

48. If the events are independent and the number of ways that each event can occur is known, then it is easier to use the additive counting principle.

49. $5! = 120$ different ways that the race could end.

50. $3 \cdot 2 \cdot 1 = 6$ different ways that the race could end. (Assuming there are no other ties.)

51. 3. A 4th, B 5th; B 4th, A 5th and a tie for 4th place.

52. 3. Cumberland 4th, Thora 5th; Thora 4th, Cumberland 5th and a tie for 4th place.

53. If one of the persons is seated, then the others can be seated in $(n-1)!$ ways. Except for rotation around the table, this is the total number of ways in which the n persons could be seated.

54. After A is seated, there is one way to seat B so that B faces A. Then there are two ways of seating the remaining two persons. Thus, there are $1 \cdot 2 = 2$ ways of seating the four persons.

55. After A is seated, there are two ways to seat B next to A (so that B does not face A). Then there are two ways of seating the remaining two persons. Thus, there are $2 \cdot 2 = 4$ ways of seating the four persons.

56. After A is seated, there are two ways to seat B next to A. Then there are two ways of seating the remaining two persons. Thus, there are $2 \cdot 2 = 4$ ways of seating the four persons.

Calculator Corner

1. Problem 7:
   $8 \boxed{2nd} \boxed{!} = 40{,}320$
   Problem 14:
   $9 \boxed{_nP_r} \boxed{4} = 3024$

Collaborative Learning

1. $P(5,3) = 5 \cdot 4 \cdot 3 = 60$

2. List: abc, acb, abe, aeb, etc.

3. Yes, abc is a different selection from cba.

4. $P(5,3) = 5 \cdot 4 \cdot 3 = 60$

5. List: abc, acb, abe, aeb, etc.

6. Yes, abc is a different selection from cba.

7. For the letters, a, b, c, there are 6 combinations if order is important: abc, acb, cab, cba, bac, bca. Thus, $60 \div 6 = 10$ different choices.

8. List: abc, acb, cab, cba, bac, bca, etc.

9. No. abc is the same choice as cba.

Section 10.3 Combinations

1. $C(5,2) = \dfrac{5 \cdot 4}{2 \cdot 1} = 10$; $P(5,2) = 5 \cdot 4 = 20$

2. $C(6,4) = \dfrac{6 \cdot 5 \cdot 4 \cdot 3}{4 \cdot 3 \cdot 2 \cdot 1} = 15$;
   $P(6,4) = 6 \cdot 5 \cdot 4 \cdot 3 = 360$

3. $C(7,3) = \dfrac{7 \cdot 6 \cdot 5}{3 \cdot 2 \cdot 1} = 35$;
   $P(7,3) = 7 \cdot 6 \cdot 5 = 210$

4. $C(5,0) = \dfrac{5!}{0!5!} = 1$; $P(5,0) = \dfrac{5!}{5!} = 1$

5. $C(9,6) = \dfrac{9 \cdot 8 \cdot 7}{3 \cdot 2 \cdot 1} = 84$;
   $P(9,6) = 9 \cdot 8 \cdot 7 \cdot 6 \cdot 5 \cdot 4 = 60{,}480$

6. $C(7,0) = \dfrac{7!}{0!7!} = 1$; $P(7,0) = \dfrac{7!}{7!} = 1$

7. $C(5,4) = \dfrac{5 \cdot 4!}{4! \, 1!} = 5$ combinations with 4 of the 5 tips given in the list.

8. $C(5,2) = \dfrac{5!}{2!3!} = 10$ combinations with 2 of the 5 tips given in the list.

9. $C(5,3) = \dfrac{5!}{3!2!} = 10$ combinations if the 5 tips in the list are taken 3 at a time.

10. $C(5,3) = \dfrac{5!}{3!2!} = 10$ combinations with 3 of the 5 tips given in the list.

11. $C(8,2) = \dfrac{8 \cdot 7 \cdot 6!}{2 \cdot 1 \cdot 6!} = \dfrac{56}{2} = 28$ subsets of 2 elements from a set of 8 elements.

12. $C(7,5) = \dfrac{7 \cdot 6 \cdot 5!}{5!2!} = 21$ subsets of 5 elements from a set of 7 elements.

13. $C(12,8) = \dfrac{12 \cdot 11 \cdot 10 \cdot 9 \cdot 8!}{4 \cdot 3 \cdot 2 \cdot 1 \cdot 8!} = 495$ different 8-element subsets from a set of 12 elements.

14. $C(15,10) = \dfrac{15 \cdot 14 \cdot 13 \cdot 12 \cdot 11 \cdot 10!}{10!5!} = 3003$ different 10-element subsets from a set of 15 elements.

15. a. $C(12,3) = \dfrac{12 \cdot 11 \cdot 10 \cdot 9!}{3!9!} = 220$ subsets of 3 elements.

    b. $C(12,0) + C(12,1) + C(12,2)$
       $= 1 + 12 + \dfrac{12 \cdot 11 \cdot 10!}{2!10!} = 13 + 66 = 79$

subsets of less than 3 elements.

c. $C(12,0) = \dfrac{12!}{0!12!} = 1$ subset with no elements.

d. $C(12,10) + C(12,11) + C(12,12)$

$= \dfrac{12 \cdot 11 \cdot 10!}{10!2!} + \dfrac{12 \cdot 11!}{11!1!} + \dfrac{12!}{12!0!}$

$= 66 + 12 + 1 = 79$ subsets of more than 9 elements.

16. $C(5,3) = \dfrac{5!}{3!2!} = 10$ different sums of money if exactly 3 coins are used.

17. $C(5,4) = \dfrac{5!}{4!1!} = 5$ different sums of money if 4 coins are used.

18. $C(5,2) + C(5,3) + C(5,4) + C(5,5)$

$= 10 + 10 + 5 + 1 = 26$ different sums of money if at least 2 coins are used.

19. a. $C(5,3) = C(5,2) = \dfrac{5 \cdot 4}{2 \cdot 1} = 10$ subsets of 3 elements.

b. $C(5,0) + C(5,1) + C(5,2) + C(5,3)$

$= 1 + 5 + 10 + 10 = 26$ subsets that have no more than 3 elements.

20. $C(20,2) = \dfrac{20 \cdot 19 \cdot 18!}{2! \, 18!} = 190$ handshakes.

21. $C(24,3) = \dfrac{24 \cdot 23 \cdot 22 \cdot 21!}{3 \cdot 2 \cdot 1 \cdot 21!} = 2024$ ways to select 3 different Greek letters when order does not matter.

22. $C(10,5) = \dfrac{10 \cdot 9 \cdot 8 \cdot 7 \cdot 6 \cdot 5!}{5!5!} = 252$ different sets of 5 members.

23. $C(10,3) = \dfrac{10 \cdot 9 \cdot 8 \cdot 7!}{3!7!} = 120$ different committees.

24. $C(40,3) = \dfrac{40 \cdot 39 \cdot 38 \cdot 37!}{3!37!} = 9880$ different selections of 3 different books.

25. $C(52,5) = \dfrac{52 \cdot 51 \cdot 50 \cdot 49 \cdot 48 \cdot 47!}{5 \cdot 4 \cdot 3 \cdot 2 \cdot 1 \cdot 47!}$

$= 2,598,960$ different 5-card poker hands.

26. $C(8,2) = \dfrac{8 \cdot 7 \cdot 6!}{2!6!} = 28$ different sets of 2 sandwiches.

27. $C(100,5) = \dfrac{100 \cdot 99 \cdot 98 \cdot 97 \cdot 96 \cdot 95!}{5 \cdot 4 \cdot 3 \cdot 2 \cdot 1 \cdot 95!}$

$= 75,287,520$ different 5-member committees.

28. $C(12,7) = \dfrac{12 \cdot 11 \cdot 10 \cdot 9 \cdot 8 \cdot 7!}{7!5!} = 792$ different subcommittees of 7.

29. $C(4,1) + C(4,2) + C(4,3) + C(4,4)$

$= 2^4 - 1 = 16 - 1 = 15$ different sums of money.

30. $C(6,2) = \dfrac{6 \cdot 5 \cdot 4!}{2!4!} = 15$ different sums of money.

31. $C(6,1) + C(6,2) + C(6,3) + C(6,4)$

$\quad + C(6,5) + C(6,6)$

$= 2^6 - 1 = 64 - 1 = 63$ different sums of money.

32. $C(8,3) + C(8,4) + C(8,5) + C(8,6)$

$\quad + C(8,7) + C(8,8)$

$= 56 + 70 + 56 + 28 + 8 + 1 = 219$ different committees of at least 3 people.

33. This is the number of ways that 4 of the 8 people can be selected without regard to order:

$C(8,4) = \dfrac{8 \cdot 7 \cdot 6 \cdot 5 \cdot 4!}{4 \cdot 3 \cdot 2 \cdot 1 \cdot 4!} = 70$

34. a. $C(8,2) - 8 = \dfrac{8 \cdot 7 \cdot 6!}{2!6!} - 8 = 28 - 8 = 20$

b. $C(n,2) - n = \dfrac{n \cdot (n-1) \cdot (n-2)!}{2!(n-2)!} - n$

$= \dfrac{n(n-1)}{2} - \dfrac{2n}{2} = \dfrac{n^2 - n - 2n}{2}$

$= \dfrac{n^2 - 3n}{2} = \dfrac{n(n-3)}{2}$

35. Answers will vary. The important difference

is that permutations take account of order and combinations do not.

36. a.   No. It might need some other permutation of the numbers 1, 2, 3.
    b.   1, 2, 3; 2, 3, 1; 3, 1, 2; 1, 3, 2; 3, 2, 1; 2, 1, 3. Yes, one of these would open the lock because these are the only possible permutations.

37. The order of the numbers is important, so a permutation is being used.

38. a.   Since $C(n,r) = \dfrac{P(n,r)}{r!}$,

    $C(n,r) = P(n,r)$ if and only if $r! = 1$, that is, $r = 0$ or $r = 1$.

    b.   The same formula as in (a) shows that $P(n,r) = r! \cdot C(n,r)$. Hence,

    $P(n,r) > C(n,r)$ if $r > 1$.

39.

$$1+5 \quad 5+10 \quad 10+10 \quad 10+5 \quad 5+1$$
$$\downarrow \quad \downarrow \quad \downarrow \quad \downarrow \quad \downarrow$$
$$n=6 \quad 1 \quad 6 \quad 15 \quad 20 \quad 15 \quad 6 \quad 1$$

$$1+6 \quad 6+15 \quad 15+20 \quad 20+15 \quad 15+6 \quad 6+1$$
$$\downarrow \quad \downarrow \quad \downarrow \quad \downarrow \quad \downarrow \quad \downarrow$$
$$n=7 \quad 1 \; 7 \quad 21 \quad 35 \quad 35 \quad 21 \quad 7 \; 1$$

40. a. $C(6, 4) = 15$ b. $C(7, 3) = 35$

41. a. $(a+b)^4$

    $= a^4 + 4a^3b + 6a^2b^2 + 4ab^3 + b^4$

    b. $(a+b)^5 = a^5 + 5a^4b + 10a^3b^2$
    $+10a^2b^3 + 5ab^4 + b^5$

42. $(a+b)^6 = a^6 + 6a^5b + 15a^4b^2 + 20a^3b^3$
    $+15a^2b^4 + 6ab^5 + b^6$

43. $C(5,0) = \dfrac{5!}{0!5!} = 1$ different way for the outcome to be 0 heads and 5 tails.

44. $C(5,1) = \dfrac{5 \cdot 4!}{1!4!} = 5$ different ways for the outcome to be 1 head and 4 tails.

45. $C(5,3) = \dfrac{5 \cdot 4 \cdot 3!}{2 \cdot 1 \cdot 3!} = 10$ different ways for the outcome to be 31 head and 2 tails.

46. $C(5,4) = \dfrac{5 \cdot 4!}{4!1!} = 5$ different ways for the outcome to be 4 head and 1 tails.

47. $C(5,5) = \dfrac{5!}{5!0!} = 1$ different way for the outcome to be 5 heads and 0 tails.

48. The coin can fall in either of two ways. If it is flipped 5 times, the total number of possible outcomes is 2^5 or 32.

49. The left side is the sum of the number of ways in which there could be 0 heads and n tails, 1 head and $n - 1$ tails, 2 heads and $n - 2$ tails, and so on, to n heads and 0 tails. The right side is exactly the number of ways in which n coins can fall either heads or tails. Thus,

$$C(n,0) + C(n,1) + C(n,2) + \ldots + C(n,n) = 2^n$$

Calculator Corner

1. Example 6:

    a. $\boxed{26}\boxed{{}_nC_r}\boxed{3}\boxed{\text{ENTER}}$ Answer: 2600

    b. $\boxed{8}\boxed{{}_nC_r}\boxed{2}\boxed{\text{ENTER}}$ Answer: 28

Example 7:

$\boxed{52}\boxed{{}_nP_r}\boxed{2}\boxed{\div}\boxed{2!}\boxed{\text{ENTER}}$ Answer: 1326

Example 8:

    a. $\boxed{6}\boxed{{}_nC_r}\boxed{1}\boxed{\text{ENTER}}$ Answer: 6

    b. $\boxed{6}\boxed{{}_nP_r}\boxed{2}\boxed{\div}\boxed{2!}\boxed{\text{ENTER}}$ Answer: 15

    c. $\boxed{6}\boxed{{}_nP_r}\boxed{3}\boxed{\div}\boxed{3!}\boxed{\text{ENTER}}$ Answer: 20

    d. $\boxed{6}\boxed{{}_nC_r}\boxed{4}\boxed{\text{ENTER}}$ Answer: 15

    $\boxed{6}\boxed{{}_nC_r}\boxed{2}\boxed{\text{ENTER}}$ Answer: 15

Collaborative Learning

1. $10 \cdot 10 \cdot 10 \cdot 10 \cdot 10 \cdot 10 = 10^6$

2.   Answers will vary.

3.   Answer may vary. If every member of the population has at least one car,

probably not, because $2 \cdot 568,156 =$,
$1,136,312$ which is greater than 10^6.
However, the population is given as
$568,158$ but first, not all of the population
are motorists (under age, etc.) and
therefore not be in need of a license plate,
second, not all motorists have an
individual car and therefore are not in
need of a license plate, and third, not
every person who has an individual car
has multiple cars that need license plates.
Thus, there may be enough license plates
for all motorists.

4.   Answers will vary.

5.   Answers will vary.

6.   a. $10 \cdot 26 \cdot 26 \cdot 26 \cdot 10 \cdot 10 \cdot 10$
$= 175,760,000$
$26 \cdot 26 \cdot 26 \cdot 10 \cdot 10 \cdot 10 = 17,576,000$
   b.   First method; answers will vary.

Section 10.4 Miscellaneous Counting Methods

1.   a.   Order important:
$P(52,3) = 52 \cdot 51 \cdot 50 = 132,600$
different orders of 3 cards dealt.
   b.   Order not important:
$C(52,3) = \dfrac{52 \cdot 51 \cdot 50 \cdot 49!}{3 \cdot 2 \cdot 1 \cdot 49!} = 22,100$
different 3-card hands.

2.   a.   Order not important:
$C(6,4) = \dfrac{6 \cdot 5 \cdot 4!}{4!2!} = 15$ ways for 4 of
them to be assigned to the research
department.
   b.   Order important:
$P(6,3) = 6 \cdot 5 \cdot 4 = 120$ ways for 3 of
them to be assigned to different
companies.

3.   a. $50 \cdot 50 \cdot 50 = 125,000$ different ways to
select 3 plays for the next 3 downs. (The
plays do not have to be all different.)
   b.   Order not important :
$C(50,3) = \dfrac{50 \cdot 49 \cdot 48 \cdot 47!}{3 \cdot 2 \cdot 1 \cdot 47!} = 19,600$
different ways to select a set of 3

plays to study. (The plays would be
different.)

4.   a.   Order important:
$P(6,3) = 6 \cdot 5 \cdot 4 = 120$ different ways
to take 3 different courses on Mondays.
   b.   Order not important:
$C(6,3) = \dfrac{6 \cdot 5 \cdot 4 \cdot 3!}{3!3!} = 20$ different ways
to take 3 different courses on Mondays.

5. $C(5,3) = \dfrac{5 \cdot 4 \cdot 3!}{2 \cdot 1 \cdot 3!} = 10$ different ways
to take 3 different courses on Mondays.

6.   a.   Order important: $P(3,3) = 3 \cdot 2 \cdot 1 = 6$
different schedules.
   b.   Order important: $P(2,2) = 2 \cdot 1 = 2$
different schedules with mathematics at
11 am with Mr. Eldridge.

7.   a.   Order not important:
$C(7,3) = \dfrac{7 \cdot 6 \cdot 5 \cdot 4!}{3 \cdot 2 \cdot 1 \cdot 4!} = 35$ ways to select 3
electives from a group of 7 courses.
   b.   Peter can select the 3 hours in
$P(7,4) = 840$ ways.

8.   a.   Order not important:
$C(100,3) = \dfrac{100 \cdot 99 \cdot 98 \cdot 97!}{3!97!} = 161,700$
choices in order to take 3 courses in area
V.
   b.   Order not important:
$C(40,2) \cdot C(100,2)$
$= \dfrac{40 \cdot 39 \cdot 38!}{2!38!} \cdot \dfrac{100 \cdot 99 \cdot 98!}{2!98!}$
$= 780 \cdot 4950 = 3,861,000$ choices in order
to take the minimum number of courses in
areas IV and V.

9.   a. $P(14,2) \cdot P(10,2) = 14 \cdot 13 \cdot 10 \cdot 9 = 16,380$
possibilities.
   b. $P(12,2) \cdot P(10,2) = 12 \cdot 11 \cdot 10 \cdot 9 = 11,880$
possibilities if 2 of the boys refuse to
participate.

10.   a.   Order not important:

$$C(6,2) \cdot C(4,2) = \frac{6 \cdot 5 \cdot 4!}{2!4!} \cdot \frac{4 \cdot 3 \cdot 2!}{2!2!}$$
$$= 15 \cdot 6 = 90 \text{ ways for a}$$

committee of 4 where 2 members are officers and 2 are directors.

b.   Order not important:

$$C(6,3) \cdot C(4,1) = \frac{6 \cdot 5 \cdot 4 \cdot 3!}{3!3!} \cdot \frac{4 \cdot 3!}{1!3!}$$
$$= 20 \cdot 4 = 80 \text{ ways for a committee of}$$

4 where 3 members are officers and 1 is a director.

c.   Order not important:

$$C(6,4) = \frac{6 \cdot 5 \cdot 4 \cdot 3 \cdot 2!}{4!2!} = 15 \text{ ways for}$$

a committee of 4 where all members are officers.

d.   Order not important:

$$C(10,4) = \frac{10 \cdot 9 \cdot 8 \cdot 7 \cdot 6!}{4!6!} = 210 \text{ ways}$$

for a committee of 4 with no restrictions.

11. a. $$C(7,3) \cdot C(8,1) = \frac{7 \cdot 6 \cdot 5 \cdot 4!}{3 \cdot 2 \cdot 1 \cdot 4!} \cdot \frac{8}{1} = 280$$

ways to fill 4 vacancies with 1 woman and 3 men if 7 men and 8 women are available to serve.

h. $$C(5,3) \cdot C(2,1) = \frac{5 \cdot 4 \cdot 3!}{2 \cdot 1 \cdot 3!} \cdot \frac{2}{1} = 20$$

ways to fill 4 vacancies with 1 woman and 3 men if 5 men and 2 women are available to serve.

12. $$C(6,3) \cdot C(6,2) \cdot C(5,1)$$

$$= \frac{6 \cdot 5 \cdot 4 \cdot 3!}{3!3!} \cdot \frac{6 \cdot 5 \cdot 4!}{2!4!} \cdot \frac{5 \cdot 4!}{1!4!}$$
$$= 20 \cdot 15 \cdot 5 = 1500 \text{ ways to choose a meal}$$
consisting of a pizza with 3 toppings, 2 beverages, and a dessert.

13. There are 11 letters in all: 1 T, 3 A's, 2 L's, 1 H, 2 S's, and 2 E's, so the answer is

$$\frac{11!}{1!3!2!1!2!2!} = 831,600$$

14. There are 11 letters in all: 1 M, 4 I's, 4 S's, and 2 P's, so the answer is

$$\frac{11!}{1!4!4!2!} = 34,650$$

15. There are 9 letters in all: 2 R's, 2E's, 2 D's. 2 I's, and 1 V, so the answer is

$$\frac{9!}{2!2!2!2!1!} = 22,680$$

16. There are 12 letters in all: 1 I, 1 J, 3 O's, 3 U's, 1 A, 2 E's, and 1 N, so the answer is

$$\frac{12!}{1!1!3!3!1!2!1!} = 6,652,800$$

17. The contractor can select 2 components from the first subcontractor in C(7, 2) ways, 3 components from the second subcontractor in C(5, 3) ways, and 2 components from the third subcontractor in C(2, 2) ways. Thus, he can select his 7 components in

$$C(7,2) \cdot C(5,3) \cdot C(2,2)$$

$$= \frac{7 \cdot 6}{2 \cdot 1} \cdot \frac{5 \cdot 4 \cdot 3}{3 \cdot 2 \cdot 1} \cdot \frac{2 \cdot 1}{2 \cdot 1} = 21 \cdot 10 \cdot 1 = 210 \text{ ways.}$$

18. We have to choose the least value of n for which $C(n, 3) \geq 20$, that is, for which $$\frac{n(n-1)(n-2)}{3!} \geq 20. \text{ To simplify the}$$ calculation, multiply both sides by $3! = 6$: $n(n-1)(n-2) \geq 120$. Try $n = 5$. The left side becomes $5 \cdot 4 \cdot 3 = 60$. Too small! Try $n = 6$. The left side becomes $6 \cdot 5 \cdot 4 = 120$. Thus, to carry out the contract, the network must have at least 6 different ads.

19. We have to choose the least value of n for which $C(n, 5) \geq 21$, that is, for which $$\frac{n(n-1)(n-2)(n-3)(n-4)}{5!} \geq 21. \text{ To}$$ simplify the calculation, multiply both sides by $5! = 120$: $$n(n-1)(n-2)(n-3)(n-4) \geq 2520.$$ Try $n = 6$. The left side becomes $6 \cdot 5 \cdot 4 \cdot 3 \cdot 2 = 720$. Too small! Try $n = 7$. The left side becomes $7 \cdot 6 \cdot 5 \cdot 4 \cdot 3 = 2520$. Thus, to carry out the program, the network must have at least **7** different movies.

20. We have to choose the least value of n for which $C(n, 5) \geq 56$, that is, for which $$\frac{n(n-1)(n-2)(n-3)(n-4)}{5!} \geq 56. \text{ To}$$ simplify the calculation, multiply both sides by

5! = 120:

$$n(n-1)(n-2)(n-3)(n-4) \geq 6720.$$

Try $n = 7$. The left side becomes
$7 \cdot 6 \cdot 5 \cdot 4 \cdot 3 = 2520$. Too small!
Try $n = 8$. The left side becomes
$8 \cdot 7 \cdot 6 \cdot 5 \cdot 4 = 6720$. Thus, to carry out the
program, the network must have at least 8
different movies.

21. She can select 2 of the 3 courses and the
order in which they come in the morning.
Then she can select 2 of the 4 morning
hours for these 2 courses. That leaves her
the choice of 1 of the 2 afternoon hours
for the third course. Thus, she has

$$P(3,2) \cdot C(4,2) \cdot C(2,1) = 3 \cdot 2 \cdot \frac{4 \cdot 3}{2 \cdot 1} \cdot \frac{2}{1}$$

$$= 6 \cdot 6 \cdot 2 = 72 \text{ choices.}$$

22. Roy can select 1 course from Group I and
2 from group II or 2 courses from Group I
and 1 from Group II. Thus, Roy has

$$C(4,1) \cdot C(3,2) + C(4,2) \cdot C(3,1)$$

$$= \frac{4!}{1!3!} \cdot \frac{3!}{2!1!} + \frac{4!}{2!2!} \cdot \frac{3!}{1!2!}$$

$$= 4 \cdot 3 + 6 \cdot 3 = 12 + 18 = 30$$

23. a. The first decision is to select a mutual
fund (M), a management company
(C) or a CD. The mutual fund can
have high (10%) or low (6%) yields,
the management company can have
high (10%) or low yields (5%) and
the CD can have high (4%) or low
(3%) yield. The highest (↑) and
lowest (↓) investments are shown in
the tree diagram:

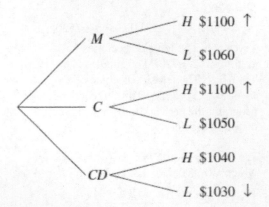

b. $1100. Mutual Fund ($M$), high ($H$) or
management co. (C), high (H)

c. $1030. CD, low (L)

24. a.

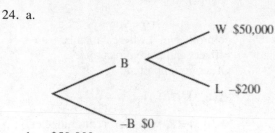

b. $50,000

c. –$200

25. a. The market for the product may be
extremely high (EH) or low (LO). From
there, sales can be high (H), medium (M)
or low (L)   The highest and lowest
amounts are shown in the tree diagram:

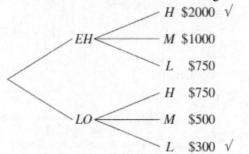

b. $2000. Market size extremely high (EH),
sales high (H).

c. $300. Market size low ($LO$), sales low
(L)

26. a.

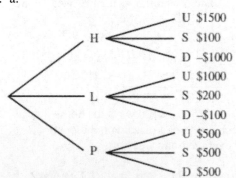

b. $1500. High stocks that go up.

c. –$1000. High stocks that go down.

27. Answers will vary. Read the text to see what
each of the SCP, $P(n, k)$ and $C(n, k)$ formulas
calculates.

28. If a set of n objects consists of r different
types, with objects of the same type being
indistinguishable, let n_k be the number of

objects of type k for $k = 1, 2, 3, \ldots, r$. Then the total number of distinct permutations of the n objects is given by the formula $\dfrac{n!}{n_1!\,n_2!\ldots n_r!}$.

29. $144 = 2^4 \cdot 3^2$. The factor 2 can be used 0, 1, 2, 3, or 4 times, and the factor 3 can be used 0, 1, or 2 times. So the number of exact divisors is $(4+1)(2+1) = 5 \cdot 3 = 15$.

30. $2520 = 2^3 \cdot 3^2 \cdot 5 \cdot 7$. The factor 2 can be used 0, 1, 2, or 3 times, the factor 3 can be used 0, 1, or 2 times, the factor 5 can be used 0 or 1 time, and the factor 7 can be used 0 or 1 time. So the number of exact divisors is $(3+1)(2+1)(1+1)(1+1)$
$= 4 \cdot 3 \cdot 2 \cdot 2 = 48$.

31. The 2 can be a factor 0, 1, 2, . . ., or a times; $(a + 1)$ choices.
The 3 can be a factor 0, 1, 2, . . ., or b times; $(b + 1)$ choices.
The 5 can be a factor 0, 1, 2, . . ., or c times; $(c + 1)$ choices.
The 7 can be a factor 0, 1, 2, . . ., or d times; $(d + 1)$ choices.
Thus, the number of exact divisors is
$$(a+1)(b+1)(c+1)(d+1).$$

32. For the number $2^4 \cdot 3^2 \cdot 7^3$, the factor 2 can be used 0, 1, 2, 3, or 4 times, the factor 3 can be used 0, 1, or 2 times, and the factor 7 can be used 0, 1, 2, or 3 times. So the number of exact divisors is $(4+1)(2+1)(3+1) = 5 \cdot 3 \cdot 4 = 60$.

Collaborative Learning

1.   10. Vaccinate, no complications, no disease or don't vaccinate, no disease.

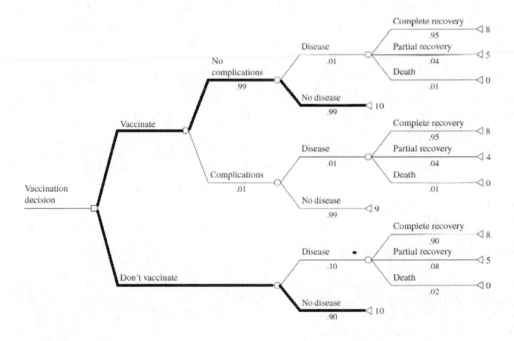

2.   Answers will vary.

3.   0. There are 3 ways to get a score of 0: Vaccinate, no complications, disease, death; Vaccinate, complications, disease, death; or Don't vaccinate, disease, death (See the diagram.)

4. Answer will vary. The two ways to get a score of 5: Vaccinate, no complications, disease, partial recovery or vaccinate, complications, disease, partial recovery; or don't vaccinate, disease, partial recovery.

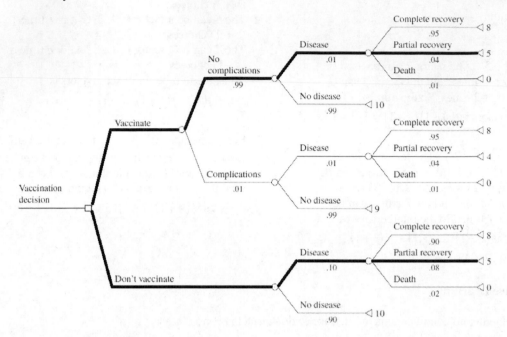

Chapter 10 Practice Test

1.

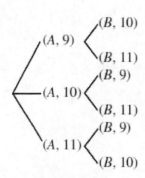

(A, 9)
    (B, 10)
    (B, 11)
(A, 10)
    (B, 9)
    (B, 11)
(A, 11)
    (B, 9)
    (B, 10)

2. $2 \cdot 3 \cdot 5 = 30$ different meals are possible.

3. a. Since each die can fall in 6 different ways, $6 \cdot 6 = 36$ different results are possible.
   b. To get a sum of 5, one die must come up 1 and the other 4, or one must come up 2 and the other 3. Since each of these events can occur in 2 ways, the total number of ways is $2 \cdot 2 = 4$.

4. There are 2 black jacks and 26 red cards, so the total number of ways to get a black jack followed by a red card is $2 \cdot 26 = 52$.

5. You have a choice of 3 flights followed by a choice of 5 flights, so the answer is $3 \cdot 5 = 15$.

6. a. $7! = 7 \cdot 6 \cdot 5 \cdot 4 \cdot 3 \cdot 2 \cdot 1 = 5040$
   b. $\dfrac{7!}{4!} = \dfrac{7 \cdot 6 \cdot 5 \cdot 4 \cdot 3 \cdot 2 \cdot 1}{4 \cdot 3 \cdot 2 \cdot 1} = 210$

7. a. $3! \cdot 4! = 3 \cdot 2 \cdot 1 \cdot 4 \cdot 3 \cdot 2 \cdot 1 = 144$
   b. $3! + 4! = 3 \cdot 2 \cdot 1 + 4 \cdot 3 \cdot 2 \cdot 1$
   $$= 6 + 24 = 30$$

8. a. $P(5,5) = 5! = 5 \cdot 4 \cdot 3 \cdot 2 \cdot 1 = 120$
   b. $P(6,6) = 6! = 6 \cdot 5 \cdot 4 \cdot 3 \cdot 2 \cdot 1 = 720$

9. a. $P(8,2) = 8 \cdot 7 = 56$
   b. $P(7,3) = 7 \cdot 6 \cdot 5 = 210$

10. They can be arranged in $P(4,4) = 4! = 4 \cdot 3 \cdot 2 \cdot 1 = 24$ ways.

11. Each couple can be seated in 2 ways, and the 3 couples can be arranged in $P(3, 3)$ ways, so the answer is $2^3 \cdot 3! = 8 \cdot 6 = 48$.

12. There are 2 white birds to choose from and 3 ways to select them (first, second or third) and there are $P(4,2)$ ways of selecting two non-white birds. Thus, the number of ways to select exactly one white bird is $2 \cdot 3 \cdot P(4,2) = 6 \cdot 12 = 72$.

13. 24 of the numbers are divisible by 2, 9 of the numbers are divisible by 5, and 4 of the numbers are divisible by both 2 and 5. Thus, the number divisible by 2 or by 5 is $24 + 9 - 4 = 29$.

14. The number of different sums is
$$C(4,2) = \frac{4 \cdot 3}{2 \cdot 1} = 6.$$

15. The number of subsets is
$$C(6,3) = \frac{6 \cdot 5 \cdot 4}{3 \cdot 2 \cdot 1} = 20.$$

16. a. $C(5,2) = \frac{5 \cdot 4}{2 \cdot 1} = 10$

   b. $C(6,4) = C(6,2) = \frac{6 \cdot 5}{2 \cdot 1} = 15$

17. a. $C(6,0) = 1$

   b. $C(5,4) = C(5,1) = 5$

   $C(5,3) = C(5,2) = \frac{5 \cdot 4}{2 \cdot 1} = 10$

   $\frac{C(5,4)}{C(5,3)} = \frac{5}{10} = \frac{1}{2}$

18. The number of different sets is
$$C(52,2) = \frac{52 \cdot 51}{2 \cdot 1} = 1326.$$

19. The number of different schedules is
$$P(4,4) = 4! = 4 \cdot 3 \cdot 2 \cdot 1 = 24.$$

20. The number of different sums is
$$C(5,1) + C(5,2) + C(5,3)$$
$$= \frac{5}{1} + \frac{5 \cdot 4}{2 \cdot 1} + \frac{5 \cdot 4 \cdot 3}{3 \cdot 2 \cdot 1} = 5 + 10 + 10 = 25.$$

21. There are 5 choices for the foreman, followed by $C(4, 2)$ choices for the helpers. Thus, the total number of choices is
$$5 \cdot C(4,2) = 5 \cdot \frac{4 \cdot 3}{2 \cdot 1} = 30.$$

22. The number of choices is
$$C(8,4) = \frac{8 \cdot 7 \cdot 6 \cdot 5}{4 \cdot 3 \cdot 2 \cdot 1} = 70.$$

23. There are 8 letters: 2 B's, 4 O's, 1 G and 1 A, so the number of distinct arrangements is
$$\frac{8!}{2!4!1!1!} = \frac{8 \cdot 7 \cdot 6 \cdot 5 \cdot 4 \cdot 3 \cdot 2 \cdot 1}{2 \cdot 1 \cdot 4 \cdot 3 \cdot 2 \cdot 1 \cdot 1 \cdot 1} = 840.$$

24. There are 11 letters: 4 M's, 4 A's, 2 D's and 1 I, so the number of distinct arrangements is
$$\frac{11!}{4!4!2!1!} = \frac{11 \cdot 10 \cdot 9 \cdot 8 \cdot 7 \cdot 6 \cdot 5 \cdot 4 \cdot 3 \cdot 2 \cdot 1}{4 \cdot 3 \cdot 2 \cdot 1 \cdot 4 \cdot 3 \cdot 2 \cdot 1 \cdot 2 \cdot 1 \cdot 1}$$
$$= 34,650.$$

25. There are 1977 marks in all: 1189 a's, 460 d's, and 328 n's, so the number of distinct arrangements is $\dfrac{1977!}{1189!460!328!}$.

Chapter 11 Probability

Section 11.1 Sample Spaces and Probability

1. There are 6 possible outcomes of which exactly one is favorable, so $P(E) = \dfrac{1}{6}$.

2. There are 3 possible outcomes of which exactly one is favorable, so
$$P(E) = \frac{3}{6} = \frac{1}{2}.$$

3. There are 2 favorable outcomes and 6 possible outcomes, so $P(E) = \dfrac{2}{6} = \dfrac{1}{3}$.

4. There are 4 favorable outcomes and 6 possible outcomes, so $P(E) = \dfrac{4}{6} = \dfrac{2}{3}$.

5. There are 10 possible outcomes of which exactly one is favorable, so $P(E) = \dfrac{1}{10}$.

6. There are 5 favorable outcomes and 10 possible outcomes, so $P(E) = \dfrac{5}{10} = \dfrac{1}{2}$.

7. There are 9 favorable outcomes and 10 possible outcomes, so $P(E) = \dfrac{9}{10}$.

8. There are 9 favorable outcomes and 10 possible outcomes, so $P(E) = \dfrac{9}{10}$.

9. There are no favorable outcomes possible, so $P(E) = 0$.

10. There are 7 favorable outcomes and 10 possible outcomes, so $P(E) = \dfrac{7}{10}$.

11. There are 4 aces and 52 cards in all, so $P(\text{ace}) = \dfrac{4}{52} = \dfrac{1}{13}$.

12. There is one king of spades and 52 cards in all, so $P(\text{king of spades}) = \dfrac{1}{52}$.

13. There are 13 spades out of 52 cards, so
$$P(\text{spade}) = \frac{13}{52} = \frac{1}{4}.$$

14. There are 12 face cards out of 52 cards, so
$$P(\text{face card}) = \frac{12}{52} = \frac{3}{13}.$$

15. There are 13 spades and 9 face cards that are not spades, so there are 13 + 9 = 22 favorable outcomes out of 52 possible outcomes.
Therefore, $P(E) = \dfrac{22}{52} = \dfrac{11}{26}$.

16. There are 26 red cards and 6 picture cards that are not red, so there are 26 + 6 = 32 favorable outcomes out of 52 possible outcomes.
Therefore, $P(E) = \dfrac{32}{52} = \dfrac{8}{13}$.

17. a. There is 1 favorable outcome out of 5 possible outcomes, so $P(E) = \dfrac{1}{5}$.

    b. There are 3 favorable outcomes out of 5 possible outcomes so $P(E) = \dfrac{3}{5}$.

    c. There are 4 favorable outcomes out of 5 possible outcomes, so $P(E) = \dfrac{4}{5}$.

18. a.

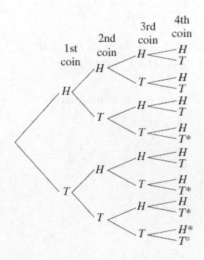

b. There are 11 favorable outcomes out of 16 possible outcomes so

$$P(E) = \frac{11}{16}.$$

c. There are 4 favorable outcomes out of 16 possible outcomes so

$$P(E) = \frac{4}{16} = \frac{1}{4}.$$

19. a. There is 1 favorable outcome out of 3 possible outcomes, so $P(E) = \frac{1}{3}.$

b. There is 1 favorable outcome out of 3 possible outcomes, so $P(E) = \frac{1}{3}.$

20. There is 1 favorable outcome and 8 possible outcomes, so $P(E) = \frac{1}{8}.$

21. There is 1 favorable outcome and 8 possible outcomes, so $P(E) = \frac{1}{8}.$

22. There is 7 favorable outcomes and 8 possible outcomes, so $P(E) = \frac{7}{8}.$

23. There are 3 favorable outcomes and 8 possible outcomes, so $P(E) = \frac{3}{8}.$

24. a.

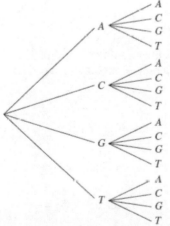

b. There is 1 favorable outcome and 16 possible outcomes, so $P(E) = \frac{1}{16}.$

c. There is 1 favorable outcome and 16 possible outcomes, so $P(E) = \frac{1}{16}.$

d. There is 1 favorable outcome and 16 possible outcomes, so $P(E) = \frac{1}{16}.$

25. A sum of 7 is either a 1 and 6, 2 and 5, 3 and 4, 4 and 3, 5 and 2, or 6 and 1. There are 6 favorable outcomes and 36 possible outcomes, so $P(E) = \frac{6}{36} = \frac{1}{6}.$

26. A sum of 2 is a 1 and 1. There is 1 favorable outcome and 36 possible outcomes, so

$$P(E) = \frac{1}{36}.$$

27. There are 6 possible ways to have the same number on both dice and there are 36 possible outcomes. So, $P(E) = \frac{6}{36} = \frac{1}{6}.$

28. There are 30 possible ways to have the different numbers on the two dice and there are 36 possible outcomes. So, $P(E) = \frac{30}{36} = \frac{5}{6}.$

29. There are 18 possible ways to obtain an even sum on the dice and there are 36 possible outcomes. So, $P(E) = \frac{18}{36} = \frac{1}{2}.$

30. There are 18 possible ways to obtain an odd sum on the dice and there are 36 possible outcomes. So, $P(E) = \frac{18}{36} = \frac{1}{2}.$

31. a. $P(B) = \frac{25}{100} = \frac{1}{4}$

b. $P(R) = \frac{28}{100} = \frac{7}{25}$

c. $P(G) = \frac{24}{100} = \frac{6}{25}$

d. $P(Y) = \frac{23}{100}$

c. Theoretical probabilities: $\frac{1}{4}$ for each

f. $P(B)$

32. a. $P(Y) = \dfrac{15}{100} = \dfrac{3}{20}$

b. $P(B) = \dfrac{18}{100} = \dfrac{9}{50}$

c. $P(G) = \dfrac{20}{100} = \dfrac{1}{5}$

d. $P(W) = \dfrac{13}{100}$

e. $P(O) = \dfrac{15}{100} = \dfrac{3}{20}$

f. $P(R) = \dfrac{19}{100}$

33.

Outcome	Empirical Probability	Theoretical Probability
a. Red	$\dfrac{24}{100} = \dfrac{6}{25}$	$\dfrac{1}{6}$
b. Blue	$\dfrac{9}{100}$	$\dfrac{1}{9}$
c. Green	$\dfrac{29}{100}$	$\dfrac{5}{18}$
d. White	$\dfrac{20}{100} = \dfrac{1}{5}$	$\dfrac{2}{9}$
e. Yellow	$\dfrac{18}{100} = \dfrac{9}{50}$	$\dfrac{2}{9}$

34.

Outcome	Empirical Probability	Theoretical Probability
a. Sum = 2	$\dfrac{3}{100}$	$\dfrac{1}{36}$
b. Sum = 5	$\dfrac{3}{25}$	$\dfrac{1}{9}$
c. Sum = 7	$\dfrac{17}{100}$	$\dfrac{1}{6}$
d. Sum = 9	$\dfrac{13}{100}$	$\dfrac{1}{9}$
e. Sum = 12	$\dfrac{1}{50}$	$\dfrac{1}{36}$
f. Sum > 10	$\dfrac{2}{25}$	$\dfrac{1}{12}$
g. Sum < 4	$\dfrac{7}{100}$	$\dfrac{1}{12}$
h. Sum > 2	$\dfrac{97}{100}$	$\dfrac{35}{36}$
i. Sum < 12	$\dfrac{49}{50}$	$\dfrac{35}{36}$

35. a. $P(11) = \dfrac{6}{50} = \dfrac{3}{25}$ b. $P(7) = \dfrac{9}{50}$

c. $P(O)$

$= P(3) + P(5) + P(7) + P(9) + P(11)$

$= \dfrac{4}{50} + \dfrac{4}{50} + \dfrac{9}{50} + \dfrac{3}{50} + \dfrac{6}{50} = \dfrac{26}{50} = \dfrac{13}{25}$

d. $P(\sim O) = 1 - P(O) = 1 - \dfrac{13}{25} = \dfrac{12}{25}$

e. Getting a sum of 8.
f. Getting a sum of 2 or 4 or 12.
g. Getting a sum of 2 or 4 or 12.
h. No

36. a. $P(\text{sum of } 2 \text{ or } 12) = \dfrac{2}{36} = \dfrac{1}{18}$

b. $P(\text{sum odd and} > 8) = \dfrac{7}{36}$

c. $P(\text{sum even and} < 5) = \dfrac{4}{36} = \dfrac{1}{9}$

d. $P(\text{sum} < 12) = \dfrac{35}{36}$

e. $P(\text{sum} = 1) = \dfrac{0}{36} = 0$

f.   2, 3, 4, 7, 11, 12

37. a. $P(\text{None}) = \dfrac{172}{502} = \dfrac{86}{251}$

b. $P(1) = \dfrac{73}{502}$

c.   Having exactly 4 credit cards.

d.   Having no credit cards.

e. $P(\text{at least } 1) = 1 - P(\text{None})$

$= 1 - \dfrac{86}{251} = \dfrac{165}{251}$

38. a. $P(\text{hot dogs}) = \dfrac{75}{1510} = \dfrac{15}{302}$

b. $P(\text{sandwiches}) = \dfrac{45}{1510} = \dfrac{9}{302}$

c. $P(\text{chicken}) = \dfrac{560}{1510} = \dfrac{56}{151}$

d. $P(\text{fish sticks or sandwiches})$

$= \dfrac{75 + 45}{1510} = \dfrac{120}{1510} = \dfrac{12}{151}$

39. a. $P(\text{Victim}) = \dfrac{75}{500} = \dfrac{3}{20}$

b. $P(\text{Not a victim}) = \dfrac{370}{500} = \dfrac{37}{50}$

c. $P(\text{Not sure}) = \dfrac{55}{500} = \dfrac{11}{100}$

40. a.   0.22   b.   0.25

c.   TV viewing at 28%

41. a. $P(\text{Reading}) = \dfrac{89}{239}$

b. $P(\text{Watch movie}) = \dfrac{33}{239}$

c. $P(\text{Not watch movie})$

$= 1 - P(\text{Watch movie})$

$= 1 - \dfrac{33}{239} = \dfrac{206}{239}$

d. $P(\text{Sleeping}) = \dfrac{24}{239}$

42. a. $P(\text{Conservationist}) = \dfrac{490}{1323} = \dfrac{10}{27}$

b. $P(\text{Environmentalist}) = \dfrac{416}{1323}$

c. $P(\text{Green}) = \dfrac{417}{1323} = \dfrac{139}{441}$

43. a. $P(\text{Very often}) = \dfrac{140}{5543}$

b. $P(\text{Never}) = \dfrac{2804}{5543}$

c. $P(\text{Regift}) = 1 - P(\text{Never})$

$= 1 - \dfrac{2804}{5543} = \dfrac{2739}{5543}$

44. a. $P(\text{rarely}) = \dfrac{2443}{8523}$

b. $P(\text{very often}) = \dfrac{2137}{8523}$

c. $P(\text{never}) = \dfrac{1532}{8523}$

45. a.   There are 650 favorable outcomes and 850 possible outcomes, so

$P(E) = \dfrac{650}{850} = \dfrac{13}{17}.$

b.   There are 200 favorable outcomes and 850 possible outcomes, so

$P(E') = \dfrac{200}{850} = \dfrac{4}{17}.$

This problem can also be done by using the result of part (a) and the equation

$P(E') = 1 - P(E)$ to get the same

answer: $P(E') = 1 - \dfrac{13}{17} = \dfrac{4}{17}.$

46. $100\% - 35\% - 10\% = 55\%$

47. a. $P(\text{NL player home run}) = \dfrac{150}{5493} = \dfrac{50}{1831}$

b. $P(\text{AL player home run}) = \dfrac{158}{5533}$

48. a. $P(\text{Bautista home run}) = \dfrac{54}{559}$

b. $P(\text{Pujols home run}) = \dfrac{42}{587}$

49. AL players; their probability of hitting a

   home run $\dfrac{158}{5533} = 0.029$ is higher than that

   of NL players $\dfrac{150}{5493} = 0.027$.

50. Jose Bautista; his probability of hitting a

   home run $\dfrac{54}{559} = 0.10$ is higher than that

   of Albert Pujols $\dfrac{42}{587} = 0.07$.

51. Answers will vary. Experimental
   (empirical) probablity is based on actual
   results from an experiment, whereas,
   theoretical probablity is based on logical
   reasoning.

52. Answers will vary. Tossing a coin is a
   simple probability experiment. The
   sample space, which consists of all
   possible outcomes, for tossing a coin is
   {H, T}.

53. The probability formula does not apply if
   the events are not all equally likely to
   occur. For example, if a die is weighted so
   that a 6 is twice as likely to come up as
   any other number, then to calculate the
   probability that an even number comes up,
   it would be wrong to use the fact that
   three of the six faces are even so that the
   probability is 1/2. Instead, the 6 face must
   be given a weight of 2 and the other faces
   weights of 1. Then the weight of the even
   faces is 1 + 1 + 2 = 4 and the weight of all
   the faces is 1 + 1 + 1 + 1 + 1 + 2 = 7. This
   means that the probability that an even

   number comes up is $\dfrac{4}{7}$.

54. a. Rolling a pair of dice is an
      experiment.
   b. Choosing two cards from a deck of
      cards is an experiment.
   c. Landing on black when a roulette
      wheel is spun is an outcome.
   d. Choosing 2 marbles from a jar is an
      experiment.

55. a. Choosing a number at random from 1 to 7
      has an equally likely outcome.
   b. Tossing a fair coin has an equally likely
      outcome.
   c. Choosing a letter at random from
      MISSISSIPPI does not have equally likely
      outcomes, because each letter does not
      occur the same number of times.
   d. Choosing a number at random from 1 to
      10 has an equally likely outcome.

56. Think of a red and a green die. Then, the
   possible outcomes will be: 7 = 1 + 6 =
   2 + 5 = 3 + 4 = 4 + 3 = 5 + 2 = 6 + 1

57. There were 465,300 successes and 472,000
   operations, so the probability of a success is

   $P(S) = \dfrac{465300}{472000} = \dfrac{4653}{4720} \approx 0.986$.

58. There were 781,000 successes and 784,000
   operations, so the probability of a success is

   $P(S) = \dfrac{781,000}{784,000} = \dfrac{781}{784} \approx 0.996$.

59. There were 506,000 successes and 508,000
   operations, so the probability of a success is

   $P(S) = \dfrac{506000}{508000} = \dfrac{253}{254} \approx 0.996$.

Collaborative Learning

1. a. $\dfrac{1}{200}$

   For parts b, c and d, go to:
   **http://www.dartmouth.edu/~chance/chance
   _news/recent_news/chance_news_8.01.html
   #be robbed**

2. a. The sample space is $\{BB, BG, GB\}$, so

      the probability of two boys is $\dfrac{1}{3}$.

   b. Answers will vary.

**Section 11.2 Counting Techniques and
Probability**

1. The total number of possibilities is
   $3 \cdot 2 \cdot 3 = 18$ and the number favorable

   is 1. Therefore, the probability is $\dfrac{1}{18}$.

2. The total number of possibilities is
$5 \cdot 2 = 10$ and the number favorable is 1.

Therefore, the probability is $\dfrac{1}{10}$.

3. In 1 throw, $P(\text{even number}) = \dfrac{1}{2}$, so in 3

throws, $P(\text{Even}) = \left(\dfrac{1}{2}\right)^3 = \dfrac{1}{8}$.

4. The total number of possible choices for
the committee of three is $C(40, 3)$ and the
number of choices if Jim is one of the
three selected is $C(3, 1)$. So the
probability that Jim is 1 of the 3 selected

members is $\dfrac{C(3,1)}{C(40,3)} = \dfrac{3}{9880}$.

5. The total number of possible choices for
the committee of four is $C(25, 4)$. The
number of choices to select both Helen
and Patty are $C(2, 2)$, and the total
number of choices of the remaining
committee members is $C(23, 2)$. So the
probability that both Helen and Patty will
be selected is

$$P(E) = \frac{C(2,2)C(23,2)}{C(25,4)}$$

$$= \frac{1 \cdot 23 \cdot 22}{2 \cdot 1} \cdot \frac{4 \cdot 3 \cdot 2 \cdot 1}{25 \cdot 24 \cdot 23 \cdot 22} = \frac{1}{50}.$$

6. a. The number of ways in which the ace
   of spades and a king is selected is
   $1 \cdot 4 = 4$.

   b. $P(\text{ace of spades and a king}) = \dfrac{1}{52} \cdot \dfrac{4}{51}$

   $$= \dfrac{4}{2651} = \dfrac{1}{663}.$$

7. a. Suppose that Mr. C. Nile chooses a
   restaurant. The probability that Mr.
   D. Mented goes to that restaurant is
   $\dfrac{1}{5}$.

   b. The probability that they miss each

   other is $1 - \dfrac{1}{5} = \dfrac{4}{5}$.

8. The total number of possible choices for
selecting 4 classes is $C(100, 4)$ and the total
number of choices of selecting 4 classes that
are not mathematics classes is $C(75, 4)$. So the
probability that the selection will not include a
mathematics course is

$$\frac{C(75,4)}{C(100,4)} = \frac{75 \cdot 74 \cdot 73 \cdot 72}{100 \cdot 99 \cdot 98 \cdot 97}.$$

9. a. To get 35¢, a person must get first a dime
   and then a quarter or first a quarter and
   then a dime. Since there are 2 dimes and 2
   quarters, there are $2 \cdot (2 \cdot 2) = 8$ ways of
   getting 35¢. There are 7 coins, so there are
   $7 \cdot 6 = 42$ ways of getting 2 coins. Thus,

   $$P(35¢) = \frac{8}{42} = \frac{4}{21}.$$

   b. To get 50¢, a person must get the 2
   quarters in either order, and there are 2
   ways of doing this. Hence

   $$P(50¢) = \frac{2}{42} = \frac{1}{21}.$$

10. The total number of possible choices for the
committee of two is $C(11, 2)$ and the total
number of choices of selecting 1 man is
$C(5, 1)$ and 1 woman is $C(6, 1)$. So the
probability that the committee will consist of

1 man and 1 woman is $\dfrac{C(5,1)C(6,1)}{C(11,2)} = \dfrac{6}{11}$.

11. $P(2 \text{ kings}) = \dfrac{P(4,2)}{P(52,2)} = \dfrac{C(4,2)}{C(52,2)} = \dfrac{1}{221}$

You can also use the SCP. There are 4
possibilities for selecting the first king and 3
for selecting the second king. Thus, there are
$4 \cdot 3$ favorable ways of selecting the two kings.
Since there are $52 \cdot 51$ ways of selecting two
cards from a deck, the answer is

$$\frac{4 \cdot 3}{52 \cdot 51} = \frac{1}{221}.$$

12. The total number of possible choices for
drawing two spades is $C(13, 2)$ and the total
number of possible choices for drawing 2
cards is $C(52, 2)$. So the probability of drawing

2 spades is $P(2 \text{ spades}) = \dfrac{C(13,2)}{C(52,2)} = \dfrac{1}{17}$.

13. There are 13 spades and 3 kings (other than the king of spades), so there are $13 \cdot 3$ ways of getting a spade and one of the 3 kings in that order. The number of ways of drawing 2 cards is $52 \cdot 51$. Thus, the probability of drawing a spade and one of the other 3 kings, in that order, is

$$\frac{13 \cdot 3}{52 \cdot 51} = \frac{1}{68}.$$

14. There are 13 spades and 3 kings not spades. The total number of possible choices for drawing one spades is $C(13, 1)$, for drawing 1 king is $C(3, 1)$ and the total number of possible choices for drawing 2 cards is $C(52, 2)$. So the probability of drawing 1 spade and 1 king other than the king of spades is

$$\frac{C(13,1)C(3,1)}{C(52,2)} = \frac{1}{34}.$$

15. Since there are 26 red cards and 52 cards in all, the probability of drawing 2 red cards in 2 draws is

$$P(2\text{ red cards}) = \frac{P(26,2)}{P(52,2)} = \frac{C(26,2)}{C(52,2)} = \frac{25}{102}.$$

16. a. $P(4, 2) = 12$ b. $P(15, 2) = 210$

   c. $\dfrac{P(4,2)}{P(15,2)} = \dfrac{12}{210} = \dfrac{2}{35}$

17. a. There are 5 $50 bills and 3 $10 bills, so there are $5 \cdot 3 = 15$ ways of getting a $50 bill and a $10 bill in that order.

   b. There are $5 + 4 + 3 + 2 + 1 = 15$ bills in all, so there are $15 \cdot 14$ ways of selecting 2 bills. Thus, the probability of getting a $5 bill and a $10 bill, in that order, is $\dfrac{5 \cdot 3}{15 \cdot 14} = \dfrac{1}{14}$.

   c. Since there are 2 ways to get a specific $50 bill and a $10 bill (without regard to order), the probability is twice that found in part b: $2 \cdot \dfrac{1}{14} = \dfrac{1}{7}$.

18. If 2% are defective then 98% are not defective. The probability of 2 tires randomly selected such that neither are defective is $0.98 \cdot 0.98 = 0.9604$.

19. The probability that at least one of the two tires is defective is

$$1 - P(\text{neither defective}) = 1 - (0.98)^2$$
$$= 1 - 0.9604 = 0.0396$$

20. The probability of 2 of the 10 CD-R disks is defective is $\dfrac{C(2,2)}{C(10,2)} = \dfrac{1}{45}$.

21. The probability is

$$\frac{6}{100} \cdot \frac{8}{10,000} = \frac{3}{62,500} = 0.000048.$$

22. For parts a – c, order does not matter so we can use combinations rather than permutations.

   a. The probability of both ball white is

$$\frac{C(5,2)}{C(8,2)} = \frac{5}{14}.$$

   b. The probability of both ball black is

$$\frac{C(3,2)}{C(8,2)} = \frac{3}{28}.$$

   c. The probability of one ball white and the other black is $\dfrac{C(5,1)C(3,1)}{C(8,2)} = \dfrac{15}{28}.$

23. a. Since the order does not matter, we can use combinations rather than permutations. There are 4 kings and 4 aces and 44 other cards in the deck of 52 cards. Therefore, the probability of getting 2 kings, 2 aces, and one other card is

$$\frac{C(4,2)C(4,2)C(44,1)}{C(52,5)}.$$

   b. The probability of getting 3 kings and 2 aces is $\dfrac{C(4,3)C(4,2)}{C(52,5)}.$

24. The number of different combinations of 3 of the 315 houses is $C(315, 3) = 5,159,805$. There are $C(70, 2) = 2415$ ways of selecting a house that tested positive and $C(245, 1) = 245$ ways of selecting a house that did not test positive. Thus, the probability of that 2 test positive for corrosion problems and 1 does not is

$$\frac{C(70,2) \cdot C(245,1)}{C(315,3)} = \frac{591,675}{5,159,805} = \frac{5635}{49,141}$$
$$\approx 0.115.$$

25. The number of different combinations of 2 of the 4 crew members is $C(4, 2) = 6$. There are $C(3, 1) = 3$ ways of selecting 1 of the 3 men and $C(4, 2) = 6$ ways of selecting 1 woman. Thus, the probability that 1 man and the 1 woman are selected for the space walk is

$$\frac{C(3,1) \cdot C(1,1)}{C(4,2)} = \frac{3 \cdot 1}{6} = \frac{3}{6} = \frac{1}{2}.$$

26. a. The probability that all 3 cans selected are legally labeled is

$$\frac{C(3,3)}{C(10,3)} = \frac{1}{120}.$$

   b. The probability that 2 cans selected are legally labeled and one is illegally labeled is $\dfrac{C(3,2) \cdot C(7,1)}{C(10,3)} = \dfrac{7}{40}.$

27. There are 4 possible royal flushes, so the probability of getting a royal flush is

$$P(\text{royal flush}) = \frac{4}{C(52,5)} = \frac{1}{649,740}$$

$$\approx 0.0000015$$

28. There are $10 \cdot 4 = 40$ possible straight flushes, so the probability of getting a straight flush is

$$P(\text{straight flush}) = \frac{40}{C(52,5)}$$

$$= \frac{1}{64,974} \approx 0.000015$$

29. There are 13 sets of four of a kind and if one of these occurs, the fifth card can be any one of the remaining 48 cards. Thus, the probability of getting four of a kind is

$$P(4 \text{ of a kind}) = \frac{13 \cdot 48}{C(52,5)}$$

$$= \frac{1}{4165} \approx 0.00024$$

30. There are 13 sets of two of a kind and 12 sets of 3 of a kind to choose from in order to get a full house. Thus, the probability of getting a full house is

$$\frac{13 \cdot C(4,2) \cdot 12 \cdot C(4,3)}{C(52,5)} = \frac{6}{4165} \approx 0.0014$$

31. The number of combinations of 5 cards in a given suit is $C(13, 5)$ and 10 of these are straights (including a royal flush). Thus, the number of flushes that are not straights is $C(13, 5) - 10$. The probability of getting such a flush is

$$P(E) = \frac{4\left[C(13,5) - 10\right]}{C(52,5)} = \frac{5148 - 40}{C(52,5)}$$

$$= \frac{5108}{C(52,5)} = \frac{1277}{649,740} \approx 0.0020$$

32. The number of combinations of 5 consecutive cards is $10 \cdot 4^5$ and 40 of these are straight flushes. Thus, the number of straights, not all of the same suit, is $10 \cdot 4^5 - 40$. The probability of getting such a straight is

$$\frac{10 \cdot 4^5 - 40}{C(52,5)} = \frac{5}{1274} \approx 0.0039$$

33. The total probability for a low-producing well (See Example 9) is

$$0.6(0.25) + 0.4(0.125) = 0.2$$

34. The total probability for a high-producing well (See Example 9) is

$$0.6(0.15) + 0.4(0.025) = 0.1$$

35. Dome structure, dry with probability

$$0.6(0.6) = 0.36$$

36. a.

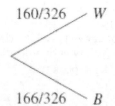

   b. The probability that a person selected at random is white is $\dfrac{160}{326}$.

   c. The probability that a person selected at random is black is $\dfrac{166}{326}$.

37.

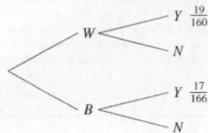

   a.   The probability that a white convict received the death penalty is $\dfrac{19}{160}$.

   b.   The probability that a black convict received the death penalty is $\dfrac{17}{166}$.

38.

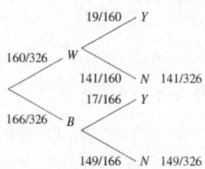

The probability that a convict did not receive the death penalty is

$$\frac{141}{326}+\frac{149}{326}=\frac{290}{326}=\frac{145}{163}.$$

39. The number of convicts that did not received the death penalty is $141 + 149$. The total number of convicts is 326. Thus, the probability that a convict of either race did not receive the death penalty is

$$\frac{141+149}{326}=\frac{290}{326}=\frac{145}{163}.$$

40. Yes. The information used to create the diagram was obtained from the table, so the result would be identical.

41. No. The coin is probably weighted to come up heads. Bet on heads.

42. Yes, bet on heads. Coin is probably weighted to come up heads.

43. No. The coin is probably weighted to come up heads as the odds of obtaining this result from a 'fair' coin is $\dfrac{1}{2^{10}}$. Bet on heads.

44. a. Bet on heads.   b. Don't bet.
    c. Bet on tails.

45. The number of combinations of 150 women that could be selected is $C(40{,}000, 150)$ and the number of combinations of 150 men is $C(36{,}000, 150)$. The number of combinations of 300 persons that could be selected is $C(76{,}000, 300)$. Hence, the probability that 150 men and 150 women will be selected is

$$\frac{C\left(40{,}000,150\right)C\left(36{,}000,150\right)}{C\left(76{,}000,300\right)}.$$

46. The number of combinations of 15 women that could be selected is $C(160, 15)$ and the number of combinations of 15 men is $C(140, 15)$. The number of combinations of 30 persons that could be selected is $C(300, 30)$. Hence, the probability that 15 men and 15 women will be selected is $\dfrac{C\left(160,15\right)C\left(140,15\right)}{C\left(300,30\right)}.$

47. The number of possible combinations of six women is $C(16, 6)$ and of six men is $C(14, 6)$. The number of combinations of 12 people selected from the 30 is $C(30, 12)$. Thus, the probability that the final jury will consist of six men and six women is $\dfrac{C\left(16,6\right)C\left(14,6\right)}{C\left(30,12\right)}.$

Calculator Corner

$\boxed{52}\ \boxed{{}_nC_r}\ \boxed{5}\ \boxed{\text{ENTER}}$ Answer: 2,598,960

Collaborative Learning

2. The probability that in a group of 23 students all will have different birthdays is

$$\frac{365\times364\times\cdots\times\left(365-23+1\right)}{365^{23}}$$

$$=\frac{365!}{365^{23}\left(365-23\right)!}=\frac{P\left(365,23\right)}{365^{23}}$$

$$=0.4927027657$$

3. The probability that in a group of 23 students that at least 2 will have the same birthday is $1 - 0.4927027657 = 0.5072972343$.

4. Yes.

Go to **http://www.mste.uiuc.edu/reese/ birthday/intro.html** for further discussion. If you assume N people are in a room, what is the smallest N such that there is at least probability 0.5 that M people have the same birthday? Assuming that the birthday distribution is uniform over 365 days, we have:

M	N	Probability
2	23	0.507297234324
2	22	0.475695307663
3	88	0.511065110625
3	87	0.499454850632
4	187	0.502685373189
4	186	0.495825706383

Section 11.3 Computation of Probabilities

1. $E = \varnothing$, so $P(E) = 0$; *Property 1*

2. The probability of rolling an odd number is $\dfrac{1}{2}$ and the probability of rolling an even number is $\dfrac{1}{2}$. Thus, the probability of rolling an odd number or an even number is $P(E) = \dfrac{1}{2} + \dfrac{1}{2} = 1$; *Property 4*

3. Since the sum is always between 0 and 13, $P(E) = 1$; *Property 2*

4. Since there are only 4 Aces in a regular deck, $E = \varnothing$, so $P(E) = 0$.; *Property 1*

5. Let A be the event that the number is even and B the event that the number is greater than 7. Then $P(A) = \dfrac{5}{10}, P(B) = \dfrac{3}{10}$,

   $P(A \cap B) = \dfrac{2}{10}$. Now, we use *Property 3*,

   $P(A \cup B) = P(A) + P(B) - P(A \cap B)$,

   to get $P(A \cup B) = \dfrac{5}{10} + \dfrac{3}{10} - \dfrac{2}{10} = \dfrac{6}{10} = \dfrac{3}{5}$.

6. Let A be the event that the number is odd and B the event that the number is less than 5. Then $P(A) = \dfrac{5}{10}, P(B) = \dfrac{4}{10}$,

   $P(A \cap B) = \dfrac{2}{10}$. Now, we use *Property 3*,

   $P(A \cup B) = P(A) + P(B) - P(A \cap B)$, to get

   $P(A \cup B) = \dfrac{5}{10} + \dfrac{4}{10} - \dfrac{2}{10} = \dfrac{7}{10}$.

7. Since E is certain to occur, $P(E) = 1$.

8. Let A be the event that the number is greater than 7 and B the event that the number is less than 5. Then $P(A) = \dfrac{3}{10}, P(B) = \dfrac{4}{10}$,

   $P(A \cap B) = \dfrac{2}{10}$. Now, we use *Property 4*,

   $P(A \cup B) = P(A) + P(B)$, to get

   $P(A \cup B) = \dfrac{3}{10} + \dfrac{4}{10} = \dfrac{7}{10}$.

9. There are 14 favorable outcomes and 52 possible outcomes, so $P(E) = \dfrac{14}{52} = \dfrac{7}{26}$.

10. There are 4 favorable outcomes and 52 possible outcomes, so $P(E) = \dfrac{4}{52} = \dfrac{1}{13}$.

11. There are 13 diamonds and 52 cards in all, so $P(E) = \dfrac{13}{52} = \dfrac{1}{4}$.

12. There are 26 favorable outcomes and 52 cards in all, so $P(E) = \dfrac{26}{52} = \dfrac{1}{2}$.

13. There are 12 picture cards and 52 cards in all, so $P(E) = \dfrac{12}{52} = \dfrac{3}{13}$.

14. The probability that it rains in winter is $\dfrac{40}{90} = \dfrac{4}{9}$ and the probability that it snows is

$\dfrac{50}{90} = \dfrac{5}{9}$, and the probability that it rains

and snows is $\dfrac{10}{90} = \dfrac{1}{9}$. Thus, the

probability that it will rain or snow is

$\dfrac{4}{9} + \dfrac{5}{9} - \dfrac{1}{9} = \dfrac{8}{9}$.

15. Let N be the event that the stock remained unchanged. Since 9 stocks remained

unchanged, $P(N) = \dfrac{9}{50}$. The event that

the stock did not change is N', so the probability that a randomly selected stock did change is

$P(N') = 1 - P(N) = 1 - \dfrac{9}{50} = \dfrac{41}{50}$.

16. From the table, the probability of exactly 2 persons in line is 0.20.

17. Let E_4 be the event that more than 3 persons are in line. From the table, we read that $P(E_4) = 0.20$.

18. The table gives 0.15 as the probability that 1 person is in line, 0.20 that 2 persons are in line, 0.35 that 3 persons are in line, and 0.20 that 4 or more persons are in line. The probability of at least 1 person in line would be the sum of these probabilities: $0.15 + 0.20 + .035 + 0.20 = 0.90$

19. The table gives 0.10 as the probability that 0 persons are in line, and 0.15 that 1 person is in line, so the probability that less than 2 persons are in line is $0.10 + 0.15 = 0.25$. Since the event E_4 that more than 3 persons are in line and the event, say E_2, that less than 2 persons are in line are mutually exclusive, $E_2 \cap E_4 = \varnothing$. Therefore, the probability that more than 3 or less than 2 persons are in line is $P(E_2 \cup E_4) = P(E_2) + P(E_4)$
$= 0.25 + 0.20 = 0.45$

20. More than 2 persons or fewer than 3 persons in line would include all of the possibilities, this probability would be $0.10 + 0.15 + 0.20 + .035 + 0.20 = 1$.

21. a. Using Table 11.4, we find the probability that a male who is alive at 20 is alive at

age 60 is $P(E) = \dfrac{85,227}{98,541}$. Hence, the

probability that a male who is alive at age 20 is not alive at age 60 is

$P(E') = 1 - P(E) = 1 - \dfrac{85,227}{98,541}$

$= \dfrac{13,314}{98,541} = \dfrac{4438}{32,847}$

b. Using Table 11.4, we find the probability that a female who is alive at 20 is alive at

age 60 is $P(E) = \dfrac{91,220}{98,983}$. Hence, the

probability that a female who is alive at age 20 is not alive at age 60 is

$P(E') = 1 - P(E) = 1 - \dfrac{91,220}{98,983}$

$= \dfrac{7763}{98,983}$

22. a. Using Table 11.4, we find the probability that a male who is alive at 30 is alive at

age 70 is $P(E) = \dfrac{72,066}{97,147}$.

b. Using Table 11.4, we find the probability that a female who is alive at 30 is alive at

age 70 is $P(E) = \dfrac{81,944}{98,466} = \dfrac{40,972}{49,233}$.

23. a. Using Table 11.4, we find the probability that a male who is alive at 30 is alive at

age 70 is $P(E) = \dfrac{72,066}{97,147}$. Hence, the

probability that a male who is alive at age 30 is not alive at age 70 is

$P(E') = 1 - P(E) = 1 - \dfrac{72,066}{97,147} = \dfrac{25,081}{97,147}$.

b. Using Table 11.4, we find the probability that a female who is alive at 30 is alive at

age 70 is $P(E) = \dfrac{81,944}{98,466}$. Hence, the

probability that a female who is alive at age 30 is not alive at age 70 is

$P(E') = 1 - P(E) = 1 - \dfrac{81,944}{98,466}$

$$= \frac{16,522}{98,466} = \frac{8261}{49,233}$$

24. a. Using Table 11.4, we find the probability that a male who is alive at 50 is alive at age 130 is
$$P(E) = \frac{0}{92,224} = 0.$$

    b. Using Table 11.4, we find the probability that a female who is alive at 50 is alive at age 130 is
$$P(E) = \frac{0}{95,530} = 0.$$

25. a. Since the assumption is that no one attained 130 years of age, then the probability that a male will live less than 80 more years after attaining age 50 is $P(E) = 1$.

    b. Since the assumption is that no one attained 130 years of age, then the probability that a female will live less than 80 more years after attaining age 50 is $P(E) = 1$.

26. The table gives that the number of long forms as $60 + 20 = 80$, which includes both incorrectly and correctly filled out forms. The additional incorrectly filled out forms (short forms) is 5. Since the total number of forms is 100, the probability that a form was a long form or an incorrectly filled out form is
$$P(E) = \frac{80+5}{100} = \frac{85}{100} = \frac{17}{20}.$$

27. The table gives the number of correct forms with no itemized deductions as $15 + 40 = 55$. Since the total number of forms is 100, the probability that a form had no itemized deductions and was correctly filled out is $P(E) = \frac{55}{100} = \frac{11}{20}.$

28. The number of form not filled out incorrectly is those that are filled out correctly. The table gives the number of correctly filled out forms as 65. Hence, the probability that a form is not incorrectly filled out is
$$P(E) = \frac{65}{100} = \frac{13}{20}.$$

29. The table gives the number of short forms as 20, so the number of long forms was 80. Hence, the probability that a form was not a short form is $P(E) = \frac{80}{100} = \frac{4}{5}.$

30. The table gives the number of long forms with no itemized deductions and filled out incorrectly as 20. Hence, the probability that a form is a long form with no itemized deductions and filled out incorrectly is
$$P(E) = \frac{20}{100} = \frac{1}{5}.$$

31. The green and yellow lights are on for a total of 65 seconds and the entire cycle takes 85 seconds. Thus, the probability of finding the light green or yellow is $P(E) = \frac{65}{85} = \frac{13}{17}.$

32. The yellow light is 5 seconds, so for the driver to make it through the intersection before it turns red, he would have to be at most 59 seconds in the green light cycle. Thus, the probability that the driver makes it through intersection before the light turns red is $\frac{59}{85}.$

33. The probability of an event being 0, means that the event cannot occur.

34. If the probability of an event is 1, then the event is certain to occur.

35. If A and B have no elements in common, so that $A \cap B = \varnothing$, then
$$P(A \cup B) = P(A) + P(B).$$

36. An event is either possible or not possible. If the event is impossible, its probability is 0. If the event is possible, then the probability is a positive fraction not greater than 1. In any case, the probability cannot be negative.

37. We can tabulate John Dough's points as follows:

Item	Points
Age 27	5
Time at Address, 3 yr.	5
Age of Auto, 2 yr.	16
Monthly Auto Payment $200	0
Housing Cost $130/month	10
Checking Account Only	2
No Finance Co. Reference	15
Major Credit Cards 1	5
Debt to Income Ratio 12%	20
Total Score	78

From the table showing the probability of repayment, we estimate that John's probability is between 0.81 and 0.84, say about 0.83.

38. We can retabulate John Dough's points as follows:

Item	Points
Age 27	5
Time at Address, 3 yr.	5
Age of Auto, None	0
Monthly Auto Payment None	18
Housing Cost $130/month	10
Checking Account Only	2
No Finance Co. Reference	15
Major Credit Cards 1	5
Debt to Income Ratio 12%	20
Total Score	80

From the table showing the probability of repayment, we estimate that John's probability is about 0.84.

39. Answer will depend on the number of points you score but if you want to see a real way of scoring your credit history go to **http://www.myfico.com/** . Generally speaking, five factors are taken into account: Payment history, how much you owe, the length of time of your credit history, how much new credit you have established and the type of credit you have (credit cards, mortgages, finance companies, etc.)

The Venn diagram shows the data given for problems 40 – 42.

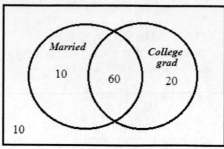

40. Refer to the Venn diagram. The number of persons in $M \cap C$ is 60, so the probability that a person selected at random is married and a college graduate is $P(M \cap C) = \dfrac{60}{100} = \dfrac{3}{5}$.

41. Refer to the Venn diagram. The number of persons in $M \cup C$ is $10 + 60 + 20 = 90$, so the probability that a person selected at random is married or a college graduate is

$$P(M \cup C) = \frac{90}{100} = \frac{9}{10}.$$

42. Refer to the Venn diagram. The number of person that are not married and not a college graduate is 10, the probability that a person selected at random is not married and not a college graduate is $P(\overline{M} \cup \overline{C}) = \dfrac{10}{100} = \dfrac{1}{10}$.

The Venn diagram shows how the voters voted for problems 43 – 47.

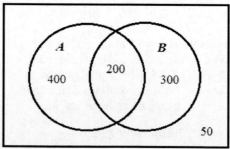

43. Refer to the Venn diagram. Note that the numbers add up to 950, so 50 persons did not vote at all. The diagram shows that 400 voted for *A* and not *B*. Thus, the probability that an eligible voter selected at random voted for *A* and not for *B* is $P(E) = \dfrac{400}{1000} = \dfrac{2}{5}$.

44. Refer to the Venn diagram. The diagram shows that 300 voted for B and not A. Thus, the probability that an eligible voter selected at random voted for B and not for A is $P(E) = \dfrac{300}{1000} = \dfrac{3}{10}$.

45. Refer to the Venn diagram. Since 200 voted for both A and B, the probability that an eligible voter selected at random voted for both A and B is

$$P(E) = \frac{200}{1000} = \frac{1}{5}.$$

46. Refer to the Venn diagram. There are 50 voters outside of those voting for A or B. Thus, the probability that an eligible voter selected at random voted against A and B is $P(E) = \dfrac{50}{1000} = \dfrac{1}{20}$.

47. Refer to the Venn diagram. Since 50 did not vote at all, the probability that an eligible voter selected at random did not vote at all is $P(E) = \dfrac{50}{1000} = \dfrac{1}{20}$.

Section 11.4 Conditional Probability

1. Let F be the event that a 5 came up and let E be the event that an even number came up. Then $F \cap E = \varnothing$, so $P(F \cap E) = 0$ and $P(F|E) = 0$.

2. Let F be the event obtaining a 7 and let E be the event that tails came up. Then $F \cap E = \varnothing$, so $P(F \cap E) = 0$ and $P(F|E) = 0$.

3. a. Let A be the event that the numbers coming up were identical, and let B be the event that the sum was 8. There is only one way for the sum to be 8 and the numbers to be identical: that is for both numbers to be 4. Since the probability that both numbers were 4's is 1/36, and the probability that the numbers were identical is 1/6, we have

$$P(B|A) = \frac{P(A \cap B)}{P(A)} = \frac{\frac{1}{36}}{\frac{1}{6}} = \frac{1}{6}.$$

b. It is impossible to get a sum of 9 if the two numbers coming up are identical, so $P(9|\text{numbers identical}) = 0$.

c. If the two numbers coming up are identical, then the sum is even, so $P(\text{even sum}|\text{numbers identical}) = 1$.

d. It is impossible to get an odd sum if the two numbers coming up are identical, so $P(\text{odd sum}|\text{numbers identical}) = 0$.

4. a. Since two b genes will always produce blue eyes, the probability of a person with two b genes having brown eyes is 0.

b. Since two b genes will always produce blue eyes, the probability of a person with two b genes having blue eyes is 1.

5. $P(BB|BB \text{ or } BG)$

$$= \frac{P(BB \text{ and } (BB \text{ or } BG))}{P(BB \text{ or } BG)} = \frac{\frac{1}{4}}{\frac{1}{2}} = \frac{1}{2}.$$

6. a. $P(GGG|G) = \dfrac{P(GGG \text{ and } G)}{P(G)} = \dfrac{\frac{1}{8}}{\frac{1}{2}} = \dfrac{1}{4}.$

b. If the first child is a boy, it is impossible to have three girls. The probability is 0.

7. If the first child is a girl and there are exactly two girls, then we must have GGB or GBG. Since there are $2^3 = 8$ possibilities, $P(GGB \text{ or } GBG) = \dfrac{1}{4}$. The probability that the first child is a girl is 1/2. Therefore, the probability that there are exactly 2 girls given that the first child is a girl is

$P(\text{exactly } 2\,G\,|1^{st} \text{ child is } G)$

$$= \frac{P(GGB \text{ or } GBG)}{P(|1^{st} \text{ child is } G)} = \frac{\frac{1}{4}}{\frac{1}{2}} = \frac{1}{2}.$$

8. a. $P(25-45 | \text{United States}) = \dfrac{20}{100,000}$

$= 0.0002$

b. $P(25-45 | \text{Canada}) = \dfrac{15}{100,000}$

$= 0.00015$

c. The number of suicides in Germany is $20 + 30 + 50 + 50 = 150$.

$P(15-65 \text{ and over} | \text{Germany})$

$= \dfrac{150}{100,000} = 0.0015$

9. a. From the table, we have the probability that an employee missed 6–10 days, given that the employee is a woman, $P = \dfrac{20\%}{100\%} = \dfrac{1}{5}$.

b. Suppose there were 100 men and 100 women employees. The table shows that 40 men and 20 women missed 6-10 days. Thus, the probability that the employee is a woman, given that the employee missed 6-10 days is

$P = \dfrac{20}{60} = \dfrac{1}{3}$.

10. a. From the table we have $15 + 10 + 8 + 7 = 40$ females and the total number of students is 100. The probability that a randomly selected student is female is $P = \dfrac{40}{100} = 0.4$.

b. From the table we have $12 + 8 = 20$ juniors and the total number of students is 100. The probability that a randomly selected student is a junior is $P = \dfrac{20}{100} = 0.2$.

c. From the table we have $12 + 8 = 20$ juniors and 8 juniors are females. The probability that a selected student is a female given the student is a junior is $P = \dfrac{8}{20} = 0.4$.

11. Use the following table.

Reason to Work	AGE	
	16–64	65+
Need Money (N)	49	17
Wants to (W)	20	54
Both (B)	31	27

a. The table shows that $49 + 17 = 66$ people work because they need the money (N). 17 of those are 65+ in age. Thus, the probability that a randomly selected person is 65+ given that they work because they need money is

$P(65+ | N) = \dfrac{P(65+ \cap N)}{P(N)} = \dfrac{17}{66}$.

b. The table shows that $49 + 17 = 66$ people work because they need the money (N). 49 of those are 16-64 in age. Thus, the probability that a randomly selected person is 16-64 given that they work because they need money is

$P(16-64 | N) = \dfrac{P(16\text{-}64 \cap N)}{P(N)} = \dfrac{49}{66}$

c. The table shows that 17 of the 98 people 65+ in age are those that work because they need money (N). Thus, the probability that a randomly selected person works because they need money given that they are 65+ is $\dfrac{17}{98} = 17.3\%$.

12. If the first card was the ace of spaces, there one ace of hearts in the remaining 51 cards, so the probability that the second card is the ace of hearts is $P = \dfrac{1}{51}$.

13. If the first card was a king, there are 3 kings left in the remaining 51 cards, so the probability that the second card is a king is

$P = \dfrac{3}{51} = \dfrac{1}{17}$.

14. If the first card was a 6, there are four 7 cards left in the remaining 51 cards, so the probability that the second card is a 7 is

$P = \dfrac{4}{51}$.

15. There are 25 low-risk stocks, of which 5 are computer stocks, so the probability that the person selected a computer stock, given that the person selected a low-risk stock is $P = \dfrac{5}{25} = \dfrac{1}{5}$.

16. There are 25 high-risk stocks, of which 15 are petroleum stocks, so the probability that the person selected a petroleum stock, given that the person selected a high-risk stock is $P = \dfrac{15}{25} = \dfrac{3}{5}$.

17. $P(B|A) = \dfrac{P(A \cap B)}{P(A)} = \dfrac{0.4}{0.6} = \dfrac{2}{3}$

18. $P(\text{Busch} | \text{Disney}) = \dfrac{P(\text{Busch} \cap \text{Disney})}{P(\text{Disney})}$

$$= \dfrac{0.2}{0.5} = \dfrac{2}{5}$$

19. a. $P(\text{Good} | \text{Tenured})$

$$= \dfrac{P(\text{Good} \cap \text{Tenured})}{P(\text{Tenured})}$$

$$= \dfrac{72}{72 + 168} = \dfrac{72}{240} = \dfrac{3}{10}$$

b. $P(\text{Good}) = \dfrac{72 + 84}{72 + 84 + 168 + 76}$

$$= \dfrac{156}{400} = \dfrac{39}{100}$$

20. a. $P(\text{Poor} | \text{Tenured})$

$$= \dfrac{P(\text{Poor} \cap \text{Tenured})}{P(\text{Tenured})}$$

$$= \dfrac{168}{240} = \dfrac{7}{10}$$

b. $P(\text{Poor}) = \dfrac{168 + 76}{72 + 84 + 168 + 76}$

$$= \dfrac{244}{400} = \dfrac{61}{100}$$

21. a. $P(\text{None} | 65+) = \dfrac{P(\text{None} \cap 65+)}{P(65+)}$

$$= \dfrac{280}{70 + 287 + 280} = \dfrac{280}{637} \approx 0.44 = 44\%$$

b. $P(\text{None} | 18\text{-}24) = \dfrac{P(\text{None} \cap 18\text{-}24)}{P(18\text{-}24)}$

$$= \dfrac{11}{108 + 101 + 11} = \dfrac{11}{220} = 0.05 = 5\%$$

22. a. $P(65+ | \text{Smart}) = \dfrac{P(65+ \cap \text{Smart})}{P(\text{Smart})}$

$$= \dfrac{70}{108 + 144 + 124 + 110 + 95 + 70}$$

$$= \dfrac{70}{651} \approx 0.11 = 11\%$$

b. $P(18\text{-}24 | \text{Smart}) = \dfrac{P(18\text{-}24 \cap \text{Smart})}{P(\text{Smart})}$

$$= \dfrac{108}{108 + 144 + 124 + 110 + 95 + 70}$$

$$= \dfrac{108}{651} \approx 0.17 = 17\%$$

23. a. The table shows that 135 of the 200 patients have improved. Thus, the probability that a patient chosen at random has improved is

$$P(I) = \dfrac{70 + 65}{200} = \dfrac{135}{200} = \dfrac{27}{40}.$$

b. The table shows that 70 of the 100 patients taking the experimental drug have improved, so the probability that one of these patients chosen at random has improved is $P(I|E) = \dfrac{70}{100} = \dfrac{7}{10}$.

24. a. $P(1^{\text{st}} \text{floor}) = 20\% + 30\% + 10\%$

$$= 60\% = 0.6$$

b. $P(1^{\text{st}} \text{floor, 3-bed}) = 10\% = 0.1$

c. $P(2^{\text{nd}} \text{floor} | 1\text{-bed}) = \dfrac{P(2^{\text{nd}} \text{floor} \cap 1\text{-bed})}{P(1\text{-bed})}$

$$= \dfrac{15}{20 + 15} = \dfrac{15}{35} = \dfrac{3}{7}$$

d. $P\left(2 \text{ or } 3\text{-bed}|1^{st}\text{floor}\right)$

$$= \frac{P\left(2 \text{ or } 3\text{-bed} \cap 1^{st}\text{floor}\right)}{P\left(1^{st}\text{floor}\right)}$$

$$= \frac{30+10}{20+30+10} = \frac{40}{60} = \frac{2}{3}$$

25. $P(D|W)$ is the probability that the person gets the death penalty (D) given that the person is white (W). In the first column of the table, there are 160 whites of which 19 got the death penalty, thus

$$P\left(D|W\right) = \frac{19}{160} \approx 0.119.$$

26. $P(D|B)$ is the probability that the person gets the death penalty (D) given that the person is black (B). In the first column of the table, there are 166 blacks of which 17 got the death penalty, thus

$$P\left(D|B\right) = \frac{P\left(D \cap B\right)}{P\left(B\right)} = \frac{17}{166} \approx 0.102.$$

27. For these 326 convicted murderers,

$$P\left(D|W\right) = \frac{19}{160} \approx 0.119 \text{ and}$$

$$P\left(D|B\right) = \frac{17}{166} \approx 0.102. \text{ There is not}$$

much difference $(0.119 - 0.102 = 0.017)$ between outcomes for whites and blacks.

28. $P(D|WW)$ means the probability that the person gets the death penalty (D) given that the defendant is white and the victim is white (WW). From the first table, where the race of the victim is white, and the defendant is white, we see that there are 19 whites that got the death penalty out of the 151 in the column. Thus,

$$P\left(D|WW\right) = \frac{19}{151} \approx 0.126.$$

29. $P(D|BW)$ means the probability that the person gets the death penalty (D) given that the defendant is black and the victim is white (BW). From the first table, where the race of the victim is white, and the defendant is black (last column), we see that there are 11 blacks that got the death penalty out of the 63 in the column. Thus,

$$P\left(D|BW\right) = \frac{11}{63} \approx 0.175.$$

30. $P(D|WB)$ means the probability that the person gets the death penalty (D) given that the defendant is white and the victim is black (WB). From the second table, where the race of the victim is black, and the defendant is white, we see that there are 0 whites that got the death penalty out of the 9 in the column. Thus,

$$P\left(D|WB\right) = \frac{0}{9} = 0.$$

31. $P(D|BB)$ means the probability that the person gets the death penalty (D) given that the defendant is black and the victim is black (BB). From the second table, where the race of the victim is black, and the defendant is black, (last column), we see that there are 6 blacks that got the death penalty out of the 103 in the

column. Thus, $P\left(D|BB\right) = \frac{6}{103} \approx 0.058.$

32. Given the race of the victim, blacks get the death penalty more often out of the 326 convicted murderers.

33. Answers will vary.

34. A: A die coming up an even number.
B: A die coming up 1, 2, 3, 4, 5, 6.
If A and B are independent events or if A is a subset of B and B is the universal set, then $P(A|B) = P(A)$.

35. The total number of crimes listed in the table is 128.
a. The probability that the victim of one of these crimes was a male is

$$P\left(\text{male}\right) = \frac{5+18+52}{128} = \frac{75}{128}.$$

b. The probability that the victim was a female is $P\left(\text{female}\right) = \frac{2+9+42}{128} = \frac{53}{128}$

c. Male; $[P(\text{male}) > P(\text{female})]$

36. a. The probability of the victim being a male given that an assault was committed is

$$P\left(\text{male}|\text{assault}\right) = \frac{P\left(\text{male} \cap \text{assault}\right)}{P\left(\text{assault}\right)}$$

$$= \frac{18}{18+9} = \frac{18}{27} = \frac{2}{3}$$

b. The probability of the victim being a female given that an assault was committed is

$$P(\text{female}|\text{assault}) = \frac{P(\text{female} \cap \text{assault})}{P(\text{assault})}$$

$$= \frac{9}{18+9} = \frac{9}{27} = \frac{1}{3}.$$

37. $P(\text{assault}|\text{female})$

$$= \frac{P(\text{assault} \cap \text{female})}{P(\text{female})} = \frac{9}{2+9+42} = \frac{9}{53}$$

38. $P(\text{robbery}|\text{male}) = \frac{P(\text{robbery} \cap \text{male})}{P(\text{male})}$

$$= \frac{5}{5+18+52} = \frac{5}{75} = \frac{1}{15}$$

Section 11.5 Independent Events

1. Yes. $P(E_1|E_2) = P(E_1)$, so E_1 and E_2 are independent.

2. a. $(0.06+0.44) \cdot (0.06+0.44)$

$$= (0.5) \cdot (0.5) = 0.25$$

b. $(0.06+0.44) \cdot (0.05+0.32)$

$$= (0.5) \cdot (0.37) = 0.185$$

c. $(0.06) \cdot (0.06) = 0.0036$

d. $(0.05) \cdot (0.05) = 0.0025$

e. $(0.44) \cdot (0.05) = 0.022$

3. a. Since the three events are independent

$P(\text{bad modem, bad CPU, bad drive})$

$$= \frac{1}{4} \cdot \frac{1}{8} \cdot \frac{1}{3} = \frac{1}{96}.$$

b. We need
$P(\text{bad modem, bad CPU, good drive})$

$$= \frac{1}{4} \cdot \frac{1}{8} \cdot \frac{2}{3} = \frac{1}{48}.$$

c. Here we need
$P(\text{gd modem, gd CPU, gd drive})$

$$= \frac{3}{4} \cdot \frac{7}{8} \cdot \frac{2}{3} = \frac{7}{16}.$$

4. a. These are independent events, so
$P(\text{both work}) = 0.49 \cdot 0.17 = 0.0833.$

b. These are independent events, so
$P(\text{younger need, older want}) = 0.49 \cdot 0.54$

$$= 0.2646$$

c. $P(\text{younger need, older want})$

$+P(\text{younger want, older need})$

$$= 0.49 \cdot 0.54 + 0.20 \cdot 0.17 = 0.2986$$

5. a. $P(HTH) = \frac{1}{2} \cdot \frac{1}{2} \cdot \frac{1}{2} = \frac{1}{8}$

b. If a coin is tossed three times the possible outcomes are: {*HHH, HHT, HTH, THH, TTH, THT, HTT, TTT*}
The favorable outcomes are {*HHH, HHT, HTH, THH*}. Since the events are independent

$P(HHH) + P(HHT) + P(HTH) + P(THH)$

$$= \frac{4}{8} = \frac{1}{2}. \text{ Thus, the probability of at least}$$

2 heads is $\frac{1}{2}$.

c. $P(HHH) = \frac{1}{8}.$ Therefore the probability of at most two heads is

$$1 - P(HHH) = 1 - \frac{1}{8} = \frac{7}{8}.$$

6. a. $P(\text{odd, odd, odd}) = \frac{1}{2} \cdot \frac{1}{2} \cdot \frac{1}{2} = \frac{1}{8}$

b. $P(\text{odd, odd, even}) = \frac{1}{2} \cdot \frac{1}{2} \cdot \frac{1}{2} = \frac{1}{8}$

c. $P(\text{odd, odd, odd}) + P(\text{odd, odd, even})$

$+P(\text{odd, even, odd}) + P(\text{even, odd, odd})$

$$= \frac{1}{2} \cdot \frac{1}{2} \cdot \frac{1}{2} + \frac{1}{2} \cdot \frac{1}{2} \cdot \frac{1}{2} + \frac{1}{2} \cdot \frac{1}{2} \cdot \frac{1}{2} + \frac{1}{2} \cdot \frac{1}{2} \cdot \frac{1}{2}$$

$$= \frac{1}{8} + \frac{1}{8} + \frac{1}{8} + \frac{1}{8} = \frac{4}{8} = \frac{1}{2}$$

7. a. There are 13 spades and 52 cards in all, so the probability that the first card is a spade is $\dfrac{13}{52} = \dfrac{1}{4}$.

   b. Since the first card is returned to the deck, the probability that the second card is a spade is also $\dfrac{1}{4}$.

   c. The probability that both cards are spades is $\dfrac{1}{4} \cdot \dfrac{1}{4} = \dfrac{1}{16}$.

   d. The probability that the first card is not a spade is $1 - \dfrac{1}{4} = \dfrac{3}{4}$. This is also the probability that the second card is not a spade. Thus, the probability that neither card is a spade is $\dfrac{3}{4} \cdot \dfrac{3}{4} = \dfrac{9}{16}$.

8. a. There are 13 spades and 52 cards in all, so the probability that the first card is a spade is $\dfrac{13}{52} = \dfrac{1}{4}$.

   b. Make a tree diagram. Let S = spade and NS = not a spade.

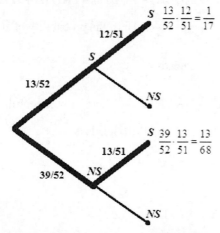

$$S \quad \dfrac{13}{52} \cdot \dfrac{12}{51} = \dfrac{1}{17}$$

$$S \quad \dfrac{39}{52} \cdot \dfrac{13}{51} = \dfrac{13}{68}$$

   We see that there are two paths to follow in order to have the second card drawn a spade. The sum of these probabilities is $\dfrac{1}{17} + \dfrac{13}{68} = \dfrac{1}{4}$.

   c. Drawing without replacement,
   $$P(\text{spade, spade}) = \dfrac{13}{52} \cdot \dfrac{12}{51} = \dfrac{1}{17}.$$

   d. Drawing without replacement,

$$P(\text{not spade, not spade}) = \dfrac{39}{52} \cdot \dfrac{38}{51} = \dfrac{19}{34}.$$

9. a. At most one girl means either no girls or exactly one girl, that is, BBB, GBB, BGB, BBG. Thus, $P(M) = \dfrac{1}{8} + \dfrac{3}{8} = \dfrac{1}{2}$. (Note that the probability that the first child is a girl and the other two are boys is $\dfrac{1}{2} \cdot \dfrac{1}{2} \cdot \dfrac{1}{2} = \dfrac{1}{8}$. This is also the probability that the second child is a girl and the other two are boys and also is the probability that the third child is a girl and the other two are boys. Hence, the probability that there is exactly one girl is $\dfrac{3}{8}$. You can verify this by making a tree diagram.)

   b. $P(B) = 1 - P(\text{no boys}) - P(\text{no girls})$
   $$= 1 - \dfrac{1}{8} - \dfrac{1}{8} = \dfrac{3}{4}$$

   c. M is the event that the family has at most 1 girl, and B is the event that the family has children of both sexes, so $M \cap B$ is the event that the family has exactly 1 girl.

   From part a, $P(1 \text{ girl}) = \dfrac{3}{8}$, so
   $$P(M \cap B) = \dfrac{3}{8}.$$

   d. In part a, we found $P(M) = \dfrac{1}{2}$ and from part b, $P(B) = \dfrac{3}{4}$. Since
   $$\dfrac{3}{8} = \dfrac{1}{2} \cdot \dfrac{3}{4}, P(M \cap B) = P(M)P(B)$$
   which shows that M and B are independent.

10. a. There are 4 kings and 4 aces in a deck of 52 cards. Since this is without replacement,
   $$P(\text{king, ace}) = \dfrac{4}{52} \cdot \dfrac{4}{51} = \dfrac{4}{663}.$$

   b. There are 4 aces in a deck of 52 cards and after the 1st draw there are 3 aces. Thus, $P(\text{ace, ace}) = \dfrac{4}{52} \cdot \dfrac{3}{51} = \dfrac{1}{221}.$

   c. There are 48 cards that are not aces in a deck of 52 cards and after the 1st draw that is not an ace, there remain 47 non-ace cards. Thus,

$$P(\text{not ace, not ace}) = \frac{48}{52} \cdot \frac{47}{51} = \frac{188}{221}.$$

d. The ace could either be the 1ˢᵗ card drawn with the 2ⁿᵈ card not an ace or the 1ˢᵗ card not an ace and the 2ⁿᵈ card an ace. This gives the probability

$$P(\text{ace, not ace}) + P(\text{not ace, ace})$$

$$= \frac{4}{52} \cdot \frac{48}{51} + \frac{48}{52} \cdot \frac{4}{51} = \frac{32}{221}.$$

11. $P(GR) = P(G) \cdot P(R) = \frac{5}{18} \cdot \frac{1}{6} = \frac{5}{108}$

12. $P(WB) = P(W) \cdot P(B) = \frac{2}{9} \cdot \frac{1}{9} = \frac{2}{81}$

13. $P(GG) = P(G) \cdot P(G) = \frac{5}{18} \cdot \frac{5}{18} = \frac{25}{324}$

14. $P(\text{Not } W) = 1 - P(W) = 1 - \frac{2}{9} = \frac{7}{9}$, so

the probability of not landing on the white sector if the spinner is spun twice is

$$P(\text{Not } W) \cdot P(\text{Not } W) = \frac{7}{9} \cdot \frac{7}{9} = \frac{49}{81}.$$

15. $P(R'R') = (1 - P(R))^2 = \left(1 - \frac{1}{6}\right)^2$

$$= \left(\frac{5}{6}\right)^2 = \frac{25}{36}$$

16. There are 5 red marbles out of 20, so $P(R) = \frac{5}{20}$. There are 4 red marbles out of the remaining 19 marbles, so $P(R) = \frac{4}{19}$. Thus, $P(RR) = \frac{5}{20} \cdot \frac{4}{19} = \frac{1}{19}$.

17. There are 5 red marbles out of 20, so $P(R) = \frac{5}{20}$. There are 9 blue marbles out of the remaining 19 marbles, so $P(B) = \frac{9}{19}$. Thus, $P(RB) = \frac{5}{20} \cdot \frac{9}{19} = \frac{9}{76}$.

18. There are 15 marbles that are not red (R') out of 20, so $P(R') = \frac{15}{20}$. There are 14 non-red marbles out of the remaining 19 marbles, so $P(R') = \frac{14}{19}$. Thus, $P(R',R') = \frac{15}{20} \cdot \frac{14}{19} = \frac{21}{38}$.

19. There are 3 green marbles out of 20, so $P(G) = \frac{3}{20}$. There are 3 yellow marbles out of the remaining 19 marbles, so $P(Y) = \frac{3}{19}$. Thus,

$$P(GY) = \frac{3}{20} \cdot \frac{3}{19} = \frac{9}{380}.$$

20. The probability of 2 marbles of the same color is the sum of the probabilities $P(BB)$, $P(RR), P(YY)$, and $P(GG)$. Thus, without replacement,

$$P(BB) + P(RR) + P(YY) + P(GG)$$

$$= \frac{9}{20} \cdot \frac{8}{19} + \frac{5}{20} \cdot \frac{4}{19} + \frac{3}{20} \cdot \frac{2}{19} + \frac{3}{20} \cdot \frac{2}{19} = \frac{26}{95}.$$

21. There are 7 red marbles out of 25, so $P(R) = \frac{7}{25}$. Since the marble is replaced, there are 4 yellow marbles out of 25 marbles, so $P(Y) = \frac{4}{25}$. Thus, $P(RY) = \frac{7}{25} \cdot \frac{4}{25} = \frac{28}{625}$.

22. There are 4 yellow marbles out of 25, so $P(Y) = \frac{4}{25}$. Since the marble is replaced, there are still 4 yellow marbles out of 25 marbles, so $P(Y) = \frac{4}{25}$. Thus,

$$P(YY) = \frac{4}{25} \cdot \frac{4}{25} = \frac{16}{625}.$$

23. Since no blue marble is chosen, one of the remaining 17 marbles is chosen. So, $P(B') = \frac{17}{25}$. Thus,

$$P(B'B') = \frac{17}{25} \cdot \frac{17}{25} = \frac{289}{625}.$$

24. The probability of 2 marbles of the same color is the sum of the probabilities

$P(RR), P(GG), P(BB),$ and $P(YY)$.

Thus, with replacement,

$$P(RR) + P(GG) + P(BB) + P(YY)$$

$$= \frac{7}{25} \cdot \frac{7}{25} + \frac{6}{25} \cdot \frac{6}{25} + \frac{8}{25} \cdot \frac{8}{25} + \frac{4}{25} \cdot \frac{4}{25} = \frac{33}{125}.$$

25. $P(\text{at least 1 red}) = 1 - P(\text{no reds})$

$$= 1 - P(R'R') = 1 - \frac{18}{25} \cdot \frac{18}{25}$$

$$= 1 - \frac{324}{625} = \frac{301}{625}.$$

26. $P(\text{all healthcare}) = (0.41)(0.41)(0.41)$

$$= 0.068921$$

27. $P(\text{none healthcare})$

$$= (0.59)(0.59)(0.59)$$

$$= 0.205379$$

28. $P(\text{healthcare, finance, direct products})$

$$= (0.41)(0.31)(0.14)$$

$$= 0.017794$$

29. $P(\text{none direct product})$

$$= (0.86)(0.86)(0.86) = 0.636056$$

30. Healthcare since it has the largest percent.

31. a. $P(3 \text{ successful}) = \frac{1}{4} \cdot \frac{2}{3} \cdot \frac{1}{2} = \frac{1}{12}$

   b. $P(0 \text{ successful})$

$$= \left(1 - \frac{1}{4}\right)\left(1 - \frac{2}{3}\right)\left(1 - \frac{1}{2}\right)$$

$$= \frac{3}{4} \cdot \frac{1}{3} \cdot \frac{1}{2} = \frac{1}{8}$$

32. $P(1 \text{ successful})$

$$= \frac{1}{4} \cdot \frac{1}{3} \cdot \frac{1}{2} + \frac{3}{4} \cdot \frac{2}{3} \cdot \frac{1}{2} + \frac{3}{4} \cdot \frac{1}{3} \cdot \frac{1}{2} = \frac{10}{24} = \frac{5}{12}$$

33. a. $P(2 \text{ tails}) = \frac{1}{2} \cdot \frac{1}{2} = \frac{1}{4}$

   b. $P(H \text{ and } 6) = \frac{1}{2} \cdot \frac{1}{6} = \frac{1}{12}$

   c. $P(H \text{ and even no.}) = \frac{1}{2} \cdot \frac{3}{6} = \frac{1}{4}$

34. a. Yes. $P(S \cap L) = \frac{42}{100} = \frac{21}{50}$ and

$$P(S) \cdot P(L) = \frac{42 + 28}{100} \cdot \frac{42 + 18}{100}$$

$$= \frac{70}{100} \cdot \frac{60}{100} = \frac{21}{50}$$

Since $P(S \cap L) = P(S) \cdot P(L)$,

S and L are independent.

   b. Yes. $P(S' \cap L') = \frac{12}{100} = \frac{3}{25}$ and

$$P(S') \cdot P(L') = \frac{18 + 12}{100} \cdot \frac{28 + 12}{100}$$

$$= \frac{30}{100} \cdot \frac{40}{100} = \frac{3}{25}$$

Since $P(S' \cap L') = P(S') \cdot P(L')$,

S' and L' are independent.

35. $\dfrac{91{,}220}{98{,}466} \cdot \dfrac{91{,}220}{97{,}586} \approx 0.86579$

36. $\dfrac{81{,}944}{98{,}466} \cdot \dfrac{81{,}944}{97{,}586} \approx 0.6988$

37. $(0.90)^5 \approx 0.59$

38. $P(A \cap B) = \dfrac{1}{4}$ and

$$P(A) \cdot P(B) = \left(\frac{1}{8} + \frac{1}{8} + \frac{1}{4}\right) \cdot \left(\frac{1}{8} + \frac{1}{8} + \frac{1}{4}\right)$$

$$= \frac{1}{2} \cdot \frac{1}{2} = \frac{1}{4}$$

Since $P(A \cap B) = P(A) \cdot P(B)$, A and B are independent.

39. a. $P(\text{all 3 fail}) = \left(\dfrac{1}{20}\right)^3 = \dfrac{1}{8000}$

   b. $P(\text{exactly 2 fail})$

$$= C(3,1) \cdot \frac{1}{20} \cdot \frac{1}{20} \cdot \frac{19}{20} = 3 \cdot \frac{19}{8000} = \frac{57}{8000}$$

40. $P(\text{caught and convicted})$

$= 0.30 \cdot 0.60 = 0.18$

41. a.   National League:

$P(\text{hit}) = \dfrac{54}{254} \approx 0.2126$

American League:

$P(\text{hit}) = \dfrac{66}{274} \approx 0.2409$

b.   The probability of getting a hit in the postseason is higher in the American League.

c.   National League:

$P(4 \text{ hits}) = (0.2126)^4 \approx 0.00204$

American League:

$P(4 \text{ hits}) = (0.2409)^4 \approx 0.00337$

42.   a. Probability Yankees beat the Twins at home is $\dfrac{2}{3}$.

b. Probability Yankees beat the Twins away is $\dfrac{2}{3}$.

c. $P(2 \text{ away}, 1 \text{ home wins})$

$= \left(\dfrac{2}{3}\right)^3 = \dfrac{8}{27}$

43.

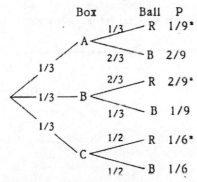

Add the starred items to get:

$P = \dfrac{1}{9} + \dfrac{2}{9} + \dfrac{1}{6} = \dfrac{2}{18} + \dfrac{4}{18} + \dfrac{3}{18} = \dfrac{9}{18} = \dfrac{1}{2}$

44. I(A, A), II(0, 0), III(A, 0)

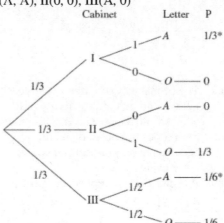

The starred probabilities may be taken as the weights for the corresponding events. Thus, the required probability P is given by:

$$\dfrac{\dfrac{1}{3}}{\dfrac{1}{3} + \dfrac{1}{6}} = \dfrac{\dfrac{2}{6}}{\dfrac{3}{6}} = \dfrac{2}{3}.$$

45. Draw a tree diagram, letting F be the fair coin and U the unbalanced coin:

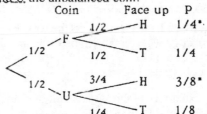

Use the starred numbers as weights to get:

$$P(U|H) = \dfrac{P(U \cap H)}{P(H)} = \dfrac{\dfrac{1}{2} \cdot \dfrac{3}{4}}{\dfrac{3}{8} + \dfrac{1}{4}} = \dfrac{\dfrac{3}{8}}{\dfrac{5}{8}} = \dfrac{3}{5}$$

46.

As in problem 44, the starred probabilities may be taken as the weights for the corresponding events. Thus, the probability P is

$$\frac{\dfrac{3}{10}}{\dfrac{3}{10}+\dfrac{1}{10}}=\frac{\dfrac{3}{10}}{\dfrac{4}{10}}=\frac{3}{4}.$$

47. a.   The probability of either event does not depend on the probability of the other event. The occurrence of either event does not depend on the occurrence or non-occurrence of the other event.

 b.   If A and B are independent events, then $P(A\cap B)=P(A)\cdot P(B)$.

48. Based on this information, the probability that a hurricane in the Atlantic basin hits the United States was $\dfrac{0}{12}=0$. If you assume these probabilities hold for next year, the probability of at least one hurricane in the Atlantic basin hitting the United States is 1 – probability none hitting $= 1 - 0 = 1$.

49. $C(50, 25)$ is the number of ways to get exactly 25 heads and 2^{50} is the total number of ways in which the coin can fall. Thus, $P(\text{exactly 25 heads})=\dfrac{C(50,25)}{2^{50}}$.

We can arrive at the same result by using the formula. Letting

$$n = 50,\ x = 25,\ p = \frac{1}{2},\ \text{and } q = \frac{1}{2},$$

we have

$$C(50,25)\left(\frac{1}{2}\right)^{25}\left(\frac{1}{2}\right)^{50-25}$$

$$=C(50,25)\left(\frac{1}{2}\right)^{25}\left(\frac{1}{2}\right)^{25}$$

$$=C(50,25)\left(\frac{1}{2}\right)^{50}=\frac{C(50,25)}{2^{50}}.$$

50. The probability of getting at least 3 heads if a fair coin is tossed 6 times is

$$\frac{C(6,3)+C(6,4)+C(6,5)+C(6,6)}{2^6}$$

$$=\frac{42}{64}=\frac{21}{32}.$$

51. The numbers of ways of getting 0, 1, or 2 heads (without regard to order) out of the 6 tosses are $C(6, 0)$, $C(6, 1)$, and $C(6, 2)$, respectively. Thus, for the biased coin, the probability of getting less than 3 heads is

$$C(6,0)\left(\frac{1}{3}\right)^{6}+C(6,1)\left(\frac{1}{3}\right)^{5}\left(\frac{2}{3}\right)$$

$$+C(6,2)\left(\frac{1}{3}\right)^{4}\left(\frac{2}{3}\right)^{2}$$

$$=1\cdot\frac{1}{729}+6\cdot\frac{1}{243}\cdot\frac{2}{3}+\frac{6\cdot5}{2\cdot1}\cdot\frac{1}{81}\cdot\frac{4}{9}$$

$$=\frac{1+12+60}{729}=\frac{73}{729}$$

Thus, the probability of getting at least 3 heads is: $1-\dfrac{73}{729}=\dfrac{656}{729}$.

52. Probability gets less and less.

53. The number of ways (without regard to order) of getting exactly two 3's out of 5 tosses is $C(5, 2)$, so the probability is:

$$C(5,2)\cdot\left(\frac{1}{6}\right)^{2}\left(\frac{5}{6}\right)^{3}=\frac{5\cdot4}{2\cdot1}\cdot\frac{1}{36}\cdot\frac{125}{216}$$

$$=\frac{625}{3888}$$

54. Subtract the number of ways (without regard to order) of getting at one 3 and zero 3's out of 5 tosses from 1, so the probability is:

$$1-C(5,1)\left(\frac{1}{6}\right)\left(\frac{5}{6}\right)^{4}-C(5,0)\left(\frac{5}{6}\right)^{5}$$

$$=\frac{763}{3888}\approx 0.196$$

55. The probability that a person fools the first machine is $1 - 0.98 = 0.02$.

56. The probability that a person fools the first two machines is $(0.02)^{2} = 0.0004$.

57. The probability that a person fools all three machines is $(0.02)(0.02)(0.02) = 0.000008$.

58. The system is $1 - 0.000008 = 0.999992 = 99.9992\%$ reliable.

Section 11.6 Odds and Mathematical Expectation

1. There is 1 favorable outcome and there are 5 unfavorable outcomes, so the odds are 1 to 5 in favor of getting a 2.

2. There is 3 favorable outcomes and there are 3 unfavorable outcomes, so the odds are 3 to 3 or 1 to 1 in favor of getting an even number in one roll of a single die.

3. There are 4 aces and 48 other cards, so the odds are 4 to 48 or 1 to 12 in favor of getting an ace.

4. There are 26 red cards and 26 other cards, so the odds are 26 to 26 or 1 to 1 in favor of getting a red card.

5. You can get *TT*, *TH*, *HT*, *HH*, so there is 1 favorable outcome and 3 unfavorable outcomes. Thus, the odds in favor of getting 2 tails are 1 to 3.

6. You can get *TT*, *TH*, *HT*, *HH*, so there are 3 favorable outcomes and 1 unfavorable outcomes. Thus, the odds in favor of getting at least 1 tail is 3 to 1.

7. There are 5 vowels {a, e, i, o, u} and 21 other letters, so the odds in favor of getting a vowel are 5 to 21. (For this problem, do not include the letter y, as it is only sometimes a vowel.)

8. There are 5 unfavorable outcomes and 1 favorable outcome, so the odds are 5 to 1 against getting a 4 in one roll of a single die.

9. There are 3 odd numbers and 3 even numbers, so the odds against getting an odd number are 1 to 1.

19. For the probability $\dfrac{1}{2} = \dfrac{1}{1+1}$, the odds in favor of having complications are 1 to 1.

20. For the probability $\dfrac{1}{4} = \dfrac{1}{3+1}$, the odds in favor of having high cholesterol levels are 1 to 3.

10. There are 51 unfavorable outcomes and 1 favorable outcome, so the odds are 51 to 1 against getting a king of spades.

11. There are 12 picture cards and 40 other cards in the deck, so the odds against getting a picture card are 40 to 12 or 10 to 3.

12. You can get *TT*, *TH*, *HT*, *HH*, so there is 1 unfavorable outcome and 3 favorable outcomes. Thus, the odds against getting at most 1 tail is 1 to 3.

13. To win $5 you need to get 3 out of 6 numbers and the probability of that is:
$$\frac{C(6,3)\cdot C(47,3)}{C(53,6)} = \frac{324{,}300}{22{,}957{,}480} = \frac{32{,}430}{2{,}295{,}748}$$
The odds in favor are 32,430 to 2,263,318.

14. To win $70 you need to get 4 out of 6 numbers and the probability of that is:
$$\frac{C(6,4)\cdot C(47,2)}{C(53,6)} = \frac{16{,}215}{22{,}957{,}480} = \frac{3243}{4{,}591{,}496}$$
The odds in favor are 3243 to 4,588,253.

15. The probability that he wins is $\dfrac{3}{3+2} = \dfrac{3}{5}$.

16. For the probability $\dfrac{1}{20} = \dfrac{1}{19+1}$, the odds of being a victim are 1 to 19.

17. Probability is $\dfrac{630}{100{,}000} = \dfrac{63}{10{,}000}$; the odds in favor of being a victim are 63 to 9937.

18. For the odds 1 to 4, the probability of having complications is $\dfrac{1}{4+1} = \dfrac{1}{5}$.

21. For the odds 10 to 4867, the probability of publishing 1 of the 10 best-selling novels of the year is $\dfrac{10}{4867+10} = \dfrac{10}{4877}$.

22. For the odds 41 to 9, the probability of getting rich by hard work is $\dfrac{41}{41+9} = \dfrac{41}{50}$.

23. For the odds 3 to 21, the probability of being a top executeive is $\dfrac{3}{21+3} = \dfrac{3}{24} = \dfrac{1}{8}$.

24. For the probability $0.19 = \dfrac{19}{100} = \dfrac{19}{19+81}$, the odds in favor completing 4 years of college are 19 to 81.

25. For the probability $0.33 = \dfrac{33}{100} = \dfrac{19}{33+67}$, the odds in favor of growing up incompetent in math are 33 to 67.

26. The probability that heads comes up either time is $\dfrac{3}{4}$, and the probability of no heads is $\dfrac{1}{4}$, so the expected value is
$$E = \$2 \cdot \dfrac{3}{4} - \$4 \cdot \dfrac{1}{4} = \$1.50 - \$1 = \$0.50.$$

27. The probability that the sum is even is $\dfrac{1}{2}$, and this is also the probability that the sum is not even, so the expected value is
$$E = \$10 \cdot \dfrac{1}{2} - \$20 \cdot \dfrac{1}{2} = \$5 - \$10 = -\$5.$$

28. The probability for each number is $\dfrac{1}{6}$, so the expected value is
$$E = \$1 \cdot \dfrac{1}{6} + \$2 \cdot \dfrac{1}{6} + \$3 \cdot \dfrac{1}{6} + \$4 \cdot \dfrac{1}{6}$$
$$+ \$5 \cdot \dfrac{1}{6} + \$6 \cdot \dfrac{1}{6} = \$0.17 + \$0.33 + \$0.50$$
$$+ \$0.67 + \$0.83 + \$1 = \$3.50.$$
To make the game fair, a player should pay $3.50.

29. a. The expected value of the policy is
$$\$300,000(1-0.998349) = \$300,000(0.001651)$$
$$= \$495.30$$
   b. The fair price for the annual premium is $495.30.
   c. The monthly payment is $495.30 \div 12 = \$41.28$.

30. a. The expected value of the policy is
$$\$200,000(1-0.989302) = \$200,000(0.010698)$$
$$= \$2139.60$$
   b. The fair price for the annual premium is $2139.60.
   c. The revenue from the monthly payment is $200 \cdot 12 = \$2400$. The profit is $2400.00 - \$2139.60 = \$260.40$.

31. Expected value is
$$3 \cdot 0.25 + 4 \cdot 0.375 + 5 \cdot 0.375 = 4.125 \text{ games.}$$

32. Expected value is
$$4 \cdot 0.125 + 5 \cdot 0.25 + 6 \cdot 0.3125 + 7 \cdot 0.3125$$
$$= 5.8125 \text{ games.}$$

33. For the first location,
$$E_1 = \$100,000 \cdot \dfrac{2}{3} - \$50,000 \cdot \dfrac{1}{3} = \$50,000.$$
For the second location,
$$E_2 = \$150,000 \cdot \dfrac{2}{5} - \$80,000 \cdot \dfrac{3}{5} = \$12,000.$$
Since $E_1 > E_2$, the first location should be chosen.

34. a. $E_1 = \$20,000 \cdot \dfrac{4}{5} - \$10,000 \cdot \dfrac{1}{5}$
$$= \$14,000$$
   b. $E_2 = \$30,000 \cdot \dfrac{4}{5} + \$5,000 \cdot \dfrac{1}{5}$
$$= \$25,000$$
   c. Since continuing the campaign would result in an expected gain of $14,000, and discontinuing the campaign would result in an expected gain of $25,000. The company should discontinue the campaign.

35. a. $E_1 = \$20,000 \cdot \dfrac{1}{5} - \$10,000 \cdot \dfrac{4}{5}$
$$= -\$4000$$
   b. $E_2 = \$30,000 \cdot \dfrac{1}{5} - \$5000 \cdot \dfrac{4}{5} = \$2000$
   c. Since continuing the campaign would result in an expected loss of $4000, and discontinuing the campaign would result in an expected gain of $2,000, the campaign

should be discontinued.

36.

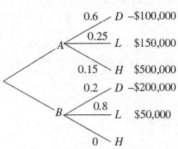

a. The expected value for Site A is
$$E = -\$100,000 \cdot 0.6 + \$150,000 \cdot 0.25$$
$$+ \$500,000 \cdot 0.15 = \$52,500$$

b. The expected value for Site B is
$$E = -\$200,000 \cdot 0.2 + \$50,000 \cdot 0.8 = \$0$$

c. Site A has an expected value that is greater than Site B. The company should select Site A.

37.

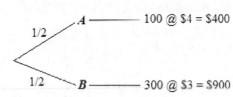

a. $E_A = \$400 \cdot \dfrac{1}{2} = \$200$

b. $E_B = \$900 \cdot \dfrac{1}{2} = \$450$

c. Location B has the better expected value.

38. If the odds in favor of an event are p to q, then the probability of the event is $\dfrac{p}{p+q}$.

39. The mathematical expectation is that you lose $0.58 per $2 bet on the average, so it is not a fair bet. (For a fair bet, the mathematical expectation is 0.)

40. Need to know the gain or loss that depends on how the problem is decided and need to know the odds (or the probability) for the gain or loss.

41. a. The curve shows that the probability of winning is about 0.81.
b. The probability of losing is $1 - 0.81 = 0.19$.

42. a. The probability of winning is about
$$0.81 = \frac{81}{100} \approx \frac{4}{5} \text{, so the odds of winning}$$
are about 4 to 1.
b. The odds against would be 1 to 4.

43. Odds against you are 9 to 1, so put up $1 for each $9. Thus, you should bet $\left(\dfrac{1}{9}\right) \cdot \$10$, or about $1.11, to make the bet fair.
Alternative method:
The curve shows that the probability of winning is 0.9, so the probability of losing is $1 - 0.9 = 0.1$. If $x is put up against the man's $10, the expected value is
$$E = \$x(0.9) - \$10(0.1). \text{ For the bet to be fair,}$$
E must be 0, so we have
$$0.9x - 1 = 0$$
$$9x - 10 = 0$$
$$9x = 10$$
$$x = \frac{10}{9} = 1.111...$$
and (to the nearest cent) $1.11 should be put up against the man's $10.

44. The probability of a black number is $\dfrac{18}{38}$, of a red number is $\dfrac{18}{38}$, and of either 0 or 00 is $\dfrac{2}{38}$.
If 0 or 00 turns up, then the player gets his money back (but gains nothing) if a black number comes up next and loses his $1 if a red number comes up next. Thus, the expected value is
$$E = 1 \cdot \frac{18}{38} - 1 \cdot \frac{18}{38} + 0 \cdot \frac{2}{38} \cdot \frac{18}{38} - 1 \cdot \frac{2}{38} \cdot \frac{18}{38}$$
$$= -\$1 \cdot \frac{9}{19 \cdot 19} \approx -0.025.$$

45. The probability of a black or a red number is $\dfrac{36}{38}$ and if one of these colors comes up, player wins $0.50 and loses $0.50, so he breaks even.
The probability of 0 or 00 is $\dfrac{2}{38}$ and if 0 or 00 turns up, then the player gets his money back (but gains nothing) on one color and loses $0.50 on the other color. Thus, the expected value is

$$E = 0 \cdot \frac{36}{38} - \$0.50 \cdot \frac{2}{38} \cdot \frac{36}{38} = -\frac{\$9}{361}$$
$$\approx -\$0.025 \approx -2.5\text{¢}$$

Collaborative Learning

1. The probability that you lose money given that you choose A is 0.

2. The probability that you make more than $50 given that you choose A is 0.

3. Answers will vary.

4. The probability that you do not make any money given that you choose B is 0.60.

5. The probability that you make more than $50 given that you choose B is 0.40.

6. Answers will vary.

7 – 10. Answers will vary.
NOTE: The probability of winning the lottery varies, depending on the number of balls used in the drawing and how many balls you have to guess. For the sake of argument, suppose there are 40 balls (numbers) in your state and it takes 6 correct numbers to win. The probability that you win is

$$\frac{1}{C(40,6)} = \frac{1}{3,838,380} \approx 0.0000002605. \text{ The}$$

probability that you win with 50 dollars is
$$\frac{50}{C(40,6)} = 0.0000130263288\ldots$$

The probability of winning *at least once* in 50 tries is the same as the probability of *not losing* 50 times in a row. The probability of *losing* is
$1 - 0.0000002605\ldots = 0.9999997394\ldots$

The probability of *losing 50 times in a row* is 0.9999997394... to the 50th power or 0.99998697...

The probability of *not losing 50 times in a row* is $1 - 0.99998697\ldots = 0.0000130262457\ldots$
Note that this is the probability of winning at least once in 50 tries.

So, since the probability of winning at least once in 50 tries is 0.0000130262457... and the

probability of winning one lottery with 50 dollars is 0.0000130263288..., the odds are very slightly more favorable by playing all 50 dollars in one lottery than spreading it out among 50 lotteries.

Author's Note   Is it possible that the small discrepancy is due to rounding? Does it matter what numbers you select? Discuss.

Chapter 11 Practice Test

1. a. This event is certain, so $P(E) = 1$.
   b. 4 of the 6 numbers are greater than 2, so the probability is $\frac{4}{6} = \frac{2}{3}$.

2. a. Of the 5 balls 2 are even numbered, so the probability is $\frac{2}{5}$.
   b. There is just 1 ball numbered 2, so the probability is $\frac{1}{5}$.
   c. The probability is $1 - \frac{1}{5} = \frac{4}{5}$.

3. a. There are 5 possible outcomes on the first draw and 4 possible outcomes on the second draw, so the sample space has $5 \cdot 4 = 20$ elements.
   b. There are 5 possible outcomes on each of the two draws, so the sample space has $5 \cdot 5 = 25$ elements.

4. a. The probability that the first card is red is $\frac{26}{52} = \frac{1}{2}$. If the first card is red, there are 25 red cards out of the 51 cards left, so the probability that the second card is red is $\frac{25}{51}$. Thus, the probability that both cards are red is $\frac{26}{52} \cdot \frac{25}{51} = \frac{1}{2} \cdot \frac{25}{51} = \frac{25}{102}$.
   b. The probability that the first card is not an ace is $\frac{48}{52} = \frac{12}{13}$. The probability that the second card is not an ace is then $\frac{47}{51}$. Thus, the probability that neither card is an ace is $\frac{48}{52} \cdot \frac{47}{51} = \frac{12}{13} \cdot \frac{47}{51} = \frac{188}{221}$.

5. a. 26 of the 52 cards are red, so the probability that both cards will be red is $\dfrac{26}{52} \cdot \dfrac{26}{52} = \dfrac{1}{2} \cdot \dfrac{1}{2} = \dfrac{1}{4}$.

   b. If neither card is red then both cards must be black. The probability that both cards are black is the same as the probability that both cards are red, that is $\dfrac{1}{4}$.

6. $P(\text{no heads}) = \left(\dfrac{1}{2}\right)^5 = \dfrac{1}{32}$. Therefore,

   $P(\text{at least one head}) = 1 - \dfrac{1}{32} = \dfrac{31}{32}$.

7. a. There are 5 white and 3 black balls out of a total of 10 balls, so

   $P(\text{white or black}) = \dfrac{8}{10} = \dfrac{4}{5}$.

   b. This is the same as part a, so the probability is $\dfrac{4}{5}$.

8. There are 12 face cards and a total of 52 cards in the deck, so

   $P(3 \text{ face cards}) = \dfrac{12}{52} \cdot \dfrac{11}{51} \cdot \dfrac{10}{50}$

   $= \dfrac{3}{13} \cdot \dfrac{11}{51} \cdot \dfrac{1}{5} = \dfrac{11}{1105} \approx 0.01$

9. Let E stand for passing English and M stand for passing math. Then, $P(E \cup M) = 0.9, P(E) = 0.8$, and $P(E \cap M) = 0.6$ are all given. Use the equation

   $P(E \cup M) = P(E) + P(M) - P(E \cap M)$

   to get $0.9 = 0.8 + P(M) - 0.6$, which gives $P(M) = 0.7$.

10. This is just the probability that the second die comes up 6, that is, $\dfrac{1}{6}$.

11. In order to get a sum of 11 and have the second die come up an even number, this die must come up 6. Since there are 3 even numbers, the probability that the die comes up 6, given that it is an even number is $1/3$. To get a sum of 11, the first die must come up 5. The probability of this is $\dfrac{1}{6}$. Thus, the probability that the sum is eleven given that the second die comes up an even number is $\dfrac{1}{6} \cdot \dfrac{1}{3} = \dfrac{1}{18}$.

12. a. There are 3 ways to get a sum of 10: 1st die 4, 2nd die 6; 1st die 5, 2nd die 5; 1st die 6, 2nd die 4. Since the dice can come up in 36 ways, the probability of getting a sum of 10 is $\dfrac{3}{36} = \dfrac{1}{12}$.

    b. 3 of the 6 numbers are odd, so the probability of getting an odd number is $\dfrac{3}{6} = \dfrac{1}{2}$.

    c. No. Let A be the event that the sum is 10 and B the event that the first die comes up an odd number. If the first number is odd, then the sum of 10 can be obtained only if both numbers are 5's. From part a, we see that the probability of this is $\dfrac{1}{36}$. Thus, we have $P(A \cap B) = \dfrac{1}{36}$ and $P(A)P(B) = \dfrac{1}{12} \cdot \dfrac{1}{2} = \dfrac{1}{24}$. Since these two results are not equal, A and B are not independent.

13. a. $P = (0.04)^3 = 0.000064$

    b. $P = (1 - 0.04)^3 = (0.96)^3 = 0.884736$

14. There are 2 courses and 3 possible hours. This makes $2 \cdot 3 = 6$ possible arrangements. Thus, the probability that Roland will have English at 8 A.M. and history at 3 P.M. is $\dfrac{1}{6}$.

15. $P = (1 - 0.97)^2 = (0.03)^2 = 0.0009$

16. a. There are 4 kings and 48 other cards, so the odds in favor of selecting a king are 4 to 48 or (dividing by 4) 1 to 12.

    b. The odds against selecting a king are just reversed from the answer in part a. The answer is 12 to 1.

17. a.   Since $P(E) = \frac{3}{7}, P(E') = 1 - \frac{3}{7} = \frac{4}{7}$.

   Thus, the odds in favor of E are 3 to 4.

   b.   The odds against E are 4 to 3 (just the reverse of the answer in part a).

18. a.   If the odds in favor are 3 to 7, the odds against the event are 7 to 3.

   b.   The probability that the event will not occur is $\dfrac{7}{7+3} = \dfrac{7}{10}$.

19. The expected value of this game is

   $$E = \$5 \cdot \frac{1}{2} + \$5 \cdot \frac{1}{4} = \$2.50 + \$1.25 = \$3.75$$

   so we should be willing to pay $3.75 to play this game.

20. From Example 4, you pay $1 to play the Florida Lottery. Thus, the mathematical expected value of winning as an "instant winner" is

   $$E = \$2 \cdot \frac{1}{10} + \$5 \cdot \frac{1}{50} + \$25 \cdot \frac{1}{600} + \$50 \cdot \frac{1}{1200} - \$1$$

   $$= \$0.20 + \$0.10 + \$\frac{1}{24} + \$\frac{1}{24} - \$1$$

   $$= \$0.30 + \$\frac{1}{12} - \$1 = \$0.38\frac{1}{3} - \$1$$

   $$= -\$0.61\frac{2}{3}, \text{ or } -61\frac{2}{3} \text{ cents}$$

Chapter 12 Statistics

Section 12.1 Sampling, Frequency Distributions, and Graphs

1. Descriptive statistics is the science of collecting, organizing and summarizing data.

2. Inferential statistics is the science of drawing conclusions from an organized set of data.

3. A sample usually consists of just a part of the target population.

4. a. The population is the 116 million U.S. households with a TV set.
    b. The sample is the households that agree to use the NPM.

5. a. The implied population is all households in the U. S.
    b. The sample is the 1006 households surveyed.

6. a. The population is all the colleges of the nation.
    b. The sample is the 50 colleges in the sample from which the students took information.

7. a. No, this is not a random sample.
    b. The sample includes only those viewers who are willing to pay for the call.

8. a. The population is adults in the United States.
    b. The sample is the 1015 adults interviewed.
    c. No, this is not a random sample. This is not a random sample because each adult in the United States did not have the same chance of being chosen. Did the sample include homeless, working, out of the country?

9. a. Make a card for each student, number the cards and mix them up. Then draw ten cards at random and select the corresponding students.
    b. Make a card for each student, number the cards and:
       i. Pick only even numbered cards.
       ii. Pick only odd numbered cards.
       iii. Don't mix the cards and pick the first 10.

10. a. The sample is the 50,000 households.
    b. The population is the 120 million total households.

11. a. The target population is all TV watchers.
    b. The sample population is people who visit the Web site and are willing to participate in the survey.
    c. No. Respondents do not necessarily represent the target population (all TV watchers). Those in the target population may not have internet access, may not use that provider, may not hit that pop-up, and so on.

12. a. No. The sample surveys students at the bookstore and would probably not include those who bought books online.
    b. The target population is the students at the school.
    c. The sample population is the students at the bookstore.
    d. No. Some students may not go to the bookstore.

13. Although both surveys ultimately had 50 responses, the second survey should produce more accurate results because $\dfrac{50}{75} \approx 67\%$ of the people responded compared with only $\dfrac{50}{100} = 50\%$ for the first survey.

14. a. The target population is all Americans. The sample population is the group of constituents surveyed.
    b. No. The sample is only of those who live in a particular area, not a sample of the whole U.S.

15. a. Attended a football game last year?

Y	720
N	160
NR	120
Total	1000

    b. So the total will add to 1000.

16. Y $\dfrac{720}{1000} = 0.72 = 72\%$

N $\dfrac{160}{1000} = 0.16 = 16\%$

NR $\dfrac{120}{1000} = 0.12 = 12\%$

17. a.

Number of Hours	Tally Marks	Frequency
0	I	1
1	I	1
2	III	3
3	III	3
4	III	3
5	III	3
6	IIII	4
7	II	2

b.   The most frequent number is 6 hours.

c.   6 people spend more than the 5.18 hr
daily average; $\dfrac{6}{20} = 0.3 = 30\%$

d.   14 people spend few than the 5.18 hr
daily average; $\dfrac{14}{20} = 0.7 = 70\%$

18. a.

Number of Hours	Tally Marks	Frequency
0	I	1
1	I	1
2	I	1
3	II	2
4	I	1
5	III	3
6	II	2
7	I	1
8	I	1
9	I	1
10	II	2
11	III	3
12	IIII	4
13	IIII	4
14	II	2
15	I	1

b.   The most frequent number of hours
spent online person is 12 and 13
hours.

c. $4 + 4 + 2 + 1 = 11$ people are online
more than 11 hours;

$\dfrac{11}{30} \approx 0.367 = 36.7\%$

d. $1 + 1 + 1 + 2 + 1 + 3 = 9$ people;

$\dfrac{9}{30} \approx 0.3 = 30\%$

19. a.

Outcome	Tally Marks	Frequency
1	IIII IIII I	11
2	II	2
3	IIII I	6
4	II	2
5	IIII III	8
6	I	1

b.   The most frequent outcome is the 1. It
occurred 11 times.

c.   The least frequent outcome is the 6. It
occurred 1 time.

20. a.

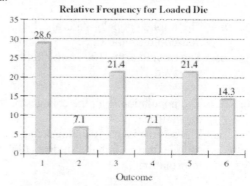

b.   The 1 occurs 28.6% of the time.

c.   The 4 occurs 7.1% of the time.

d.   You can only if you know the total
number of outcomes.

21. a.

Number of Hours	Tally Marks	Frequency
0	II	2
1	III	3
2	II	2
3	III	3
4	III	3
5	II	2
6	II	2
7	II	2
8	IIII	4
9	I	1
10	II	2
11		0
12	II	2
13		0
14	I	1
15	I	1

b. The most frequent number of hours watched is 8.

c. $0 + 2 + 0 + 1 + 1 = 4$ students watched television more than 10 hr.

d. $2 + 3 + 2 + 3 + 3 + 2 = 15$ students watched television 5 hr or less.

e. $4 + 1 + 2 + 0 + 2 + 0 + 1 + 1 = 11$ students watched television more than 7 hr, which is $\dfrac{11}{30} \approx 0.367 = 36.7\%$.

22.

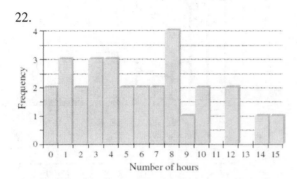

23. a.

b. There were 18 out of 50 patients, that is, $\dfrac{18}{50} = 0.36 = 36\%$, who waited 7.0 min or less.

c. There were 26 out of 50 patients, that is, $\dfrac{26}{50} = 0.52 = 52\%$ who had to wait more than 10.5 min.

24. a.

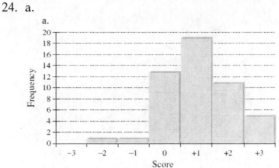

b. There were $19 + 11 + 5 = 35$ tasters that liked Solid H, that is, $\dfrac{35}{50} = 0.70 = 70\%$.

c. There were $\dfrac{13}{50} = 0.26 = 26\%$ undecided tasters.

25. a.

Age	Tally Marks	Frequency
6	I	1
7	I	1
8	III	3
9	III	3
10	II	2

b.

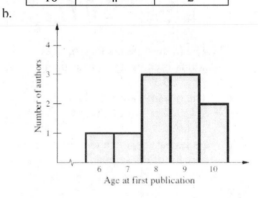

c. From the histogram, we see that $\dfrac{2}{10} = 0.20 = 20\%$ authors were less than 8 years old when they published their first book.

26. a.

Height (in.)	Tally Marks	Frequency
62	III	3
63	II	2
64	II	2
65	I	1
66	II	2

b.

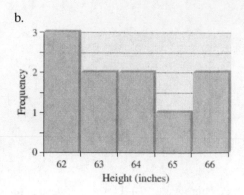

27. a.

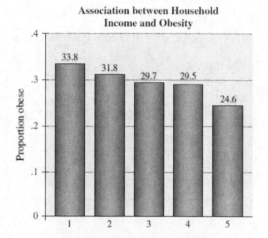

Association between Household Income and Obesity

b. The highest percentage of obese adults is category 1: Less than $15,000.

c. The obesity rate for adults making $50,000 or more (Category 5) is 24.6%.

d. As household income *increases*, the percent of obese people *decreases*.

28. a.

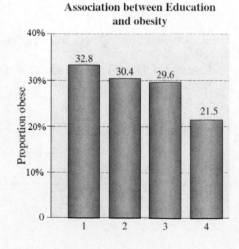

Association between Education and obesity

b. The most obese people are in category 1: Did not graduate High School.

c. The obesity rate for people who attended College or Technical School is 29.6%.

d. As the level of schooling *increases*, the percent of obese people *decreases*.

29.

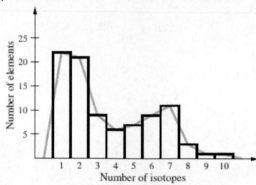

30. a.

Inches	Tally Marks	Frequency
0.245	I	1
0.246	I	1
0.247	II	2
0.248	I	1
0.249	IIII	4
0.250	II	2
0.251	IIII	4
0.252	II	2
0.253	II	2
0.254	I	1

b. The measurement 0.250 in. has 9 measurements below and 9 above it.

c. Between 0.249 and 0.251, inclusive, there are $4 + 2 + 4 = 10$ measurements, which is $\dfrac{10}{20} = 0.50 = 50\%$ of the measurements.

d. The best estimate of the diameter would be 0.250 in. because it is the median (middle value).

31. a.

Letter	Frequency	Letter	Frequency
a	10	n	13
b	4	o	14
c	3	p	2
d	4	q	0
e	18	r	7
f	2	s	10
g	3	t	17
h	9	u	5
i	12	v	2
j	0	w	5
k	1	x	0
l	4	y	2
m	4	z	0

b.   The letter e occurs most frequently.
c.   The vowels are a, e, i, o, and u, of which there is $10 + 18 + 12 + 14 + 5 = 59$. Thus, $\dfrac{59}{151} \approx 0.391 = 39.1\%$ of the letters are vowels.

32.

No. of Heads	Tally Marks	Frequency
0	‖	2
1	ⵌ ‖‖	8
2	ⵌ ⵌ ‖	12
3	ⵌ ‖‖	8
4	‖	2

33. a. and b.

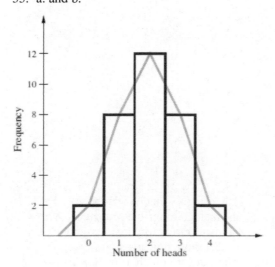

34.

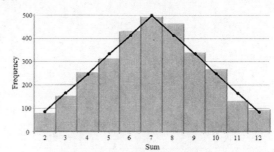

Histogram shows actual frequency; line shows theoretical frequency.

35. a.

Concentration	Tally Marks	Frequency
0.00-0.04	ⵌ ‖	6
0.05-0.09	ⵌ ⵌ ‖‖‖	13
0.10-0.14	ⵌ	5
0.15-0.19	‖‖‖‖	4
0.20-0.24	‖	2

b.   The concentration of sulfur dioxide was more than 0.14 part per million $4 + 2 = 6$ times, or $\dfrac{6}{30} = 0.20 = 20\%$ of the time.

c.   The frequency distribution groups data so use the raw data for the exact count. The concentration of sulfur dioxide was more than 0.075 part per million 17 times, or $\dfrac{17}{30} \approx 0.567 = 56.7\%$ of the time.

36.

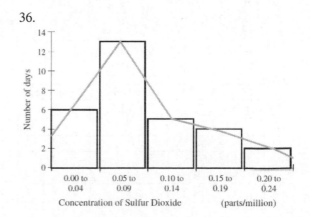

37. a.

Weekly Salary	Tally Marks	Frequency
$600-$2400	ⵌ ‖‖‖‖	9
$2400-$4200		0
$4200-$6000	‖	2
$6000-$7800	‖	1

b.

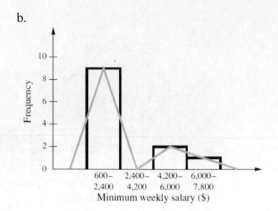

b.

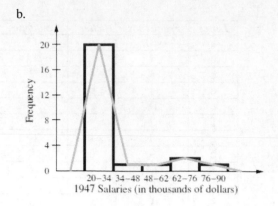

38. a.

Salaries (millions)	Tally Marks	Frequency
$7^+ - 8$	|||||	5
$8^+ - 9$	|||||	5
$9^+ - 10$	|||	3
$10^+ - 11$	||	2

b.

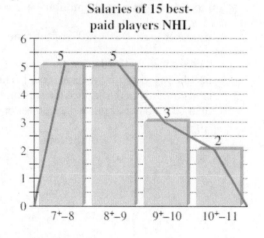

Salaries of 15 best-paid players NHL

39. a.

Salary (X 1000)	Tally Marks	Frequency
$20-$34	||||| ||||| ||||| |||||	20
$34-$48			1
$48-$62			1
$62-$76	||	2
$76-$90			1

40. a.

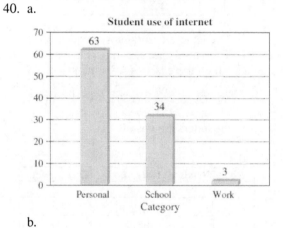

b.

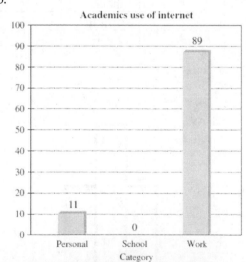

c. The category that has the shortest bar in the histogram for the students is Work. Students rarely use the internet for work, or that most students do not work.

d. The category that has the longest bar in the histogram for the students is Work. Academics use the internet mostly for work.

41. a.   The class width is

$$(550 - 180) \div 5 = 370 \div 5 = \$74.$$

   b.

Price	Tally Marks	Frequency
$180-$254	⊪	5
$254-$328	⊪ II	7
$328-$402		0
$402-$476	I	1
$476-$550	II	2

   c.

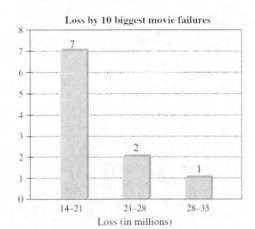

Cost of netbooks ($)

42. a.   The class width is

$$(35 - 14) \div 3 = 21 \div 3 = \$7 \text{ million.}$$

   b.

Loss (millions)	Tally Marks	Frequency
14 – 21	⊪ II	7
21 – 28	II	2
28 – 35	I	1

   c.

Loss by 10 biggest movie failures

Loss (in millions)

43. a.   The class width is

$$(122 - 115) \div 4 = 7 \div 4 = 1.75 \approx 2 \text{ years.}$$

   b.

Age	Tally Marks	Frequency
115–117	⊪ ⊪ ⊪ IIII	19
117–119	IIII	4
119–121	I	1
121–123	I	1

   c.

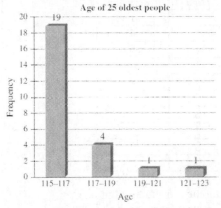

Age of 25 oldest people

44. Tract 1305 has the most renter-occupied homes.

45. Tract 1304 has the fewest renter-occupied homes.

46. Tract 1304 has the fewest vacant homes.

47. Chose tract 1305 as it has the most renter-occupied homes.

48. a.   The sample size is 198 + 2 = 200.
    b.   The test was incorrect 1 time when test says not pregnant but was actually pregnant.
    c. $\dfrac{1}{200} = 0.005 = 0.5\%$

49. No. The women were not selected at random. Only women who thought that they might be pregnant would chose to buy the test.

50. They only surveyed Midway travelers.

51. No. Not all members of the population had the same chance of being chosen.

52. This is done so that there will be no space between adjacent bars.

53. The lower and upper class limits, respectively, are the least and the greatest values in that class. Each class boundary is the midpoint

between the upper limit of the respective class and the lower limit of the next class.

54. $130 + 123 = 253 \neq 200$; somebody can't count!

55.

Digit	Frequency
0	1
1	4
2	5
3	6
4	4
5	4
6	3
7	3
8	5
9	5

56. The most frequent digit is 3. The least frequent digit is 0.

57. Yes, the jump in sales from first 9 months to first quarter is $3{,}205{,}000 - 3{,}104{,}729 = 100{,}271$.

58. Yes, the percent rise is
$$\frac{100{,}271}{3{,}104{,}729} \approx 0.032 = 3.2\%$$

59. Yes. In each case, most of the bar is omitted.

60. a. It can be either frequencies or relative frequencies. The y-axis needs to start at 0, so that the bars are not distorted.
    b. The percent difference is about $62\% - 54\% = 8\%$, based on the graph.
    c. They could be very close. The Democrats could be lower, $62\% - 7\% = 55\%$ and the Republicans could be higher, $54\% + 7\% = 61\%$, for a difference of only 6%.
    d. Start the y-axis at zero, not 53.

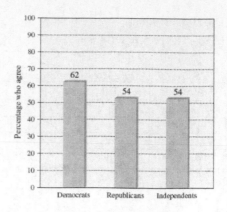

Collaborative Learning

1. Answers will vary.   2. Answers will vary.

3. Makeup and deodorant cause the most allergies. To sell hypoallergenic products concentrate on manufacturing shampoo and aftershave as they are the products that cause allergies the least amongst those considered on this chart.

4. No. There is space between bars. The figure is a bar graph. It makes no difference.

5.

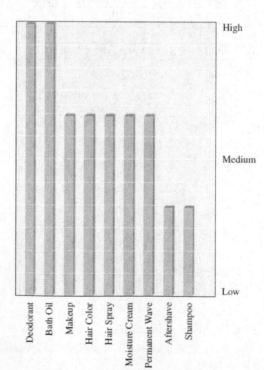

**Section 12.2 Measures of Central Tendency:
The Mean, Median, and Mode**

1. a. Mean $= \dfrac{1+5+9+13+17}{5} = \dfrac{45}{5} = 9$

   and median is the 5th term: 9

   b. Mean $=$
   $\dfrac{1+5+9+27+81}{5} = \dfrac{121}{5} = 24.2$

   and median is the 5th term: 9

   c. Mean $= \dfrac{1+4+9+16+25}{5} = \dfrac{55}{5} = 11$

   and median is the 5th term: 9

   d. The mean and medium are the same
   for part a only. The median is 9 for all
   three. None has a mode.

2. Order the numbers: 1, 2, 4, 8, 16, 32. The
   median is the average of the 3rd and 4th

   terms: $\dfrac{4+8}{2} = \dfrac{12}{2} = 6$. The mean $=$

   $\dfrac{1+2+4+8+16+32}{6} = \dfrac{63}{6} = 10.5$. Thus,

   the median of this set is less than the
   mean.

3. Mean $= \dfrac{121}{20} = 6.05$, the median is the

   average of the 10th and 11th terms:

   $\dfrac{6+7}{2} = \dfrac{13}{2} = 6.5$, and the mode is the

   most frequent score, 8. The mode is the
   least representative.

4. Mean $= \dfrac{568}{11} \approx 51.6$ and the median is the
   6th term: 60.

5. Betty is correct. She took account of the
   number of students making each score,
   and Agnes did not.

6. Average cost per share is
   $\dfrac{50 \cdot \$60 + 60 \cdot \$50 + 40 \cdot \$75}{50+60+40}$

   $= \dfrac{\$3000 + \$3000 + \$3000}{150} = \dfrac{9000}{150} = \$60$

7. The frequency distribution is

Number of Letters	Frequency
2	1
3	5
4	4
5	5
6	0
7	3
8	2
9	0
10	0
11	1

   a. There are two modes: 3 and 5.
   b. The sum of the frequencies is 21, so add
   the numbers in the frequency column until
   we first get a sum of 11 or more. This
   occurs in the row where the number of
   letters is 5, so the median is 5.
   c. The mean is

   $\dfrac{2 \cdot 1 + 3 \cdot 5 + \cdots + 10 \cdot 0 + 11 \cdot 1}{21} = \dfrac{106}{21} \approx 5.05$

   d. No. There is too much repetition for this
   to be representative of ordinary English
   writing.

8. The frequency distribution is

Temperatures	Frequency
64	2
65	1
66	2
69	1
71	3
74	1
75	1
76	1
79	1
81	1
86	1
89	1
90	1
91	2
92	2

   a. $\bar{x} = \dfrac{1623}{21} \approx 77.3$, median is 11th term: 75

   b. $\bar{x} = \dfrac{791}{9} \approx 87.9$, median is 5th term: 90

   c. $\bar{x} = \dfrac{472}{7} \approx 67.4$, median is 4th term: 66

9. b. – c. Answers will vary, but should be
   approximately 8.

10. The sum of the test scores is
$20 \cdot 75 = 1500$.

11. If the mean in 81, then
$$\frac{1560 + x}{20} = 81$$
$$1560 + x = 1620$$
$$x = 60$$
The grade on the lost paper is 60.

12. If the mean in 82, then
$$\frac{1560 + x}{20} = 82$$
$$1560 + x = 1640$$
$$x = 80$$
The grade on the lost paper is 80.

13. Company A: $20 \cdot \$90 = \$1800$
Company B: $30 \cdot \$80 = \$2400$
The new mean salary is
$$\frac{1800 + 2400}{50} = \frac{1200}{50} = \$84 \text{ per week}$$

14.
$$\frac{5 \cdot 88 + x}{6} = 80$$
$$\frac{440 + x}{6} = 80$$
$$440 + x = 480$$
$$x = 40$$
She must obtain a score of 40.

15. a. The proportion of families that have incomes of at least $25,000 is the sum of the last five items:
$0.11 + 0.10 + 0.07 + 0.05 + 0.01 = 0.34$
   b. Locate the bracket that contains 0.50 by starting at the top and adding down. Thus $20,000–$24,999 is the median income range.
   c. The mean of the lower income levels in thousands of dollars is
$$\frac{\text{sum of lower limits}}{9} = \frac{355,000}{9} \approx \$39,444$$
   d. The sum of the first three proportions is 0.36 which means that 36% have incomes less than $20,000.

16. a.
$$\bar{x} = \frac{5.34 + 4.55 + 4.41 + 4.38 + 4.35}{5}$$
$$= \frac{23.03}{5} \approx \$4.61$$
Median is 3rd term: $4.41
No mode.
   b. No. The mean, median and mode are not close.
   c. The median is most representative.
   d. Without Hong Kong:
$$\bar{x} = \frac{4.55 + 4.41 + 4.38 + 4.35}{5}$$
$$= \frac{17.69}{4} \approx \$4.42$$
Median is average of the 2nd and 3th terms: $\frac{4.38 + 4.41}{2} \approx \$4.40$
No mode. The mean and median are most representative.

17. a.
$$\bar{x} = \frac{0.28 + 0.74 + 0.75 + 0.77 + 0.82}{5}$$
$$= \frac{3.36}{5} \approx \$0.67$$
Median is 3rd term: $0.75
No mode.
   b. No. The mean, median and mode are not close.
   c. The median is most representative.
   d. Without Caracas:
$$\bar{x} = \frac{0.74 + 0.75 + 0.77 + 0.82}{4}$$
$$= \frac{3.08}{4} = \$0.77$$
Median is average of the 2nd and 3th terms: $\frac{0.75 + 0.77}{2} = \$0.76$
No mode. The mean and median are most representative.

18. Statement (d) applies.

19. a.
$$\bar{x} = \frac{1553 + 1449 + 1411 + 1311}{5}$$
$$= \frac{7199}{5} \approx \$1439.80$$
Arrange the weekly salaries in order of magnitude: $1311, $1411, $1449, $1475, $1553. The median is 3rd term: $1449
No mode.

b. The median is higher.

20. a. $\bar{x} = \dfrac{2085 + 1954 + 1935 + 1788 + 1550}{5}$

$= \dfrac{9312}{5} \approx \$1862.40$

Arrange the weekly salaries in order of magnitude: \$1550, \$1788, \$1935, \$1954, \$2085. The median is 3rd term: \$1935

No mode.

b. The median is higher.

21. $\bar{x} = \dfrac{247 + 481 + 817 + 764}{4}$

$= \dfrac{2309}{4} = 577.25$

Arrange the number of houses in order of magnitude: 247, 481, 764, 817. The median is average between the 2nd and 3rd

terms: $\dfrac{481 + 764}{2} = \dfrac{1245}{2} = 622.5$

22. $\bar{x} = \dfrac{367 + 611 + 1315 + 900}{4}$

$= \dfrac{3193}{4} = 798.25$

Arrange the number of houses in order of magnitude: 367, 611, 900, 1315. The median is average between the 2nd and 3rd

terms: $\dfrac{611 + 900}{2} = \dfrac{1511}{2} = 755.5$

23. The mean is

$\bar{x} = \dfrac{-18 + 8 + 5 + 46 + 62}{5} = \dfrac{103}{5} = 20.6$

24. The mean is

$\bar{x} = \dfrac{-13 + 16 + 45}{3} = \dfrac{48}{3} = 16$

25. The mean number of spams in July is

$\bar{x} = \dfrac{14 + 28 + 18 + 40 + 2 + 30 + 16 + 28 + 24}{9}$

$= \dfrac{200}{9} \approx 22.2$

26. Arrange the number of spams in July in order of magnitude: 2, 14, 16, 18, 24, 28, 28, 30, 40. The median is the 5th term: 24

27. The mode is 28, since it occurs twice.

28. The categories in which the number of spams received did not change from July to August are Products and Spiritual.

29. The category that increased the most from July to August was Internet.

30. Magic Kingdom:

$\bar{x} = \dfrac{11.2 + 12.9 + 13.8 + 17.0}{4}$

$= \dfrac{54.9}{4} = 13.725$ million

Arrange the attendance in order of magnitude: 11.2, 12.9, 13.8, 17.0. The median is average between the 2nd and 3rd terms:

$\dfrac{12.9 + 13.8}{2} = \dfrac{26.7}{2} = 13.35$ million.

The current attendance is greater than the averages, so attendance has increased.

31. Disneyland:

$\bar{x} = \dfrac{10.3 + 14.1 + 15.0 + 14.3}{4}$

$= \dfrac{53.7}{4} = 13.425$ million

Arrange the attendance in order of magnitude: 10.3, 14.1, 14.3, 15.0. The median is average between the 2nd and 3rd terms:

$\dfrac{14.1 + 14.3}{2} = \dfrac{28.4}{2} = 14.2$ million.

The current attendance is greater than the averages, so attendance has increased.

32. Epcot:

$\bar{x} = \dfrac{9.7 + 10.7 + 11.2 + 11.8}{4}$

$= \dfrac{43.4}{4} = 10.85$ million

Arrange the attendance in order of magnitude: 9.7, 10.7, 11.2, 11.8. The median is average between the 2nd and 3rd terms:

$\dfrac{10.7 + 11.2}{2} = \dfrac{21.9}{2} = 10.95$ million.

The current attendance is smaller than the averages, so attendance has decreased.

33. Disney-MGM:

$$\overline{x} = \frac{8.0 + 9.5 + 10.0 + 10.5}{4}$$

$$= \frac{38}{4} = 9.5 \text{ million}$$

Arrange the attendance in order of magnitude: 8.0, 9.5, 10.0, 10.5. The median is average between the 2nd and 3rd terms: $\frac{9.5 + 10.0}{2} = \frac{19.5}{2} = 9.75$ million.

The current attendance is greater than the mean, so attendance has increased.

34. Universal Studios Florida:

$$\overline{x} = \frac{7.7 + 8.0 + 8.4 + 8.9}{4}$$

$$= \frac{33}{4} = 8.25 \text{ million}$$

Arrange the attendance in order of magnitude: 7.7, 8.0, 8.4, 8.9. The median is average between the 2nd and 3rd terms:

$$\frac{8.0 + 8.4}{2} = \frac{16.4}{2} = 8.2 \text{ million}.$$

The current attendance is smaller than the averages, so attendance has decreased.

35. The average number of visitors to the top 10 Web sites overall is

$$\overline{x} = \frac{\text{sum of unique visitors}}{10}$$

$$= \frac{4750}{10} = 475 \text{ million}$$

36. The average number of visitors to the top 10 education sites is

$$\overline{x} = \frac{\text{sum of unique visitors}}{10}$$

$$= \frac{28.5}{10} = 2.85 \text{ million}$$

37. $\overline{x} =$

$$\frac{39,468 + 39,276 + 40,827 + 46,778 + 49,733}{5}$$

$$= \frac{216,082}{5} = \$43,216.40$$

Arrange the salaries in order of magnitude: $39,276, $39,468, $40,827, $46,778, $49,733. The median is the 3rd term: $40,827. There is no mode.

b. The median is most representative of the person's salary.

38. a. $\overline{x} =$

$$\frac{20,484 + 19,935 + 21,611 + 22,679 + 23,845}{5}$$

$$= \frac{108,554}{5} = \$21,710.80$$

Arrange the salaries in order of magnitude: $19,935, $20,484, $21,611, $22,679, $23,845. The median is the 3rd term: $21,611. There is no mode.

b. Either mean or median depending upon use.

39. The median of a set of scores is the middle number (if there is one) when the scores are arranged in order of magnitude. If there is no middle number, the median is the average of the two middle numbers. The median is not a good measure of a set of scores as it gives no indication of how the scores are spread. (The median could be considered a good measure of a set of scores if one wants to negate the effect of outliers, that is, scores that are either very high or low as compared to the other scores.)

40. The mode of the set of scores is the score that occurs most often. This could be a good measure. If the mode is a failing score on a statistics test, this could mean that the class needed more help to understand the subject. The mode uniformly works best with nominal (non-numeric) data such as names for babies, types of cars, school colors, etc.

41. a. The average (mean) number of people in line is $\overline{x} = \dfrac{2 + 3 + 2 + 3 + 2}{5} = \dfrac{12}{5} = 2.4$

b. The mode is 2 because there are 2 people in line in three of the five minutes.

42. a.

		E	F		
		D	E	F	
A	B	C	D	E	
1	2	3	4	5	

b. The average (mean) number of people in line is

$$\overline{x} = \frac{1 + 1 + 3 + 3 + 2}{5} = \frac{10}{5} = 2$$

c. There are two modes, 1 and 3, because there is one person in line in two of the five minutes and 3 people in line also in two of the five minutes.

43. This "average" is the mean in dollars as shown.

$$\overline{x} =$$

$$\frac{100,000 + 50,000 + 25,000 + 2 \cdot 10,000 + 6 \cdot 6000}{11}$$

$$= \frac{231,000}{11} = \$21,000$$

Scrooge is using the mean of all the salaries.

44. Manny Chevitz uses either the mode or the median as his "average." The median and mode are both $6000.

45. B. Crooked is using the mean of a secretary's and a worker's salary as his "average" as shown.

$$\overline{x} = \frac{10,000 + 6000}{2} = \frac{16,000}{2} = \$8000$$

Collaborative Learning

	RACE	SEX
1.	29,764.6	24,900.2
2.	31,182.6	26,735.6
3.	$36.42 million	$46.26 million

Section 12.3 Measures of Dispersion: The Range and Standard Deviation

1. a. Range = 21 − 3 = 18
   b.

x	$x - \overline{x}$	$(x - \overline{x})^2$
3	−7	49
5	−5	25
8	−2	4
13	3	9
21	11	121
50		**208**

$$\overline{x} = \frac{50}{5} = 10 \qquad \frac{208}{4} = 52$$

$$s = \sqrt{52} \approx 7.21$$

2. a. Range = 25 − 1 = 24
   b.

x	$x - \overline{x}$	$(x - \overline{x})^2$
1	−10	100
4	−7	49
9	−2	4
16	5	25
25	14	196
55		**374**

$$\overline{x} = \frac{55}{5} = 11 \qquad \frac{374}{4} = 93.5$$

$$s = \sqrt{93.5} \approx 9.67$$

3. a. Range = 25 − 5 = 20
   b.

x	$x - \overline{x}$	$(x - \overline{x})^2$
5	−10	100
10	−5	25
15	0	0
20	5	25
25	10	100
75		**250**

$$\overline{x} = \frac{75}{5} = 15 \qquad \frac{250}{4} = 62.5$$

$$s = \sqrt{62.5} \approx 7.91$$

4. a. Range = 18 − 6 = 12
   b.

x	$x - \overline{x}$	$(x - \overline{x})^2$
6	−6	36
9	−3	9
12	0	0
15	3	9
18	6	36
60		**90**

$$\overline{x} = \frac{60}{5} = 12 \qquad \frac{90}{4} = 22.5$$

$$s = \sqrt{22.5} \approx 4.74$$

5. a. Range = 9 – 5 = 4

    b.

x	$x - \overline{x}$	$\left(x - \overline{x}\right)^2$
5	–2	4
6	–1	1
7	0	0
8	1	1
9	2	4
35		**10**

$$\overline{x} = \frac{35}{5} = 7 \qquad \frac{10}{4} = 2.5$$

$$s = \sqrt{2.5} \approx 1.58$$

6. a. Range = 12 – 4 = 8

    b.

x	$x - \overline{x}$	$\left(x - \overline{x}\right)^2$
4	–4	16
6	–2	4
8	0	0
10	2	4
12	4	16
40		**40**

$$\overline{x} = \frac{40}{5} = 8 \qquad \frac{40}{4} = 10$$

$$s = \sqrt{10} \approx 3.16$$

7. a. Range = 9 – 1 = 8

    b.

x	$x - \overline{x}$	$\left(x - \overline{x}\right)^2$
5	0	0
9	4	16
1	–4	16
3	–2	4
8	3	9
7	2	4
2	–3	9
35		**58**

$$\overline{x} = \frac{35}{7} = 5 \qquad \frac{58}{6} \approx 9.67$$

$$s = \sqrt{9.67} \approx 3.11$$

8. a. Range = 10 – 0 = 10

    b.

x	$x - \overline{x}$	$\left(x - \overline{x}\right)^2$
2	–3	9
0	–5	25
4	–1	1
6	1	1
8	3	9
10	5	25
8	3	9
2	–3	9
40		88

$$\overline{x} = \frac{40}{8} = 5 \qquad \frac{88}{7} \approx 12.57$$

$$s = \sqrt{12.57} \approx 3.55$$

9. a. Range = 3 – (–3) = 6

    b.

x	$x - \overline{x}$	$\left(x - \overline{x}\right)^2$
–3	–3	9
–2	–2	4
–1	–1	1
0	0	0
1	1	1
2	2	4
3	3	9
0		**28**

$$\overline{x} = \frac{0}{7} = 0 \qquad \frac{28}{6} \approx 4.67$$

$$s = \sqrt{4.67} \approx 2.16$$

10. a. Range = 6 – (–6) = 12

     b.

x	$x - \overline{x}$	$\left(x - \overline{x}\right)^2$
–6	–6	36
–4	–4	16
–2	–2	4
0	0	0
2	2	4
4	4	16
6	6	36
0		**112**

$$\overline{x} = \frac{0}{7} = 0 \qquad \frac{112}{6} \approx 18.67$$

$$s = \sqrt{18.67} \approx 4.32$$

11. a. The most frequent number is the mode, 8.

     b. The number of students is even, so the
         median is the average of the 10th and 11th

terms: $\dfrac{6+7}{2} = \dfrac{13}{2} = 6.5$

c. The mean is $\overline{x} = \dfrac{\text{sum}}{20} = \dfrac{120}{20} = 6.$

d.

x	$x - \overline{x}$	$\left(x - \overline{x}\right)^2$
0	–6	36
0	–6	36
1	–5	25
2	–4	16
4	–2	4
4	–2	4
5	–1	1
6	0	0
6	0	0
6	0	0
7	1	1
8	2	4
8	2	4
8	2	4
8	2	4
9	3	9
9	3	9
9	3	9
10	4	16
10	4	16
10	4	16
120		**198**

$\overline{x} = \dfrac{120}{20} = 6$ $\qquad$ $\dfrac{198}{19} \approx 10.42$

$s = \sqrt{10.42} \approx 3.23$

e. The table shows that 14 of the 20 scores, or $\dfrac{14}{20} = 0.7 = 70\%$ of the scores, lie within 1 standard deviation of the mean.

f. The table shows that 20 of the 20 scores, or $\dfrac{20}{20} = 100\%$ of the scores, lie within 2 standard deviations of the mean.

12. a. The most frequent number is the mode, 8.

b. The number of students is even, so the median is the average of the 8th and 9th terms: $\dfrac{8+8}{2} = \dfrac{16}{2} = 8$

c. The mean is $\overline{x} = \dfrac{\text{sum}}{16} = \dfrac{117}{16} \approx 7.31.$

d.

x	$x - \overline{x}$	$\left(x - \overline{x}\right)^2$
4	–3.3125	10.97265625
4	–3.3125	10.97265625
5	–2.3125	5.34765625
6	–1.3125	1.72265625
6	–1.3125	1.72265625
6	–1.3125	1.72265625
7	–0.3125	0.09765625
8	0.6875	0.47265625
8	0.6875	0.47265625
8	0.6875	0.47265625
8	0.6875	0.47265625
9	1.6875	2.84765625
9	1.6875	2.84765625
9	1.6875	2.84765625
10	2.6875	7.22265625
10	2.6875	7.22265625
117		**57.4375**

$\overline{x} = \dfrac{117}{16} \approx 7.31$ $\qquad$ $\dfrac{57.4375}{15} \approx 3.83$

$s = \sqrt{3.83} \approx 1.96$

e. The table shows that 11 of the 16 scores, or $\dfrac{11}{16} = 0.6875 = 68.75\%$ of the scores, lie within 1 standard deviation of the mean.

f. The table shows that 16 of the 16 scores, or $\dfrac{16}{16} = 100\%$ of the scores, lie within 2 standard deviations of the mean.

13. a. The most frequent number is the mode, 110.

b. Arrange the hours in order of magnitude: 102, 103, 105, 106, 110, 110, 110, 110, 111, 113. The number of terms is even, so the median is the average of the 5th and 6th terms: $\dfrac{110+110}{2} = \dfrac{220}{2} = 110$

c. The mean is $\overline{x} = \dfrac{\text{sum}}{10} = \dfrac{1080}{10} = 108.$

d.

x	$x-\overline{x}$	$\left(x-\overline{x}\right)^2$
103	–5	25
110	2	4
113	5	25
102	–6	36
105	–3	36
110	2	4
111	3	9
110	2	4
106	–2	4
110	2	4
1080		**124**

$$\overline{x}=\frac{1080}{10}=108 \qquad \frac{124}{9}\approx 13.78$$

$$s=\sqrt{13.78}\approx 3.71$$

e. The values more than 1 standard deviation of the mean are 102, 103, and 113. Thus, $\frac{3}{10}=0.30=30\%$ of the values are more than 1 standard deviation of the mean.

14. a. The most frequent number is the mode, 110.

   b. Arrange the hours in order of magnitude: 102, 103, 105, 106, 110, 110, 110, 110. The number of terms is even, so the median is the average of the 4th and 5th terms:
   $$\frac{106+110}{2}=\frac{216}{2}=108$$

   c. The mean is $\overline{x}=\frac{\text{sum}}{8}=\frac{856}{8}=107$.

   d.

x	$x-\overline{x}$	$\left(x-\overline{x}\right)^2$
103	–4	16
110	3	9
102	–5	25
105	–2	4
110	3	9
110	3	9
106	–1	1
110	3	9
856		**82**

$$\overline{x}=\frac{856}{8}=107 \qquad \frac{82}{7}\approx 11.71$$

$$s=\sqrt{11.71}\approx 3.42$$

e. The values more than 1 standard deviation of the mean are 102 and 103. Thus, $\frac{2}{8}=0.25=25\%$ of the values are more than 1 standard deviation of the mean.

15. Range = 17 – 2 = 15
   $$\text{Mean}=\overline{x}=\frac{6+2+17+3+5+9}{6}=\frac{42}{6}=7$$

x	$x-\overline{x}$	$\left(x-\overline{x}\right)^2$
6	–1	1
2	–5	25
17	10	100
3	–4	16
5	–2	4
9	2	4
42		**150**

$$\overline{x}=\frac{42}{6}=7 \qquad \frac{150}{5}=30$$

$$s=\sqrt{30}\approx 5.48$$

16. Range = 44 – 30 = 14
   $$\text{Mean}=\overline{x}=\frac{\text{sum of values}}{10}=\frac{370}{10}=37$$

x	$x-\overline{x}$	$\left(x-\overline{x}\right)^2$
30	–7	49
30	–7	49
32	–5	25
35	–2	4
37	0	0
40	3	9
40	3	9
40	3	9
42	5	25
44	7	49
370		**228**

$$\overline{x}=\frac{370}{10}=37 \qquad \frac{228}{9}\approx 25.33$$

$$s=\sqrt{25.33}\approx 5.03$$

17. Range = 12 – 3 = 9
   $$\text{Mean}=\overline{x}=\frac{6+7+9+12+3+5}{6}=\frac{42}{6}=7$$

x	$x-\overline{x}$	$(x-\overline{x})^2$
6	−1	1
7	0	0
9	2	4
12	5	25
3	−4	16
5	−2	4
42		**50**

$$\overline{x}=\frac{42}{6}=7 \qquad \frac{50}{5}=10$$

$$s=\sqrt{10}\approx 3.16$$

18. Range = $60-11=49$

$$\text{Mean} = \overline{x}=\frac{\text{sum of values}}{12}=\frac{542}{12}\approx 45.17$$

x	$x-\overline{x}$	$(x-\overline{x})^2$
11	−34.17	1167.59
47	1.83	3.35
29	−16.17	261.47
60	14.83	219.93
54	8.83	77.97
54	8.83	77.97
59	13.83	191.27
46	0.83	0.69
41	−4.17	17.39
49	3.83	14.67
46	0.83	0.69
46	0.83	0.69
542		**2033.67**

$$\overline{x}=\frac{542}{12}\approx 45.17 \qquad \frac{2033.67}{11}=184.88$$

$$s=\sqrt{184.88}\approx 13.60$$

19. Coral Reef: Range = $150 - $70 = 80
Waikiki: Range = $495 - $105 = 390
Radisson: Range = $215 - $215 = 0
Waikiki Parkside: Range = $148 - $59 = 89
Pagoda: Range = $145 - $68 = 77

20. Coral Reef: $\overline{x}=\dfrac{70+150}{2}=\dfrac{220}{2}=\$110$

Waikiki: $\overline{x}=\dfrac{105+495}{2}=\dfrac{600}{2}=\$300$

Radisson: $\overline{x}=\dfrac{215+215}{2}=\dfrac{430}{2}=\$215$

Waikiki Parkside:

$$\overline{x}=\frac{59+148}{2}=\frac{207}{2}=\$103.50$$

Pagoda: $\overline{x}=\dfrac{68+145}{2}=\dfrac{213}{2}=\$106.50$

21. The average of the price averages is

$$\overline{x}=\frac{110+300+215+103.5+106.5}{5}=\frac{835}{5}=\$167$$

22. a. The standard deviation is $87.94.

x	$x-\overline{x}$	$(x-\overline{x})^2$
110	−57	3249
300	133	17,689
215	48	2304
103.50	−63.5	4032.25
106.50	−60.5	3660.25
835		**30,934.5**

$$\overline{x}=\frac{835}{5}=167 \qquad \frac{30,934.5}{4}=7733.625$$

$$s=\sqrt{7733.625}\approx 87.94$$

b. The table shows that 4 of the 5 prices,

or $\dfrac{4}{5}=0.80=80\%$ of the prices, lie

within 1 standard deviation of the mean.

c. The table shows that 5 of the 5 prices,

or $\dfrac{5}{5}=100\%$ of the prices, lie within

2 standard deviations of the mean.

23. Renting for 1 day:
Range = $37.99 - $23.99 = 14

24. Average for renting a compact car:

$$\overline{x}=\frac{23.99+26.99+34.98+37.99+36.99}{5}$$

$$=\frac{160.94}{5}\approx \$32.19$$

25.

x	$x - \overline{x}$	$\left(x - \overline{x}\right)^2$
23.99	–8.2	67.24
26.99	–5.2	27.04
34.98	2.79	7.7841
37.99	5.8	33.64
36.99	4.8	23.04
160.94		**158.7441**

$$\overline{x} = \frac{160.94}{5} = 32.19 \qquad \frac{158.7441}{4} \approx 39.67$$

$$s = \sqrt{39.67} \approx 6.30$$

The standard deviation of the prices for renting a compact car for 1 day is $6.30.

26. a. The table shows that 4 of the 5 prices, or $\dfrac{4}{5} = 0.80 = 80\%$ of the prices, lie within 1 standard deviation of the mean.

 b. The table shows that 5 of the 5 prices, or $\dfrac{5}{5} = 100\%$ of the prices, lie within 2 standard deviations of the mean.

27. The numbers are all the same. If zero is the standard deviation, then $\left(x - \overline{x}\right)^2 = 0$ for all x in the set.

28. Answers will vary. All will be positive; the more things are from the mean, the bigger the value for the standard deviation.

29. Choose the numbers 1, 1, 5, and 5 (remember, repetitions are allowed). The mean of these numbers is 3 and 1, 1, 5, and 5 are as far from the mean 3 (2 units) as possible.

30. For the first class, $x + s = 80$, $x + 2s = 85$, so the probability of scores ≥ 90 is very small. For the second class, $x + s = 85$, $x + 2s = 100$, so we would expect several scores ≥ 90.

31. $s = \sqrt{180 \cdot \dfrac{1}{6} \cdot \dfrac{5}{6}} = \sqrt{\dfrac{900}{36}} = \sqrt{25} = 5$

32. $s = \sqrt{18 \cdot \dfrac{2}{6} \cdot \dfrac{4}{6}} = \sqrt{\dfrac{144}{36}} = \sqrt{4} = 2$;

 The mean is $np = 18\left(\dfrac{2}{6}\right) = 6$, so more than 12 successes would be above 2 standard deviations away from the mean and we should become suspicious of the die's honesty.

33. $s = \sqrt{400 \cdot \dfrac{1}{4} \cdot \dfrac{3}{4}} = \sqrt{\dfrac{1200}{16}} = \sqrt{75} \approx 8.66$

34. The standard deviation stays the same because the differences from the mean will remain the same.

35. If you multiply each data point by 1.1 (100% + 10% = 1.1), it increases the spread of the points by a factor of 1.1. For example, let the mean be $64,000, and one standard deviation below the mean is at $44,000. We see that one standard deviation is $20,000. So if two employees making $64,000 and $44,000 are given a 10% raise, they are
$1.1 \times 64,000 - 1.1 \times 44,000$
$= 1.1 \times \left(64,000 - 44,000\right)$, or $22,000, apart.
This is an increase of $2000, or
$\dfrac{2000}{20,000} = 0.1 = 10\%$. Thus, the standard deviation increases by 10%.

Collaborative Learning

1. Mean:
$$\overline{x} = \frac{85.7\% + 6.6\% + 5.2\% + 2.5\%}{4} = \frac{100\%}{4} = 25\%$$
Arrange the percents in order of magnitude: 2.5%, 5.2%, 6.6%, 85.7%. The median is the average of the 2nd and 3rd terms:
$$\frac{5.2\% + 6.6\%}{2} = \frac{11.8\%}{2} = 5.9\%$$
Range: 85.7% − 2.5% = 83.2%

2.

x	$x - \overline{x}$	$\left(x - \overline{x}\right)^2$
86	60.75	3690.5625
7	–18.25	333.0625
5	–20.25	410.0625
3	–22.25	495.0625
101		**4928.75**

$$\overline{x} = \frac{101}{4} = 25.25 \qquad \frac{4928.75}{3} \approx 1642.92$$

$$s = \sqrt{1642.92} \approx 40.5$$

The standard deviation is 40.5% (Using 86, 7, 5 and 3).

3. The table shows that 3 of the 4 percents,

or $\dfrac{3}{4} = 0.75 = 75\%$ of the percents, lie

within 1 standard deviation of the mean.

4. The table shows that 4 of the 4 percents,

or $\dfrac{4}{4} = 100\%$ of the percents, lie within 2

standard deviations of the mean.

Section 12.4 The Normal Distribution: A Problem-Solving Tool

1. a. The mean is under the highest point on the graph, $35,987.
   b. From the graph, it appears that the value $34,772 is approximately 2 standard deviations from the mean, $35,987. Thus, the standard deviation

   is $\dfrac{\$35,987 - \$34,772}{2} = \dfrac{\$1215}{2}$

   $= \$607.50$.
   c. There are two standard deviations between $34,772 and $35,987. Refer to the Figure 12.10 to see that the area under a normal curve for two standard deviations is 13.5% + 34% = 47.5%. Thus, 47.5% of the cars had a price between $34,772 and $35,987.

2. We are given
   $\mu = \$40,000$ and $\sigma = \$10,000$.
   a. $50,000 is 1 standard deviation above the mean, so 16% of the teachers would have incomes over $50,000.
   b. $20,000 is 2 standard deviations below the mean, so 2.5% of the

   teachers would have incomes less than $20,000.
   c. $60,000 is 2 standard deviations above the mean, so the probability that the annual income was more than $60,000 is $0.025 = 2.5\%$.
   d. No. If the distribution is normal, we would expect only 16% to have incomes over $50,000.

3. We are given $\mu = 120\ \text{sec}$ and $\sigma = 15\ \text{sec}$.
   a. 90 sec is 2 standard deviations below the mean, so 2.5% of the children, or $0.025 \cdot 1000 = 25$ children finished the puzzle in less than 90 sec.
   b. 150 sec is 2 standard deviations above the mean, so 2.5% of the children, or $0.025 \cdot 1000 = 25$ children finished the puzzle in more than 150 sec.
   c. 68% of the children, or $0.68 \cdot 1000 = 680$, are within 1 standard deviation of the mean.

4. We are given $\mu = 200$ and $\sigma = 30$.
   a. 170 is 1 standard deviation below the mean and 230 is 1 standard deviation above the mean, so 68% of the students, or $0.68 \cdot 1000 = 680$ students, are between the scores of 170 and 230.
   b. 260 is 2 standard deviations below the mean, so 2.5% of the children, or $0.025 \cdot 1000 = 25$ children are expected to score above 260.
   c. The scores will fall between 3 standard deviations above and below the mean: 110 to 290. The range is $290 - 110 = 180$.

5. We are given $\mu = 50$ and $\sigma = 10$.
   A: 2.5% get this grade. 2.5% of 500 = 12.5, so 12 or 13 get A.
   B: 13.5% get this grade. 13.5% of 500 = 67.5, so 67 or 68 get B.
   C: 68% get this grade. 68% of 500 = 340, so 340 get C.
   D: 13.5% get this grade. 13.5% of 500 = 67.5, so 67 or 68 get D.
   F: 2.5% get this grade. 2.5% of 500 = 12.5, so 12 or 13 get F.
   (Of course, the teacher's choices must add up to 500.)

6. We are given $\mu = \$35,987$ and $\sigma = \$607.50$.
   a. Yes. The MSRP price is $37,995, which is

$$\frac{\$37,998-\$35,987}{607.50}=\frac{\$2011}{607.50}\approx 3.31$$

standard deviations above the mean.

b. $35,987 is the mean, then since it is a normal distribution 50% of the cars are priced below $35,987.

c. Cars with a great price ranged from $34,772 to $35,987. This is

$$\frac{\$35,987-\$34,772}{607.50}=\frac{\$1215}{607.50}=2$$

standard deviations from the mean. Refer to the Figure 12.10 to see that the area under a normal curve for two standard deviations is 13.5% + 34% = 47.5%. Thus, 47.5% of the cars had a price between $34,772 and $35,987.

d. The starting price for "great price" cars is $34,772.

7. Given $\mu = 26,000$ mi and $\sigma = 2500$ mi. 21,000 mi is

$$\frac{26,000-21,000}{2500}=\frac{5000}{2500}=2\text{ standard}$$

deviations below the mean. Thus, $0.025\cdot 200 = 5$ tires gave out before 26,000 mi.

8. Since 95% is 2 standard deviations below and above the mean, we have

$$\$25,000-2\left(\$600\right)=\$23,800$$

$$\$25,000+2\left(\$600\right)=\$26,200$$

The price range expected 95% of the time is $23,800 to $26,200.

9. Since $\mu = 20$ ft and $\sigma = 0.5$ in. , almost all the measurements fall between $20\text{ft}-3\left(0.5\text{in.}\right)$ and $20\text{ft}+3\left(0.5\text{in.}\right)$, that is, between 19 ft, 10.5 in. and 20 ft, 1.5 in.

10. a. Since $\mu = 50$ and $\sigma = 5$, 95% of the time the number of heads fall between $50-2\left(5\right)=50-10=40$ and $50+2\left(5\right)=50+10=60$.

    b. Since 45 is 1 standard deviation below and 55 is 1 standard deviation above the mean, you would expect heads 68% of the time.

    c. The coin needs to turn up heads more than 3 standard deviations above

the mean, or $50+3\left(5\right)=65$ times.

11. The purchasing director will decide to buy. If the lifetimes are normally distributed, 2.5% will last for 30 + 2(5) = 40 or more days. Thus, of the 8000 ball bearings, about $8000\cdot 0.025=200$ would last for 40 or more days, so the purchasing director would decide to buy.

12. a. 360 is 1 standard deviation above the mean, so 16% of the time, or $50\cdot 0.16=8$ days, the road will be used by more than 360 vehicles.

    b. 340 is 1 standard deviation below the mean (34%) and 380 is 3 standard deviations above the mean (50%). There are $50\cdot \left(0.34+0.50\right)=50\cdot 0.84=42$ days where between 340 and 380 vehicles are using the road.

    c. The lowest number of vehicles on this road on any given day is $350-3\left(10\right)=320$.

    d. The highest number of vehicles on this road on any given day is $350+3\left(10\right)=380$.

13. For the S.A.T., the z-score is $z=\frac{635-514}{117}\approx 1.03$. For the A.C.T., the z-score is $z=\frac{26.2-21}{5.2}=1$. Thus, the student who scored 635 on the S.A.T. has the higher score relative to the test.

14. The setting should be $16+3\left(0.05\right)=16.15\text{ oz}$ to ensure that all of the packages contain at least 16 oz of cereal.

15. a. $\sigma = 10$ b. $\sigma = 5$
    c. $\mu = 40$ d. $\mu = 65$
    e. A z-score of +2 corresponds to

    $$\frac{x-40}{10}=2$$

    $$x-40=20$$

    $$x=60$$

    A z-score of –1 corresponds to

$$\frac{x-40}{10} = -1$$

$$x - 40 = -10$$

$$x = 30$$

f. A z-score of +2 corresponds to

$$\frac{x-65}{5} = 2$$

$$x - 65 = 10$$

$$x = 75$$

A z-score of –1 corresponds to

$$\frac{x-65}{5} = -1$$

$$x - 65 = -5$$

$$x = 60$$

16. a. From 40 and 50 is 1 standard deviation, so the 34% of the scores would be between 40 and 50.
    b. From 20 to 40 is 2 standard deviations below the mean (47.5%) and from 40 to 50 is 1 standard deviation above the mean (34%), so 47.5% + 34% = 81.5% of the scores are between 20 and 50.
    c. From 10 to 40 is 3 standard deviations below the mean (50%) and from 40 to 70 is 3 standard deviations above the mean (50%), so 50% + 50% = 100% of the scores are between 10 and 70.

17. Given $\mu = 16.15$ oz and $\sigma = 0.05$ oz, a z-score of 0 corresponds to

$$\frac{x-16.15}{0.05} = 0$$

$$x - 16.15 = 0$$

$$x = 16.15$$

The weight of a box with a z-score 0 is 16.15 oz.

18. a. Given $\sigma = 5, x = 170$ lb, and z-score is +2, we have

$$\frac{170-\mu}{5} = 2$$

$$170 - \mu = 10$$

$$\mu = 160$$

The mean weight for Bernie's breed and age is 160 lb.
    b. From –2 to 2 is 4 standard deviations, so Bernie's weight after the diet is

$$170 - 4(5) = 150 \text{ lb.}$$

19. Given $\sigma = 10$, $\mu = 70$, and z-score is +2, we have $\dfrac{x-70}{10} = 2$

$$x - 70 = 20$$

$$x = 90$$

Pedro's exam score is 90.

20. If your score x equals mean score μ, then your z-score is $z = \dfrac{x-\mu}{\sigma} = \dfrac{0}{\sigma} = 0$.

21. Given $\mu = 5$ and $\sigma = 1.25$.
    a. If $x = 6$, then $z = \dfrac{6-5}{1.25} = \dfrac{1}{1.25} = 0.8$
    b. If $x = 7$, then $z = \dfrac{7-5}{1.25} = \dfrac{2}{1.25} = 1.6$
    c. If $x = 7.5$, then $z = \dfrac{7.5-5}{1.25} = \dfrac{2.5}{1.25} = 2$

22. Given $\mu = \$19,310, \sigma = \$574$, and $x = \$19,482$, then

$$z = \frac{\$19,482 - \$19,310}{\$574} = \frac{\$172}{\$574}$$

$$\approx 0.2997 \approx 0.300$$

23. For the German test, the z-score is $z = \dfrac{85-75}{20} = 0.5$. For the English test, the z-score is $z = \dfrac{85-80}{15} = \dfrac{5}{15} \approx 0.33$. Thus, the German test score is the better score relative to the test.

24. For the Spanish test, the z-score is $z = \dfrac{88-78}{7.5} \approx 1.33$. For the algebra test, the z-score is $z = \dfrac{90-82}{6.5} \approx 1.23$. Thus, the Spanish test score is the better score relative to the test.

25. 20 minutes is 2 standard deviations from the mean of 30 minutes. Thus, it has a z-score of –2. The probability of arriving at school in 20 to 30 minutes is 47.7%, using the values of 34.1% and 13.6% instead of the approximate 34% and for 13.5%, respectively.

26. From 30 min to 35 min is 1 standard deviation away from the mean, thus the probability that Latasha completes the workout in 30 to 35 min is 34%.

27. Find the z-score for values of $\mu = 4.5$ min, $\sigma = 1.5$ min, and $x = 5$ min.

$$z = \frac{5-4.5}{1.5} = \frac{0.5}{1.5} \approx 0.33$$

From Table II the probability associated with 0.33 is 0.129. So the probability of being served within 5 minutes is $0.50 + 0.129 = 0.629 = 62.9\%$.

28. The time period that you would be certain to be served has a probability of 100%, or 3 standard deviations above the mean. Thus, the time period is

$$4.5 \text{ min} + 3(1.5 \text{ min}) = 9 \text{ min}.$$

29. Given $\mu = 100$ and $\sigma = 15$.
   a. The z-score for $x = 110$ is

   $$z = \frac{110-100}{15} = \frac{10}{15} \approx 0.667$$

   From Table II, we find the probability that a randomly selected score is between the mean and 0.667 standard deviation above the mean to be 0.249.
   b. The z-score for $x = 130$ is

   $$z = \frac{130-100}{15} = \frac{30}{15} = 2$$

   Again, from Table II, we find the probability that a randomly selected score is between the mean and 2 standard deviations above the mean to be 0.477.

30. Given $\mu = 100$ and $\sigma = 15$. The z-score for $x = 80$ is

   $$z = \frac{80-100}{15} = -\frac{20}{15} \approx -1.33$$

   and for $x = 120$ is

$$z = \frac{120-100}{15} = \frac{20}{15} \approx 1.33$$

From Table II, we find the probability that a randomly selected score between the mean and 1.33 standard deviations above the mean is about 0.408. By symmetry of the normal curve, we have that the probability that a randomly selected score is between 80 and 120 is about $2 \cdot 0.408 = 0.816$.

31. a. Since $z = \frac{55-100}{15} = -\frac{45}{15} = -3$ and

   $z = \frac{145-100}{15} = \frac{45}{15} = 3$, 55 and 145 are

   each 3 standard deviations from the mean. From Table II, we find the probability that a randomly selected score falls between the mean and 3 standard deviations above the mean to be 0.499. This means that the probability that the score is between 100 and 145 is 0.499. Because of the symmetry of the normal curve, the probability that the score is between 55 and 100 is also 0.499. Therefore, the probability that the score is between 55 and 145 is $0.499 + 0.499 = 0.998$.

   b. $z = \frac{60-100}{15} = -\frac{40}{15} = -2.67$. So 60 is

   2.67 standard deviations "below" the mean. Table II gives 0.496 as the probability that a randomly selected score is between the mean and 2.67 standard deviations from the mean. Since the probability that such a score is below the mean is 0.5, the probability that the score is below 60 is $0.5 - 0.496 = 0.004$.

32. a. Since $z = \frac{75-100}{15} = -\frac{25}{15} \approx -1.667$ and

   the mean is 100, 75 is –1.667 standard deviations from the mean. From Table II, we find the probability that a randomly selected score falls between the mean and 1.667 standard deviations below the mean to be about 0.452. This means that the probability that the score is between 75 and is 0.452.

   b. $z = \frac{80-100}{15} = -\frac{20}{15} \approx -1.333$. So 80 is

   –1.333 standard deviations from the mean. Table II gives about 0.409 as the probability that a randomly selected score is between 1.333 standard deviations below the mean and the mean. Since the probability that a score above the mean is 0.5, the probability that the score is above 80 is about $0.409 + 0.5 = 0.909$.

33. In problem 29, we found 0.249 to be the probability that a randomly selected score is between 100 and 110, and 0.477 to be the corresponding probability for the score to be between 100 and 130. Consequently, the probability that the score is between 110 and 130 is $0.477 - 0.249 = 0.228$.

34. To determine the probability of getting 60 heads if 100 fair coins are tossed, find the area between these z-scores.

$$z = \frac{59.5 - 50}{5} = \frac{9.5}{5} = 1.9 \text{ and}$$

$$z = \frac{60.5 - 50}{5} = \frac{10.5}{5} = 2.1$$

From Table II, the probability between the mean and 2.1 standard deviations above the mean is 0.482. The probability between the mean and 1.9 standard deviations above the mean is 0.471. Thus, the probability of getting 60 heads if 100 fair coins are tossed is about $0.482 - 0.471 = 0.011$.

35. This student is to be shortest of the tallest 20%. From Table II, the area from the mean to the top 20% is found by finding the z-score corresponding to $0.5 + 0.3 = 0.8$. Thus, the z-score of his height must be greater than 0.8. The height x in. of the shortest student in this group must be such that $\dfrac{x - 5\,\text{ft } 7\,\text{in.}}{3\,\text{in.}} = \dfrac{x - 67\,\text{in.}}{3\,\text{in.}} = 0.8$

$$x - 67\,\text{in.} = 2.4\,\text{in.}$$

$$x = 69.4\,\text{in. or } 5\,\text{ft } 9\tfrac{1}{2}\,\text{in.}$$

Thus, the shortest student in the tallest group is about 5 ft 9 ½ in. tall.

36. The z-score relating to 6 ft 3 in. is

$$z = \frac{6\,\text{ft } 3\,\text{in.} - 5\,\text{ft } 7\,\text{in.}}{3\,\text{in.}} = \frac{5\,\text{ft } 15\,\text{in.} - 5\,\text{ft } 7\,\text{in.}}{3\,\text{in.}}$$

$= \dfrac{8}{3} \approx 2.667$ Table II gives the area between the mean and 2.667 as 0.496, so the area above 2.667 would be $0.5 - 0.496 = 0.004$. If the number of male students is x, we have $0.004 \cdot x = 10$, or $x = 2500$. There are $(10 + 2490)$ or 2500 males students at this college.

37. $z = \dfrac{4400 - 4200}{200} = \dfrac{200}{200} = 1$.
A z-value of 1 indicates that the value \$4400 is one standard deviation above the mean of \$4200. (Someone with this income is earning more than 84% of other budget analysts.)

38. $z = \dfrac{3800 - 4200}{200} = -\dfrac{400}{200} = -2$. A z-value of -2 indicates that the value \$3800 is two standard deviation below the mean of \$4200. (Someone with this income is earning more than 2.5% of other budget analysts, or earning less than 97.5% of other budget analysts.)

39. We can be certain that the ice cream will be within 3 standard deviations of the mean. Since the mean is 8 oz and the standard deviation is 0.25 oz, the weight of the ice cream must be between $8 - 3(0.25) = 7.25$ oz and $8 + 3(0.25) = 8.75$ oz.

40. a. $z = \dfrac{30 - 45}{10} = -\dfrac{15}{10} = -1.5$. So 30 is -1.5 standard deviations from the mean. Table II gives about 0.433 as the probability that a randomly selected time is between 1.5 standard deviations below the mean and the mean. The probability that the professor get to work in 30 min or less would be about $0.5 - 0.433 = 0.067$.

   b. We want to know the probability of the professor getting to work in 60 min or more. $z = \dfrac{60 - 45}{10} = \dfrac{15}{10} = 1.5$. So 60 is 1.5 standard deviations from the mean, as in part a, the probability that the professor get to work in 60 min or more would be about $0.5 - 0.433 = 0.067$ or 6.7% of the time.

41. Find the z-scores for the values of $x = 8$ and $x = 8.4$ given that $\mu = 8\,\text{hr}$ and $\sigma = 0.25\,\text{hr}$.

$$z = \frac{8-8}{0.25} = \frac{0}{0.25} = 0$$

$$z = \frac{8.4-8}{0.25} = \frac{.4}{0.25} = 1.6$$

From Table II the probability associated with 1.6 is 0.445. So the probability of Caruca will get her restorative sleep is 0.445 or 44.5%.

42. At least 50% of the students scored less than you did.

43. Since 68% of the values on the normal curve are within one standard deviation (10 gal) of the mean (110 gal), the daily water usage lies between $110 - 10 = 100$ gal and $110 + 10 = 120$ gal.

44. Since 95% of the values on the normal curve are within two standard deviation ($2 \cdot 10 = 20$ gal) of the mean (110 gal), the daily water usage lies between $110 - 20 = 90$ gal and $110 + 20 = 130$ gal. 99% of the values on the normal curve are within about 2.57 standard deviations ($2.57 \cdot 10 = 25.7$ gal) of the mean (110 gal). Thus, the daily water usage lies between $110 - 25.7 = 84.3$ gal and $110 + 25.7 = 135.7$ gal.

45. Since 110 gal is the mean and 50% of all values in the normal curve are to the left of the mean, the probability that a person selected at random will use less than 110 gal per day is 50%.

46. Since 110 gal is the mean and 50% of all values in the normal curve are to the right of the mean, the probability that a person selected at random will use more than 110 gal per day is 50%.

47. Since the mean is 110, and the standard deviation is 10, the value 100 is one standard deviation below the mean. Thus, 34% of the people use between 100 gal and 110 gal.

48. Since the mean is 110, and the standard deviation is 10, the value 100 is 1 standard deviation below the mean and the value of

120 is one standard deviation above the mean. Thus, $34\% + 34\% = 68\%$ of the people use between 100 gal and 120 gal.

49. She has provided poor service if her tips are less than $70. The z-value for $70 is

$$z = \frac{70-100}{20} = -\frac{30}{20} = -1.5.$$

From Table II, the value for 1.5 is 0.433, so the probability that the waitress provided poor service is $0.5 - 0.433$ or 0.067, that is, 6.7%. (Remember, you are looking for the area under the normal curve that is to the left of the z-score corresponding to -1.5).

50. The z-value for $70 is

$$z = \frac{70-100}{10} = -\frac{30}{10} = -3.$$

From Table II, the value for 3 is 0.499, so the probability that the waitress provided poor service is $0.5 - 0.499 = 0.001$, that is, 1%.

51. Yes. See Figure 12.14 on page 708. Here both curves have the mean 0. The standard deviation for A is $\frac{1}{3}$ unit while that for B is 1 unit.

52. Yes. Each item of the second set could be some constant greater than the corresponding item of the first set. In this case, the mean for the second set would be greater than the mean for the first set, but the standard deviations would be equal.

53. No. If curve A in Figure 12.14 on page 708 is moved 2 units to the right, this would be an example. The standard deviation for A would be $\frac{1}{3}$ unit and that for B would be 1 unit, while the mean for A would be 2 and that for B would be 0.

54. A z-score is the number of standard deviations that the corresponding score is from the mean.

55. $\text{Percentile} = \frac{40}{50} \cdot 100 = 0.8 \cdot 100 = 80$. Her percentile is 80th.

56. $\text{Percentile} = \frac{80-9}{80} \cdot 100 = \frac{71}{80} \cdot 100$
    $= 0.8875 \cdot 100 = 88.75$
    His percentile is no higher than 88.75th.

57.   a.   There are 2 scores less than 90, so the percentile is

$$\frac{2}{10} \cdot 100 = 0.2 \cdot 100 = 20^{\text{th}}.$$

b.   There are 6 scores less than 97, so the percentile is

$$\frac{6}{10} \cdot 100 = 0.6 \cdot 100 = 60^{\text{th}}.$$

c.   There are 9 scores less than 100, so the percentile is

$$\frac{9}{10} \cdot 100 = 0.9 \cdot 100 = 90^{\text{th}}.$$

d.   There are 0 scores less than 83, so the percentile is

$$\frac{0}{10} \cdot 100 = 0 \cdot 100 = 0^{\text{th}}.$$

58.   50% of the scores were less than 90 and 10% of the scores were less than 30. So 40% of the scores were between 30 and 90 (with the 30 included but not the 90).

59.   a.   40 and 60 are each 2 standard deviations from the mean, so we use Chebyshev's theorem with $h = 2$ and $N = 100$:

$$\left(1 - \frac{1}{2^2}\right) \cdot 100 = \left(1 - \frac{1}{4}\right) \cdot 100$$

$$= \left(\frac{3}{4}\right) \cdot 100 = 75$$

Thus, at least 75 of the measurements must be between 40 and 60.

b.   35 and 65 are each 3 standard deviations from the mean, so we use Chebyshev's theorem with $h = 3$ and $N = 100$:

$$\left(1 - \frac{1}{3^2}\right) \cdot 100 = \left(1 - \frac{1}{9}\right) \cdot 100$$

$$= \left(\frac{8}{9}\right) \cdot 100 \approx 89$$

Thus, at least 89 of the measurements must be between 35 and 65.

c.   43 and 57 are each $\dfrac{7}{5}$ standard deviations from the mean, so we use Chebyshev's theorem with $h = \dfrac{7}{5}$ and $N = 100$:

$$\left(1 - \frac{1}{\left(\frac{7}{5}\right)^2}\right) \cdot 100 = \left(1 - \frac{25}{49}\right) \cdot 100$$

$$= \left(\frac{24}{49}\right) \cdot 100 \approx 49$$

Thus, at least 49 of the measurements must be between 43 and 57.

60.   a. $\left(1 - \dfrac{1}{h^2}\right) \cdot 100 = 96$

$$1 - \frac{1}{h^2} = 0.96$$

$$h^2 = \frac{1}{0.04} = 25$$

$$h = 5$$

b. $\left(1 - \dfrac{1}{h^2}\right) \cdot 100 = 91$

$$1 - \frac{1}{h^2} = 0.91$$

$$h^2 = \frac{1}{0.09} = \frac{100}{9}$$

$$h = \frac{10}{3}$$

c. $\left(1 - \dfrac{1}{h^2}\right) \cdot 100 = 64$

$$1 - \frac{1}{h^2} = 0.64$$

$$h^2 = \frac{1}{0.36} = \frac{25}{9}$$

$$h = \frac{5}{3}$$

61.

x	$x - \overline{x}$	$\left(x - \overline{x}\right)^2$
1	–5	25
1	–5	25
1	–5	25
2	–4	16
6	0	0
10	4	16
11	5	25
11	5	25
11	5	25
54		**182**

$$\overline{x} = \frac{54}{9} = 6 \qquad \frac{182}{8} = 22.75$$

$$s = \sqrt{22.75} \approx 4.77$$

Three of the numbers (2, 6, and 10) lie within 1 standard deviation from the mean, and all 9 of the numbers lie within 2 standard deviations from the mean. The theorem makes no prediction for 1 standard deviation; it predicts at least 75% for 2 standard deviations.

62. No. Suppose that $\left|x_n - \overline{x}\right|$ is the largest deviation and that $\sigma > \left|x_n - \overline{x}\right|$. Then,

$$n\sigma^2 > n\left|x_n - \overline{x}\right|^2$$

$$\geq \left|x_1 - \overline{x}\right|^2 + \left|x_2 - \overline{x}\right|^2 + \ldots + \left|x_n - \overline{x}\right|^2$$

which is a contradiction because $n\sigma^2$ is exactly this last sum.

63. No; the theorem predicts the least number that must lie within 2 standard deviations from the mean, and it predicts the least number that must lie within 3 standard deviations from the mean, but it does not predict how many must lie between 2 and 3 standard deviations from the mean. However, since at least 75% of the numbers must lie within 2 standard deviations from the mean, the number of numbers between 2 and 3 standard deviations from the mean cannot be more than 25% of all the numbers.

Collaborative Learning

3. The mean, median, and mode is 100.

4. The suggested standard deviation is 10.

5. $z = \dfrac{120 - 100}{10} = \dfrac{20}{10} = 2$

6. $z = \dfrac{80 - 100}{10} = -\dfrac{20}{10} = -2$

7. 68% of the people have IQ scores between 90 and 110. From the figure, 50% of the total population distribution is in that range. Yes, the percents are different.

8. $z = \dfrac{125 - 100}{10} = \dfrac{25}{10} = 2.5.$ and

$$z = \dfrac{130 - 100}{10} = \dfrac{30}{10} = 3$$

From Table II, 0.499 is the probability 3 standard deviations above the mean and 0.494 is the probability 2.5 standard deviations above the mean. The probability between 2.5 and 3 standard deviation above the mean is 0.499 – 0.494 = 0.005, or 0.05% of the people have IQ scores between 125 and 130. 5% of the total population distribution is shown in that range. Yes, the percents are different.

Section 12.5 Statistical Graphs:
A Problem-Solving Tool

1.

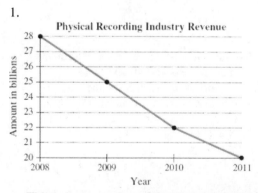

This is just a portion of the complete graph.

2.

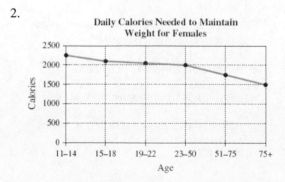

3.

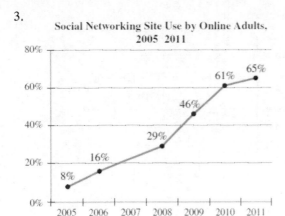

Social Networking Site Use by Online Adults,
2005 2011

6.

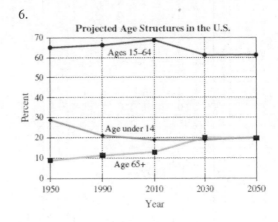

Projected Age Structures in the U.S.

4.

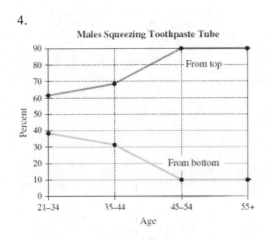

Males Squeezing Toothpaste Tube

7.

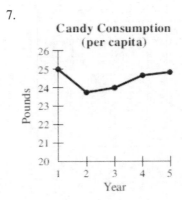

Candy Consumption
(per capita)

5.

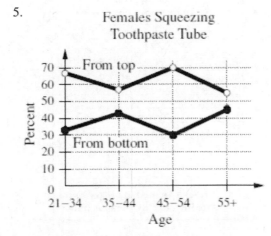

Females Squeezing
Toothpaste Tube

8.

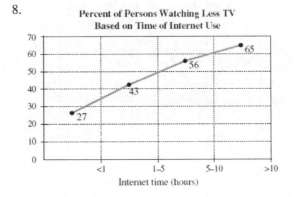

Percent of Persons Watching Less TV
Based on Time of Internet Use

9.

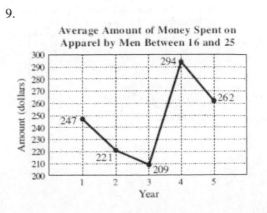

Average Amount of Money Spent on
Apparel by Men Between 16 and 25

10.

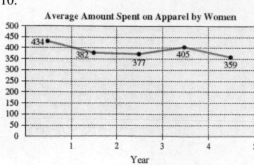

11.

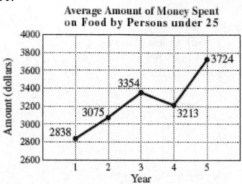

12.

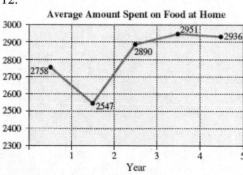

13.

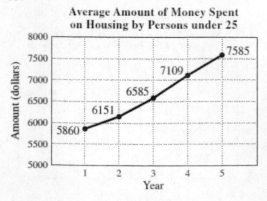

14.

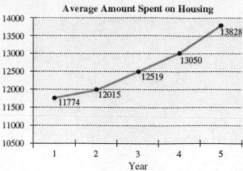

15.

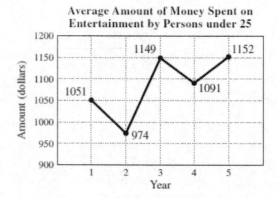

16.

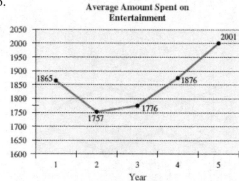

17.

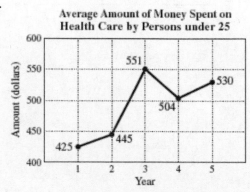

18.

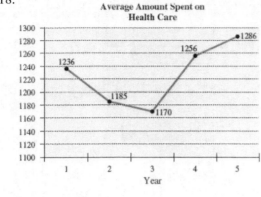

Average Amount Spent on
Health Care

19.

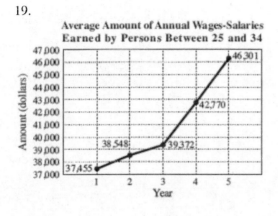

Average Amount of Annual Wages-Salaries
Earned by Persons Between 25 and 34

20.

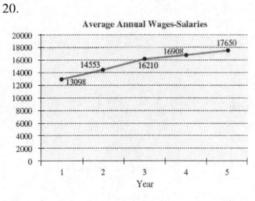

Average Annual Wages-Salaries

21.

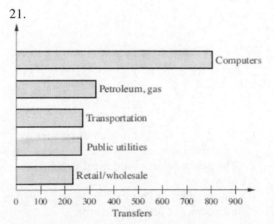

22. a.

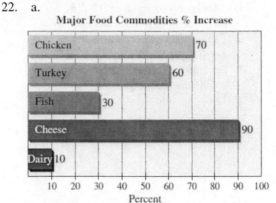

Major Food Commodities % Increase

b.   Choose the Cheese business; avoid
the Dairy business.

23. a.

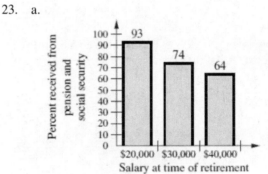

b.   You should expect
$0.93 \cdot \$20,000 = \$18,600$ from your
pension and Social Security.

24.

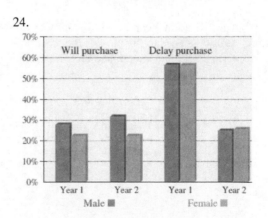

25. a.

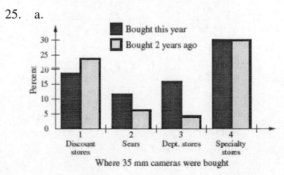

b.   Most people buy their 35-mm
     cameras at specialty stores.
c.   Department stores lost the most in the
     2-year interval.
d.   Specialty stores had the most
     consistent sales.

26.   a.

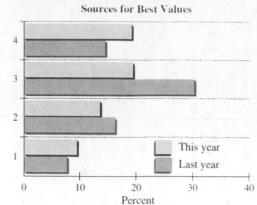

Sources for Best Values

b.   Electronic stores provided the best value
     for home electronics.

27.   a.

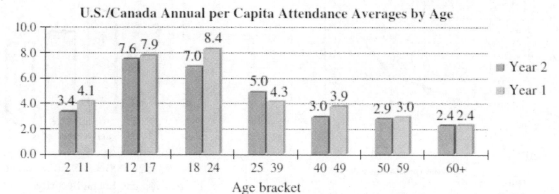

U.S./Canada Annual per Capita Attendance Averages by Age

b.   Ages 18-24 in Year 1 go to the movies most frequently.
c.   Ages 60+ goes to the movies the least.
d.   Ages 25-39 had attendance increase from Year 1 to Year 2.

28.   a.

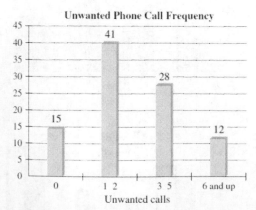

Unwanted Phone Call Frequency

b.   1-2 calls is the most common number
     of calls.
c.   15% of the people received no
     unwanted calls.

29.   a.

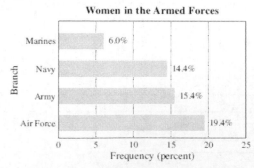

Women in the Armed Forces

b.   The Air Force has the highest percentage
     of women.
c.   The Marines have the lowest percentage
     of women.
d.   No, we need to know the total
     numbers, not just the percents.

30. a.

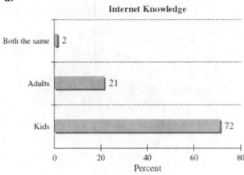

b. Kids have the most Internet knowledge.

c. 2% of the people think that kids and adults have the same knowledge.

31.

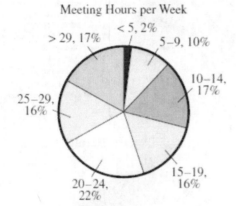

32.

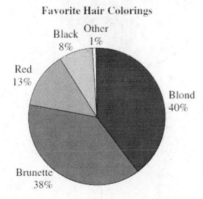

33.

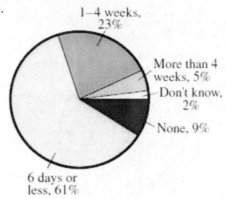

34.

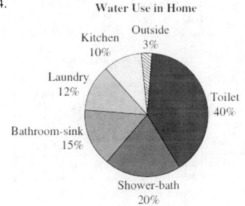

35.

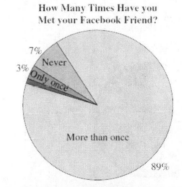

Note: Figures do not add to 100% due to rounding

36.

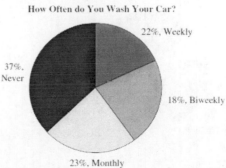

37. a.

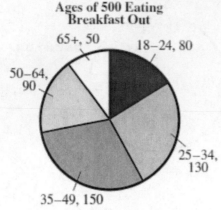

Ages of 500 Eating Breakfast Out

65+, 50
18–24, 80
50–64, 90
25–34, 130
35–49, 150

b.   You should cater to the 35-49 age group.

38.

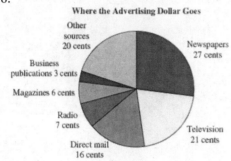

Where the Advertising Dollar Goes

Other sources 20 cents
Newspapers 27 cents
Business publications 3 cents
Magazines 6 cents
Radio 7 cents
Direct mail 16 cents
Television 21 cents

39.

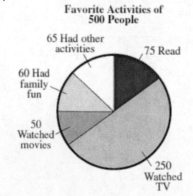

Favorite Activities of 500 People

65 Had other activities
75 Read
60 Had family fun
50 Watched movies
250 Watched TV

40.

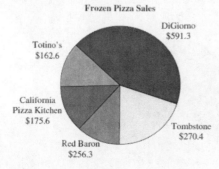

Frozen Pizza Sales

DiGiorno $591.3
Totino's $162.6
California Pizza Kitchen $175.6
Red Baron $256.3
Tombstone $270.4

41.

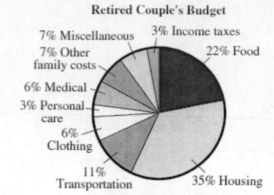

Retired Couple's Budget

7% Miscellaneous
7% Other family costs
6% Medical
3% Personal care
6% Clothing
11% Transportation
3% Income taxes
22% Food
35% Housing

42.

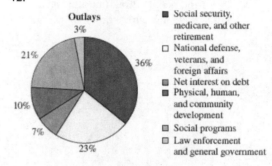

Outlays
3%
21%
36%
10%
7%
23%

■ Social security, medicare, and other retirement
□ National defense, veterans, and foreign affairs
▦ Net interest on debt
▨ Physical, human, and community development
▥ Social programs
□ Law enforcement and general government

43. a.

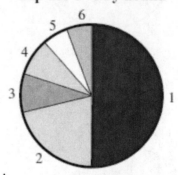

Top Six TVs by Brand

6
5
4
3
2
1

b.

6
5
4
3
2
1

Brand

0 10 20 30 40 50 60
Percent

c.   The circle graph. The area corresponding

to brand 1 overshadows all the rest of the chart.

44.

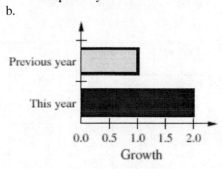

Do Women Like Housework?

Unqualified liking 67%

Unqualified dislike 4%

Other 29%

45. a. Yes. To give a correct visual impression, only the height should be doubled. If both the height and the radius are doubled, the volume is multiplied by 8.

b.

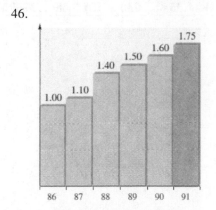

Previous year

This year

0.0   0.5   1.0   1.5   2.0
Growth

46.

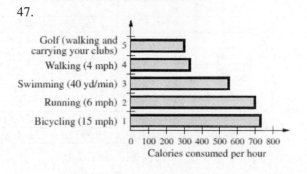

1.00   1.10   1.40   1.50   1.60   1.75

86   87   88   89   90   91

47.

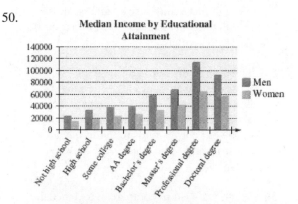

Golf (walking and carrying your clubs) 5

Walking (4 mph) 4

Swimming (40 yd/min) 3

Running (6 mph) 2

Bicycling (15 mph) 1

0   100   200   300   400   500   600   700   800
Calories consumed per hour

48.

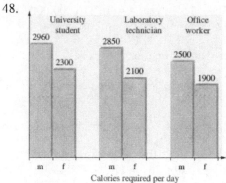

University student   Laboratory technician   Office worker

2960   2300   2850   2100   2500   1900

m   f   m   f   m   f
Calories required per day

Percent more calories required by males

Student: About 28.7%

Technician: About 35.7%

Office Worker: About 31.6%

49.

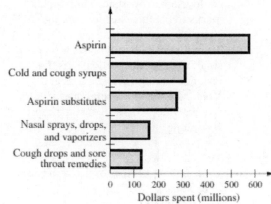

Aspirin

Cold and cough syrups

Aspirin substitutes

Nasal sprays, drops, and vaporizers

Cough drops and sore throat remedies

0   100   200   300   400   500   600
Dollars spent (millions)

50.

Median Income by Educational Attainment

■ Men
□ Women

Not high school   High school   Some college   AA degree   Bachelor's degree   Master's degree   Professional degree   Doctoral degree

Education	
Women's Income as a percentage of men's	
Not high school	58.4%
High school	59.8%
Some college	59.0%
AA degree	64.3%
Bachelor's degree	57.8%
Master's degree	61.4%
Professional degree	55.1%
Doctoral degree	61.8%

51. a.   The sales in year 4 were $16,000,000.
    b.   The sales started to level off in year 6.

52. The percent of time for classes is

$\dfrac{3}{24} = 0.125 = 12.5\%$ and the percent of

time for study is $\dfrac{6}{24} = 0.25 = 25\%$. Thus,

the percent of the time Harry is allowing
for classes and study is 12.5% + 25% =
37.5%.

53. a.   To make sales look better, use a large
         scale on the vertical axis, for instance,
         start the vertical axis at 19. You
         could use narrow spaced horizontal
         marks to obtain a steeper looking
         slope.
    b.   To make sales look flat, use a very
         small scale on the vertical axis, for
         instance start the vertical axis at 0.
         You could use horizontal marks
         spaced widely apart to obtain almost
         zero slope.

54. a.   To make sales look better, use a large
         scale and cut off part of the zero end
         of each bar.
    b.   To give the impression that sales are
         not increasing, use a small scale so
         that the bars appear to be about of the
         same length.

55. The area of the bar in a bar graph
    indicates the amount of the item that is
    graphed. For this reason, the bars are
    usually shaded. In a histogram, the height
    of the bar corresponds to the frequency in
    question and there is no space between
    bars.

56. When we wish to compare at a glance the
    magnitudes of the categories involved.

57. One of the graphs has a very much
    compressed vertical scale, which
    diminishes the visual effect of each
    increase or decrease.

Skill Checker

1. $\dfrac{3-0}{0-2} = -\dfrac{3}{2} = -1.5$

2.   The y-intercept is 3.

3. $y = -1.5x + 3$

4. $\dfrac{6-2}{4-0} = \dfrac{4}{4} = 1$

5.   The y-intercept is 2.

6. $y = x + 2$

Section 12.6 Making Predictions: Linear Regression

*For calculations, non-rounded numbers are
used in the intermediate steps.*

1. a.

Person	x	y	x^2	xy
1	462	30	213444	13860
2	488	50	238144	24400
3	503	70	253009	35210
4	517	90	267289	46530
5	525	110	275625	57750
6	529	130	279841	68770
7	536	150	287296	80400
Totals	**3560**	**630**	**1814648**	**326920**

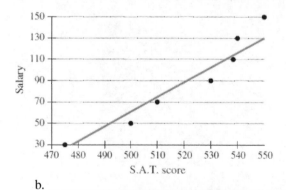

b.

Person	x	y	x^2	xy
1	475	30	225625	14250
2	497	50	247009	24850
3	512	70	262144	35840
4	528	90	278784	47520
5	538	110	289444	59180
6	542	130	293764	70460
7	550	150	302500	82500
Totals	**3642**	**630**	**1899270**	**334600**

$$m = \dfrac{7(334600) - (3642)(630)}{7(1899270) - (3642)^2} = \dfrac{47{,}740}{30{,}726} \approx 1.554$$

$$b = \frac{630 - 1.554(3642)}{7} = -\frac{5028.686}{7} \approx -718.4$$

The regression line is $y = 1.554x - 718.4$.

See part a for the graph.

c. Let $x = 500$, then

$y = 1.554(500) - 718.4 = 58.6$

The salary of a person with a S.A.T of 500 is predicted to be $58,600.

Let $x = 540$, then

$y = 1.554(540) - 718.4 = 120.76$

The salary of a person with a S.A.T of 540 is predicted to be $120,760.

2. a.

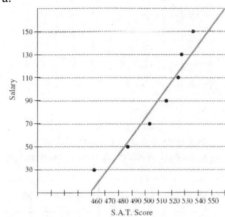

S.A.T. Score

b.

$$m = \frac{7(326920) - (3560)(630)}{7(1814648) - (3560)^2} = \frac{45,640}{28,936} \approx 1.577$$

$$b = \frac{630 - 1.577(3560)}{7} = -\frac{4985.12}{7} \approx -712.2$$

The regression line is $y = 1.577x - 712.2$.

See part a for the graph.

c. Let $x = 500$, then

$y = 1.577(500) - 712.2$

$= 76.3$

The salary of a person with a S.A.T of 500 is predicted to be $76,300.

Let $x = 540$, then

$y = 1.577(540) - 712.2 = 139.38$

The salary of a person with a S.A.T of 540 is predicted to be $139,380.

3. a.

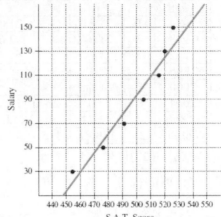

S.A.T. Score

b.

Person	x	y	x^2	xy
1	453	30	205209	13590
2	476	50	226576	23800
3	481	70	241081	34370
4	505	90	255025	45450
5	516	110	266256	56760
6	520	130	270400	67600
7	527	150	277729	79050
Totals	**3488**	**630**	**1742276**	**320620**

$$m = \frac{7(320620) - (3488)(630)}{7(1742276) - (3488)^2} = \frac{46,900}{29,788} \approx 1.574$$

$$b = \frac{630 - 1.577(3488)}{7} = -\frac{4861.71}{7} \approx -694.5$$

The regression line is $y = 1.574x - 694.5$.

See part a for the graph.

c. Let $x = 500$, then

$y = 1.574(500) - 694.5 = 92.5$

The salary of a person with a S.A.T of 500 is predicted to be $92,500.

Let $x = 540$, then

$y = 1.574(540) - 694.5 = 155.46$

The salary of a person with a S.A.T of 540 is predicted to be $155,460.

4. a.

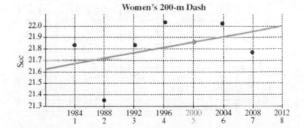

© 2014 Cengage Learning. All Rights Reserved. May not be scanned, copied or duplicated, or posted to a publicly accessible website, in whole or in part.

b.

Year	x	y	x^2	xy
1984	1	21.81	1	21.81
1988	2	21.34	4	42.68
1992	3	21.81	9	65.43
1996	4	22.12	16	88.48
2000	5	Vacant		
2004	6	22.05	36	132.3
2008	7	21.74	49	152.18
Totals	**23**	**130.87**	**115**	**502.88**

$$m = \frac{6(502.88) - (23)(130.87)}{6(115) - (23)^2} = \frac{7.27}{161} \approx 0.045$$

$$b = \frac{130.87 - 0.045(23)}{6} = \frac{129.83}{6} \approx 21.64$$

The regression line is $y = 0.045x + 21.64$.

See part a for the graph.

c. For 2000, let $x = 5$, then

$$y = 0.045(5) + 21.64 = 21.865$$

The time for the 2000 Olympics is 21.865 sec.

d. For 2012, let $x = 8$, then

$$y = 0.045(8) + 21.64 = 22$$

The time for the 2012 Olympics is 22 sec.

5. a.

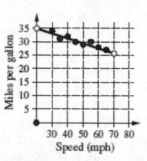

b. If your speed were 70 mph, you would get about 26 mi/gal (may vary).

c.

Car	x	y	x^2	xy
1	30	34	900	1020
2	35	31	1225	1085
3	40	32	1600	1280
4	45	30	2025	1350
5	50	29	2500	1450
6	55	30	3025	1650
7	60	28	3600	1680
8	65	27	4225	1755
Totals	**380**	**241**	**19100**	**11270**

$$m = \frac{8(11270) - (380)(241)}{8(19100) - (380)^2} = -\frac{1420}{8400} \approx -0.169$$

$$b = \frac{241 + 0.169(380)}{8} = \frac{305.24}{8} \approx 38.155$$

The regression line is $y = -0.169x + 38.155$.

Let $x = 70$, then

$$y = -0.169(70) + 38.155 = 26.3$$

When the speed is 70 mi/hr, you should get 26.3 mi/gal.

6. a.

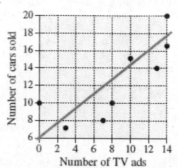

b. For only 6 ads per week, 10 or 11 cars will be sold (Answers will vary).

c.

Ads	x	y	x^2	xy
1	3	7	9	21
2	10	15	100	150
3	0	10	0	0
4	7	8	49	56
5	13	14	169	182
6	8	10	64	80
7	14	20	196	280
Totals	**55**	**84**	**587**	**769**

$$m = \frac{7(769) - (55)(84)}{7(587) - (55)^2} = \frac{763}{1084} \approx 0.704$$

$$b = \frac{84 - 0.704(55)}{7} = \frac{45.287}{7} \approx 6.470$$

The regression line is $y = 0.704x + 6.470$.

Let $x = 6$, then

$$y = 0.704(6) + 6.470 = 10.694$$

When the number of ads is 6, about 10.7 cars will be sold.

7. a.

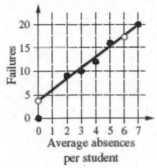

b. For 6 absences per student, about 18 students will fail.

c.

Absences	x	y	x^2	xy
1	5	16	25	80
2	7	20	49	140
3	2	9	4	18
4	4	12	16	48
5	3	10	9	30
Totals	**21**	**67**	**103**	**316**

$$m = \frac{5(316) - (21)(67)}{5(103) - (21)^2} = \frac{173}{74} \approx 2.338$$

$$b = \frac{67 - 2.338(21)}{5} = \frac{17.91}{5} \approx 3.581$$

The regression line is $y = 2.338x + 3.581$.
Let $x = 6$, then

$$y = 2.338(6) + 3.581 = 17.609$$

When the number of ads is 6, about 18 students fail.

8. a.

Game	x	y	x^2	xy
1	23	16	529	368
2	32	23	1024	736
3	19	13	361	247
4	29	22	841	638
5	20	16	400	320
Totals	**123**	**90**	**3155**	**2309**

$$m = \frac{5(2309) - (123)(90)}{5(3155) - (123)^2} = \frac{475}{646} \approx 0.735$$

$$b = \frac{90 - 0.735(123)}{5} = -\frac{0.441}{5} = -0.088$$

The regression line is $y = 0.735x - 0.088$.

b. For 26,000 tickets, let $x = 26$, then

$$y = 0.735(26) - 0.088 = 19.022$$

When 26,000 tickets are sold, the concessionaire should buy 19.022 hot dogs.

9. a.

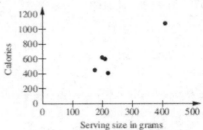

b.

Item	x	y	x^2	xy
1	168	450	28224	75600
2	222	590	49284	130980
3	418	1120	174724	468160
4	209	625	43681	130625
5	231	430	53361	99330
Totals	**1248**	**3215**	**349274**	**904695**

$$m = \frac{5(904695) - (1248)(3215)}{5(349274) - (1248)^2} = \frac{511,155}{188,866} \approx 2.706$$

$$b = \frac{3215 - 2.706(1248)}{5} = -\frac{162.64}{5} \approx -32.5$$

The regression line is $y = 2.706x - 32.5$.

c. Let $x = 300$, then

$$y = 2.706(300) - 32.5 = 779.3$$

When you consume 300 gm of a Burger King sandwich, you will intake about 779 cal.

10. a.

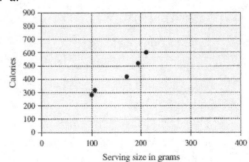

b.

Item	x	y	x^2	xy
1	102	280	10404	28560
2	116	330	13456	38280
3	166	430	27556	71380
4	194	530	37636	102820
5	215	590	46225	126850
Totals	**793**	**2160**	**135277**	**367890**

$$m = \frac{5(367890) - (793)(2160)}{5(135277) - (793)^2} = \frac{126,570}{47,536} \approx 2.663$$

$$b = \frac{2160 - 2.663(793)}{5} = \frac{48.547}{5} \approx 9.709$$

The regression line is $y = 2.663x + 9.709$.

c. Let $x = 300$, then

$$y = 2.663(300) + 9.709 \approx 808.61$$

When you consume 300 gm of McDonald's sandwich, you will intake about 808.61 cal.

11. a.

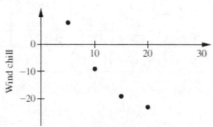

b.

Item	x	y	x^2	xy
1	5	6	25	30
2	10	−9	100	−90
3	15	−18	225	−270
4	20	−24	400	−480
Totals	50	−45	750	−810

$$m = \frac{4(-810) - (50)(-45)}{4(750) - (50)^2} = \frac{-990}{500} = -1.98$$

$$b = \frac{-45 - (-1.98)(50)}{4} = \frac{54}{4} = 13.5$$

The regression line is $y = -1.98x + 13.5$.

c. Let $x = 25$, then

$$y = -1.98(25) + 13.5 = -36$$

When the wind speed is 25 mph, the wind chill is −36° F.

12. a.

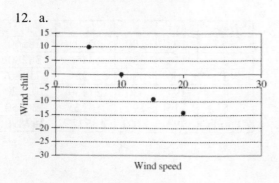

b.

Item	x	y	x^2	xy
1	5	10	25	50
2	10	0	100	0
3	15	−8	225	−120
4	20	−14	400	−280
Totals	50	−12	750	−350

$$m = \frac{4(-350) - (50)(-12)}{4(750) - (50)^2} = -\frac{800}{500} = -1.6$$

$$b = \frac{-12 - (-1.6)(50)}{4} = \frac{68}{4} = 17$$

The regression line is $y = -1.6x + 17$.

c. Let $x = 25$, then $y = -1.6(25) + 17 = -23$

When the wind speed is 25 mph, the wind chill is −23° F.

d. The current wind chill is −36° F, so −23° F is higher.

13. a.

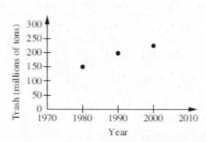

b. Let x be the number of years after 1980.

x	y	x^2	xy
0	150	0	0
10	200	100	2000
20	220	400	4400
30	570	500	6400

$$m = \frac{3(6400) - (30)(570)}{3(500) - (30)^2} = \frac{2100}{600} = 3.5$$

$$b = \frac{570 - 3.5(30)}{3} = \frac{465}{3} = 155$$

The regression line is $y = 3.5x + 155$.

c. For 2010, let $x = 30$, then

$$y = 3.5(30) + 155 = 260$$

In 2010, the amount of trash will be 260 million tons.

For 2015, let $x = 35$, then

$$y = 3.5(35) + 155 = 277.5$$

In 2015, the amount of trash will be 277.5 million tons.

14. a.

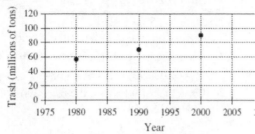

  b. Let x be the number of years after 1990.

x	y	x^2	xy
−10	55	100	−550
0	70	0	0
10	90	100	900
0	**215**	**200**	**350**

$$m = \frac{3(350) - (0)(215)}{3(200) - (0)^2} = \frac{1050}{600} = 1.75$$

$$b = \frac{215 - 1.75(0)}{3} = \frac{215}{3} \approx 71.667$$

The regression line is $y = 1.75x + 71.667$.

  c. For 2010, let $x = 20$, then

$$y = 1.75(20) + 71.667 = 106.667$$

In 2010, the amount of trash will be 106.667 million tons.

For 2015, let $x = 25$, then

$$y = 1.75(25) + 71.667 = 115.417$$

In 2015, the amount of trash will be 115.417 million tons.

15. a.

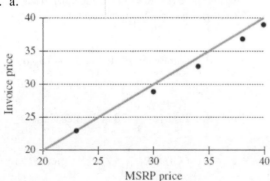

  b.

Model	x	y	x^2	xy
1	23	22	529	506
2	30	29	900	870
3	38	36	1444	1368
4	34	33	1156	1122
5	41	39	1681	1599
Totals	**166**	**159**	**5710**	**5465**

$$m = \frac{5(5465) - (166)(159)}{5(5710) - (166)^2} = \frac{931}{994} = 0.94$$

$$b = \frac{159 - 0.94(166)}{5} = \frac{3.52}{5} \approx 0.7$$

The regression line is $y = 0.94x + 0.7$.

  c. For \$30,000 MSRP, let $x = 30$, then

$$y = 0.94(30) + 0.7 = 28.9$$

For a \$30,000 MSRP, the invoice price will be \$28,900.

16. a.

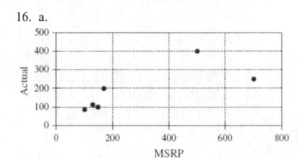

  b.

x	y	x^2	xy
500	400	250000	200000
700	250	490000	175000
100	90	10000	9000
170	200	28900	34000
130	120	16900	15600
150	100	22500	15000
1750	**1160**	**818300**	**448600**

$$m = \frac{6(448,600) - (1750)(1160)}{6(818,300) - (1750)^2}$$

$$= \frac{661,600}{1,847,300} \approx 0.358$$

$$b = \frac{1160 - 0.358(1750)}{6} = \frac{533.247}{6} \approx 88.875$$

The regression line is $y = 0.358x + 88.875$.

  c. For \$300 MSRP, let $x = 300$, then

$$y = 0.358(300) + 88.875 \approx 196.28$$

For a \$300 MSRP, the actual price will be \$196.28.

17. a.

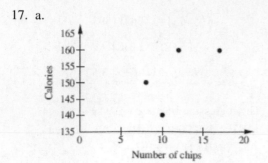

b.

Brand	x	y	x^2	xy
Terra	10	140	100	1400
Taro	10	140	100	1400
Sweet Potato	17	160	289	2720
Glenny's	12	160	144	1920
Sesame	9	150	81	1350
Total	**58**	**750**	**714**	**8790**

$$m = \frac{5(8790) - (58)(750)}{5(714) - (58)^2} = \frac{450}{206} \approx 2.184$$

$$b = \frac{750 - 2.184(58)}{5} = \frac{623.301}{5} \approx 124.66$$

The regression line is $y = 2.184x + 124.66$.

c. For a serving of 15 chips, let $x = 15$, then $y = 2.184(15) + 124.66 \approx 157$.

For a serving of 15 chips, there will be about 157 cal.

18. a.

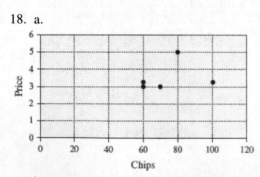

b.

Brand	x	y	x^2	xy
Terra	80	5.00	6400	400
Taro	60	3.25	3600	195
Sweet Potato	100	3.25	10000	325
Glenny's	60	3.00	3600	180
Sesame	70	3.00	4900	210
Total	**370**	**17.5**	**28500**	**1310**

$$m = \frac{5(1310) - (370)(17.5)}{5(28500) - (370)^2} = \frac{75}{5600} \approx 0.013$$

$$b = \frac{17.5 - 0.013(370)}{5} = \frac{12.54}{5} \approx 2.509$$

The regression line is $y = 0.013x + 2.509$.

c. For a bag of 90 chips, let $x = 90$, then

$y = 0.013(90) + 2.509 \approx 3.68$

For a bag of 90 chips, the price will be about $3.68.

19. $\dfrac{12}{50} \cdot 3000 = 720$ students would be expected to prefer their hamburgers plain.

20. $\dfrac{9}{150} \cdot 10{,}000 = 600$ people would expected to be guilty of fraud.

21. $\dfrac{3}{150} \cdot 10{,}000 = 200$ tires are expected to be defective.

22. $\dfrac{5}{150} \cdot 5000 \approx 166.67$ cars should be expected to have defective steering assemblies.

23. $0.727 \cdot 586 \approx 426$ baskets would be expected to be made.

24. $\dfrac{9}{50} \cdot 200 = 36$ males and $\dfrac{19}{50} \cdot 200 = 76$ females would be expected to be squeezing their toothpaste tubes from the bottom.

25. a. Punxsutawney Phil: $\dfrac{10}{15} \cdot 20 \approx 13$ times right

b. Sun Prairie: $\dfrac{3}{7} \cdot 20 \approx 9$ times right

c. West Orange: $\dfrac{6}{13} \cdot 20 \approx 9$ times wrong

d. Staten Island: $\dfrac{1}{7} \cdot 20 \approx 3$ times wrong

e. Lilburn: $\dfrac{1}{7} \cdot 20 \approx 3$ times wrong

f. Chicago: $\dfrac{1}{6} \cdot 20 \approx 3$ times right

26. $0.14 \cdot 500 = 70$ African American and $0.09 \cdot 1500 = 135$ white students would be expected to drop out.

27. $0.20 \cdot 500 = 100$ liberals and $0.32 \cdot 500 = 160$ conservatives would be expected.

28. a.

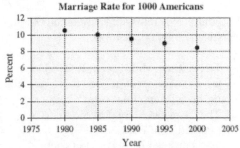

Marriage Rate for 1000 Americans

b. For every 5 yr, the marriage rate lowers by 0.5%. For 2010, the rate would be 7.5% and for 2015, the rate would be 7%.

c. In 2015 about $0.07 \cdot 5000 = 350$ Americans would be expected to marry.

29. a.

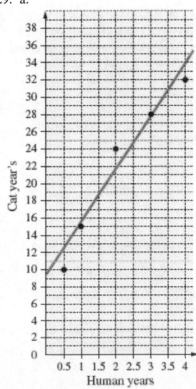

b.

x	y	x^2	xy
0.5	10	0.25	5
1	15	1	15
2	24	4	48
3	28	9	84
4	32	16	128
10.5	**109**	**30.25**	**280**

$$m = \frac{5(280) - (10.5)(109)}{5(30.25) - (10.5)^2} = \frac{255.5}{41} \approx 6.2$$

$$b = \frac{109 - 6.2(10.5)}{5} = \frac{43.567}{5} \approx 8.7$$

The regression line is $y = 6.2x + 8.7$.

c. For a 2-yr old cat, let $x = 2$, then
$$y = 6.2(2) + 8.7 = 21.1$$
From the formula, a 2-yr old cat would be 21.1 years old.

30. a. From the chart, a dog that is 9 yr old in human years would be 60 yr old in dog years.

b. From the chart, a dog that is 65 yr old in dog years would be 10 yr old in human years.

31. Find 21 on the vertical axis, move to the right to the line, then down to find the corresponding horizontal axis value. The human age 21 corresponds to about 2 yr in human years.

32.

x	y	x^2	xy
1	12	1	12
3	30	9	90
4	40	16	160
9	60	81	540
11	70	121	770
28	**212**	**228**	**1572**

$$m = \frac{5(1572) - (28)(212)}{5(228) - (28)^2} = \frac{1924}{356} \approx 5.4$$

$$b = \frac{212 - 5.4(28)}{5} = \frac{60.67}{5} \approx 12$$

The regression line is $y = 5.4x + 12$.

33. a. Use the regression line from problem 32. For dog 15 yr old in human years, let $x = 15$, then $y = 5.4(15) + 12 = 93$.

A dog that is 15 yr old in human years would be 93 yr old in dog years.

b. Find 15 on the horizontal axis, go up to the line, then left to the vertical axis to find the corresponding value. Thus, for 15 human years, the dog would be 90 yr in dog years.

34.

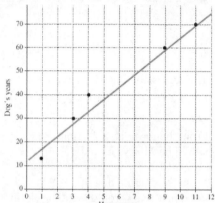

35. a. Refer to problem 34. The coordinates of the point closest to being on the line is (9, 60).

b. Let $x = 9$, then $y = 5.4(9) + 12 = 60.6$. The coordinates are (9, 60.6).

36. a. The wind speed was 75 mph.
b. There was no change in hurricane intensity from 48 to 72 hours.
c. The hurricane was decreasing in intensity from Now to 48 hours.

37. a. Since we only have two points, we can find the equation of the line through those points.

$$m = \frac{75 - 60}{0 - 36} = -\frac{15}{36} \approx -0.417$$

Using $m = -0.417$ and point (0, 75):
$$y = mx + b$$
$$75 = -0.417(0) + b$$
$$b = 75$$

The regression line is $y = -0.417x + 75$.

b. Let $x = 24$, then
$$y = -0.417(24) + 75 = 64.992 \approx 65 \text{ mph}$$

c. From the graph, the wind velocity between 48 and 72 hr after the beginning of the forecast was 50 mph.

d. The equation of the regression line between 48 and 72 hr is the horizontal line $y = 50$.

38. From February to May the increase is about $73° - 50° = 23°$.

39. Procedure (d) is the most appropriate to obtain a statistically unbiased sample.

40. Procedure (c) is most appropriate to obtain a statistically unbiased sample.

41. a. The women who shop in Rodeo Drive are not necessarily a good representation of the entire population of California.
b. The same can be said of the male population of Berkeley.
c. The same can be said of the people attending an Oakland baseball game.
In general not all elements of the population participate in these activities and, therefore, have zero chance of being selected. The procedures might yield a representative sample, but it is not a random sample because not all elements have an equal chance of selection.

42. Assume that the sample is a random sample of the entire population that is being surveyed. If the population is not too large, use the entire population. Otherwise, put all the names in a box and draw a random sample as large as is feasible.

43. The point (0, 19.9) is a y intercept, so the y intercept b of the line is 19.9.

44. The slope of the line is
$$m = \frac{19.9 - 19.58}{0 - 7} = -\frac{0.32}{7} \approx -0.046.$$

45. The equation of the line is $y = -0.046x + 19.9$.

46. For the year 2012, let $x = 8$, then
$$y = -0.046(8) + 19.9 = 19.532 \text{ sec.}$$

47. The predicted winning time in the year 2012 using $y = -0.048x + 19.914$ is
$$y = -0.048(8) + 19.914 = 19.53 \text{ sec.}$$

48. The difference between problem 46 and 47 answers is 19.532 sec − 19.53 sec = 0.002 sec.

Section 12.7 Scattergrams and Correlation

1. No. Too many data points lie below the line.

2. Good. Roughly as many points above as below the line.

3. Good. Roughly as many points above as below the line.

4. Not good. Too many points above the line.

5. Positive

6. Positive

7. None

8. Positive

9. Negative

10. Negative

11. Positive

12. Negative

13. The value of the linear correlation coefficient r is always (c) between -1 and 1, inclusive.

14. The linear correlation coefficient r measures (d) the direction and strength of the linear relationship. 15. Let $x = 90$, then $y = 10 + 0.9(90) = 91$. The predicted value of Maria's score on the final exam is (c) 91.

16. A hotdog containing 100 cal would have a sodium content of about (b) 350.

17. The least-squares line would predict (a) 1.1 gm of nitrogen oxide per mile driven.

18. The scatter gram indicates (a) a positive association between height and volume.

19. A plausible value r would be (c) -0.9.

20. The correlation would be (c) positive, but we cannot say what the exact value would be.

21. The true statement is (c) There is a positive correlation between the heights of men and women on a date.

22. The valid conclusion is (d) None of the above.

23. a.

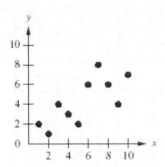

b.

x	y	x^2	xy	y^2
2	1	4	2	1
4	3	16	12	9
7	8	49	56	64
3	4	9	12	16
1	2	1	2	4
5	2	25	10	4
8	6	64	48	36
10	7	100	70	49
6	6	36	36	36
9	4	81	36	16
55	**43**	**385**	**284**	**235**

$$m = \frac{10(284) - (55)(43)}{10(385) - (55)^2} = \frac{475}{825} \approx 0.58$$

$$b = \frac{43 - 0.58(55)}{10} = \frac{11.333}{10} \approx 1.133$$

The regression line is $y = 0.58x + 1.133$.

c. $$r = \frac{10(284) - (55)(43)}{\sqrt{10(385) - (55)^2} \cdot \sqrt{10(235) - (43)^2}}$$

$$= \frac{475}{\sqrt{825} \cdot \sqrt{501}} \approx \frac{475}{642.9} \approx 0.7388$$

d. We can be 95% confident that there is a significant positive linear correlation.

24. a.

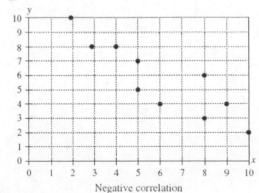

Negative correlation

b.

x	y	x^2	xy	y^2
9	4	81	36	16
10	2	100	20	4
8	3	64	24	9
8	6	64	48	36
6	4	36	24	16
4	8	16	32	64
5	7	25	35	49
5	5	25	25	25
3	8	9	24	64
2	10	4	20	100
60	**57**	**424**	**288**	**383**

$$m = \frac{10(288)-(60)(57)}{10(424)-(60)^2} = -\frac{540}{640} \approx -0.84$$

$$b = \frac{57+0.84(60)}{10} \approx \frac{107.625}{10} \approx 10.76$$

The regression line is $y = -0.84x + 10.76$.

c.

$$r = \frac{10(288)-(60)(57)}{\sqrt{10(424)-(60)^2} \cdot \sqrt{10(383)-(57)^2}}$$

$$= -\frac{540}{\sqrt{640} \cdot \sqrt{581}} \approx -\frac{540}{609.79} \approx -0.886$$

d. Since $|-0.866| > 0.765$, we can be 99% confident that there is a significant negative linear correlation.

b. Let $x =$ weight (lb) and $y =$ mpg.

x	y	x^2	xy	y^2
2800	19	7840000	53200	361
1900	34	3610000	64600	1156
2000	28	4000000	56000	784
3300	19	10890000	62700	361
3100	24	9610000	74400	576
2900	23	8410000	66700	529
4000	16	1600000	64000	256
2600	24	6760000	62400	576
22600	**187**	**67120000**	**504000**	**4599**

$$m = \frac{8(504,000)-(22,600)(187)}{8(67,120,000)-(22,600)^2}$$

$$= -\frac{194,200}{26,200,000} \approx -0.01$$

$$b = \frac{187-(-0.01)(22,600)}{8} \approx \frac{354.52}{8} \approx 44.315$$

The regression line is $y = -0.01x + 44.315$.

c.

$$r = \frac{8(504000)-(22600)(187)}{\sqrt{8(67120000)-(22600)^2} \cdot \sqrt{8(4599)-(187)^2}}$$

$$= -\frac{194,200}{\sqrt{26,200,000} \cdot \sqrt{1823}} \approx -\frac{194,200}{218,546.56} \approx -0.889$$

d. Since $|-0.889| > 0.834$, we can be 99% confident that there is a significant negative linear correlation.

25. a.

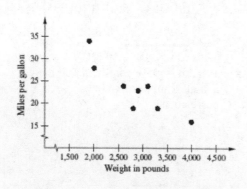

26. a.

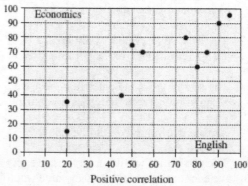

b. Let x = English score and
    y = economics score.

x	y	x^2	xy	y^2
50	75	2500	3750	5625
95	95	9025	9025	9025
55	70	3025	3850	4900
20	36	400	700	1225
85	70	7225	5950	4900
75	80	5625	6000	6400
45	40	2025	1800	1600
20	15	400	300	225
80	60	6400	4800	3600
90	90	8100	8100	8100
615	**630**	**44725**	**44275**	**45600**

$$m = \frac{10(44,275)-(615)(630)}{10(44,725)-(615)^2} = \frac{55,300}{69,025} \approx 0.80$$

$$b = \frac{630-0.80(615)}{10} \approx \frac{137.29}{10} \approx 13.73$$

The regression line is $y = 0.80x + 13.73$

c.

$$r = \frac{10(44275)-(615)(630)}{\sqrt{10(44725)-(615)^2} \cdot \sqrt{10(45600)-(630)^2}}$$

$$= \frac{55,300}{\sqrt{69,025} \cdot \sqrt{59,100}} \approx \frac{55,300}{63,870.0} \approx 0.866$$

d. Since $|0.866| > 0.765$, we can be
    99% confident that there is a
    significant linear correlation.

e. Let $x = 70$, then
    $y = 0.80(70) + 13.73 = 69.73 \approx 70$
    The predicted economics score would
    be about 70.

27. a.

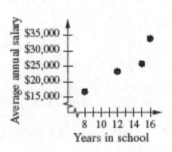

b. Let x = years of schooling and
    y = average salary in thousands.

x	y	x^2	xy	y^2
8	16.8	64	134.4	282.24
12	23.3	144	279.6	542.89
15	25.8	225	387	665.64
16	33.9	256	542.4	1149.21
51	**99.8**	**689**	**1343.4**	**2639.98**

$$m = \frac{4(1343.4)-(51)(99.8)}{4(689)-(51)^2} = \frac{283.8}{155} \approx 1.83$$

$$b = \frac{99.8-1.83(51)}{4} \approx \frac{6.421}{4} \approx 1.605$$

The regression line is $y = 1.83x + 1.605$
thousands.

c.

$$r = \frac{4(1343.4)-(51)(99.8)}{\sqrt{4(689)-(51)^2} \cdot \sqrt{4(2639.98)-(99.8)^2}}$$

$$= \frac{283.8}{\sqrt{155} \cdot \sqrt{599.88}} \approx \frac{283.8}{304.929} \approx 0.9307$$

d. Since $|0.9307| < 0.950$, we cannot be
    certain that there is a significant
    positive linear correlation at the 95%
    or 99% confidence level.

e. Let $x = 10$, then
    $y = 1.83(10) + 1.605 = 19.905$
    The predicted salary would be $19,905.

28. a.

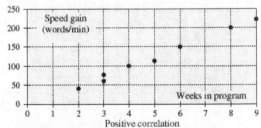

Positive correlation

b. Let x = weeks in program and
    y = speed gain (words per minute).

x	y	x^2	xy	y^2
2	40	4	80	1600
3	60	9	180	3600
3	80	9	240	6400
4	100	16	400	10000
5	110	25	550	12100
6	150	36	900	22500
8	190	64	1520	36100
9	220	81	1980	48400
40	**950**	**244**	**5850**	**140700**

$$m = \frac{8(5850) - (40)(950)}{8(244) - (40)^2} = \frac{8800}{352} = 25$$

$$b = \frac{950 - 25(40)}{8} = -\frac{50}{8} = -6.25$$

The regression line is $y = 25x - 6.25$.

c.

$$r = \frac{8(5850) - (40)(950)}{\sqrt{8(244) - (40)^2} \cdot \sqrt{8(140,700) - (950)^2}}$$

$$= \frac{8800}{\sqrt{352} \cdot \sqrt{223,100}} \approx \frac{8800}{8861.783} \approx 0.993$$

d. Since $|0.933| > 0.834$, we can be
    99% confident that there is a
    significant linear correlation.

e. Let $x = 7$, then
    $$y = 25(7) - 6.25 = 168.75 \approx 169$$
    The expected gain in reading speed
    would be about 169 wpm.

29. a.

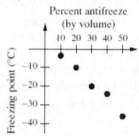

Percent antifreeze
(by volume)

b. Let x = percent of antifreeze and
    y = freezing point (degrees C).

x	y	x^2	xy	y^2
10	−4	100	−40	16
20	−10	400	−200	100
30	−20	900	−600	400
40	−24	1600	−960	576
50	−36	2500	−1800	1296
150	**−94**	**5500**	**−3600**	**2388**

$$m = \frac{5(-3600) - (150)(-94)}{5(5500) - (150)^2} = -\frac{3900}{5000} = -0.78$$

$$b = \frac{-94 - (-0.78)(150)}{5} = \frac{23}{5} = 4.6$$

The regression line is $y = -0.78x + 4.6$.

c.

$$r = \frac{5(-3600) - (150)(-94)}{\sqrt{5(5500) - (150)^2} \cdot \sqrt{5(2388) - (-94)^2}}$$

$$= -\frac{3900}{\sqrt{5000} \cdot \sqrt{3104}} \approx -\frac{3900}{3939.54} \approx -0.99$$

d. Since $|-0.99| > 0.959$, we can be
    99% confident that there is a
    significant negative linear correlation.

e. Let $x = 25$, then
    $$y = -0.78(25) + 4.6 = -14.9$$
    The predicted freezing point would be
    $-14.9°C$.

30. a.

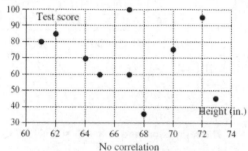

No correlation

b. Let x = height (in.) and y = test score.

x	y	x^2	xy	y^2
62	85	3844	5270	7225
67	60	4489	4020	3600
70	75	4900	5250	5625
64	70	4096	4480	4900
72	95	5184	6840	9025
68	35	4624	2380	1225
65	60	4225	3900	3600
61	80	3721	4880	6400
73	45	5329	3285	2025
67	100	4489	6700	10000
669	**705**	**44901**	**47005**	**53625**

$$m = \frac{10(47,005) - (669)(705)}{10(44,901) - (669)^2} = -\frac{1595}{1449} \approx -1.10$$

$$b = \frac{705 - (-1.10)(669)}{10} \approx \frac{1441.4}{10} \approx 144.14$$

The regression line is $y = -1.10x + 144.14$.

c. $r =$

$$\frac{10(47005) - (669)(705)}{\sqrt{10(44901) - (669)^2} \cdot \sqrt{10(53625) - (705)^2}}$$

$$= -\frac{1595}{\sqrt{1449} \cdot \sqrt{39,225}} \approx -\frac{1595}{7539.03} \approx -0.2116$$

d. Since $|-0.2116| \not> 0.632$, we cannot
    conclude that there is a linear correlation
    between the variables.

e. Let $x = 66$, then

$y = -1.10(66) + 144.14 \approx 71.5$

The predicted score would be about 71.5.

31. a. There was no outage during the 7th week.
    b. The greatest number of outages occurred during the 11th week.
    c. A decline in the number of outages seemed to start after the 2nd week.
    d. No correlation is shown by the chart.

32. a. The chart shows a positive correlation.
    b. The student would be expected to score in the 70's.

33. a. No, correlation does not mean that one variable causes the other.
    b. Answers may vary. It is possible that the number of cars with air bags being sold is increasing at a rate that makes them representative of the entire population of cars.

34. a. As one variable increases, the related variable also increases at an approximately constant rate for linear correlations.
    b. As one variable increases, the related variable decreases at an approximately constant rate for linear correlations.

35. Using a grapher, $r \approx 0.2236$. We cannot be certain that there is a significant linear correlation.

36. Deleting Northern Ireland from the sample, $r \approx 0.78$.

37. No. inclusion of Ireland makes it appear as though there is no linear correlation.

38. Answers will vary.

Chapter 12   Practice Test

1. No. Not all members of the student body had the same chance of being chosen (only those in the English Department).

2.

Scores	Tally Marks	Frequency
$60 < s \le 65$	II	2
$65 < s \le 70$	III	3
$70 < s \le 75$	III	3
$75 < s \le 80$	II	2
$80 < s \le 85$	III	3
$85 < s \le 90$	IN II	7
$90 < s \le 95$	III	3
$95 < s \le 100$	II	2

3. a. – b.

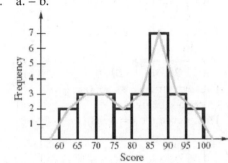

4. a. The mean =
$$\frac{69 + 70 + 71 + 73 + 78 + 82 + 82}{7} = \frac{525}{7} = 75°F.$$
   b. The mode is 82°F.
   c. Order the numbers: 69, 70, 71, 73, 78, 82, 82. The median is the 4th term: 73°F

5. a. Range = 82 – 69 = 13°F
   b.

x	$x - \overline{x}$	$(x - \overline{x})^2$
78	3	9
82	7	49
82	7	49
71	–4	16
69	–6	36
73	–2	4
70	–5	25
525		**188**
$\overline{x} = \dfrac{525}{7} = 75°F$	$\dfrac{188}{6} \approx 31.333$	
		$s = \sqrt{31.333} \approx 5.60°F$

6. We are given $\mu = 128$ and $\sigma = 8$.
   a. Almost all the measurements fall between $128 - 3(8) = 104$ and $128 + 3(8) = 152$.
   b. Find the z-score for values of $x = 112$.

$$z = \frac{112 - 128}{8} = -\frac{16}{8} = -2$$

The probability associated with 2 standard deviations below the mean is 0.5 – 0.475 = 0.025 = 2.5%.

7. Given $\mu = 100$ and $\sigma = 20$.

a. The z-score for $x = 140$ is
$$z = \frac{140 - 100}{20} = \frac{40}{20} = 2$$
Thus, about 2.5% of 1000 = 25 scores are above 140.

b. The z-score for $x = 80$ is
$$z = \frac{80 - 100}{20} = -\frac{20}{20} = -1$$
Thus, about 16% of 1000 = 160 scores are below 80.

c. The z-score for $x = 60$ is
$$z = \frac{60 - 100}{20} = -\frac{40}{20} = -2$$
About 2.5% of 1000 = 25 scores are below 60. In part b, we found that about 160 scores are below 80. Thus, about 160 – 25 = 135 scores are between 60 and 80.

8. Given $\mu = 10$ lb and $\sigma = 1$ lb.

a. The z-score for $x = 10$ is
$$z = \frac{10 - 10}{1} = \frac{0}{1} = 0$$
The probability is that 0.5, or 50%, of the lines has a breaking point of more than 10 lb.

b. The z-score for $x = 8$ is
$$z = \frac{8 - 10}{1} = -\frac{2}{1} = -2$$
The probability is that 0.025, or 2.5%, of the lines has a breaking point of less than 8 lb.

9. Given $\mu = 50$ and $\sigma = 5$.

a. $z = \frac{58 - 50}{5} = \frac{8}{5} = 1.6$

b. $z = \frac{62 - 50}{5} = \frac{12}{5} = 2.4$

10. For the French test, the z-score is

$$z = \frac{88 - 76}{18} \approx 0.667 \text{ For the psychology test,}$$

the z-score is $z = \frac{90 - 80}{16} = \frac{10}{16} = 0.625$. Thus,

the student who scored 88 on the French test has the better score relative to the test.

11. Given $\mu = 50$ and $\sigma = 5$.

For $x = 50$: $z = \frac{50 - 50}{5} = \frac{0}{5} = 0.$

For $x = 62$: $z = \frac{62 - 50}{5} = \frac{12}{5} = 2.4.$

From Table II, we find the probability that a randomly selected score is between the mean and 2.4 standard deviation above the mean to be 0.492.

12. a.

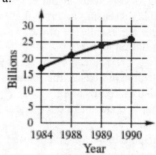

b. In 1986 about $19 billion was spent on education.

13.

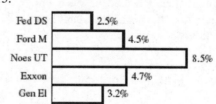

14.

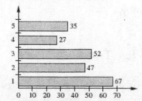

Features that Patrons Liked

1 Low-calorie entrees   4 All-you-can-eat specials

2 Varied portion sizes   5 Self-service soup bar

3 Cholesterol-free entrees

15. The percentage increase is
$$\frac{15-10}{10} = \frac{5}{10} = 0.5 = 50\%.$$

16.

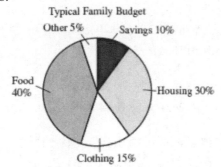

Typical Family Budget

Other 5%
Savings 10%
Food 40%
Housing 30%
Clothing 15%

17. For $x = 6$, $y \approx 0$.

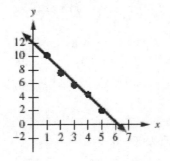

18.

x	y	x^2	xy
1	10.2	1	10.2
2	7.6	4	15.2
3	5.8	9	17.4
4	4.4	16	17.6
5	2.0	25	10
15	**30**	**55**	**70.4**

$$m = \frac{5(70.4) - (15)(30)}{5(55) - (15)^2} = -\frac{98}{50} = -1.96$$

$$b = \frac{30 - (-1.96)(15)}{5} = \frac{59.4}{5} = 11.88$$

The regression line is $y = -1.96x + 11.88$.

c. Let $x = 6$, then
$$y = -1.96(6) + 11.88 = 0.12$$

19. $\dfrac{3}{150} \cdot 10,000 = 200$ tires are expected to be defective.

20. $\dfrac{4000}{50,000} \cdot 100 = 8$ students should be expected to have gotten an excellent rating on this test.

21. The best representation for the data is (b). The slope follows the direction of the line and has about the same number of points above and below the line.

22. a. Positive correlation
    b. Negative correlation
    c. None
    d. Negative correlation

23. The graph shows a strong negative linear correlation. Thus, the coefficient of correlation r is (c) -0.94.

24. Let x = the year and y = the product sales (in billions of dollars).

x	y	x^2	xy	y^2
2	4	4	8	16
3	4.2	9	12.6	17.64
4	5	16	20	25
5	5.8	25	29	33.64
14	**19**	**54**	**69.6**	**92.28**

$$m = \frac{4(69.6) - (14)(19)}{4(54) - (14)^2} = \frac{12.4}{20} = 0.62$$

$$b = \frac{19 - 0.62(14)}{4} = \frac{10.32}{4} = 2.58$$

The regression line is $y = 0.62x + 2.58$.

25. Refer to table in problem 24.

$$r = \frac{4(69.6) - (14)(19)}{\sqrt{4(54) - (14)^2} \cdot \sqrt{4(92.28) - (19)^2}}$$

$$= \frac{12.4}{\sqrt{20} \cdot \sqrt{8.12}} \approx \frac{12.4}{12.743} \approx 0.97$$

We can be 95% confident that there is a significant correlation between the year x and the sales y.

Chapter 13 Your Money and Your Math

Section 13.1 Interest, Taxes, and Discounts

1. a. $I = Prt = 3000(0.08)(1) = \$240$
    b. $I = Prt = 3000(0.04)(1) = \$120$

2. a. $I = Prt = 4500(0.07)(1) = \$315$
    b. $I = Prt = 4500(0.035)(1) = \$157.50$

3. a. $I = Prt = 2000(0.09)(3) = \$540$
    b. $I = Prt = 2000(0.045)(3) = \$270$

4. a. $I = Prt = 6200(0.08)(4) = \$1984$
    b. $I = Prt = 6200(0.04)(4) = \$992$

5. a. $I = Prt = 4000(0.10)\left(\dfrac{1}{2}\right) = \$200$
    b. $I = Prt = 4000(0.035)\left(\dfrac{1}{2}\right) = \$70$

6. a. $I = Prt = 6000(0.12)\left(\dfrac{1}{3}\right) = \$240$
    b. $I = Prt = 6000(0.015)\left(\dfrac{1}{3}\right) = \$30$

7. a. $I = Prt = 2500(0.10)\left(\dfrac{1}{4}\right) = \$62.50$
    b. $I = Prt = 2500(0.025)\left(\dfrac{1}{4}\right) = \$15.63$

8. a. $I = Prt = 12,000(0.09)\left(\dfrac{1}{12}\right) = \$90$
    b. $I = Prt = 12,000(0.02)\left(\dfrac{1}{12}\right) = \$20$

9. a. $I = Prt = 16,000(0.07)\left(\dfrac{5}{12}\right)$
        $= \$466.67$
    b. $I = Prt = 16,000(0.03)\left(\dfrac{5}{12}\right) = \$200$

10. a. $I = Prt = 30,000(0.08)\left(\dfrac{2}{12}\right) = \$400$
    b. $I = Prt = 30,000(0.015)\left(\dfrac{2}{12}\right) = \$75$

11. a. Sales tax $= 0.06(40.20) = \$2.41$
    b. $40.20 + 2.41 = \$42.61$

12. a. Sales tax $= 0.04(666) = \$26.64$
    b. $666 + 26.64 = \$692.64$

13. a. FICA tax $= 0.0565(24,000) = \$1356$
    b. FICA tax $= 0.0765(24,000) = \$1836$

14. FICA tax $= 0.0765(30,000) = \$2295$

15. Maybelle's estimated tax was
    $850 + 0.15(25,850 - 8500)$
    $= 850 + 0.15(17,350) = 850 + 2602.50 = \$3452.50$

16. Rob's estimated tax was
    $850 + 0.15(9500 - 8500)$
    $= 850 + 0.15(1000) = 850 + 150 = \$1000$

17. a. Discount $= 0.20(200) = \$40$
    b. $200 - 40 = \$160$
    c. $160 + 0.05(160) = 160 + 8 = \$168$

18. a. Discount $= 0.50(900) = \$450$
    b. $900 - 450 = \$450$
    c. $450 + 0.06(450) = 450 + 27 = \$477$

19. a. Discount $= 0.25(500) = \$125$
    b. $500 - 125 = \$375$

20. a. Discount $=$
        $4(45 - 0.10 \cdot 45) = 4(40.5) = \$162$
    b. $4(0.10 \cdot 45) = \$18$
    c. $162 + 0.06(162) = 162 + 9.72 = \$171.72$

21. a. Discount $= 0.05(28.40) = \$1.42$
    b. $28.40 - 1.42 = \$26.98$

22. a. First discount:
        $350 - 0.20 \cdot 350 = 350 - 70 = \$280$
        Second discount:
        $280 - 0.10 \cdot 280 = 280 - 28 = \$252$
    b. Since $350 - 0.28 \cdot 350 = 350 - 98 = \$252$,
        it makes no difference.

NOTE: Problems 23 – 32 can be done using a

calculator and the formula: $A_n = P\left(1 + \dfrac{r}{m}\right)^n$,

where P is the principal, r the annual interest
rate, m the number of compoundings per year
and n the number of periods.

23. a. Amount = ($100)(1.5938) = $159.38
        Interest = $159.38 – $100 = $59.38
        With a calculator, rounded to
        hundreths:
        $A_n = 100(1 + 0.06)^8 = \$159.38$
        $I = 159.38 - 100 = \$59.38$
    b. Amount = ($100)(1.3686) = $136.86
        Interest = 136.86 – 100 = $36.86
        With a calculator, rounded to
        hundreths:
        $A_n = 100(1 + 0.04)^8 = \$136.86$
        $I = 136.86 - 100 = \$36.86$

24. a. Amount = ($1000)(2.5804)
            =$2580.40
        Interest = $2580.4 – $1000 = $1580.40
        With a calculator, rounded to
        hundreths:
        $A_n = 1000(1 + 0.09)^{11} = \$2580.43$
        $I = 2580.43 - 1000 = \$1580.43$
    b. Amount = ($1000)(1.3842)
            =$1384.20
        Interest = 1384.20 – 1000 = $384.20
        With a calculator, rounded to
        hundreths:
        $A_n = 1000(1 + 0.03)^{11} = \$1384.23$
        Interest = 1384.23 – 1000 = $384.23

25. a. Amount = ($2580)(2.7731)
            = $7154.60
        Interest = 7154.60 – 2580 = $4574.60
        With a calculator, rounded to
        hundreths:
        $A_n = 2580(1 + 0.12)^9 = \$7154.54$
        $I = 7154.54 - 2580 = \$4574.54$

b. Amount = ($2580)(1.1951) = $3083.30
    Interest = 3083.30 – 2580 = $503.30
    With a calculator, rounded to hundreths:
    $A_n = 2580(1 + 0.02)^9 = \$3083.34$
    $I = 3083.34 - 2580 = \$503.34$

26. a. Amount = ($6230)(3.4985) = $21,796
        Interest = 21,796 – 6230 = $15,566
        With a calculator, rounded to hundreths:
        $A_n = 6230(1 + 0.11)^{12} = \$21,795.35$
        $I = 21,795.35 - 6230 = \$15,565.35$
    b. Amount = ($6230)(1.2682) = $7900.10
        Interest = 7900.10 – 6230 = $1670.10
        With a calculator, rounded to hundreths:
        $A_n = 6230(1 + 0.02)^{12} = \$7901.15$
        $I = 7901.15 - 6230 = \$1671.15$

27. a. Amount = ($12,000)(2.1829) = $26,195
        Interest = 26,195 – 12,000 = $14,195
        With a calculator:
        $A_n = 12,000\left(1 + \dfrac{0.10}{2}\right)^{16} = \$26,195$
        $I = 26,195 - 12,000 = \$14,195$
    b. Amount = ($12,000)(1.3728) = $16,473
        Interest = 16,473 – 12,000 = $4473
        With a calculator:
        $A_n = 12,000\left(1 + \dfrac{0.04}{2}\right)^{16} = \$16,473$
        $I = 16,473 - 12,000 = \$4473$

28. a. Amount = ($15,000)(3.8697) = $58,046
        Interest = 58,046 – $15,000 = $43,046
        With a calculator:
        $A_n = 15,000\left(1 + \dfrac{0.14}{2}\right)^{20} = \$58,045$
        $I = 58,045 - 15,000 = \$43,045$
    b. Amount = ($15,000)(1.4859) = $22,289
        Interest = 22,289 – $15,000 = $7289
        With a calculator:
        $A_n = 15,000\left(1 + \dfrac{0.04}{2}\right)^{20} = \$22,289$
        $I = 22,289 - 15,000 = \$7289$

29. a. Amount = ($20,000)(1.2682) = $25,364
        Interest = $25,364 – $20,000 = $5364
        With a calculator:

$$A_n = 20,000\left(1+\frac{0.08}{4}\right)^{12} = \$25,365$$

$$I = 25,365 - 20,000 = \$5365$$

b. Amount = (\$20,000)(1.0615)
$$= \$21,230$$
Interest = \$21,230 - \$20,000 = \$1230
With a calculator:

$$A_n = 20,000\left(1+\frac{0.02}{4}\right)^{12} = \$21,234$$

$$I = 21,234 - 20,000 = \$1234$$

30. a. Amount = (\$30,000)(1.6047)
$$= \$48,141$$
Interest = \$48,141 - \$30,000
$$= \$18,141$$
With a calculator:

$$A_n = 30,000\left(1+\frac{0.12}{4}\right)^{16} = \$48,141$$

$$I = 48,141 - 30,000 = \$18,141$$

b. Amount = (\$30,000)(1.1726)
$$= \$35,178$$
Interest = \$35,178 - \$30,000 = \$5178
With a calculator:

$$A_n = 30,000\left(1+\frac{0.04}{4}\right)^{16} = \$35,177$$

$$I = 35,177 - 30,000 = \$5177$$

31. a. Amt = (\$40,000)(97.0172)
$$= \$3,880,688$$
Int = \$3,880,688 - \$40,000
$$= \$3,840,688$$
With a calculator:

$$A_n = 40,000\left(1+\frac{0.20}{2}\right)^{48} = \$3,880,689$$

$$I = 3,880,689 - 40,000 = \$3,840,689$$

b. Amt = (\$40,000)(2.5871) = \$103,484
Int = \$103,484 - \$40,000 = \$63,484
With a calculator:

$$A_n = 40,000\left(1+\frac{0.04}{2}\right)^{48} = \$103,483$$

$$I = 103,483 - 40,000 = \$63,483$$

32. a. Amt = (\$50,000)(10.0627)
$$= \$503,135$$
Int = \$503,135 - \$50,000 = \$453,135
With a calculator:

$$A_n = 50,000\left(1+\frac{0.16}{2}\right)^{30} = \$503,133$$

$$I = 503,133 - 50,000 = \$453,133$$

b. Amt = (\$50,000)(2.4273) = \$121,365
Int = \$121,365 - \$50,000 = \$71,365
With a calculator:

$$A_n = 50,000\left(1+\frac{0.06}{2}\right)^{30} = \$121,363$$

$$I = 121,363 - 50,000 = \$71,363$$

33. a. Amt = (\$1000)(2.8543) = \$2854.30
With a calculator, rounded to hundreths:

$$A_n = 1000(1+0.06)^{18} = \$2854.34$$

b. Amount = (1000)(2.8983) = \$2898.30
With a calculator, rounded to hundreths:

$$A_n = 1000\left(1+\frac{0.06}{2}\right)^{36} = \$2898.28$$

34. a. Amt = (\$100)(1.7908) = \$179.08
With a calculator, rounded to hundreths:

$$A_n = 100(1+0.06)^{10} = \$179.08$$

b. Amount = (179.08)(2.1829) = \$390.91
With a calculator, rounded to hundreths:

$$A_n = 179.08\left(1+\frac{0.10}{2}\right)^{16} = \$390.91$$

35. a. Amount = (\$3000)(1.3310) = \$3993
b. Interest = 3993 - 3000 = \$993
With a calculator:

$$A_n = 3000(1+0.10)^{3} = \$3993$$

Interest = 3993 - 3000 = \$993

36. a. Amount = (\$1000)(1.4859) = \$1485.90
With a calculator, rounded to hundreths:

$$A_n = 1000\left(1+\frac{0.08}{4}\right)^{20} = \$1485.95$$

b. Amount = (\$1000)(1.6289) = \$1628.90
With a calculator, rounded to hundreths:

$$A_n = 1000\left(1+\frac{0.10}{2}\right)^{10} = \$1628.89$$

c. Deposit your money in Bank B.

37. (\$1000)(1.8061 - 1.7908)
$$= \$1000(0.0153) = \$15.30$$
With a calculator, rounded to hundreths:
$$1000\left(1.03^{20} - 1.06^{10}\right) = \$15.26$$

38.

n	6% Compounded	6.5% Simple
1	$60	$65
2	$123.60	$130
3	$191.02	$195
4	$262.48	$260

The table shows that at the end of four years, the 6% compounded interest exceeds the accumulated 6.5% simple interest by $2.48. Because interest is being paid on the accumulated interest, the compounded interest will continue to exceed the simple interest by an increasing amount after this time.

39. $A = Pe^{rt}$, where $P = 2000$, $r = 0.08$ and $t = \dfrac{1}{2} = 0.5$.

$A = 2000e^{0.08(0.5)} = 2000e^{0.04}$
$= 2000(1.0408108) = \$2081.62$

40. $A = Pe^{rt}$, where $P = 3000$, $r = 0.08$ and $t = 5$.

$A = 3000e^{0.08(5)} = 3000e^{0.4}$
$= 3000(1.491824698) = \$4475.47$

41. $A = P\left(1+\dfrac{r}{m}\right)^n$, where $P = \$10,000$,

$r = 0.11$, $m = 2$, $n = 4$

$A = 10,000\left(1+\dfrac{0.11}{2}\right)^4 = \$12,388.25$

$A = Pe^{rt}$, where $P = 10,000$, $r = 0.105$ and $t = 2$

$A = 10,000e^{0.105(2)} = \$12,336.78$

The first investment of 11% semiannually yields $12,388.25 - 12,336.78 = \$51.47$ more.

42. $A = P\left(1+\dfrac{r}{m}\right)^n$, where $P = \$1000$,

$r = 0.05$, $m = 360$, $n = 180$

$A = 1000\left(1+\dfrac{0.05}{360}\right)^{180} = \$1025.313341$

$A = Pe^{rt}$, where $P = 1000$, $r = 0.05$ and $t = \dfrac{180}{360} = 0.5$

$A = 1000e^{0.05(0.5)} = \$1025.315121$
The difference is
$1025.313341 - 1025.315121 = \$0.0018$.

$A = P\left(1+\dfrac{r}{m}\right)^n$, where $P = \$2,000,000$,

$r = 0.05$, $m = 360$, $n = 180$

$A = 2,000,000\left(1+\dfrac{0.05}{360}\right)^{180} = \$2,050,626.68$

$A = Pe^{rt}$, where $P = \$2,000,000$, $r = 0.05$ and $t = \dfrac{180}{360} = 0.5$

$A = 2,000,000e^{0.05(0.5)} = \$2,050,630.24$
The difference is
$2,050,630.24 - 2,050,626.68 = \$3.56$

43. $r = 0.02$, $k = 360$

$APY = \left(1+\dfrac{r}{k}\right)^k - 1 = \left(1+\dfrac{0.02}{360}\right)^{360} - 1$
$= (1.00006)^{360} - 1 \approx 0.02020 = 2.020\%$

44. $r = 0.03$, $k = 360$

$APY = \left(1+\dfrac{r}{k}\right)^k - 1 = \left(1+\dfrac{0.03}{360}\right)^{360} - 1$
$= (1.00008)^{360} - 1 \approx 0.03045 = 3.045\%$

45. $r = 0.06$, $k = 2$

$APY = \left(1+\dfrac{r}{k}\right)^k - 1 = \left(1+\dfrac{0.06}{2}\right)^2 - 1$
$= (1.03)^2 - 1 = 0.0609 = 6.09\%$

46. $r = 0.06$, $k = 12$

$APY = \left(1+\dfrac{r}{k}\right)^k - 1 = \left(1+\dfrac{0.06}{12}\right)^{12} - 1$
$= (1.005)^{12} - 1 = 0.06168 = 06.17\%$

47. $r = 0.08$, $k = 4$

$APY = \left(1+\dfrac{r}{k}\right)^k - 1 = \left(1+\dfrac{0.08}{4}\right)^4 - 1$
$= (1.02)^4 - 1 = 0.0824 = 8.24\%$

48. $r = 0.12$, $k = 12$

$$APY = \left(1 + \frac{r}{k}\right)^k - 1 = \left(1 + \frac{0.12}{12}\right)^{12} - 1$$

$$= (1.01)^{12} - 1 = 0.1268 = 12.68\%$$

49. $r = 0.09, k = 4$

$$APY = \left(1 + \frac{r}{k}\right)^k - 1 = \left(1 + \frac{0.09}{4}\right)^4 - 1$$

$$= (1.0225)^4 - 1 \approx 0.0931 = 9.31\%$$

50. $r = 0.15, k = 2$

$$APY = \left(1 + \frac{r}{k}\right)^k - 1 = \left(1 + \frac{0.15}{2}\right)^2 - 1$$

$$= (1.075)^2 - 1 = 0.1556 = 15.56\%$$

51. $r = 0.18, k = 12$

$$APY = \left(1 + \frac{r}{k}\right)^k - 1 = \left(1 + \frac{0.18}{12}\right)^{12} - 1$$

$$= (1.015)^{12} - 1 \approx 0.1956 = 19.56\%$$

52. $r = 0.15, k = 12$

$$APY = \left(1 + \frac{r}{k}\right)^k - 1 = \left(1 + \frac{0.15}{12}\right)^{12} - 1$$

$$= (1.0125)^{12} - 1 = 0.1608 = 16.08\%$$

53. Simple interest means that the interest does not earn additional interest, while compound interest means that the interest earns interest at the same rate as the original principal. For instance, $100 at 10% simple interest would earn $20 in two years, while $100 at compound interest would earn $21 in two years.

54. No. If the price P is increased by 10%, the new price is $(1 + 0.10)P = 1.10P$. If this new price is decreased by 10%, the final price is

$$(1 - 0.10)(1.10P) = (0.90)(1.10P) = 0.99P.$$

Thus, the final price is 1% less than the starting price.

55. $r = 0.0398, k = 12$

$$APY = \left(1 + \frac{r}{k}\right)^k - 1 = \left(1 + \frac{0.0398}{12}\right)^{12} - 1$$

$$= (1.003317)^{12} - 1 \approx 0.0405 = 4.05\%,$$

instead of 4.06%.

56. $r = 0.0392, k = 2$

$$APY = \left(1 + \frac{r}{k}\right)^k - 1 = \left(1 + \frac{0.0392}{52}\right)^{52} - 1$$

$$= (1.0399631)^{52} - 1 \approx 0.03996 = 4.00\%,$$

as stated.

57. $r = 0.0390, k = 52$

$$APY = \left(1 + \frac{r}{k}\right)^k - 1 = \left(1 + \frac{0.039}{2}\right)^2 - 1$$

$$= (1.0195)^2 - 1 \approx 0.03938 = 3.94\%,$$

instead of 3.98%.

58. $r = 0.0388, k = 360$

$$APY = \left(1 + \frac{r}{k}\right)^k - 1 = \left(1 + \frac{0.0388}{360}\right)^{360} - 1$$

$$= (1.00010)^{360} - 1 \approx 0.0396 = 3.96\%,$$

as stated.

Collaborative Learning

1. $t = \dfrac{\ln 2}{r}$ 2. $t = \dfrac{0.69315}{r}$

3. a. $t = \dfrac{\ln 2}{0.04} \approx 17.3$ yr

   b. $t = \dfrac{\ln 2}{0.08} \approx 8.7$ yr

   c. $t = \dfrac{\ln 2}{0.12} \approx 5.8$ yr

Section 13.2 Credit Cards and Consumer Credit

1. Since the couple's combined gross income must be at least $40,000, Susan must earn at least $15,000 per year for them to qualify.

2. Since the couple's combined gross income must be at least $40,000, they must each earn at least $20,000 per year for them to qualify.

3. $1\frac{1}{2}\%$ of ($100 − $10) = (0.015)($90) = $1.35
   New balance = $90 + $1.35 + $50 = $141.35

4. $1\frac{1}{2}\%$ of ($300 − $190) = (0.015)($110)

$$= \$1.65$$

New balance = $110 + $1.65 + $25

$$= \$136.65$$

5. $1\frac{1}{2}\%$ of ($134.39 − $25)

$$= (0.015)(\$109.39) = \$1.64$$

New balance = $109.39 + $1.64 + $73.98

$$= \$185.01$$

6. $1\frac{1}{2}\%$ of ($145.96 − $55)

$$= (0.015)(\$90.96) = \$1.36$$

New balance = $90.96+ $1.36+ $44.97

$$= \$137.29$$

7. $1\frac{1}{2}\%$ of ($378.93 − $75)

$$= (0.015)(\$303.93) = \$4.56$$

New balance

= $303.93 + $4.56 + $248.99 = $557.48

8. a. $1\frac{1}{2}\%$ of $50.40 = (0.015)($50.40)

$$= \$0.76$$

   b. $50.40 + $0.76 + $173 = $224.16

   c. 5% of $224.16 = (0.05)($ 224.16)

$$= \$11.21$$

9. a. $1\frac{1}{2}\%$ of $85 = (0.015)($85) = $1.28

   b. $85 + $1.28 + $150 = $236.28

   c. 5% of $236.28 = (0.05)($236.28)

$$= \$11.81$$

10. a. $1\frac{1}{2}\%$ of $154 = (0.015)($154)

$$− \$2.31$$

    b. $154+ $2.31+ $75 = $231.31

    c. 5% of $231.31= (0.05)($ 231.31)

$$= \$11.57$$

11. a. $1\frac{1}{2}\%$ of $344 = (0.015)($344)

$$= \$5.16$$

    b. $344 + $5.16 + $60 = $409.16

    c. 5% of $409.16 = (0.05)($409.16)

$$= \$20.46$$

12. a. 1% of ($666.80) = (0.01)($666.80)

$$= \$6.67$$

    b. $666.80 + $6.67 + $53.49 = $726.96

    c. 5% of $726.96 = (0.05)($726.96)

$$= \$36.35$$

13. a. $1\frac{1}{2}\%$ of $80.45 = (0.015)($80.45)

$$= \$1.21$$

b. $80.45 + $1.21 + $98.73 = $180.39

c. The new balance is under $200, so the minimum payment is $10.

14. a. $1\frac{1}{2}\%$ of $34.97 = (0.015)($ 34.97)

$$= \$0.52$$

    b. $34.97 + $0.52+ $50 = $85.49

    c. The new balance is under $200, so the minimum payment is $10.

15. a. $1\frac{1}{2}\%$ of $55.90 = (0.015)($55.90)

$$= \$0.84$$

    b. $55.90 + $0.84 + $35.99 = $92.73

    c. The new balance is under $200, so the minimum payment is $10.

16. a. $1\frac{1}{2}\%$ of $98.56 = (0.015)($98.56)

$$= \$1.48$$

    b. $98.56 + $1.48+ $45.01 = $145.05

    c. The new balance is under $200, so the minimum payment is $10.

17. a. $1\frac{1}{2}\%$ of $34.76 = (0.015)($34.76)

$$= \$0.52$$

    b. $34.76 + $0.52 + $87.53 = $122.81

    c. The new balance is under $200, so the minimum payment is $10.

18. Finance charge

$$= 1\frac{1}{2}\% \text{ of } \$300 + 1\% \text{ of } (\$685 − \$300)$$

$$= (0.015)(\$300) + 0.01(\$385) = \$8.35$$

19. Finance charge

$$= 1\frac{1}{2}\% \text{ of } \$190 = (0.015)(\$190) = \$2.85$$

20. Rate $\cdot$ Balance = Finance charge

$$x \cdot \$100 = \$1.5$$

$$x = 0.015$$

$$x = 1\frac{1}{2}\%$$

21. Finance charge = $1\frac{1}{2}\%$ of $90

$$= (0.015)(\$90) = \$1.35$$

22. Finance charge = 1.25% of $90

$$= (0.0125)(\$90) = \$1.13$$

23. a. Balance = $9000 − $1600 = $7400. Add-on interest is ($7400)(0.09)(3) = $1998.

    b. Total to be paid in 36 months is $7400 + $1998 = $9398.

$\dfrac{9398}{36} = 261.06$, so the monthly payment (to the nearest dollar) is $261.

c.   Use
   http://www.onlineloadcalculator.org
   Total interest paid is $1071.45. The monthly payment is $235.32.

24. a.   Balance = $400 − $40 = $360. Add-on interest is ($360)(0.1)(1) = $36.

   b.   Total to be paid in 12 months is $360 + $36 = $396.

   $\dfrac{396}{12} = 33$, so the monthly payment (to the nearest dollar) is $33.

25. a.   Balance = $2400 − $400 = $2000. Add-on interest is ($2000)(0.15)(1.5) = $450.

   b.   Total to be paid in 18 months is $2000 +$450 = $2450.

   $\dfrac{2450}{18} = 136.11$, so the monthly payment (to the nearest dollar) is $136.

26. a.   Balance = $8500 − $1500 = $7000. Add-on interest is ($7000)(0.18)(3) = $3780.

   b.   Total to be paid in 36 months is $7000 + $3780 = $10,780. Since

   $\dfrac{10,780}{36} = 299.44$, the monthly payment (to the nearest dollar) is $299.

27. a.   Balance = $500 − $100 = $400. Add-on interest is ($400)(0.10)(1.5) = $60.

   b.   Total to be paid in 18 months is $400 + $60 = $460. Since

   $\dfrac{460}{18} = 25.56$, the monthly payment (to the nearest dollar) is $26.

28.

n	Int	Bal Due	Payment	New Bal
1	15.00	1015.00	200.00	815.00
2	12.23	827.23	200.00	627.23
3	9.41	636.64	200.00	436.64
4	6.55	443.19	200.00	243.19
5	3.65	246.84	200.00	46.84
6	0.70	47.54	47.54	0.00

Total interest paid $47.54.

n	Int	Bal Due	Payment	New Bal
1	15.00	1015.00	215.00	800.00
2	12.00	812.00	212.00	600.00
3	9.00	609.00	209.00	400.00
4	6.00	406.00	206.00	200.00
5	3.00	203.00	203.00	0.00
6	0.00	0.00	0.00	0.00

Total interest paid $45.00. Cissie would save $2.54 because she would not have to pay interest on the accumulated interest.

29. This procedure gives the longest possible time between the purchase date and the date when payment must be made to avoid a finance charge.

30. This would make the unpaid balance as small as possible and thus would avoid some of the finance charge.

31. ($47)(24) = $1128.
   Interest = $1128 − $1000 = $128. Since this is for 2 years, the interest rate is

   $\dfrac{\$128}{(\$1000)(2)} = 0.064 = 6.4\%.$

32. ($64)(18) = $1152.
   Interest = $1152 − $1000 = $152. Since this is for 18 months or 1.5 years, the interest rate is

   $\dfrac{\$152}{(\$1000)(1.5)} = 0.101 = 10.1\%.$

33. ($50)(24) = $1200.
   Interest = $1200 − $1000 = $200. Since this is for 2 years, the interest rate is

   $\dfrac{\$200}{(\$1000)(2)} = 0.10 = 10\%.$

34. ($48)(24) = $1152.
   Interest = $1152 − $1000 = $152. Since this is for 18 months or 1.5 years, the interest rate is

$$\frac{\$152}{(\$1000)(2)} = 0.076 = 7.6\%.$$

Section 13.3 Annual Percentage Rate (APR) and the Rule of 78

1. $\dfrac{194}{2500} \cdot 100 = 7.76$ = finance charge per
    $100. The nearest table entry for 12
    payments is 7.74 corresponding to an
    APR of 14%.

2. $\dfrac{166}{2000} \cdot 100 = 8.3$ = finance charge per $100.
    The nearest table entry for 12 payments is
    8.31 corresponding to 15%.

3. $\dfrac{264}{1500} \cdot 100 = 17.60$ = finance charge per
    $100. The nearest table entry for 24
    payments is 17.51 corresponding to 16%.

4. $\dfrac{675}{3500} \cdot 100 = 19.3$ = finance charge per $100.
    The nearest table entry for 24 payments is
    19.24 corresponding to $17\frac{1}{2}\%$.

5. $\dfrac{210}{1500} \cdot 100 = 14$ = finance charge per
    $100. The nearest table entry for 18
    payments is 13.99 corresponding to 17%.

6. $\dfrac{1364}{4500} \cdot 100 = 30.3$ = finance charge per $100.
    The nearest table entry for 36 payments is
    30.15 corresponding to 18%.

7. $\dfrac{1570}{4500} \cdot 100 = 34.89$ = finance charge per
    $100. The nearest table entry for 48
    payments is 34.81 corresponding to
    $15\frac{1}{2}\%$.

8. $\dfrac{170.80}{4000} \cdot 100 = 4.27$ = finance charge per $100.
    The table entry for 6 payments is 4.27
    corresponding to $14\frac{1}{2}\%$.

9. $\dfrac{1800}{5000} \cdot 100 = 36$ = finance charge per $100.
    The nearest table entry for 48 payments is
    36.03 corresponding to 16%.

10. $\dfrac{908.80}{4000} \cdot 100 = 22.7$ = finance charge per $100.
    The nearest table entry for 30 payments is 22.72
    corresponding to $16\frac{1}{2}\%$.

11. a. Here, $r = 4$ and $n = 12$, so the unearned
        finance charge is
        $$u = \frac{4 \cdot 5}{12 \cdot 13} \cdot \$15.60 = \frac{5}{39} \cdot \$15.60 = \$2.$$
    b. There are 4 payments remaining, so it will
        take $4 \cdot \$25 - \$2 = \$98$ to pay off the loan.

12. a. Here, $r = 5$ and $n = 12$, so the unearned
        finance charge is
        $$u = \frac{5 \cdot 6}{12 \cdot 13} \cdot \$23.40 = \frac{5}{26} \cdot \$23.40 = \$4.50.$$
    b. There are 5 payments remaining, so it will
        take $5 \cdot \$35 - \$4.50 = \$170.50$ to pay off
        the loan.

13. a. Here, $r = 6$ and $n = 12$, so the unearned
        finance charge is
        $$u = \frac{6 \cdot 7}{12 \cdot 13} \cdot \$31.20 = \frac{7}{26} \cdot \$31.20 = \$8.40.$$
    b. There are 6 payments remaining, so it will
        take $6 \cdot \$45 - \$8.40 = \$261.60$ to pay off
        the loan.

14. a. Here, $r = 9$ and $n = 18$, so the unearned
        finance charge is
        $$u = \frac{9 \cdot 10}{18 \cdot 19} \cdot \$52.00 = \frac{5}{19} \cdot \$52.00 = \$13.68.$$
    b. There are 9 payments remaining, so it will
        take $9 \cdot \$10 - \$13.68 = \$76.32$ to pay off
        the loan.

15. a. Here, $r = 5$ and $n = 20$, so the unearned
        finance charge is
        $$u = \frac{5 \cdot 6}{20 \cdot 21} \cdot \$58.50 = \frac{1}{14} \cdot \$58.50 = \$4.18.$$
    b. There are 5 payments remaining, so it will
        take $5 \cdot \$10 - \$4.18 = \$45.82$ to pay off
        the loan.

16. a. $u = \dfrac{6 \cdot 7}{24 \cdot 25} \cdot \$194 = \dfrac{7}{100} \cdot \$194$
$$= \$52.23$$

   b. $\text{PMT} = \dfrac{2500 + 194}{12} = \$224.50$

   $V = \$4.12$ (Table 13.3 - corresponding to 6 and 14% from APR in problem 1)
   $$u = \dfrac{6(224.50)(4.12)}{100 + 4.12} = \$53.30$$

   c. $\text{Payoff} = 6(224.50) - 52.23$
   $$= \$1294.77$$

   d. $\text{Payoff} = 224.50 \left[\dfrac{1 - \left(1 + \dfrac{0.14}{12}\right)^{-6}}{\dfrac{0.14}{12}} \right]$
   $$= \$1293.66$$

17. a. $u = \dfrac{6 \cdot 7}{24 \cdot 25} \cdot \$264 = \dfrac{7}{100} \cdot \$264$
$$= \$18.48$$

   b. $\text{PMT} = \dfrac{1500 + 264}{24} = \$73.50$

   $V = \$4.72$ (Table 13.3 - corresponding to 6 and 16% from APR in problem 3)
   $$u = \dfrac{6(73.50)(4.72)}{100 + 4.72} = \$19.88$$

   c. $\text{Payoff} = 6(73.50) - 18.48 = \$422.52$

   d. $\text{Payoff} = 73.50 \left[\dfrac{1 - \left(1 + \dfrac{0.16}{12}\right)^{-6}}{\dfrac{0.16}{12}} \right]$
   $$= \$421.13$$

18. a. $u = \dfrac{12 \cdot 13}{18 \cdot 19} \cdot \$210 = \dfrac{26}{57} \cdot \$210$
$$= \$95.79$$

   b. $\text{PMT} = \dfrac{1500 + 210}{18} = \$95$

   $V = \$9.45$ (Table 13.3 - corresponding to 12 and 17% from APR in problem 5)
   $$u = \dfrac{12(95)(9.45)}{100 + 9.45} = \$98.43$$

   c. $\text{Payoff} = 12(95) - 95.79 = \$1044.21$

   d. $\text{Payoff} = 95 \left[\dfrac{1 - \left(1 + \dfrac{0.17}{12}\right)^{-12}}{\dfrac{0.17}{12}} \right]$
   $$= \$1041.61$$

19. a. $u = \dfrac{12 \cdot 13}{48 \cdot 49} \cdot 1570 = \dfrac{13}{196} \cdot 1570 = \$104.13$

   b. $\text{PMT} = \dfrac{4500 + 1570}{48} = \$126.46$

   $V = \$8.59$ (Table 13.3 - corresponding to 12 and 15.5% from APR in problem 7)
   $$u = \dfrac{12(126.46)(8.59)}{100 + 8.59} = \$120.04$$

   c. $\text{Payoff} = 12(126.46) - 104.13 = \$1413.39$

   d. $\text{Payoff} = 126.46 \left[\dfrac{1 - \left(1 + \dfrac{0.155}{12}\right)^{-12}}{\dfrac{0.155}{12}} \right]$
   $$= \$1397.43$$

20. a.   Finance charge $= 48 \cdot 173 - 6000 = \$2304$.

   b.   Finance charge per \$100 is
   $\dfrac{2304}{6000} \cdot 100 = \$38.40$. The nearest table entry for 48 payments is \$38.50 corresponding to 17%.

21. a.   Finance charge $= 12 \cdot 27 - 300 = \$24$.

   b.   Finance charge per \$100 is
   $\dfrac{24}{300} \cdot 100 = \$8$. The nearest table entry for 12 payments is \$8.03 corresponding to $14\frac{1}{2}\%$.

22. a.   Finance charge $= 48 \cdot 159 - 5500 = \$2132$.

   b.   Finance charge per \$100 is
   $\dfrac{2132}{5500} \cdot 100 = \$38.80$. The nearest table entry for 48 payments is \$38.50 corresponding to 17%.

23. a.   Finance charge $= 18 \cdot 63 - 1000 = \$134$.

   b.   Finance charge per \$100 is

$\dfrac{134}{1000} \cdot 100 = \$13.40.$

The nearest table entry for 18 payments is \$13.57 corresponding to $16\frac{1}{2}\%$.

24. Finance charge per \$100 is $\dfrac{195}{2000} \cdot 100 = \$9.75.$

The nearest table entry for 12 payments is \$9.73 corresponding to $17\frac{1}{2}\%$.

25. a. Here, $r = 4$ and $n = 12$, so the unearned finance charge is

$\dfrac{4 \cdot 5}{12 \cdot 13} \cdot 31.20 = \dfrac{5}{39} \cdot 31.20 = \$4.$

b. There are 4 payments remaining, so it will take $4 \cdot 50 - 4 = \$196$ to pay off the loan.

26. a. Here, $r = 5$ and $n = 12$, so the unearned finance charge is

$\dfrac{5 \cdot 6}{12 \cdot 13} \cdot 46.80 = \dfrac{5}{26} \cdot 46.80 = \$9.$

b. There are 5 payments remaining, so it will take $5 \cdot 70 - 9 = \$341$ to pay off the loan.

27. a. Finance charge

$= 0.10(800 - 80) = 0.10(720) = \$72.$

b. Monthly payment $= \dfrac{720 + 72}{12} = \$66$

c. Here $r = 4$ and $n = 12$, so the interest refund is $\dfrac{4 \cdot 5}{12 \cdot 13} \cdot 72 = \dfrac{5}{39} \cdot 72 = \$9.23.$

d. There are 4 payments remaining, so it will take $4 \cdot 66 - 9.23 = \$254.77$ to pay off the loan.

28. a. Finance charge

$= 0.15(1200 - 200)(1.5)$

$= 0.15(1000)(1.5) = \$225$

b. Monthly payment

$= \dfrac{1000 + 225}{18} = \$68.06$

c. Here $r = 9$ and $n = 18$, so the interest refund is

$\dfrac{9 \cdot 10}{18 \cdot 19} \cdot 225 = \dfrac{5}{19} \cdot 225 = \$59.21.$

d. There are 9 payments remaining, so it will take $9 \cdot 68.09 - 59.21 = \$553.33$ to pay off the loan.

29. a. Finance charge

$0.10(1000 - 200)(1.5) = \$120.$

b. Monthly payment $= \dfrac{800 + 120}{18} = \$51.11.$

c. Here, $r = 3$ and $n = 18$, so the interest refund is $\dfrac{3 \cdot 4}{18 \cdot 19} \cdot 120 = \dfrac{2}{57} \cdot 120 = \$4.21.$

d. It will take $3 \cdot 51.11 - 4.21 = \$149.12$ to pay off the loan.

For problems 30 – 35, use the links given in the text. Some answers are rounded to the nearest dollar.

30. a. The total purchase cost is \$23,532.
    b. The monthly payment is \$570.
    c. With a \$510 monthly payment, you can afford a car worth \$18,184.

31. a. If the interest rate is 7%, the monthly payment \$562.
    b. If the interest rate is 6%, the monthly payment \$554.

32. a. The interest rate is lowered by \$570 – \$562 = \$8.
    b. You would need to negotiate an interest rate of about 4% (\$537 payment).

33. a. When the interest rate is 4%, the total cost to purchase the car is \$22,344.
    b. When the interest rate is 5%, the total cost to purchase the car is \$22,637.
    c. When the interest rate is 6%, the total cost to purchase the car is \$22,932.92, or \$22,933.
    d. We see that with each 1% increase, the differences are \$22,932 – \$22,637 = \$295 and \$22,637 – \$22,344 = \$293. The total cost to purchased when the rate increases by 1% is about \$300.

34. The lease payment would be \$367.47 and the net cost of the lease is \$14,228.80.

35. The loan payment would be \$632.99 and the net cost of the loan is \$10,423.67.

36. Answers will vary. If the loan required n payments and the debtor wishes to pay off the

loan with r payments remaining, the debtor may feel that he is due a refund of r/n of the finance charge. The Rule of 78 would give the debtor a refund of only

$$\frac{r(r+1)}{n(n+1)}$$ of the finance charge. Thus, the Rule of 78 charges the debtor the

additional fraction $\dfrac{n-r}{n+1}$ of the finance charge as a penalty for the early pay-off.

37. $\text{APR} = \dfrac{2mI}{P(n+1)} = \dfrac{2 \cdot 12 \cdot 194}{2500 \cdot 13} = 0.143$

$= 14.3\%$
(0.3% more than the answer to problem 1)

38. $\text{APR} = \dfrac{2mI}{P(n+1)} = \dfrac{2 \cdot 12 \cdot 166}{2000 \cdot 13} = 0.153$

$= 15.3\%$
(0.3% more than answer to problem 2)

39. $\text{APR} = \dfrac{2mI}{P(n+1)} = \dfrac{2 \cdot 12 \cdot 264}{1500 \cdot 25} = 0.169$

$= 16.9\%$
(0.9% more than the answer to problem 3)

40. $\text{APR} = \dfrac{2mI}{P(n+1)} = \dfrac{2 \cdot 12 \cdot 675}{3500 \cdot 25} = 0.185$

$= 18.5\%$
(1% more than answer to problem 4)

41. $\text{APR} = \dfrac{2mI}{P(n+1)} = \dfrac{2 \cdot 12 \cdot 210}{1500 \cdot 19} = 0.177$

$= 17.7\%$
(0.7% more than the answer to problem 5)

42. $\text{APR} = \dfrac{2mI}{P(n+1)} = \dfrac{2 \cdot 12 \cdot 1364}{4500 \cdot 37} = 0.197$

$= 19.7\%$
(1.7% more than answer to problem 6)

43. $\text{APR} = \dfrac{2mI}{P(n+1)} = \dfrac{2 \cdot 12 \cdot 1570}{4500 \cdot 49} = 0.171$

$= 17.1\%$
(1.6% more than the answer to problem 7)

44. $\text{APR} = \dfrac{2mI}{P(n+1)} = \dfrac{2 \cdot 12 \cdot 170.80}{4000 \cdot 7} = 0.146$

$= 14.6\%$
(0.1% more than answer to problem 8)

45. $\text{APR} = \dfrac{2mI}{P(n+1)} = \dfrac{2 \cdot 12 \cdot 1800}{5000 \cdot 49} = 0.176$

$= 17.6\%$
(1.6% more than the answer to problem 9)

46. $\text{APR} = \dfrac{2mI}{P(n+1)} = \dfrac{2 \cdot 12 \cdot 908.80}{4000 \cdot 31} = 0.176$

$= 17.6\%$
(1.1% more than answer to problem 10)

Web It Exercises

Use the link given in the text.

1. Answers may vary. Some expenses might be license plates (tags), tax, title, and so on.

2. Answers may vary.

3. a. The first year depreciation is $2167 for the lease and $2250 for the loan.
   b. The net cost of leasing is $10,283.
   c. The net cost of buying is $7533.
   d. Buying is cheaper.

4. Answers may vary.

Section 13.4 Buying a House

1. a. Yes. The maximum they can spend according to the first criterion is

   $2.5(40,000) = \$100,000$, so they can afford this house.

   b. Yes. $\dfrac{40,000}{52} = \$769.23 > \$750$, so,

   according to the second criterion, they can afford this house.

   c. Yes. $0.28 \cdot \dfrac{40,000}{12} = \$933.33 > \$750$, so,

   according to the third criterion, they can afford this house.

2. a. No. The maximum they can spend according to the first criterion is

   $2.5(36,000) = \$90,000$, so they cannot afford this house.

b. Yes. $\dfrac{36,000}{52} = \$692.31 > \$570$, so, according to the second criterion, they can afford this house.

c. Yes. $0.28 \cdot \dfrac{36,000}{12} = \$840 > \$570$, so, according to the third criterion, they can afford this house.

3. a. Amount of loan:
$$= 0.80(77,000) = \$61,600.$$

   b. Down payment:
$$= 77,000 - 61,600 = \$15,400$$

   c. For an FHA loan, down payment:
$$= 0.03(77,000) = \$2310$$

4. a. Amount of loan:
$$= 0.95(60,000) = \$57,000.$$

   b. Down payment:
$$= 60,000 - 57,000 = \$3000$$

   c. For an FHA loan, down payment:
$$= 0.03(60,000) = \$1800$$

5. Using Table 13.5 with 6% interest rate and 20 year payment period, the cost is $7.16 per $1000. The monthly payment is then $7.16(60) = \$429.60$ for principal and interest. Taxes and insurance are $1160 per year or $96.67 per month. The total monthly payment is $429.60 + \$96.67 = \$526.27.

6. Using Table 13.5 with $6\frac{1}{2}$ % interest rate and 30 year payment period, the cost is $6.32 per $1000. The monthly payment is then $6.32(80) = \$505.60$ for principal and interest. Taxes and insurance are $1580 per year or $131.67 per month. The total monthly payment is $505.60 + \$131.67 = \$637.27.

7. Using Table 13.5 with 9% interest rate and 25 year payment period, the cost is $8.39 per $1000. The monthly payment is then $8.39(90) = \$755.10$ for principal and interest. Taxes and insurance are $2160 per year or $180 per month. The total monthly payment is $755.10 + \$180 = \$935.10.

8. Using Table 13.5 with $9\frac{1}{2}$ % interest rate and 20 year payment period, the cost is $9.32 per $1000. The monthly payment is then $9.32(80) = \$745.60$ for principal and interest. Taxes and insurance are $2140 per year or $178.33 per month. The total monthly payment is $745.60 + \$178.33 = \$923.93.

9. Using Table 13.5 with 5.5% interest rate and 30 year payment period, the cost is $5.68 per $1000. The monthly payment is then $5.68(173) = \$982.64$ for principal and interest. Taxes and insurance are $3600 per year or $300 per month. The total monthly payment is $982.64 + \$300 = \$1282.64.

10. Using Table 13.5 with $10\frac{1}{2}$ % interest rate and 15 year payment period, the cost is $11.05 per $1000. The monthly payment is then $11.05(80) = \$884$ for principal and interest. Taxes and insurance are $1390 per year or $115.83 per month. The total monthly payment is $884 + \$115.83 = \$999.83.

11. a. $0.03(45,000) = \$1350$

    b. $0.9875(45,000) = \$44,437.50$

12. a. $0.03(150,000) = \$4500$

    b. $0.9775(150,000) = \$146,625$

13. a. $0.03(75,000) = \$2250$

    b. $0.9765(75,000) = \$73,237.50$

14. a. $0.03(95,000) = \$2850$

    b. $0.9775(95,000) = \$92,862.50$

15. a. $45,000 + 1200 = \$46,200$

    b. $0.9875(45,000) = \$44,437.50$

    c. $M = \dfrac{44,437.50(0.005)}{1 - (1+0.005)^{-180}} = \$374.99$

16. a. $150,000 + 6000 = \$156,000$

    b. $0.9775(150,000) = \$146,625$

c. $M = \dfrac{146{,}625\left(\dfrac{0.06}{12}\right)}{1-\left(1+\dfrac{0.06}{12}\right)^{-360}} = \$879.09$

17. a. $75{,}000 + 100 = \$75{,}100$

b. $75{,}100 - 0.03(75{,}000)$

$= 75{,}100 - 2250 = \$72{,}850$

c. $M = \dfrac{72{,}850(0.00625)}{1-(1+0.00625)^{-300}} = \$538.36$

18. a. $95{,}000 + 500 = \$95{,}500$

b. $0.9775(95{,}000) = \$92{,}862.50$

c. $M = \dfrac{92{,}862.50\left(\dfrac{0.09}{12}\right)}{1-\left(1+\dfrac{0.09}{12}\right)^{-120}} = \$1176.34$

19. a.   95% of \$60,000 = (0.95)(\$60,000)
= \$57,000, so the down payment is
\$60,000 – \$57,000 = \$3000.

b.   Table 13.5 gives \$9.52 as the monthly
payment per \$1000 loan at 11% for
30 years. Hence, the mortgage
payment is $57(9.52) = \$542.64$.

Taxes and insurance amount to
\$1500/12 = \$125 per month. The total
monthly payment is
\$542.64 + \$125 = \$667.64.

20. a.   80% of \$90,000 = (0.80)(\$90,000)
= \$72,000, so the down payment is
\$90,000 – \$72,000 = \$18,000.

b.   Table 13.5 gives \$9.09 as the monthly
payment per \$1000 loan at 10% for
25 years. Hence, the mortgage
payment is $72(9.09) = \$654.48$.

Taxes and insurance amount to
\$810/12 = \$67.50 per month. The
total monthly payment is
\$654.48 + \$67.50 = \$721.98.

21. a.   3% of \$100,000 = (0.03)(\$100,000)
= \$3000 is the down payment.

b.   Table 13.5 gives \$6.32 as the monthly
payment per \$1000 loan at 6.5% for
30 years. Hence, the mortgage
payment is $97(6.32) = \$613.04$.

Taxes and insurance amount to \$2400/12
= \$200 per month. The total monthly
payment is \$613.04 + \$200 = \$813.04.

22. a.   \$95,000 – \$75,000 = \$20,000 is the down
payment.

b.   Table 13.5 gives \$9.32 as the monthly
payment per \$1000 loan at 9.5% for 20
years. Hence, the mortgage payment is
$75(9.32) = \$699$. Taxes and insurance
amount to \$1200/12 = \$100 per month.
The total monthly payment is
\$699 + \$100 = \$799.00.

23. a.   Table 13.5 gives \$8.78 as the monthly
payment per \$1000 loan at 10% for 30 years.
So, the mortgage payment is
$50(8.78) = \$439$.

b. $30 \cdot 12 = 360$ payments

c.   The total amount paid for principal and
interest is $360 \cdot 439 = \$158{,}040$.

d.   The total interest paid is
\$158,040 – \$50,000 = \$108,040.

e.   If 50,000 = 80% of x, then
$x = \dfrac{\$50{,}000}{0.8} = \$62{,}500$. Thus, the price
of the house was \$62,500, which is less
than the total interest.

24. a.   Table 13.5 gives \$8.05 as the monthly
payment per \$1000 loan at 9% for 30 years.
So, the mortgage payment is
$35(8.05) = \$281.75$.

b. $30 \cdot 12 = 360$ payments

c.   The total amount paid for principal and
interest is $360(281.75) = \$101{,}430$.

d.   The total interest paid is
\$101,430 – \$35,000 = \$66,430. If 35,000
= 80% of x, then $x = \dfrac{\$35{,}000}{0.8} = \$43{,}750$.
Thus, the price of the house was \$43,750,
which is less than the total interest.

25. a.   The down payment is 20% of \$50,000 =
\$10,000. The loan fee is 1% of
(\$50,000 – \$10,000) = \$400 which makes
the closing costs total \$45 + \$150 + \$300
+ \$50 + \$220 + \$20 + \$400 = \$1185.
Thus, the cash payment is
\$10,000 + \$1185 = \$11,185.

b.   Insurance and taxes amount to

$25 + $50 = $75 per month. Table 13.5 gives $11.85 as the monthly payment per $1000 loan at 14% for 30 years, so the mortgage payment is

$$40(11.85) = $474 .$$ The total monthly payment is thus $474 + $75 = $549.

c. Since the closing costs are $1185, there would be

$$1.185(11.85) = $14.04$$ added to the amount found in part b to give a total of $563.04.

26. a. The down payment is 10% of $75,000 = $7000. The loan fee is 1.5% of ($75,000 – $7500) = $1012.50 which makes the closing costs total $45 + $15 + $250 + $1012.5 + $210 = $1532.50. Thus, the cash payment is $7500 + $1532.50 = $9032.50.

b. Table 13.5 gives $9.09 as the monthly payment per $1000 loan at 10% for 25 years, so the monthly payment is

$$67.5(9.09) = $613.58 .$$

c. Since the closing costs are $1532.50, would be $1.5325(9.09) = 13.93 added to the amount found in part b to give a total of $627.51.

27. a. The down payment is 20% of $120,000 = $24,000. The loan amount is $120,000 – $24,000 = $96,000, so the loan fee is 1% of $96,000 = $960. The total closing costs are $45 + $25 + $250 + $960 + $350 = $1630 and the down payment plus closing costs is $24,000 + $1630 = $25,630.

b. Table 13.5 gives $8.05 as the monthly payment per $1000 loan at 9% for 30 years. The mortgage payment is

$$96(8.05) = $772.80.$$ Since taxes and insurance come to $\frac{1200}{12} = 100 per month, the total monthly payment is $100 + $772.80 = $872.80.

c. To include the closing costs, add

$$1.63(8.05) = $13.12$$ to the amount in part b to get a total of $885.92 per month.

28. a. The down payment is 25% of $150,000 = $37,500. The loan amount is $150,000 – $37,500 = $112,500, so the loan fee is 1.5% of $112,500 = $1687.50. The total closing costs are $45 + $25 + $300 + $1687.50 + $420 = $2477.50 and the down payment plus closing costs is $37,500 + $2477.50 = $39,977.50.

b. Table 13.5 gives $8.35 as the monthly payment per $1000 loan at 8% for 20 years. The mortgage payment is

$$112.5(8.35) = $939.38.$$ Since taxes and insurance come to $\frac{1500}{12} = 125 per month, the total monthly payment is $939.38 + $125 = $1064.38.

c. To include the closing costs, add

$$2.4775(8.35) = $20.69$$ to the amount in part b to get a total of $1085.06 per month.

29. a. The down payment is 10% of $84,000 = $8400. The loan amount is $84,000 – $8400 = $75,600, so the loan fee is 2% of $75,600 = $1512. This makes the total closing costs $1512 + $235 + $25 + $295 = $2067. The down payment plus closing costs is $8400 + $2067 = $10,467.

b. Table 13.5 gives $10.75 as the monthly payment per $1000 loan at 10% for 15 years. The mortgage payment is $75.6(10.75) = $812.70.

30. a. Since FHA requires a 3% down payment, the down payment is 3% of $84,000 = $2520. The loan amount is $84,000 – $2520 = $81,480, so the loan fee is 2% of $81,480 ≈ $1630. This makes the total closing costs $1630 + $200 + $25 + $295 = $2150. The down payment plus closing costs is $2520 + $2150 = $4670.

b. Table 13.5 gives $7.32 as the monthly payment per $1000 loan at 8% for 30 years. The mortgage payment is

$$81.48(7.32) = $596.43.$$

31. Answers will vary.   32. Answers will vary.

33. Table 13.5 gives $8.05 as the monthly payment per $1000 loan at 9% for 30 years. For a $100,000 loan, the monthly payment is

$100(8.05) = \$805$, and in 30 years the total payments would be $360 \cdot 805 = \$289,800$. Thus, the interest paid would be $\$289,800 - \$100,000 = \$189,800$, which is greater than the mortgage on the house. For a \$50,000 loan, the monthly payment is $50(8.05) = \$402.50$ and in 30 years, the total payments would be $360(402.50) = \$144,900$. Thus, the interest paid would be $\$144,900 - \$50,000 = \$94,900$, which is more than the price of the house.

34. Answers will vary.

Web It Exercises

For mortgage payments, try to visit *Simple Mortgage Calculator* at **http://www.mortgage-calc.com** (Click on *Simple Mortgage Calculator* to determine payment.)
Then for biweekly payments and comparison, then click on *Biweekly Mortgage Calculator*, also found at **http://www.mortgage-calc.com/mortgage/biweekly.html**

1. Answers may vary. There are 13 payments per year when paying your mortgage bi-weekly.

2. a. Your monthly payment will be \$733.76.
   b. The total interest will be \$164,155.25.
   c. If you use a biweekly schedule, you will make two extra principal payments a year of \$366.88 and the loan will terminate in 274 months (about 23 years).

3. Same

4. For a loan of \$100,000 at an interest rate of 3.8815% for 15 years the standard payment (principal and interest) will be \$733.76.

Section 13.5 Investing in Stocks, Bonds, and Mutual Funds

1. a. Total cost = cost of stock + commission
   $T = 100(\$34.78) + \$50 = \$3528$

   b. Dividend = (number of shares) $\cdot \dfrac{\text{dividend}}{\text{share}}$
   $D = 100(\$1.06) = \$106$

   c. Sell commission
   = (stock value)(commission rate)
   $S = 100(\$36.78)(0.02) = \$73.56$

   d. Capital gain =
   (change in price per share) $\cdot$ (number of shares) $-$ commisions
   $G = (\$36.78 - \$35.28) \cdot 100 - \$73.56$
   $= \$76.44$

   e. Return = capital gain + dividend
   $R = \$76.44 + \$106 = \$182.44$

   f. Percent of return = $R / (T + S)$
   $P = \dfrac{182.44}{3528 + 73.56} \approx 0.0507 = 5.07\%$

2. a. Total cost = cost of stock + commission
   $T = 100(\$16.90) + \$50 = \$1740$

   b. Dividend = (number of shares) $\cdot \dfrac{\text{dividend}}{\text{share}}$
   $D = \$0$

   c. Sell commission
   = (stock value)(commission rate)
   $S = 100(\$18.40)(0.02) = \$36.80$

   d. Capital gain =
   (change in price per share) $\cdot$ (number of shares) $-$ commisions
   $G = (\$18.40 - \$16.90) \cdot 100 - \$36.80$
   $= \$63.20$

   e. Return = capital gain + dividend
   $R = \$63.20 + \$0 = \$63.20$

   f. Percent of return = $R / (T + S)$
   $P = \dfrac{63.20}{1690 + 50 + 36.80} \approx 0.0356 = 3.56\%$

3. a. Total cost = cost of stock + commission
   $T = 200(\$28.52) + \$50 = \$5754$

   b. Dividend = (number of shares) $\cdot \dfrac{\text{dividend}}{\text{share}}$
   $D = 200(\$0.72) = \$144$

c.   Sell commission
    = (stock value)(commission rate)
$$S = 200(\$30)(0.02) = \$120$$

d.   Capital gain =
(change in price per share) · (number
of shares) – commisions
$$G = (\$30.00 - \$28.52) \cdot 200 - \$120$$
$$= \$126$$

e.   Return = capital gain + dividend
$$R = \$126 + \$144 = \$270$$

f.   Percent of return = $R / (T + S)$
$$P = \frac{270}{5754 + 120} \approx 0.0460 = 4.60\%$$

4. a.   Total cost =
    cost of stock + commission
$$T = 200(\$63.90) + \$50 = \$12,830$$

b.   Dividend =
$$\text{(number of shares)} \cdot \frac{\text{dividend}}{\text{share}}$$
$$D = 200(\$0.40) = \$80$$

c.   Sell commission
    = (stock value)(commission rate)
$$S = 200(\$64)(0.02) = \$256$$

d.   Capital gain =
(change in price per share) · (number
of shares) – commisions
$$G = (\$64.00 - \$63.90) \cdot 200 - \$50 - \$256$$
$$= -\$286$$

e.   Return = capital gain + dividend
$$R = -\$286 + \$80 = -\$206$$

f.   Percent of return = $R / (T + S)$
$$P = \frac{-206}{12,780 + 50 + 256}$$
$$\approx -0.0157 = -1.57\%$$

5. a.   Total cost =
    cost of stock + commission
$$T = 200(\$3.02) + \$604(0.02)$$
$$= \$616.08$$

b.   Dividend =
$$\text{(number of shares)} \cdot \frac{\text{dividend}}{\text{share}}$$
$$D = 200(\$0) = \$0$$

c.   Sell commission $S = \$50$

d.   Capital gain =

(change in price per share) · (number of
shares) – commisions
$$G = (\$3.02 - \$3.00) \cdot 200 - \$50 = -\$66.08$$

e.   Return = capital gain + dividend
$$R = -\$66.08 + \$0 = -\$66.08$$

f.   Percent of return = $R / (T + S)$
$$P = \frac{-66.08}{616.08 + 50} \approx -0.0992 = -9.92\%$$

6. a.   Total cost = cost of stock + commission
$$T = 200(\$58.15) + \$58.15(0.02)(200)$$
$$= \$11,862.60$$

b.   Dividend = (number of shares) · $\dfrac{\text{dividend}}{\text{share}}$
$$D = 200(\$1.10) = \$220$$

c.   Sell commission $S = \$50$

d.   Capital gain =
(change in price per share) · (number of
shares) – commisions
$$G = (\$68 - \$58.15) \cdot 200 - \$232.60 - \$50$$
$$= \$1687.40$$

e.   Return = capital gain + dividend
$$R = \$1687.40 + \$220 = \$1907.40$$

f.   Percent of return = $R / (T + S)$
$$P = \frac{1907.40}{11,862.60 + 50} \approx -0.1601 = 16.01\%$$

7. a.   Total cost = 1000 (mkt close) + $25
$$T = 1000(\$2.21) + \$25 = \$2235$$

b.   Return = 1000 (last sale) – total cost
$$R = 1000(\$2.60) - \$2235 - \$25 = \$340$$

c.   Percent of return = $R / (T + 25)$
$$P = \frac{340}{2235 + 25} \approx 0.1504 = 15.04\%$$

8. a.   Total cost = 1000 (mkt close) + $25
$$T = 1000(\$41.17) + \$25 = \$41,195$$

b.   Return = 1000 (last sale) – total cost
$$R = 1000(\$44.62) - \$41,195 - \$25$$
$$= \$3400$$

c.   Percent of return = $R / (T + 25)$
$$P = \frac{3400}{41,195 + 25} \approx 0.0825 = 8.25\%$$

9. a.   Total cost = 1000 (mkt close) + $25
$$T = 1000(\$3.01) + \$25 = \$3035$$

b. Return = 1000 (last sale) − total cost

$$R = 1000(\$3.25) - \$3035 - \$25$$

$$= \$190$$

c. Percent of return = $R / (T + 25)$

$$P = \frac{190}{3035 + 25} \approx 0.0621 \approx 6.21\%$$

10. a. Total cost = 1000 (mkt close) + \$25

$$T = 1000(\$3.50) + \$25 = \$3525$$

b. Return = 1000 (last sale) − total cost

$$R = 1000(\$3.70) - \$3525 - \$25$$

$$= \$150$$

c. Percent of return = $R / (T + 25)$

$$P = \frac{150}{3525 + 25} \approx 0.0423 = 4.23\%$$

11. a. Total cost = 1000 (mkt close) + \$25

$$T = 1000(\$18.96) + \$25 = \$18,985$$

b. Return = 1000 (last sale) − total cost

$$R = 1000(\$19.90) - \$18,985 - \$25$$

$$= \$890$$

c. Percent of return = $R / (T + 25)$

$$P = \frac{890}{18,985 + 25} \approx 0.0468 = 4.68\%$$

12. a. Total cost = 1000 (mkt close) + \$25

$$T = 1000(\$3.61) + \$25 = \$3635$$

b. Return = 1000 (last sale) − total cost

$$R = 1000(\$3.78) - \$3635 - \$25$$

$$= \$120$$

c. Percent of return = $R / (T + 25)$

$$P = \frac{120}{3635 + 25} \approx 0.0328 = 3.28\%$$

13. a. $I = Prt = \$5000(0.072)(0.5)$

$$= \$180$$

b. $I = Prt = \$5000(0.072)(5) = \$1800$

14. a. $I = Prt = \$5000(0.06125)(0.5)$

$$= \$153.13$$

b. $I = Prt = \$5000(0.06125)(5)$

$$= \$1531.25$$

15. a. $I = Prt = \$10,000(0.0675)(0.5)$

$$= \$337.50$$

b. $I = Prt = \$10,000(0.0675)(2)$

$$= \$1350$$

16. a. $I = Prt = \$10,000(0.03750)(0.5)$

$$= \$187.50$$

b. $I = Prt = \$10,000(0.03750)(2)$

$$= \$750$$

17. a. $I = Prt = \$20,000(0.0575)(0.5)$

$$= \$575$$

b. $I = Prt = \$20,000(0.0575)(5)$

$$= \$5750$$

18. a. $I = Prt = \$20,000(0.066)(0.5)$

$$= \$660$$

b. $I = Prt = \$20,000(0.066)(5)$

$$= \$6600$$

19. a. $A = 200,000,000 + 100,000,000$

$$+ 250,000 = 300,250,000$$

$$L = 10,000,000$$

$$N = 10,000,000$$

$$NAV = \frac{300,250,000 - 10,000,000}{10,000,000}$$

$$= \frac{290,250,000}{10,000,000} = \$29.025$$

b. $\dfrac{50,000}{29.025} \approx 1722.65 \approx 1722$ shares

20. a. $A = 100,000,000 + 50,000,000$

$$+ 200,000 = 150,200,000$$

$$L = 10,000,000$$

$$N = 20,000,000$$

$$NAV = \frac{150,200,000 - 10,000,000}{20,000,000}$$

$$= \frac{140,200,000}{20,000,000} = \$7.01$$

b. $\dfrac{40,000}{7.01} \approx 5706.13 \approx 5706$ shares

21. a. $A = 500,000,000 + 250,000,000$

$$+ 1,500,000 = 751,500,000$$

$L = 25,000,000$

$N = 25,000,000$

$$NAV = \frac{751,500,000 - 25,000,000}{25,000,000}$$

$$= \frac{726,500,000}{25,000,000} = \$29.06$$

b. $\dfrac{100,000}{29.06} \approx 3441.16 \approx 3441$ shares

22. a. $A = 100,000,000 + 50,000,000$

  $+ 100,000 = 150,100,000$

  $L = 5,000,000$

  $N = 5,000,000$

  $$NAV = \frac{150,100,000 - 5,000,000}{5,000,000}$$

  $$= \frac{145,100,000}{5,000,000} = \$29.02$$

b. $\dfrac{25,000}{29.02} \approx 861.47 \approx 861$ shares

23. a. $A = 400,000,000 + 200,000,000$

  $+ 1,000,000 = 601,000,000$

  $L = 20,000,000$

  $N = 20,000,000$

  $$NAV = \frac{601,000,000 - 20,000,000}{20,000,000}$$

  $$= \frac{581,000,000}{20,000,000} = \$29.05$$

b. $\dfrac{100,000}{29.05} \approx 3442.34 \approx 3442$ shares

24. a. $A = 250,000,000 + 125,000,000$

  $+ 750,000 = 375,750,000$

  $L = 10,000,000$

  $N = 10,000,000$

  $$NAV = \frac{375,750,000 - 10,000,000}{10,000,000}$$

  $$= \frac{365,750,000}{10,000,000} = \$36.575$$

b. $\dfrac{75,000}{36.575} \approx 2050.58 \approx 2050$ shares

25. a. $C = \dfrac{80 - 70}{100} = \dfrac{10}{100} = 0.10 = 10\%$

b. $Y = \dfrac{3}{80} = 0.0375 = 3.75\%$

c. $R = \dfrac{(80 - 70) \cdot 100 + 3 \cdot 100}{100 \cdot 70} = \dfrac{1300}{7000}$

  $\approx 0.1857 \approx 18.57\%$

26. a. $C = \dfrac{100 - 90}{200} = \dfrac{10}{200} = 0.05 = 5\%$

b. $Y = \dfrac{2.5}{100} = 0.025 = 2.5\%$

c. $R = \dfrac{(100 - 90) \cdot 200 + 2.50 \cdot 200}{200 \cdot 90} = \dfrac{2500}{18,000}$

  $\approx 0.1389 \approx 13.89\%$

27. a. $C = \dfrac{80 - 75}{300} = \dfrac{5}{300} \approx 0.0167 \approx 1.67\%$

b. $Y = \dfrac{1.25}{80} = 0.0156 = 1.56\%$

c. $R = \dfrac{(80 - 75) \cdot 300 + 1.25 \cdot 300}{300 \cdot 75} = \dfrac{1875}{22,500}$

  $\approx 0.0833 \approx 8.33\%$

28. a. $C = \dfrac{40 - 30}{500} = \dfrac{10}{500} = 0.02 = 2\%$

b. $Y = \dfrac{0.50}{40} = 0.0125 = 1.25\%$

c. $R = \dfrac{(40 - 30) \cdot 500 + 0.50 \cdot 500}{500 \cdot 30} = \dfrac{5250}{15,000}$

  $= 0.35 = 35\%$

29. a. $C = \dfrac{50 - 40}{400} = \dfrac{10}{400} = 0.025 = 2.5\%$

b. $Y = \dfrac{4}{50} = 0.08 - 8\%$

c. $R = \dfrac{(50 - 40) \cdot 400 + 4.00 \cdot 400}{400 \cdot 40} = \dfrac{5600}{16,000}$

  $= 0.35 = 35\%$

30. a. $C = \dfrac{25 - 20}{1000} = \dfrac{5}{1000} = 0.005 = 0.5\%$

b. $Y = \dfrac{0.75}{25} = 0.03 = 3\%$

c. $R = \dfrac{(25-20)\cdot 1000 + 0.75 \cdot 1000}{1000 \cdot 20}$

$= \dfrac{5750}{20,000} = 0.2875 = 28.75\%$

31. Answers will vary. All are long-term investments. A stock is a share in a company where you become part owner in the company in which you have invested. A bond is lending your money to a company or government. A mutual fund is a pool of many investors who pay a professional manager to purchase a variety of investments.

32. Answers will vary. Purchasing a stock gives you ownership in the company, purchasing a bond is lending money, and purchasing a mutual fund makes you one of the many investors who pay a professional manager to purchase a variety of investments.

33. Answers will vary. A dividend is the profits that a company allocates to its owners.

34. Answers will vary. Liquidity is that shares can be converted to cash at any time.

35. $CY = \dfrac{7.2}{91.242} \cdot 100 \approx 7.89\%$

36. $CY = \dfrac{0.06125}{109.195} \cdot 100 \approx 5.61\%$

37. $CY = \dfrac{6.75}{111.564} \cdot 100 \approx 6.05\%$

38. $CY = \dfrac{0.0375}{98.005} \cdot 100 \approx 3.83\%$

39. $CY = \dfrac{5.75}{108.209} \cdot 100 \approx 5.31\%$

40. $CY = \dfrac{0.066}{111.285} \cdot 100 \approx 5.93\%$

41. $P = \dfrac{100}{0.07} \approx \$1428.57$

42. $P = \dfrac{100}{0.06} \approx \$1666.67$

43. $P = \dfrac{100}{0.05} = \$2000$

44. $P = \dfrac{100}{0.11} \approx \$909.09$

45. $P = \dfrac{100}{0.12} \approx \$833.33$

46. $P = \dfrac{100}{0.13} \approx \$769.23$

Chapter 13 Practice Test

1. a. $I = Prt = 800(0.28)(2) = \$448$

    b. $I = Prt = 800(0.28)(0.25) = \$56$

    c. $\$800 + \$448 = \$1248$

2. a. $(0.06)(\$360) = \$21.60$

    b. $\$360 + \$21.60 = \$381.60$

3. a. $(0.20)(\$390) = \$78$

    b. $\$390 - \$78 = \$312$

4. a. Interest rate is 4% per period and there are 4 periods. The table gives 1.1699 for these numbers, so the accumulated amount is $100(1.1699) = \$116.99$; the interest is $16.99.

    b. Interest rate is 2% per period and there are 8 periods. The table gives 1.1717 for these numbers, so the accumulated amount is $100(1.1717) = \$117.17$; the interest is $17.17.

5. a. $0.05(185.76) = \$9.29$, so the minimum payment is $10.

    b. Finance charge $= 0.015(185.76 - 10) = \$2.64$.

6. a. $\$179.64 - \$50 = \$129.64$, so the finance charge is $0.015(129.64) = \$1.94$.

    b. New balance = $\$129.64 + \$1.94 + \$23.50 = \$155.08$.

7. a. $6500 $1500 = $5000 (unpaid
         balance)
         Interest = $(0.12)(\$5000)(4) = \$2400$

    b.   Total to be paid off is $5000 + $2400
         = $7400, so the monthly payment is
         $$\frac{7400}{48} = \$154.17.$$

8. a. $12(18.10) = \$217.20$ (total amount to
         be paid)
         $217.20 – $200 = $17.20 (interest
         charged)
         $$\frac{17.20}{200} \cdot 100 = \$8.60 \text{ (interest charge}$$
         per $100). The closest table entry is
         $8.59 corresponding to an APR of
         $15\frac{1}{2}\%$.

    b.   Here, $r = 7$ and $n = 12$, so the interest
         refund is $\dfrac{7 \cdot 8}{12 \cdot 13} \cdot 17.20 = \$6.17.$

    c. $7(18.10) - 6.17 = \$120.53$ (amount
         needed to pay off the loan.)

9. a. $(0.75)(\$50,000) = \$37,500$ (amount
         of loan)

    b. $50,000 – $37,500 = $12,500 (down
         payment)

    c. $(0.03)(\$50,000) = \$1500$ (minimum
         down payment for FHA loan)

    d. $50,000 – $1500 = $48,500
         (maximum FHA loan)

10. The table shows a payment of $12.00 per
    $1000 loan at 12% for 15 years, so the
    monthly mortgage payment (for principal
    and interest) is $37.5(12) = \$450.$

11. a.   Total cost
         = cost of stock + commission
         $T = 100(\$52.50) + \$50 = \$5300$

    b.   Dividend = (number of shares)
         $\cdot \dfrac{\text{dividend}}{\text{share}}$ $D = 100(\$1.22) = \$122$

    c.   Sell comm = (stock value)(comm
         rate)
         $S = 100(\$57.75)(0.02) = \$115.50$

    d.   Capital gain = (change in price per
         share) $\cdot$ (number of shares) –
         commisions

$$G = (57.75 - 52.50) \cdot 100 - 50 - 0.02(5775)$$
$$= \$359.50$$

    e.   Return = capital gain + dividend
         $R = \$359.50 + \$122 = \$481.50$

    f.   Percent of return $= R / (T + S)$
         $$P = \frac{481.50}{5300 + 115.50} \approx 0.0889 \approx 8.89\%$$

12. a. $I = Prt = 10,000(0.065)(0.5) = \$325$

    b. $I = Prt = 10,000(0.065)(5) = \$3250$

13. a. $A = 200,000,000 + 100,000,000$
         $+ 250,000 = 300,250,000$

    $L = 10,000,000$

    $N = 20,000,000$

    $$NAV = \frac{300,250,000 - 10,000,000}{20,000,000}$$
    $$= \frac{290,250,000}{20,000,000} = \$14.5125 \approx \$14.51$$

    b. $\dfrac{100,000}{14.51} \approx 6891.8 \approx 6891$ shares

14. a. $C = \dfrac{80 - 70}{100} = \dfrac{10}{100} = 0.10 = 10\%$

    b. $Y = \dfrac{1.50}{80} = 0.01875 = 1.875\%$

    c. $R = \dfrac{(80 - 70) \cdot 100 + 1.50 \cdot 100}{100 \cdot 70} = \dfrac{1150}{7000}$
         $\approx 0.1643 = 16.43\%$

15. a. $V = 100(70) = \$7000$

    b. $MR = 7000(0.02) = \$140$

    c.   The annual rate of return would be
         equivalent to the APY.
         $$APY = \left(1 + \frac{r}{k}\right)^k - 1 = (1 + 0.02)^{12} - 1$$
         $$= 1.02^{12} - 1 \approx 0.268 \approx 27\%$$

Chapter 14 Voting and Apportionment

Section 14.1 Voting Systems

1. a. 523,686 + 59,934,814 + 738,475 + 69,456,897 + 603,456 = 131,257,328 votes were cast.

    b. McCain:
    $$\frac{59,934,814}{131,257,328} \approx 0.46 = 46\%$$
    Obama: $\dfrac{69,456,897}{131,257,328} \approx 0.53 = 53\%$

    c. Yes, Obama won 53%.

2. a. 62,040,610 + 59,028,444 + 465,650 6 + 760,641 = 122,295,345 votes were cast.

    b. Bush: $\dfrac{62,040,610}{122,295,345} \approx 0.51 = 51\%$

    Kerry: $\dfrac{59,028,444}{122,295,345} \approx 0.48 = 48\%$

    c. Yes, Bush won 51%.

3. a. 2,911,872 + 2,910,942 + 97,419 + 17,472 = 5,937,705 total votes

    b. 2,911,872 − 2,910,942 = 930

    c. $\dfrac{930}{5.937.705} \approx 0.000157 \approx 0.016\%$

    d. Yes, the percent different does require a recount as 0.016% is less than 0.5%.

4. Bush had the most 1st place votes.

5. a. 6 + 7 + 3 + 4 = 20 votes were cast.
    b. 11 (more than half)
    c. No. Nobody had 11 or more votes.
    d. C(7 votes)

Note: T(120 + 100 = 220) *means that* T *has* 220 *votes.* S(150) *means that S has* 150 *votes.*

6. a. $\dfrac{130+120+100+150}{2} = 250$, so 251 are needed for a majority.

    b. No candidate received a majority of the first-place votes.

    c. T(120 + 100 = 220) is the winner by plurality.

7. a. T(120 + 100 = 220) and S(150)

    b. If a runoff is computed between T and S only (all others will be eliminated) the new table will look like this:

	Number of Voters			
Place	130	120	100	150
First		T	T	S
Second				
Third	S	S		
Fourth	T		S	T

The runoff results will be
$$S(130 + 150 = 280)$$
$$T(120 + 100 = 220)$$
Thus, S is the winner 280 to 220.

8. a. 13 + 12 + 10 = 35 votes

    b. $\dfrac{35}{2} = 17.5$, so 18 are needed for a majority.

    c. No brand received a majority of the first-place votes.

    d. A(13 votes) is the winner.

9. a. A(13) and C(12) have the most first-place votes.

    b. Since the top vote getters were A and C, a runoff is computed between A and C (all others are eliminated). The table now looks like this:

	Number of Voters		
Place	13	12	10
First	A	C	
Second			A
Third			
Fourth	C	A	C

The runoff results will be:
$$A(13 + 10 = 23)$$
$$C(12)$$
Thus, A is the winner 23 to 12.

10. We assign 0, 1, 2 and 3 points for last, next to last, and so on.

		Number of Voters		
Points	Place	20	15	10
3	First	D	E	S
2	Second	B	B	B
1	Third	E	D	D
0	Fourth	S	S	E

Busch Gardens (B):

$2 \cdot 20 + 2 \cdot 15 + 2 \cdot 10 = 40 + 30 + 20 = 90$ points

Disney World (D):

$3 \cdot 20 + 1 \cdot 15 + 1 \cdot 10 = 60 + 15 + 10 = 85$ points

Epcot (E):

$1 \cdot 20 + 3 \cdot 15 + 0 \cdot 10 = 20 + 45 + 0 = 65$ points

Sea World (S):

$0 \cdot 20 + 0 \cdot 15 + 3 \cdot 10 = 0 + 0 + 30 = 30$ points

The winner is Busch Gardens with 90 points, runner-up is Disney World with 85 points.

11. The vacation destinations are Busch Gardens (B), Disney World (D), Epcot (E), and Sea World (S).

	Number of Voters		
Place	20	15	10
First	D	E	S
Second	B	B	B
Third	E	D	D
Fourth	S	S	E

The number of first place votes is: D(20), E(15), S(10), so none of the destinations received a majority of the vote and B received the least amount of votes and is eliminated.

	Number of Voters		
Place	20	15	10
First	D	E	S
Second			
Third	E	D	D
Fourth	S	S	E

Now D(20), E(15), S(10), so we eliminate S. Here is the new table with D and E only.

	Number of Voters		
Place	20	15	10
First	D	E	
Second			
Third	E	D	D
Fourth			E

Now D(20 + 10 = 30) and E(15), hence

Disney World is the winner.

12. We have to compare B and D, B and E, B and S, D and E, D and S, E and S

B(15 + 10 = 25)   D(20)   B gets 1 point.
B(20 + 10 = 30)   E(15)   B gets 1 point.
B(20 + 15 = 35)   S(10)   B gets 1 point.
D(20 + 10 = 30)   E(15)   D gets 1 point.
D(20 + 15 = 35)   S(10)   D gets 1 point.
E(20 + 15 = 35)   S(10)   E gets 1 point.

The winner is Busch Gardens with three points.

13. The results are: B(5), O(11), G(8) and J(6). Thus, O, the orange juice, is the winner.

14. Since the top vote getters were O and G, we run an election between O and G (all others are eliminated). The table now looks like this:

	Number of Voters			
Place	5	11	8	6
First		O	G	
Second				G
Third	G	G	O	O
Fourth	O			

The runoff results will be:

O(11) G(5 + 8 + 6 = 19)

19 people prefer G (2 green peppers) over O (orange); G (2 green peppers) wins.

15. We assign 0, 1, 2 and 3 points for last, next to last, and so on.

		Number of Voters			
Points	Place	5	11	8	6
3	First	B	O	G	J
2	Second	J	J	J	G
1	Third	G	G	O	O
0	Fourth	O	B	B	B

1 orange (O): $0 \cdot 5 + 3 \cdot 11 + 1 \cdot 8 + 1 \cdot 6$
$= 0 + 33 + 8 + 6 = 47$ points

2 green peppers (G): $1 \cdot 5 + 1 \cdot 11 + 3 \cdot 8 + 2 \cdot 6$
$= 5 + 11 + 24 + 12 = 52$ points

1 cup cooked broccoli (B):
$3 \cdot 5 + 0 \cdot 11 + 0 \cdot 8 + 0 \cdot 6$
$= 15 + 0 + 0 + 0 = 15$ points

½ cup fresh orange juice (J):
$2 \cdot 5 + 2 \cdot 11 + 2 \cdot 8 + 3 \cdot 6$
$= 10 + 22 + 16 + 18 = 66$ points

The Borda winner is J(½ cup fresh orange juice) with 66 points.

16. The number of first place votes is: O(11), G(8), B(5), J(6), so none of the sources received a majority of the vote and B received the least amount of votes and is eliminated.

	Number of Voters			
Place	5	11	8	6
First		O	G	J
Second	J	J	J	G
Third	G	G	O	O
Fourth	O			

Now O(11), G(8), J(5 + 6 = 11), so we eliminate G. Here is the new table with O and J only.

	Number of Voters			
Place	5	11	8	6
First		O		J
Second	J	J	J	
Third			O	O
Fourth	O			

Now O(11) and J(5 + 8 + 6 = 19), hence J(½ cup fresh orange juice) is the winner.

17. We have to compare B and G, B and J, B and O, G and J, G and O, J and O
B(5) G(11 + 8 + 6 = 25): G gets 1 point.
B(5) J(11 + 8 + 6 = 25): J gets 1 point.
B(5) O(11 + 8 + 6 = 25): O gets 1 point.
G(8) J(5 + 11 + 6 = 22): J gets 1 point.
G(5 + 8 + 6 = 19) O(11): G gets 1 point.
J(5 + 8 + 6 = 19) O(11): J gets 1 point.
The winner is J(½ cup fresh orange juice) with three points.

18. Adams(6), Barnes(3), Collins(4), so Adams is the winner with approval voting.

19. If Collins drops out, Adams is the winner 6 to 3.

20. Coca-Cola(20 + 18 + 25 = 63)
5-hour Energy(12 + 7 = 19)
Gatorade(20 + 18 = 38)
Dr Pepper(18 + 23 = 41)
Pepsi(7 + 23 = 30)
The voter's favorite drink is Coca-Cola.

21. a. Latte has 12 votes.
   b. Cappuccino has 12 + 5 + 10 + 13 = 40 votes.
   c. Mocha has 5 + 10 = 15 votes.

   d. Americano has 5 + 13 = 18 votes.
   e. Cappuccino is the winner using approval voting.

22. a. Mr. Albertson has 2 + 4 = 6 votes.
   b. Ms. Baker has 3 + 4 = 7 votes.
   c. Ms. Carr has 3 + 3 = 6 votes.
   d. Mr. Davis has 4 + 3 + 1 = 8 votes.
   e. Mr. Davis is selected as faculty advisor.

23. No. You need more than 44 votes for a majority.

24. Beijing (32) has the most first place votes.

25. Beijing (BC) will be selected as it has the most votes.

26.

	Number of Voters								
	3	2	32	3	3	1	8	30	6
1ST	I	I	BC	M	BG	I	M	S	BG
2ND	BC	BC	I	BC	BC	S	S	M	S
3RD	M	BG	BG	BG	I	BC	BG	BG	M
4TH	BG	M	M	S	S	M	I	I	BC
5TH	S	S	S	I	M	BG	BC	BC	I

BC(32) BG(3 + 6 = 9) I(3 + 2 + 1 = 6)
M(3 + 8 = 11) S(30), so eliminate Istanbul (I).

	Number of Voters								
	3	2	32	3	3	1	8	30	6
1ST			BC	M	BG		M	S	BG
2ND	BC	BC		BC	BC	S	S	M	S
3RD	M	BG	BG	BG		BC	BG	BG	M
4TH	BG	M	M	S	S	M			BC
5TH	S	S	S		M	BG	BC	BC	

BC(3 + 2 + 32 = 37) BG(3 + 6 = 9)
M(3 + 8 = 11) S(30), so eliminate Berlin (BG).

	Number of Voters								
	3	2	32	3	3	1	8	30	6
1ST			BC	M			M	S	
2ND	BC	BC		BC	BC	S	S	M	S
3RD	M					BC			M
4TH		M	M	S	S	M			BC
5TH	S	S	S		M		BC	BC	

BC(3 + 2 + 32 + 3 = 40) M(3 + 8 = 11)
S(30), so eliminate Manchester (M).

	Number of Voters								
	3	2	32	3	3	1	8	30	6
1ST			BC					S	
2ND	BC	BC		BC	BC	S	S		S
3RD						BC			
4TH				S	S	M			BC
5TH	S	S	S					BC	BC

BC(3 + 2 + 32 + 3 +3 = 43) S(1 + 8 + 30 + 6 = 45), so Sydney (S) is the city selected.

27.

Pts	Number of Voters								
	3	2	32	3	3	1	8	30	6
5	I	I	BC	M	BG	I	M	S	BG
4	BC	BC	I	BC	BC	S	S	M	S
3	M	BG	BG	BG	I	BC	BG	BG	M
2	BG	M	M	S	S	M	I	I	BC
1	S	S	S	I	M	BG	BC	BC	I

BC($4 \cdot 3 + 4 \cdot 2 + 5 \cdot 32 + 4 \cdot 3 + 4 \cdot 3 + 3 \cdot 1 + 1 \cdot 8 + 1 \cdot 30 + 2 \cdot 6 = 257$)

BG($2 \cdot 3 + 3 \cdot 2 + 3 \cdot 32 + 3 \cdot 3 + 5 \cdot 3 + 1 \cdot 1 + 3 \cdot 8 + 3 \cdot 30 + 5 \cdot 6 = 277$)

I($5 \cdot 3 + 5 \cdot 2 + 4 \cdot 32 + 1 \cdot 3 + 3 \cdot 3 + 5 \cdot 1 + 2 \cdot 8 + 2 \cdot 30 + 1 \cdot 6 = 252$)

M($3 \cdot 3 + 2 \cdot 2 + 2 \cdot 32 + 5 \cdot 3 + 1 \cdot 3 + 2 \cdot 1 + 5 \cdot 8 + 4 \cdot 30 + 3 \cdot 6 = 275$

S($1 \cdot 3 + 1 \cdot 2 + 1 \cdot 32 + 2 \cdot 3 + 2 \cdot 3 + 4 \cdot 1 + 4 \cdot 8 + 5 \cdot 30 + 4 \cdot 6 = 259$)

Berlin with 277 points will be selected.

28.

Pts	Number of Voters								
	3	2	32	3	3	1	8	30	6
4	I	I	BC	M	BG	I	M	S	BG
3	BC	BC	I	BC	BC	S	S	M	S
2	M	BG	BG	BG	I	BC	BG	BG	M
1	BG	M	M	S	S	M	I	I	BC
0	S	S	S	I	M	BG	BC	BC	I

BC($3 \cdot 3 + 3 \cdot 2 + 4 \cdot 32 + 3 \cdot 3 + 3 \cdot 3 + 2 \cdot 1 + 0 \cdot 8 + 0 \cdot 30 + 1 \cdot 6 = 169$)

BG($1 \cdot 3 + 2 \cdot 2 + 2 \cdot 32 + 2 \cdot 3 + 4 \cdot 3 + 0 \cdot 1 + 2 \cdot 8 + 2 \cdot 30 + 4 \cdot 6 = 189$)

I($4 \cdot 3 + 4 \cdot 2 + 3 \cdot 32 + 0 \cdot 3 + 2 \cdot 3 + 4 \cdot 1 + 1 \cdot 8 + 1 \cdot 30 + 0 \cdot 6 = 164$)

M($2 \cdot 3 + 1 \cdot 2 + 1 \cdot 32 + 4 \cdot 3 + 0 \cdot 3 + 1 \cdot 1 + 4 \cdot 8 + 3 \cdot 30 + 2 \cdot 6 = 187$

S($0 \cdot 3 + 0 \cdot 2 + 0 \cdot 32 + 1 \cdot 3 + 1 \cdot 3 + 3 \cdot 1 + 3 \cdot 8 + 4 \cdot 30 + 3 \cdot 6 = 171$)

Berlin with 189 points will be selected.

29. Since there are five cities, there will be $\dfrac{5 \cdot 4}{2} = 10$ comparisons. They are

1) BC(3 + 2 + 32 + 3 + 1 = 41) vs. BG(3 + 8 + 30 + 6 = 47) BG gets 1 point.
2) BC(32 + 3 + 3 + 6 = 44) vs. I(3 + 2 + 1 + 8 + 8 = 22) BC gets 1 point.
3) BC(3 + 2 + 32 + 3 + 1 = 41) vs. M(3 + 8 + 30 + 6 = 47) M gets 1 point.
4) BC(3 + 2 + 32 + 3 + 3 = 43) vs. S(1 + 8 + 30 + 6 = 45) S gets 1 point.

5) BG(3 + 3 + 8 + 30 + 6 = 50) vs. I(3 + 2 + 32 + 1 = 38) BG gets 1 point.
6) BG(2 + 32 + 3 + 6 = 43) vs. M(3 + 3 + 1 + 8 + 30 = 45) M gets 1 point.
7) BG(3 + 2 + 32 + 3 + 3 + 6 = 49) vs. S(1 + 8 + 30 = 39) BG gets 1 point.
8) I(3 + 2 + 32 + 3 + 1 = 41) vs. M(3 + 8 + 30 + 6 = 47) M gets 1 point.
9) I(3 + 2 + 32 + 3 + 1 = 41) vs. S(3 + 8 + 30 + 6 = 47) S gets 1 point.
10) M(3 + 2 + 32 + 3 + 8 = 48) vs. S(3 + 1 + 30 + 6 = 40) M gets 1 point.
BC(1 pt), BG(3pts), I(0 pt), M(4 pts), and S(2 pts), so Manchester (M) is selected.

30. Refer to problem 28. The cities are ranked Berlin (189), Manchester (187), Sydney (171), Beijing (169), and Istanbul (164).

31. I(3 + 2 + 1 + 32 = 38)
S(30 + 1 + 8 + 6 = 45)
BC(32 + 3 + 2 + 3 + 3 = 43)
M(3 + 8 + 30 = 41)
BG(3 + 6 = 9)
S(Sydney) is selected with 45 votes.

32. Refer to problem 31. The cities are ranked Sydney (45), Beijing, (43), Manchester (41), Istanbul (38), and Berlin (9).

33. Rio de Janeiro won with 66 votes in the third round.

34. A majority is more than $\dfrac{94}{2} = 47$ votes.

No city received more than 47 votes in the first round.

35. A majority is more than $\dfrac{94}{2} = 47$ votes.

No city received more than 47 votes in the second round.

36. The two cities with the greatest number of votes, Madrid (28) and Rio de Janeiro (26), would face off in the runoff election.

37. Madrid with the most votes would be selected to host the 2016 Olympics.

38. a. Paris
    b. London actually won.

39. A(10), B(13), C(8 + 7 = 15), D(12).
Thus, C(Coala Cola) wins with 15.

40. Since the top vote getters were B and C, a runoff is computed between B and C (all others are eliminated). The table now looks like this:

Number of Voters				
10	13	8	7	12
	B	C	C	
B			B	
C		B		B
	C			C

The runoff results will be:
B(10 + 13 + 12 = 35) C(8 + 7 = 15)
35 consumers prefer Best Cola (B) over Coala Cola (C), so Best Cola is preferred.

41. We assign 0, 1, 2 and 3 points for last, next to last, and so on.

	Number of Voters				
Points	10	13	8	7	12
3	A	B	C	C	D
2	B	A	D	B	A
1	C	D	B	A	B
0	D	C	A	D	C

A($3 \cdot 10 + 2 \cdot 13 + 0 \cdot 8 + 1 \cdot 7 + 2 \cdot 12 = 87$ pts)
B($2 \cdot 10 + 3 \cdot 13 + 1 \cdot 8 + 2 \cdot 7 + 1 \cdot 12 = 93$ pts)
C($1 \cdot 10 + 0 \cdot 13 + 3 \cdot 8 + 3 \cdot 7 + 0 \cdot 12 = 55$ pts)
D($0 \cdot 10 + 1 \cdot 13 + 2 \cdot 8 + 0 \cdot 7 + 3 \cdot 12 = 65$ pts)
The preferred Cola is B(Best Cola) with 93 points.

42. Assign 5-4-1-0 points to first, second, third and last place. The results are:
A: 157 B: 153 C: 85 D: 105
Assigning 10-9-1-0 yields:
A: 332 B: 303 C: 160 D: 205

Section 14.2 Voting Objections

1.

		Number of Voters		
Points	Place	25	5	20
2	First	W	S	P
1	Second	P	W	S
0	Third	S	P	W

a. Using plurality W(25) is the winner.

b. Using Borda

$W (2 \cdot 25 + 1 \cdot 5 = 50 + 5 = 55)$

$S (2 \cdot 5 + 1 \cdot 20 = 10 + 20 = 30)$

$P (1 \cdot 25 + 2 \cdot 20 = 25 + 40 = 65)$

Thus, P is the winner with 65 votes.

c. Yes. W won under plurality but P wins under Borda.

d. We have to compare W and S, W and P, and S and P.

W(25)   S(5 + 20 = 25): Each gets ½ point.

W(25 + 5 = 30)   P(20): W gets 1 point.

S(5)   P(25 + 20 = 45): P gets 1 point.

W is the winner with 1½ points.

2.

		Number of Voters		
Points	Place	600	300	200
2	First	L	G	C
1	Second	G	C	L
0	Third	C	L	G

a. Using plurality L(600) is the winner.

b. Using Borda

$L(2 \cdot 600 + 1 \cdot 200 = 1400)$

$G(1 \cdot 600 + 2 \cdot 300 = 1200)$

$C(1 \cdot 300 + 2 \cdot 200 = 700)$

Thus, L (La Septima) is the winner with 1400 votes.

c. No. The Borda count winner is the same as the plurality winner.

d. We have to compare L and G, L and C, and G and C.

L(600 + 200 = 800)   G(300)

L gets 1 point.

L(600)   C(300 + 200 = 500)

L gets 1 point.

G(600 + 300 = 900)   C(200)

G gets 1 point.

L (La Septima) is the winner with 2 points.

3.

		Number of Voters			
Points	Place	10	20	30	10
3	First	C	C	L	L
2	Second	A	M	C	C
1	Third	M	A	M	A
0	Fourth	L	L	A	M

a. A (20 + 20 + 10 = 50)

C (30 + 60 + 60 + 20 = 170)

L (90 + 30 = 120)

M (40 + 10 + 30 = 80)

Under the Borda count C(Cappucino) is the winner.

b. No. L(Latte) is the plurality winner with 30 + 10 = 40 votes but C is the winner under Borda.

4. a. We have to compare C and L, C and M, and L and M. Here are the comparisons:

C(5 + 3 = 8) L(2) C gets 1 point.

C(2 + 5 = 7) M(3) C gets 1 point.

L(2 + 5 = 7) M(3) L gets 1 point.

Yes, Cats (C) is preferred.

b. Yes, the head-to-head criterion is satisfied as Cats wins under plurality.

5. a. We have to compare S and U, S and H, S and B, U and H, U and B, and H and B. Here are the comparisons:

S(50 + 25 + 15 = 90) U(10)

S gets 1 point.

S(50 + 10 = 60)   H(25 + 15 = 40)

S gets 1 point.

S(50 + 25 = 75)   B(15 + 10 = 25)

S gets 1 point.

U(50 + 10 = 60)   H(25 + 15 = 40)

U gets 1 point.

U(50 + 25 + 10 = 85)   B(15)

U gets 1 point.

H(50 + 25 = 75)   B(15 + 10 = 25)

H gets 1 point.

S(Staples) is the commercial preferred to U, H, and B.

b. Yes. S wins under plurality too.

6. First, find the plurality winner with elimination.

	Number of Voters			
Place	25	30	10	35
First	C	H	C	L
Second	H	L	L	C
Third	L	C	H	H

L(35) C(25 + 10 = 35) H(30),

so eliminate H.

Number of Voters				
Place	25	30	10	35
First	C		C	L
Second		L	L	C
Third	L	C		

L(30 + 35 = 65)   C(25 + 10 = 35)
L is the winner.

Now, the 10 voters who voted C, L, H changed their vote to L, C, H, thus, giving L additional support.

Number of Voters				
Place	25	30	10	35
First	C	H	L	L
Second	H	L	C	C
Third	L	C	H	H

L(10 + 35 = 45)   C(25)   H(30), so eliminate C.

Number of Voters				
Place	25	30	10	35
First		H	L	L
Second	H	L		
Third	L		H	H

L(10 + 35 = 45)   H(25 + 30 = 55)
H is the winner.

No, the monotonicity criterion is not satisfied. L (Los Angeles) is the winner of the first election, but does not win the second election after obtaining additional support.

7. Yes. The results of the initial election (D, A and H) are as follows: D(20), A(18) and H(12). When H is eliminated, the results are: D(20 + 12 = 32) and A(18), so D is still the winner. This means that the irrelevant alternatives criterion is satisfied.

8. No. The results of the initial election (D, A and H) are as follows: D(20), A(16) and H(14), so Washington DC (D) wins the first election. When A is eliminated, the results are: D(20) and H(16 + 14 = 30) but H wins the second election when A is removed.

9. a. Using the plurality methods the results are as follows: A(27), B(24) and C(2), so A is the winner.
    b. Yes, A does.
    c. We have to compare A and B, A and C, and B and C.
        A(27)   B(24 + 2 = 26) A gets 1 point.

A(27)   C(24 + 2 = 26) A gets 1 point.
B(24)   C(27 + 2 = 29) C gets 1 point.
A is the winner with 2 points.

d. Yes, A beats every other candidate.

e.

	Number of Voters			
Points	Place	27	24	2
2	First	A	B	C
1	Second	C	C	B
0	Third	B	A	A

A(2 · 27 = 54)
B(2 · 24 + 1 · 2 = 50)
C(1 · 27 + 1 · 24 + 2 · 2 = 55)
The winner is C.

f. The majority criterion. A wins using plurality but C wins using Borda.

g. B drops out, so we have

	Number of Voters			
Points	Place	27	24	2
1	First	A	C	C
0	Second	C	A	A

A(27)   C(24 + 2 = 26)
No. A is the new winner 27 to 26 over C.

h. Majority Criterion (A has a majority but C wins under Borda)
    Condorcet Criterion (A wins head-to-head but C wins under Borda)
    Irrelevant Alternatives (C was the winner (part e) under Borda but B's dropping out causes C to lose to A (part g)).

10. a. We have to compare A and B, A and C and B and C. Here are the comparisons:
        A(20) B(19 + 5 = 24) B gets 1 point.
        A(20) C(19 + 5 = 24) C gets 1 point.
        B(20 + 19 = 39) C(5) B gets 1 point.
        B with 2 points is the winner.

    b. Yes. B beats every other candidate in a head-to-head comparison.

    c. A(20) B(19) C(5), so A wins by plurality.

    d. Condorcet is violated. A wins under plurality but B wins under head-to-head.

    e. No. C drops out so A(20) B(19 + 5 = 24), thus B is the winner, which is not the same winner (A) as in part c.

    f. Irrelevant alternatives is violated. A wins under plurality but C dropping out causes A to lose to B.

g. Eliminate C, we have

Number of Voters			
Place	20	19	5
First	A	B	
Second	B		B
Third		A	A

A(20) B(19 + 5 =24) B is the winner.

h. Eliminate A, we have

Number of Voters			
Place	20	19	5
First		B	C
Second	B	C	B
Third	C		

B(20 + 19 = 39) C(5)
B is the winner. Yes, the winner is the same as in part g.

i. None of the criteria are violated.

11. a. The results for the first election are:
A(14) B(4) C(11) D(8)
Thus, B is eliminated.

Number of Voters					
Place	14	4	10	1	8
First	A		C	C	D
Second		D		D	C
Third	C	C	D		
Fourth	D	A	A	A	A

The results for the second election are:
A(14) C(10 + 1 = 11)
D(4 + 8 =12) Thus, C is eliminated.

Number of Voters					
Place	14	4	10	1	8
First	A				D
Second		D		D	
Third			D		
Fourth	D	A	A	A	A

The results of the third election are:
A(14) D(4 + 10 + 1 + 8 = 23)
Thus, D has a majority and is the winner.

b. We have to compare A and B, A and C, A and D, B and C, B and D, C and D. Here are the comparisons:
A(14) B(23) B gets 1 point.
A(14) C(23) C gets 1 point.
A(14) D(23) D gets 1 point.
B(18) C(19) C gets 1 point.
B(28) D(9) B gets 1 point.
C(25) D(12) C gets 1 point.

Thus, C is the pairwise comparison winner with 3 points.

c. Yes. C beats A, B and D.

d. The Condorcet criteria. C wins head to head (part c) but D wins plurality with elimination (part a).

12. a. The results for the first election are:
A(7 + 4 = 11) B(8) C(10)
Thus, B is eliminated.
The results for the second election are:
A(7 + 4 = 11) C(8 + 10 = 18)
Thus, C has a majority and is the winner.

b. The table after the new voting would be

Number of Voters			
Place	7	8	10 + 4 = 14
First	A	B	C
Second	B	C	A
Third	C	A	B

A(7) B(8) C(14), so eliminate A.

Number of Voters			
Place	7	8	10 + 4 = 14
First		B	C
Second	B	C	
Third	C		B

B(7 + 8 = 15) C(14), B is the winner.

c. Monotonicity is violated. C wins under plurality with elimination, gains additional support but loses to B.

13. a. B wins. Here are the results:
A(20) B(19) C(5).
No majority, C is eliminated.

Number of Voters			
Place	20	19	5
First	A	B	
Second	B		B
Third		A	A

A(20) B(19 + 5 = 24)
B has a majority and is the winner.

b. A drops out, we have

Number of Voters			
Place	20	19	5
First		B	C
Second	B	C	B
Third	C		

B(20 + 19 = 39) C(5), B is the winner.
Yes. After A drops out B(39) and C(5), so B still wins.

   c.   None. B wins even after A drops out.

14. a.   We have to compare A and B, A and
          C, A and D, A and E, B and C, B and
          D, B and E, C and D, C and E, and D
          and E. Here are the comparisons:
          1) A(3 + 3 + 1 = 7)
             B(3 + 1 + 1 + 3 + 9) B gets 1 point.
          2) A(3 + 3 + 3 + 3 + 1 + 1 = 14)
             C(1 + 1 = 2)   A gets 1 point.
          3) A(3 + 3 + 1 + 3 + 3 + 1 = 14)
             D(1 + 1 = 2)   A gets 1 point.
          4) A(3 + 3 + 3 + 3 + 1 + 1 = 14)
             E(1 + 1 = 2)   A gets 1 point.
          5) B(3 + 3 + 1 = 7)
             C(3 + 1 + 1 + 3 + 1 = 9)
                         C gets 1 point.
          6) B(3 + 1 + 1 + 3 + 1 = 9)
             D(3 + 3 + 1 = 7)   B gets 1 point.
          7) B(3 + 1 + 3 + 1 = 8)
             E(3 + 1 + 3 + 1 = 8)
             B gets ½ point and E gets ½ point.
          8) C(3 + 3 + 1 + 1 + 1 =9)
             D(3 + 3 + 1 = 7)   C gets 1 point.
          9) C(3 + 3 + 1 + 1 = 8)
             E(3 + 3 + 1 + 1 = 8)
             C gets ½ point and E gets ½ point.
          10) D(3 + 3 + 1 + 3 + 3 = 13)
              E(1 + 1 + 1 = 3) D gets 1 point.
          A(3 pts) B(2 ½ pts) C(2 ½ pts)
          D(1 pt)   E(1pt)   A is the winner.
    b.   C drops out, we have
          1) A(3 + 3 + 1 = 7)
             B(3 + 1 + 1 + 3 + 9)   B gets 1 point.
          3) A(3 + 3 + 1 + 3 + 3 + 1 = 14)
             D(1 + 1 = 2)   A gets 1 point.
          4) A(3 + 3 + 3 + 3 + 1 + 1 = 14)
             E(1 + 1 = 2)   A gets 1 point.
          6) B(3 + 1 + 1 + 3 + 1 = 9)
             D(3 + 3 + 1 = 7)   B gets 1 point.
          7) B(3 + 1 + 3 + 1 = 8)
             E(3 + 1 + 3 + 1 = 8)
             B gets ½ point and E gets ½ point.
          10) D(3 + 3 + 1 + 3 + 3 = 13)
             E(1 + 1 + 1 = 3)   D gets 1 point.
          A(2 pts) B(2 ½ pts) D(1 pt) E(½ pt)
          No, the winner is not the same as in
          part a.   B is the winner.
    c.   Irrelevant alternatives is violated. A
          wins under comparison, but C dropping
          out causes A to lose to B.

15. a.   For three candidates $\dfrac{3 \cdot 2}{2} = 3$
          comparisons need to be made.

    b.   For four candidates $\dfrac{4 \cdot 3}{2} = 6$
          comparisons need to be made.

    c.   For five candidates $\dfrac{5 \cdot 4}{2} = 10$
          comparisons need to be made.

    d.   For n candidates $\dfrac{n(n-1)}{2}$ comparisons
          need to be made.

16. a.   For three candidates $3 - 1 = 2$
          comparisons must be won to guarantee
          winning the election.
    b.   For four candidates $4 - 1 = 3$
          comparisons must be won to guarantee
          winning the election.
    c.   For five candidates $5 - 1 = 4$
          comparisons must be won to guarantee
          winning the election.
    d.   For n candidates $n - 1$ comparisons
          must be won to guarantee winning the
          election.

17. Answers will vary. If a candidate receives a
     majority of first-place votes, then that
     candidate should be the winner (see page
     834).

18. Answers will vary. In general, a candidate
     who holds a majority of first-place votes
     wins the election without having to hold a
     second election (see page 835).

19. Answers will vary. In general, if a candidate
     holds a majority of first-place votes, this
     candidate always wins every pairwise (head-
     to-head) comparison (see page 836).

20. Answers will vary. If a candidate is the
     winner of a first nonbinding election and
     then gains additional support without losing
     any of the original support, then the
     candidate should be the winner of the
     second election (see page 838).

21. Answers will vary. Elimination might add to
     the original plurality winner but add even
     more to the second place plurality entry,
     enough to overtake the original difference.
     Thus, plurality with elimination method will
     always satisfy the majority criterion, and
     may not satisfy the monotonicity criterion
     (see page 839).

22. Answers will vary. If a candidate is favored when compared head-to-head with every other candidate, that candidate should be the winner (see page 836).

23. Answers will vary. The winner of each pair-wise comparison would also be the winner of a head-to-head comparison (see page 838).

24. Answers will vary. If a candidate is the winner of an election and in a second election one or more of the losing candidates is removed, then the winner of the first election should be the winner of the second election (see page 840).

25. Answers will vary.

Section 14.3 Apportionment Methods

1. a. $\dfrac{2,001,102,854}{10} = \$200,110,285$

 b. $\dfrac{2,001,102,854}{216,221} = \$9255$

 c. $\dfrac{2,001,102,854}{136,363} = \$14,675$

2. University of Florida:
$\dfrac{41,652}{216,221} \cdot \$2,001,102,854 = \$385,484,926$

Florida Gulf Coast University:
$\dfrac{2893}{216,221} \cdot \$2,001,102,854 = \$26,774,414$

6. $SD = \dfrac{216,221}{200} = 1081.105$
The number of positions for each university are in the final column. Note that one additional seat was allocated to the universities with the *largest* fractional part of the standard quota.

3. University of South Florida:
$\dfrac{18,176}{136,363} \cdot 2,001,102,854 = \$266,729,578$
University of West Florida:
$\dfrac{4556}{136,363} \cdot 2,001,102,854 = \$66,858,492$

4. a. $SD = \dfrac{216,221}{200} = 1081.105$

 b. Florida Atlantic:
$SQ = \dfrac{19,153}{1081.105} = 17.716$
University of Central Florida:
$SQ = \dfrac{30,009}{1081.105} = 27.758$

5. a. $SD = \dfrac{136,363}{200} = 681.815$

 b. Florida Atlantic:
$SQ = \dfrac{10,725}{681.815} = 15.730$

University of Central Florida:
$Q = \dfrac{18,312}{681.815} = 26.858$

	Students	Quota	Initial	Extra	Final
UF	41,652	38.5272	38	1	39
FSU	30,389	28.1092	28		28
FAMU	11,324	10.4745	10		10
USF	31,555	29.1877	29		29
FAU	19,153	17.7161	17	1	18
UWF	7790	7.2056	7		7
UCF	30,009	27.7577	27	1	28
FIU	30,096	27.8382	27	1	28
UNF	11,360	10.5078	10		10
FGC	2893	2.6760	2	1	3
Total	216,221		195	5	200

7. $SD = \dfrac{136,363}{200} = 681.815$

	FTE	Quota	Initial	Extra	Final
UF	29,646	43.4810	43		43
FSU	21,195	31.0861	31		31
FAMU	8064	11.8273	11	1	12
USF	18,176	26.6583	26	1	27
FAU	10,725	15.7301	15	1	16
UWF	4556	6.6822	6	1	7
UCF	18,312	26.8577	26	1	27
FIU	17,434	25.5700	25		25
UNF	6697	9.8223	9	1	10
FGC	1558	2.2851	2		2
Total	136,363		194	6	200

The number of positions for each university are on the final column. Note that one additional seat was allocated to the universities with the *largest* fractional part of the standard quota.
No, the number of positions for each university is not the same.

8. $SD = \dfrac{90}{75} = 1.2$

SQ	R-Down	Actual
15/1.2 = 12.5	12	12
30/1.2 = 25	25	25
12/1.2 = 10	10	10
8/1.2 = 6067	6	6 + 1 = 7
25/1.2 = 20.83	20	20 + 1 = 21
	73	75

The intravenous (IV) pumps are distributed as noted in the column labeled *Actual*. One additional seat was allocated to the care unit with the *largest* fractional part of the standard quota.

9.   a.   Total population = 5637 + 5683 + 7655 + 3715 + 2061 = 24,751

$$SD = \dfrac{\text{total population}}{\text{total seats(positions, money) to be apportioned}} \text{ and } SQ = \dfrac{\text{state population}}{SD}, \text{ so that}$$

$$SQ = \dfrac{\text{state population} \cdot \text{total seats to be apportioned}}{\text{total population}}$$

CAL: $\dfrac{5637 \cdot 100}{24,751} = 22.7748$ FLA: $\dfrac{5683 \cdot 100}{24,751} = 22.9607$

NY: $\dfrac{7655 \cdot 100}{24,751} = 30.9280$ TX: $\dfrac{3715 \cdot 100}{24,751} = 15.0095$

NJ: $\dfrac{2061 \cdot 100}{24,751} = 8.3269$

b.

State	Cases	Quota	Initial	Extra	Final
CAL	5637	22.7748	22	1	23
FL	5683	22.9607	22	1	23
NY	7655	30.9280	30	1	31
TEX	3715	15.0095	15		15
NJ	2061	8.3269	8		8
Total	24,751		97	3	100

The final column shows the number of millions for each state. One additional seat was allocated to the state with the *largest* fractional part of the standard quota.

10. $SD = \dfrac{13,000}{100} = 130$; $SQ = \dfrac{Students}{130}$

College	Students	SQ	Rounded Down	Delegates
Agriculture	2500	19.23	19	19
Arts	500	3.85	3	3 + 1 = 4
Business	3000	23.08	23	23
Engineering	4000	30.77	30	30 + 1 = 31
Science	3000	23.08	23	23
Total	**13,000**		**98**	**100**

The *Delegates* column shows the number of millions for each state. One additional seat was allocated to the college with the *largest* fractional part of the standard quota.

11. a. Note: SD = 5.35; use MD = 5.25 to find $MQ = \dfrac{participants}{MD}$.

Exercise: $\dfrac{150}{5.25} = 28.5714$ Sports: $\dfrac{90}{5.25} = 17.1429$

Charity W: $\dfrac{85}{5.25} = 16.1905$ Home R: $\dfrac{130}{5.25} = 24.7619$

Computer H: $\dfrac{80}{5.25} = 15.2381$

b. Note that the modified quotas are *rounded down* in the final column.

Activity	Participants	Quota 5.35	Modified 5.25	Final
Exercise	150	28.0374	28.5714	28
Sports	90	16.8224	17.1429	17
Charity	85	15.8879	16.1905	16
Home repair	130	24.2991	24.7619	24
Computer hobbies	80	14.9533	15.2381	15
Total	**535**			**100**

According to the table, Exercise will get $28 million, Sports $17 million, Charity $16 million, Home Repair $24 million and Computer Hobbies $15 million.

12. a. Note: SD = $\dfrac{3530}{150} = 23.5333$; use MD = 23.3 to find $MQ = \dfrac{population\ in\ group}{MD}$.

Salvation Army: $\dfrac{1230}{23.3} = 52.7897$ YMCA: $\dfrac{630}{23.3} = 27.0386$

Fidelity Inv.: $\dfrac{570}{23.3} = 24.4635$ Amer. Cancer: $\dfrac{560}{23.3} = 24.0343$

Amer. Red Cross: $\dfrac{540}{23.3} = 23.1760$

b. Note that the modified quotas are *rounded down* in the final column.

Charity	Donation	Quota 23.5333	Modified 23.3	Final
Salvation Army	1,230	52.2663	52.7897	52
YMCA	630	26.7705	27.0386	27
Fidelity Inv.	570	24.221	24.4635	24
Amer. Cancer	560	23.796	24.0343	24
Amer. Red C	540	22.9462	23.1760	23
Total	**3,530**			**150**

According to the table, Salvation Army will get $52 million, YMCA $27 million, Fidelity Investments $24 million, American Cancer Society $24 million and American Red Cross $23 million.

13. a.   Use MD = 1.08 to find MQ = $\dfrac{\text{population in group}}{MD}$.

Dogs: $\dfrac{190}{1.08} = 175.9259$ Cats: $\dfrac{110}{1.08} = 101.8519$

Birds: $\dfrac{10}{1.08} = 9.2593$ Horses: $\dfrac{230}{1.08} = 212.9630$

b.   Note that the modified quotas are *rounded* in the usual manner (*up* for 0.5 or more, *down* for less than 0.5).

Pet	Cost	Quota 1.08	Modified 1.08	Final
Dogs	190	175.9259	175.9259	176
Cats	110	101.8519	101.8519	102
Birds	10	9.2593	9.2593	9
Horses	230	212.9630	212.9630	213
Total	**540**			**500**

According to the table for every $500 spent on pets, $176, $102, $9 and $213 are spent on dogs, cats, birds and horses respectively.

14. a.   Note: SD $= \dfrac{650}{700} = 0.9286$. Use MD = 0.928 to find MQ = $\dfrac{\text{population in group}}{MD}$.

Europe: $\dfrac{90}{0.928} = 96.9828$ Asia: $\dfrac{220}{0.928} = 237.0690$

North America: $\dfrac{255}{0.928} = 274.7845$ South America: $\dfrac{45}{0.928} = 48.4914$

Africa: $\dfrac{40}{0.928} = 43.1034$

b.   Note that the modified quotas are *rounded* in the usual manner (*up* for 0.5 or more, *down* for less than 0.5).

Continent	Immigration	Quota 0.9286	Modified 0.928	Final
Europe	90	96.9231	96.9828	97
Asia	220	236.9231	237.0690	237
North America	255	274.6154	274.7845	275
South America	45	48.4615	48.4914	48
Africa	40	43.0769	43.1034	43
Total	**650**			**700**

According to the table the allocation will be Europe 97 visas, Asia 247 visas, North America 275 visas, South America 48 visas, and Africa 43 visas.

15. a.   Note: SD $= \dfrac{1500}{75} = 20$. Use MD = 20.5 to find MQ = $\dfrac{\text{population in group}}{MD}$.

Lake Park: $\dfrac{600}{20.5} = 29.2683$ E.G. Simmons: $\dfrac{470}{20.5} = 22.9268$

Lettuce Lake: $\dfrac{240}{20.5} = 11.7073$ Lithia Springs: $\dfrac{160}{20.5} = 7.8049$

Eureka Springs: $\dfrac{30}{20.5} = 1.4634$

b.   Note that the modified quotas are *rounded up*. The final column shows the number of rangers assigned to each park.

Park	Acreage	Quota 20	Modified 20.5	Final
Lake Park	600	30	29.2683	30
E.G. Simmons	470	23.5	22.9268	23
Lettuce Lake	240	12	11.7073	12
Lithia Springs	160	8	7.8049	8
Eureka Springs	30	1.5	1.4634	2
Total	**1500**			**75**

16. a.   Note: $SD = \dfrac{70}{25} = 2.8$. Use MD = 3.08 to find $MQ = \dfrac{\text{population in group}}{MD}$.

Texas: $\dfrac{21}{3.08} = 6.8182$ California: $\dfrac{20}{3.08} = 6.4935$

Florida: $\dfrac{12}{3.08} = 3.8961$ Ohio: $\dfrac{10}{3.08} = 3.2468$

Colorado: $\dfrac{7}{3.08} = 2.2727$

b.   Note that the modified quotas are *rounded up*. The final column shows the number of area codes allocated to each state.

State	Area Codes	Quota 2.8	Modified 3.08	Final
Texas	21	7.5	6.8182	7
California	20	7.1429	6.4935	7
Florida	12	4.2857	3.8961	4
Ohio	10	3.5714	3.2468	4
Colorado	7	2.5	2.2727	3
Total	**70**			**25**

17. a. $SD = \dfrac{\text{total population}}{\text{total money to be apportioned}} = \dfrac{33,000+21,000+17,000+11,000+11,000}{100} = 930$

b. $SQ = \dfrac{\text{population in group}}{SD}$

Dade: $\dfrac{33,000}{930} = 35.4839$ Broward: $\dfrac{21,000}{930} = 22.5806$

Hillsborough: $\dfrac{17,000}{930} = 18.2796$ Orange: $\dfrac{11,000}{930} = 11.8280$

Pinellas: $\dfrac{11,000}{930} = 11.8280$

c.   The initial appropriation summed to 97. One additional seat was allocated to the county with the *largest* fractional part of the standard quota.

	Dade	Broward	Hills	Orange	Pinellas
SD = 930	33000	21000	17000	11000	11000
Standard Quota	35.48	22.58	18.28	11.83	11.83
Hamilton's Method	35	22 + 1 = 23	18	11 + 1 = 12	11 + 1 = 12

The bottom row shows each county's apportionment (in millions of dollars) using Hamilton's method.

18. a.   Use MD = 916.05 to find MQ = $\dfrac{\text{population in group}}{\text{MD}}$.

Dade: $\dfrac{33,000}{916.05} = 36.0242$ Broward: $\dfrac{21,000}{916.05} = 22.9245$

Hillsborough: $\dfrac{17,000}{916.05} = 18.5579$ Orange: $\dfrac{11,000}{916.05} = 12.0081$

Pinellas: $\dfrac{11,000}{916.05} = 12.0081$

b.   Note that the modified quotas are *rounded down* in the bottom row.

	Dade	Broward	Hills	Orange	Pinellas
MD = 916.05	33000	21000	17000	11000	11000
Modified Quota	36.02	22.92	18.56	12.01	12.01
Jefferson's Method	36	22	18	12	12

The bottom row shows each county's apportionment (in millions of dollars) using Jefferson's method.

19. a.   Use MD = 948.60 to find MQ = $\dfrac{\text{population in group}}{\text{MD}}$.

Dade: $\dfrac{33,000}{948.60} = 34.7881$ Broward: $\dfrac{21,000}{948.60} = 22.1379$ Hillsborough: $\dfrac{17,000}{948.60} = 17.9211$

Orange: $\dfrac{11,000}{948.60} = 11.5960$ Pinellas: $\dfrac{11,000}{948.60} = 11.5960$

b.   Results are then *rounded up* as shown.

	Dade	Broward	Hills	Orange	Pinellas
MD = 948.60	33000	21000	17000	11000	11000
Modified Quota	34.79	22.14	17.92	11.60	11.60
Adam's Method	35	23	18	12	12

The allocations are 35, 23, 18, 12 and 12 million dollars respectively as shown.

20.   SD = $\dfrac{\text{total population}}{\text{total money to be apportioned}} = \dfrac{33,000+21,000+17,000+11,000+11,000}{100} = 930$

SQ = $\dfrac{\text{population in group}}{\text{SD}}$

Dade: $\dfrac{33,000}{930} = 35.4839$ Broward: $\dfrac{21,000}{930} = 22.5806$ Hillsborough: $\dfrac{17,000}{930} = 18.2796$

Orange: $\dfrac{11,000}{930} = 11.8280$ Pinellas: $\dfrac{11,000}{930} = 11.8280$

Round each quota to the nearest integer and apportion to each group its modified rounded quota.

	Dade	Broward	Hills	Orange	Pinellas
SD = 930	33000	21000	17000	11000	11000
Standard Quota	35.48	22.58	18.28	11.83	11.83
Webster's Method	35	23	18	12	12

The allocations are 35, 23, 18, 12 and 12 million dollars respectively as shown.

21. a. $SD = \dfrac{\text{total population}}{\text{total specialists to be apportioned}} = \dfrac{100 + 72 + 62 + 56 + 50}{200} = 1.7$

 b. $SQ = \dfrac{\text{population in group}}{SD}$

 SF Gen: $\dfrac{100}{1.7} = 58.8235$ JH: $\dfrac{72}{1.7} = 42.3529$

 Mass: $\dfrac{62}{1.7} = 36.4706$ UCSF: $\dfrac{56}{1.7} = 32.9412$ Sloan: $\dfrac{50}{1.7} = 29.4118$

 c. The initial appropriation summed to 197. One additional seat was allocated to the county with the *largest* fractional part of the standard quota.

	SF Gen	JH	Mass	UCSF	Sloan
SD = 1.7	100	72	62	56	50
Standard Quota	58.82	42.35	36.47	32.94	29.41
Hamilton's Method	58 + 1 = 59	42	36 + 1 = 37	32 + 1 = 33	29

 The bottom row shows each hospital's apportionment of the 200 AIDS specialists using Hamilton's method.

22. a. Use MD = 1.6745 to find $MQ = \dfrac{\text{population in group}}{MD}$.

 SF Gen: $\dfrac{100}{1.6745} = 59.7193$ JH: $\dfrac{72}{1.6745} = 42.9979$

 Mass: $\dfrac{62}{1.6745} = 37.8260$ UCSF: $\dfrac{56}{1.6745} = 33.4428$ Sloan: $\dfrac{50}{1.6745} = 29.8597$

 b. Note that the modified quotas are *rounded down* in the bottom row.

	SF Gen	JH	Mass	UCSF	Sloan
MD = 1.6745	100	72	62	56	50
Modified Quota	59.719	42.998	37.026	33.443	29.860
Jefferson's Method	59	42	37	33	29

 The bottom row shows each hospital's apportionment of the 200 AIDS specialists using Jefferson's method.

23. a. Use MD = 1.7238 to find $MQ = \dfrac{\text{population in group}}{MD}$.

 SF Gen: $\dfrac{100}{1.7238} = 58.0114$ JH: $\dfrac{72}{1.7238} = 41.7682$

 Mass: $\dfrac{62}{1.7238} = 35.9670$ UCSF: $\dfrac{56}{1.7238} = 32.4864$ Sloan: $\dfrac{50}{1.7238} = 29.0057$

 b. Results are then *rounded up* as shown.

	SF Gen	JH	Mass	UCSF	Sloan
MD = 1.7238	100	72	62	56	50
Modified Quota	58.011	41.768	35.967	32.4586	29.006
Adams's Method	59	42	36	33	30

 The bottom row shows each hospital's apportionment of the 200 AIDS specialists using Adam's method.

24. a. Use MD = 1.6983 to find $MQ = \dfrac{\text{population in group}}{MD}$.

$$\text{SF Gen: } \frac{100}{1.6983} = 58.8824 \qquad \text{JH: } \frac{72}{1.6983} = 42.3953$$

$$\text{Mass: } \frac{62}{1.6983} = 36.5071 \qquad \text{UCSF: } \frac{56}{1.6983} = 32.9742 \qquad \text{Sloan: } \frac{50}{1.6983} = 29.4412$$

b.   Round each quota to the nearest integer and apportion to each group its modified rounded quota.

	SF Gen	JH	Mass	UCSF	Sloan
MD = 1.6983	100	72	62	56	50
Modified Quota	58.882	42.395	36.507	32.974	29.441
Adams's Method	59	42	37	33	29

The bottom row shows each hospital's apportionment of the 200 AIDS specialists using Webster's method.

25. a. $\text{Sport A gets } \dfrac{2000}{20,000} \cdot 200,000 = \$20,000 \qquad \text{Sport B gets } \dfrac{4000}{20,000} \cdot 200,000 = \$40,000$

$\text{Sport C gets } \dfrac{6000}{20,000} \cdot 200,000 = \$60,000 \qquad \text{Sport D gets } \dfrac{8000}{20,000} \cdot 200,000 = \$80,000$

b. $\text{SD} = \dfrac{\text{total population}}{\text{total money to be apportioned}} = \dfrac{2000 + 4000 + 6000 + 8000}{200,000} = 0.1$

$\text{SQ} = \dfrac{\text{population in group}}{\text{SD}}$

$\text{Sport A: } \dfrac{2000}{0.1} = 20,000 \qquad \text{Sport B: } \dfrac{4000}{0.1} = 40,000$

$\text{Sport C: } \dfrac{6000}{0.1} = 60,000 \qquad \text{Sport D: } \dfrac{8000}{0.1} = 80,000$

Since the sum of these quotas is equal to 200,000, the divisors would not need to be modified. The apportionment would be the same for Hamilton's, Jefferson's, Adam's, and Webster's methods.

c.   The answers are the same in parts a and b.

26. Answers will vary. The standard divisor is the quotient of the total population and total number to be apportioned (See page 846).

27. Answers will vary. The standard quota is the quotient of the population in the group and the standard divisor (See page 846.)

28. a.   Adam's method rounds the modified quota up.
    b.   Hamilton's and Jefferson's methods rounds the modified quota down.
    c.   Webster's method rounds the modified quota in the usual manner.

Section 14.4 Apportionment Objections

1. a.   For 30 seats: $\text{SD} = \dfrac{18,000}{30} = 600$

   For 31 seats: $\text{SD} = \dfrac{18,000}{31} = 580.6452$

	SQ (30)	Final	SQ (31)	Final
α	5.37	5 + 1 = 6	5.59	5
β	8.33	8	8.6	8 + 1 = 9
δ	16.3	16	16.8	16 + 1 = 17

Yes, the Alabama paradox occurs. α loses one seat (from 6 to 5) when seats are increased from 30 to 31.

b. For 600 seats: SD = $\dfrac{18,000}{60} = 300$ For 61 seats: SD = $\dfrac{18,000}{61} = 295.0820$

	SQ (60)	*Final*	SQ (61)	*Final*
α	10.73	10 + 1 = 11	10.91	10 + 1 = 11
β	16.67	16 + 1 = 17	16.94	16 + 1 = 17
δ	32.6	32	33.14	33

No, the Alabama paradox does not occur.

2. a. For 104 seats: SD = $\dfrac{10,000}{104} = 96.154$ For 105 seats: SD = $\dfrac{10,000}{105} = 95.238$

	SQ (104)	*Final*	SQ (105)	*Final*
A	18.72	18 + 1 = 19	18.9	18 + 1 = 19
B	38.69	38 + 1 = 39	39.06	39
C	24.23	24	24.47	24
D	22.36	22	22.58	22 + 1 = 23

No, the Alabama paradox does not occur.

b. For 114 seats: SD = $\dfrac{10,000}{114} = 87.719$ For 115 seats: SD = $\dfrac{10,000}{115} = 86.957$

	SQ (104)	*Final*	SQ (105)	*Final*
A	20.52	20 + 1 = 21	20.7	20
B	42.41	42	42.78	42 + 1 = 43
C	26.56	26 + 1 = 27	26.80	26 + 1 = 27
D	24.51	24	24.73	24 + 1 = 25

Yes, the Alabama paradox occurs. A loses one seat (from 21 to 20) when seats are increased from 114 to 115.

3. For 71 tickets: SD = $\dfrac{1020}{71} = 14.366$ For 72 tickets: SD = $\dfrac{1020}{72} = 14.167$

	SQ (71)	*Final*	SQ (72)	*Final*
B	28.19	28	28.59	28 + 1 = 29
K	21.3	21	21.6	21 + 1 = 22
W	14.2	14	14.4	14
S	7.31	7 + 1 = 8	7.41	7

Yes, the Alabama paradox does occur. Six Flags Magic Mountain goes from 8 to 7 tickets.

4. For 24 scholarships: SD = $\dfrac{65}{24} = 2.708$ For 25 scholarships: SD = $\dfrac{65}{25} = 2.6$

	SQ (24)	*Final*	SQ (25)	*Final*
W	16.25	16	16.92	16 + 1 = 17
B	1.85	1 + 1 = 2	1.92	1 + 1 = 2
H	1.48	1 + 1 = 2	1.54	1
A	4.43	4	4.62	4 + 1 = 5

Yes, the Alabama paradox does occur.
a. The Hispanic group loses 1 scholarship.
b. The White and Asian groups gain 1 scholarship.
c. The Black group stays the same.

5. a. Most recent year:

$$SD = \frac{740}{11} = 67.2727$$

	SQ	Final
DE	1.64	1
NE	3.72	3 + 1 = 4
KS	5.65	5 + 1 = 6

Delaware will receive $1 million, Nebraska $4 million, and Kansas $6 million.

b. Projected: $SD = \frac{850}{11} = 77.2727$

	SQ	Final
DE	1.58	1 + 1 = 2
NE	3.88	3 + 1 = 4
KS	5.54	5

Delaware will receive $2 million, Nebraska $4 million, and Kansas $5 million.

c. Delaware:

$$\frac{122 - 110}{110} \approx 0.1091 = 10.91\%$$

Kansas:

$$\frac{428 - 380}{380} \approx 0.1263 = 12.63\%$$

Kansas has the higher percent increase of enrollees.

d. Yes, the population paradox occurred. Kansas population increased by 12.63% but contributions decreased from $6 to $5 million, while Delaware, with a smaller 10.91% increase, got an extra million.

6. a. Most recent year:

$$SD = \frac{124,000}{100} = 1240$$

	SQ	Final
A	71.77	71 + 1 = 72
B	10.08	10
C	18.15	18

County A will receive 72 seats, county B 10 seats, and county C 18 seats.

b. 10 Years: $SD = \frac{136,200}{100} = 1362$

	SQ	Final
A	71.22	71
B	10.65	10 + 1 = 11
C	18.14	18

County A will receive 71 seats,

county B 11 seats, and county C 18 seats.

c. No, the population paradox did not occur. Even though A lost one seat and B gained one, the percent growth for A was

$$\frac{97,000 - 89,000}{89,000} \approx 0.0899 = 8.99\% \text{ while}$$

that for B was

$$\frac{145,000 - 125,000}{125,000} = 0.16 = 16\%.$$

(B deserved it more!)

7. a. Now: $SD = \frac{439,000}{13} = 33,769.23077$

	SQ	Final
A	2.64	2
B	3.70	3 + 1 = 4
C	6.66	6 + 1 = 7

County A will receive 2 seats, county B 4 seats, and county C 7 seats.

b. 10 Years: $SD = \frac{489,000}{13} = 37,615.38$

	SQ	Final
A	2.58	2 + 1 = 3
B	3.85	3 + 1 = 4
C	6.57	6

County A will receive 3 seats, county B 4 seats, and county C 6 seats.

c. Yes, the population paradox occurred. Even though C's growth rate was

$$\frac{247,000 - 225,000}{225,000} \approx 0.0978 = 9.78\%$$

and A's was

$$\frac{97,000 - 89,000}{89,000} \approx 0.0899 = 8.99\%, \text{ C}$$

lost a seat and A gained one.

d. County C will be unhappy as they had a greater increase yet lost a seat.

8. a. Now: $SD = \frac{1800}{50} = 36$

	Population	SQ	Final
A	300	8.33	8
B	156	4.33	4
C	346	9.61	9 + 1 = 10
D	408	11.33	11
E	590	16.39	16 + 1 = 17
Total	1800		50

State A will receive 8 seats, state B 4 seats, state C 10 seats, state D 11 seats, and state E 17 seats.

b.   New: SD = $\dfrac{1818}{50}$ = 36.36

	Population	SQ	*Final*
A	300	8.25	8
B	156	4.29	4 + 1 = 5
C	362	9.96	9 + 1 = 10
D	408	11.22	11
E	592	16.28	16
Total	**1818**		**50**

State A will receive 8 seats, state B 5 seats, state C 10 seats, state D 11 seats, and state E 17 seats.

c.   Yes, the population paradox occurred. Even though state B did not grow at all (0%), it gained one seat. On the other hand, E grew at a modest

$\dfrac{592-590}{590} \approx 0.0034 = 0.34\%$ rate but

lost one seat.

d.   State E will be unhappy as they had a greater increase yet lost a seat.

9.   a.   SD = $\dfrac{558}{41}$ = 13.6098

	Number	SQ	*Final*
P	402	29.54	29 + 1 = 30
S	156	11.46	11
Total	**558**		**41**

Division P will receive 30 managers and S will receive 11.

b.   SD = $\dfrac{672}{49}$ = 13.714

	Number	SQ	*Final*
P	402	29.31	29
S	156	11.38	11 + 1 = 12
A	114	8.31	8
Total	**672**		**49**

Yes, the new-states paradox occurred. The new apportionment is 29 for division P, 12 for S and 8 for A, so P lost one manager and S gained one.

10. a.   SD = $\dfrac{372}{30}$ = 12.4

	Number	SQ	*Final*
A	268	21.61	21 + 1 = 22
B	104	8.39	8
Total	**372**		**30**

State A will receive 22 seats and B 8 seats.

b.   SD = $\dfrac{448}{36}$ = 12.444

	Number	SQ	*Final*
A	268	21.54	21 + 1 = 22
B	104	8.36	8
C	76	6.11	6
Total	**448**		**36**

No, the new-states paradox does not occur. State A and B still get 22 and 8 seats, respectively.

11. a.   SD = $\dfrac{4990}{100}$ = 49.9

	Number	SQ	*Final*
A	4470	89.58	89 + 1 = 90
B	520	10.42	10
Total	**4990**		**100**

State A will receive 90 seats and B 10 seats.

b.   SD = $\dfrac{5253}{106}$ = 49.5567

	Number	SQ	*Final*
A	4470	90.20	90
B	520	10.49	10 + 1 = 11
C	263	5.31	5
Total	**5253**		**106**

Yes, the new-states paradox does occur. The new apportionment is 90 for A and 11 for B, so B gained one seat.

12. Answers will vary. The Alabama paradox occurs when an increase in the total number of items to be apportioned results in a loss of items for a group (see page 858).

13. Answers will vary. The population paradox occurs when the population of group A is increasing faster than the population of group B, yet A loses items to group B (see page 860).

14. Answers will vary. The new-states paradox occurs when the addition of a new group changes the apportionment of another group (see page 861).

Chapter 14 Practice Test

1.   a.   No. It takes over $\dfrac{10+8+7+5}{2}$ = 15, or 16

votes, for a majority.

b.   D with 7 + 5 = 12 votes

c. A with 10 votes
d. B

2. D and A have the most first place votes so they have a runoff.
8 + 7 + 5 = 20 people prefer D over A
10 people prefer A over D
D wins the runoff 20 to 10.

3. Give 3 points for first place, 2 for second 1 for third, none for last.

Points	Number of Voters			
	10	8	7	5
3	A	C	D	D
2	C	D	C	B
1	B	B	B	C
0	D	A	A	A

Here are the results:
A($3 \cdot 10 = 30$ pts)
B($1 \cdot 10 + 1 \cdot 8 + 1 \cdot 7 + 2 \cdot 5 = 35$ pts)
C($2 \cdot 10 + 3 \cdot 8 + 2 \cdot 7 + 1 \cdot 5 = 63$ pts)
D($2 \cdot 8 + 3 \cdot 7 + 3 \cdot 5 = 52$ pts)
C wins with 63 points.

4. Eliminate B first.

Number of Voters			
10	8	7	5
A	C	D	D
C	D	C	
			C
D	A	A	A

Second election. A: 10, C: 8, D: 7 + 5 = 12
Eliminate C.

Number of Voters			
10	8	7	5
A		D	D
		D	
D	A	A	A

Third election: A(10) D(8 + 7 + 5 = 20)
D is the winner.

5. a. A(5 + 9 = 14) B(3) A gets 1 point.
   b. A(5) C(3 + 9 = 12) C gets 1 point.
   c. B(5 + 3 = 8) C(9) C gets 1 point.
   d. A(1 point) C(2 points), C is the winner.

6. a. Adams has 5 votes, Barnes 3 votes, and Collins 2 votes, so Adams wins.
   b. Barnes has 3 votes and Collins 2 votes, so Barnes wins.

7. a. B with 36 votes wins using the plurality method. Yes, since 36 is more than
$$\frac{36 + 16 + 12}{2} = 32 .$$

   b. Give 2 points for first place, 1 for second none for last.

Points	Number of Voters		
	36	16	12
2	B	A	A
1	A	B	C
0	C	C	B

Here are the results:
A($1 \cdot 36 + 2 \cdot 16 + 2 \cdot 12 = 92$ pts)
B($2 \cdot 36 + 1 \cdot 16 = 88$ pts)
C($1 \cdot 12 = 12$ pts)
A is the winner. No, this method does not satisfy the majority criterion as B has the majority but A wins the Borda count.

   c. Eliminate C.

Number of Voters		
36	16	12
B	A	A
A	B	
		B

B(36) A(16 + 12 = 28)
B is the winner. Yes, the majority criterion is satisfied.

   d. We have to compare A and B, A and C, and B and C.
A(16 + 12 = 28) B(36)   B gets 1 point.
A(36 + 16 + 12 = 64) C(0)
                    A gets 1 point.
B(36 + 16 = 52) C(12) B gets 1 point.
A(1 point) B(2 points), B is the winner. Yes, the majority criterion is satisfied.

8. a. 74 voters prefer T over V.
75 voters prefer P over V.
99 voters prefer V over C.
75 voters prefer P over T.
144 voters prefer T over C.
119 voters prefer P over C.
P is the winner. Yes, the head-to-head criterion is satisfied.

   b. C with 45 votes wins using the plurality method. No, it does not satisfy the head to-head criterion.

c. Give 3 points for first place, 2 for second 1 for third, none for last.

	Number of Voters					
Points	15	25	29	30	45	
3	V	V	T	P	C	
2	T	T	V	V	P	
1	P	C	P	T	T	
0	C	P	C	C	V	

Here are the results:

$V(3 \cdot 15 + 3 \cdot 25 + 2 \cdot 29 + 2 \cdot 30 = 238 \text{ pts})$

$T(2 \cdot 15 + 2 \cdot 25 + 3 \cdot 29 + 1 \cdot 30 + 1 \cdot 45$
$\qquad = 242 \text{ pts})$

$P(1 \cdot 15 + 1 \cdot 29 + 3 \cdot 30 + 2 \cdot 45 = 224 \text{ pts})$

$C(1 \cdot 25 + 3 \cdot 45 = 160 \text{ pts})$

T is the winner using the Borda method. No, it does not satisfy the head-to-head criterion.

d. Eliminate P.

	Number of Voters				
15	25	29	30	45	
V	V	T		C	
T	T	V	V		
	C		T	T	
C		C	C	V	

Second election.

V(15 + 25 + 30 = 70)
T(29)
C(45)
Eliminate T.

	Number of Voters				
15	25	29	30	45	
V	V			C	
		V	V		
C					
C		C	C	V	

Third election.

V(15 + 25 + 29 + 30 = 99) C(45)
V wins using the plurality with elimination method. No, it does not satisfy the head-to-head criterion.

12. $SD = \dfrac{40,500}{162,000,000} = 0.00025$

Standard Quotas (in millions) for:

A: $\dfrac{15,000}{0.00025} = 60$ B: $\dfrac{8500}{0.00025} = 34$ C: $\dfrac{6500}{0.00025} = 26$

D: $\dfrac{6000}{0.00025} = 24$ E: $\dfrac{4500}{0.00025} = 18$

Note that the total is $162 million.

e. We have to compare V and T, V and P, V and C, T and P, T and C, and P and C.

1) V(15 + 25 + 30 = 70)
   T(29 + 45 = 74)   T gets 1 point.
2) V(15 + 25 + 29 = 69)
   P(30 + 45 = 75)   P gets 1 point.
3) V(15 + 25 + 29 + 30 = 99)
   C(45)   V gets 1 point.
4) T(15 + 25 + 29 = 69)
   P(30 + 45 = 75)   P gets 1 point.
5) T(15 + 25 + 29 + 30 = 99)
   C(45)   T gets 1 point.
6) P(15 + 29 + 30 = 74)
   C(25 + 45 = 70)   P gets 1 point.

T(2 points) V(1 point) P(3 points)
P wins using pairwise comparison. Yes, it does satisfy the head-to-head criterion.

9. a. Yes. C with 56 votes has the majority (more than $\dfrac{56 + 24 + 20}{2} = 50$) and wins under plurality.

   b. Yes. 56 voters prefer C over A and over B. C has the majority and wins head-to-head against all other candidates.

10. a. Yes. C will still win the second election under plurality.

    b. Yes. C will still win the second election under plurality when either A or B drops out. Note that C starts with a majority, not simply plurality, so cannot lose the majority.

11. Arrow's Impossibility Theorem states that there is no voting method that will always simultaneously satisfy each of the four fairness criteria.

13. $SD = \dfrac{180}{100} = 1.8$

Department	Faculty	SQ	RD	Actual Number
Mathematics	30	30/1.8 ≈ 16.67	16	16 + 1 = **17**
English	60	60/1.8 ≈ 33.33	33	33
Language	24	24/1.8 ≈ 13.33	13	13
Art	16	16/1.8 ≈ 8.89	8	8 + 1 = **9**
Chemistry	50	50/1.8 ≈ 27.78	27	27 + 1 = **28**
Total	**180**	**100**	**97**	**100**

14. Use 1.95 as the modified divisor then round down.

Department	Faculty	MQ	Actual
Mathematics	30	30/1.95 ≈ 15.38	15
English	**60**	60/1.95 ≈ 30.77	30
Language	24	24/1.95 ≈ 12.31	12
Art	16	16/1.95 ≈ 8.21	8
Chemistry	50	50/1.95 ≈ 25.64	25
Total	**180**	**90**	**90**

15. MD = 49,800;

$MQ = \dfrac{34,730}{49,800} \approx 0.6974$, or 1

16. Use 2.05 as the modified divisor, then round up.

Department	Faculty	MQ	Actual
Mathematics	30	30/2.05 ≈ 14.63	15
English	60	60/2.05 ≈ 29.27	30
Language	24	24/2.05 ≈ 11.71	12
Art	16	16/2.05 ≈ 7.80	8
Chemistry	50	50/2.05 ≈ 24.39	25
Total	**180**	**90**	**90**

17.

State	Population	SQ	RD	Extra	Final
A	50,4000	$\dfrac{50,400}{1960.78} \approx 25.70$	25	1	26
B	46,600	$\dfrac{46,600}{1960.78} \approx 23.77$	23	1	24
C	3000	$\dfrac{3000}{1960.78} \approx 1.53$	1	0	1
Total	**100,000**		**49**		**51**

The Alabama paradox occurs because even though the number of seats was increased from 50 to 51, state C lost one seat, from 2 to 1.

18. a.

Positions	Number	New SQ	Positions
10	484	9.6338	**9**
19	990	19.7054	**20**
71	3550	70.6608	**71**

b.   No. Even though Math's growth rate

was $\dfrac{484-476}{476} \approx 0.01681 = 1.681\%$

and English's was

$\dfrac{990-975}{975} \approx 0.01538 = 1.538\%$, Math

lost a seat and English gained one.

c.   Yes, this apportionment is an example
of the population paradox. Math lost
one position and English gained one
even though math was growing at a
faster rate, 8/476 = 1.681%, than
English 15/975 = 1.538%.

19. a. $SD = \dfrac{1116}{41} = 27.2195$

	Number	SQ	Final
A	804	29.54	29 + 1 = 30
B	312	11.46	11
Total	**1116**		**41**

State A will receive 30 seats and B will
receive 11.

b. $SD = \dfrac{1344}{49} = 27.4286$

	Number	SQ	Final
A	804	29.31	29
B	312	11.37	11 + **1** = **12**
C	228	8.31	8
Total	**1344**		**49**

Yes, the new-states paradox occurred.
The addition of the new state C caused
A to lose 1 seat (from 30 to 29) and B
to gain 1 (from 11 to 12).

20.   There is no apportionment method that
satisfies the quota rule and avoids all
paradoxes.

Chapter 15 Graph Theory

Section 15.1 Introduction to Graph Theory

1. The degree of a vertex is found by counting the number of edges that meet it. So, the degrees of the vertices A, B, C, D and E are 1, 1, 1, 0 and 3, respectively.

2. The degree of a vertex is found by counting the number of edges that meet it. So, the degrees of the vertices A, B, C, D, E and F are 3, 3, 1, 2, 4 and 1, respectively.

3. The degree of a vertex is found by counting the number of edges that meet it. So, the degrees of vertices A, B, C and D are 5, 3, 4 and 6, respectively.

4. The degree of a vertex is found by counting the number of edges that meet it. So, the degrees of each vertex is 7.

5. Since C is not one of the vertices listed, this does not determine a subgraph.

6. Since both vertices of the edges a, b, and e are included, this defines a subgraph.

7. Since both vertices of edge g are included, this defines a subgraph.

8. Edge c needs two endpoints, since F is not listed, this does not determine a subgraph.

9. By tracing along the edges listed (in order) you can see that $[a, b, c]$ is a path from A to D.

10. Getting from edge d to edge b requires a "jump," so $[a, k, d, b]$ is not a path.

11. By tracing along the edges listed (in order) you can see that $[j, d, k, a]$ is a circuit based at A.

12. Getting from edge g at H to edge f at G requires a repeat of edge g, which is not given so $[a, b, i, g, f]$ is not a path.

13. By tracing along the edges listed (in order) you can see that $[h, g]$ is a path from A to G.

14. By tracing along the edges listed (in order) you can see that $[i, c, d, k, a, j, c, i]$ is a circuit based at G.

15. Getting from edge h to edge f requires a "jump," so $[h, f, g]$ is not a path.

16. By tracing along the edges listed (in order) you can see that $[f, i, b, k, e]$ is a circuit based at F.

17. The graph consists of "one piece," so it is connected.

18. The graph consists of "two pieces," so it is disconnected.

19. The graph consists of "two pieces," so it is disconnected.

20. The graph consists of "one piece," so it is connected.

21. The graph is complete. Here's an easy way to see this: if you compare this graph with K_4 in figure 15.9 you can see that they are "the same" graph drawn in two different ways.

22. This is K_2 so it is complete (see Figure 15.9).Complete.

23. There is a pair of vertices that is not joined by any edge, so this graph is not complete.

24. There is a pair of vertices that is not joined by any edge, so this graph is not complete.

25. This is K_3 so it is complete (see Figure 15.9).

26. More than one edge is joining two vertices, so this graph is not complete.

27. Since no pair of vertices is joined by more than one edge, this graph is simple.

28. Since two pairs of vertices are joined by more than one edge, this graph is not simple.

29. Since no pair of vertices is joined by more than one edge, this graph is simple.

30. Since one pair of vertices is joined by more than one edge, this graph is not simple.

31. Answers may vary. A connected graph consists of "one piece."

32. Answers may vary. A circuit is a path with one extra condition: the starting and ending point is the same.

33. Represent each computer as a vertex and the connecting wires as edges as shown in the following diagram.

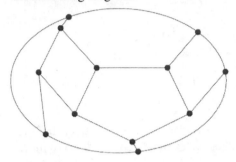

Section 15.2 Euler Paths and Euler Circuits

1. It is easy to see that [a, b, c, d, e] is a path from D to B. Since each edge is traversed once, we actually have an Euler path from D to B.

2. Neither (this sequence of edges does not even represent a path).

3. It is easy to see that [a, b, c, d, e] is a circuit based at A. Since each edge is traversed once, we actually have an Euler circuit based at A.

4. Neither (this sequence of edges represents a circuit based at A, but is not an Euler circuit because edge f is not used).

5. Every vertex in this graph has even degree. According to the traversability rules there is an Euler circuit based at any of the vertices.

6. The graph has 2 vertices of odd degree, thus according to the traversability rules there is an Euler path from either odd vertex to the other.

7. Every vertex in this graph has even degree. According to the traversability rules there is an Euler circuit based at any of the vertices.

8. The graph has 4 vertices of odd degree, so according to the traversability rules it is not traversable.

9. Every vertex in this graph has even degree. According to the traversability rules there is an Euler circuit based at any of the vertices.

10. The graph has 6 vertices of odd degree, so according to the traversability rules it is not traversable.

11. Every vertex in this graph has even degree. According to the traversability rules there is an Euler circuit based at any of the vertices. There are many correct answers (for example, [a, b, c, d, e, f, g, i, j, h]).

12. Every vertex in this graph has even degree. According to the traversability rules there is an Euler circuit based at any of the vertices. There are many correct solutions; for example, [a, b, c, d, e, f, g] is an Euler circuit.

13. Every vertex in this graph has even degree. According to the traversability rules there is an Euler circuit based at any of the vertices. There are many correct answers (for example, [a, b, e, f, h, g, d, c]).

14. Every vertex in this graph has even degree. According to the traversability rules there is an Euler circuit based at any of the vertices. There are many correct solutions: for example, [a, b, c, f, e, d, g, l, k, m, h, i, j] is an Euler circuit.

15. Every vertex in this graph has even degree. According to the traversability rules there is an Euler circuit based at any of the vertices. There are many correct answers (for example, [a, b, c, d, e, f, g, h, i]).

16. Every vertex in this graph has even degree. According to the traversability rules there is an Euler circuit based at any of the vertices. There are many correct solutions: for example, [a, b, c, d, e, f, g, h, i, j, k, l, m, n, o] is an Euler circuit.

17. Every vertex in this graph has even degree. According to the traversability rules there is an Euler circuit based at any of the vertices. There are many correct answers (for example, [a, b, c, d, e, f, g, h, i, j, k, l]).

18. Every vertex in this graph has even degree. According to the traversability rules there is an Euler circuit based at any of the vertices. There are many correct solutions; for example, [a, b, d, c, e, f] is an Euler circuit.

19. We represent the streets as labeled edges and the intersections as vertices. The result is shown.

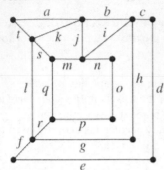

There are many correct solutions that start at either vertex of odd degree. For example, a possible Euler path is: [*s, t, a, b, c, d, e, f, g, h, i, j, k, l, r, p, o, n, m, q*].

20. We represent the streets as labeled edges and the intersections as vertices. The result is as follows.

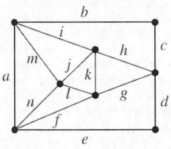

There are many correct solutions and you can start at any vertex. For example, [*a, b, c, d, e, f, g, h, i, m, j, k, l, n*] is an Euler circuit.

21. We represent the streets as labeled edges and the intersections as vertices. The result is shown.

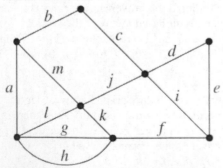

There are many correct solutions that start at either vertex of odd degree. For example,

[*a, l, m, b, c, j, k, g, h, f, i ,d, e*] is a possible Euler path.

22. We represent the streets as labeled edges and the intersections as vertices. The result is shown.

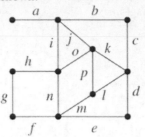

There are many correct solutions that start at either vertex of odd degree. For example, [*a, b, c, d, e, f, g, h, i, j, k, l, m, n, o, p*] is a possible Euler path.

23. Answers may vary.
    a. A graph is traversable if it has an Euler path.
    b. An Euler circuit is circuit that traverses each edge exactly one time.
    c. An Euler path is a path that traverses each edge exactly one time.
    d. If you remove an edge from a graph and get a disconnected graph, then that edge is a bridge.

24. Answers may vary. The problem asks whether it is possible to travel over each of the seven bridges of Königsberg once (and only once) and arrive back at the original starting point.

25. There are 3 regions, 5 edges and 4 vertices. Thus, $X(G) = 3 - 5 + 4 = 2$.

26. There are 4 regions, 6 edges and 4 vertices. Thus, $X(G) = 4 - 6 + 4 = 2$

27. There are 9 regions, 12 edges and 5 vertices. Thus, $X(G) = 9 - 12 + 5 = 2$.

28. There are 5 regions, 9 edges and 6 vertices. Thus, $X(G) = 5 - 9 + 6 = 2$.

29. There are 6 regions, 8 edges and 4 vertices. Thus, $X(G) = 6 - 8 + 4 = 2$.
    Possible redraw:

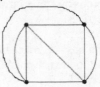

30. $X(G) = 2$ for every graph.

Section 15.3 Hamilton Paths and Hamilton Circuits

1. By tracing along the edges (in order) we see that we meet each vertex exactly once before returning to our starting point. In other words, we complete a Hamilton circuit.

2. Neither (the sequence does not even represent a path).

3. When tracing the sequence of edges [a, b, c, d, e] we land on vertex C twice: it's neither a Hamilton circuit nor a Hamilton path.

4. By tracing along the edges (in order) we see that we meet each vertex exactly once before returning to our starting point. In other words, we complete a Hamilton circuit.

5. Add the weights. The length of the path is $8 + 3 + 2 + 4 = 17$.

6. Add the weights. The length of the circuit is
$1 + 14 + 6 + 7 + 2 = 30$.

7. Add the weights. The length of the path is $5 + 5 + 7 + 4 = 21$.

8. Add the weights. The length of the path is $3 + 4 + 2 + 3 = 12$.

9. Recall that the graph K_4 has $\dfrac{(4-1)!}{2} = 3$
distinct Hamilton circuits based at vertex A. Their lengths are $5 + 7 + 5 + 5 = 22$, $5 + 3 + 5 + 4 = 17$, and $5 + 3 + 7 + 4 = 19$.

10. Recall that the graph K_4 has $\dfrac{(4-1)!}{2} = 3$
distinct Hamilton circuits based at vertex B. Their lengths are: $7 + 5 + 5 + 5 = 22$, $7 + 4 + 5 + 3 = 19$, and $5 + 4 + 5 + 3 = 17$.

11. The nearest neighbor method determines the circuit with length $2 + 2 + 4 + 6 = 14$.

12. There is more than one answer. One possibility is the circuit with length $2 + 6 + 5 + 3 = 16$.

13. There is more than one answer. One possibility is the circuit with length $2 + 1 + 1 + 5 + 2 = 11$.

14. The nearest neighbor method determines the circuit with length $1 + 1 + 1 + 5 + 2 = 10$.

15. There is more than one answer. One possibility is the circuit with length $2 + 1 + 1 + 1 + 9 + 2 = 16$.

16. There is more than one answer. One possibility is the circuit with length $3 + 5 + 3 + 1 + 2 + 5 = 19$.

17. Using the Nearest-Neighbor Method we get $8 + 12 + 19 + 11 = 50$ miles.

18. The most efficient delivery route (applying the Nearest-Neighbor Method) has length $21 + 17 + 38 + 29 = 105$ miles.

19. The most efficient delivery route (applying the Nearest-Neighbor Method) has length $15 + 13 + 17 + 25 = 70$ miles.

20. The most efficient delivery route (applying the Nearest-Neighbor Method) has length $23.5 + 18.6 + 13.9 + 29.1 = 85.1$ miles.

21. Answers may vary. How can one travel between a number of cities, visiting each destination once before returning to the starting point, in the most cost-efficient manner?

22. Answers may vary. A Hamilton path is a path that meets every vertex of the graph exactly one time. A Hamilton circuit is circuit that meets every vertex of the graph exactly one time and then directly returns to the starting (base) vertex.

23. Answers may vary. From the starting point, choose to travel along the edge of least weight -- if there is more than one, choose any of them at random. When you have arrived at a new vertex choose to travel along the edge of least weight (as long as you don't return to a vertex you have already visited). Repeat this process until all vertices have been visited, then return to the starting point along the edge of least weight (as usual, if there is more than

one of least weight, travel along any of them at random).

24. Answers may vary. An Euler circuit traverses every edge exactly one time while a Hamilton circuit meets every vertex exactly one time before returning to the base. For example, if you have two vertices joined by four edges, an Euler circuit must use all four edges, while a Hamilton circuit must use exactly two.

25. There are numerous answers, depending on your choice of starting point.

26. There are numerous answers, depending on your choice of starting point.

27. There are numerous answers, depending on your choice of starting point.

28. There are numerous answers, depending on your choice of starting point.

Section 15.4 Trees

1. This graph is a connected graph with no simple circuits, so it is a tree.

2. This graph is a connected graph with no simple circuits, so it is a tree.

3. This graph is not a tree. Here's an easy way to see this: Since there is more than one simple path from any pair of vertices, Theorem 15.1 is not satisfied – the graph can't be a tree!

4. This graph is not a tree. Since there is more than one simple path from a pair of vertices, Theorem 15.1 is not satisfied.

5. There are many correct answers. One possibility is {a, b, c}.

6. There are many correct answers. One possibility is {a, b, d, i, j}.

7. There are many correct answers. One possibility is {a, b, c, d}.

8. This graph is already a tree, so there is only one correct solution: {a, b, c, d}.

9. There are many correct answers. One possibility is {a, b, c, d}.

10. There are many correct answers. One possibility is {a, b, c, j}.

11. The graph below indicates a minimal spanning tree (there is more than one).

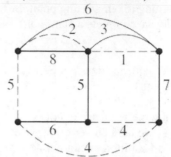

This spanning tree was found using Kruskal's algorithm. Its weight is $1 + 2 + 4 + 4 + 5 = 16$.

12. Applying Kruskal's algorithm provides the solution indicated in the graph.

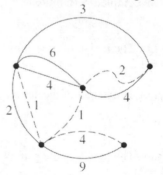

Its weight is $1 + 1 + 2 + 4 = 8$.

13. Applying Kruskal's algorithm provides the solution indicated.

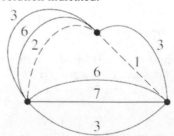

Its weight is $1 + 2 = 3$.

14. The graph below indicates a minimal spanning tree (there is more than one).

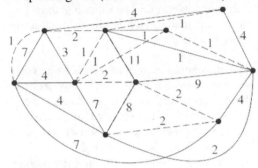

Its weight is
1 + 1 + 1 + 1 + 1 + 2 + 2 + 2 + 2 = 13.

15. Applying Kruskal's algorithm provides the solution indicated.

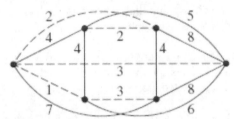

Its weight is 1 + 2 + 2 + 3 + 3 = 11.

16. Applying Kruskal's algorithm provides the solution indicated below.

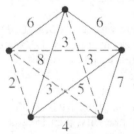

Its weight is   2 + 3 + 3 + 3 = 11.

17. Applying Kruskal's algorithm, we find that the most economical way to link all cities is a network of length 3.8 + 4.9 + 5.4 + 7.8 = 21.9 representing a cost of $21.9 million.

18. Applying Kruskal's algorithm, we find that the most economical way to link all cities is a network of length 5 + 7 + 8 + 10 + 14 = 44 representing a cost of $44 million.

19. Applying Kruskal's algorithm, we find that the most economical way to create an irrigation system has cost

126 + 132 + 135 + 141 = $534.

20. Applying Kruskal's algorithm, we find that the most economical way to create an irrigation system has cost 57 + 89 + 96 + 107 = $349.

21. Answers may vary. A spanning tree is a subgraph that is connected, has no simple circuits and contains all of the vertices of the original graph.

22. Answers may vary. See Kruskal's Algorithm on page 900.

23. Answers may vary. For each pair of vertices in a tree, there is exactly one simple path between them.

24. Answers may vary. A tree is a connected forest.

25. Neither Euler circuits nor paths would be appropriate here because, both require that every edge be used. For this problem, we are not concerned about edges and, in fact, if we can leave out an edge and still connect all the cities, it will be cheaper and thus, more desirable. The tree shown is a possible answer! Is it the cheapest way? Can you find a better way?

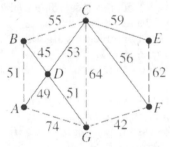

This tree has a cost of 45 + 49 + 51 + 53 + 56 + 59 = 313 million. Using Kruskal's, you can find a tree with value 42 + 45 + 49 + 51 + 53 + 59 = 299 million.

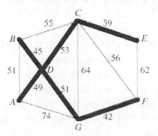

Chapter 15 Practice Test

1. To find the degree of a vertex you count the number of edges that meet it. So, the degrees of vertices *A*, *B*, *C*, *D*, *E*, *F* and *G* are 4, 4, 3, 4, 1, 2 and 0, respectively.

2. As before, count the edges: the degrees of vertices *A*, *B*, *C*, *D* and *E* are 5, 2, 4, 2 and 1, respectively.

3. If you trace along the edges *a*, *b*, *c* and *d* (in order) you find that we have a path from *A* to *B*.

4. If you trace along the edges *g*, *a*, *e* and *d* (in order) you find that we have a circuit based at *B*.

5. If you trace along the edges *b*, *c* and *f* (in order) you get a path from *B* to *E*.

6. Tracing along the edges *g* and then *d* gives us a path from *A* to *D*. BUT, there is no way to get from vertex *D* to edge *b* without lifting your pencil so this sequence of edges does not represent a path (or circuit).

7. Vertices *A* and *C* have odd degree and the others have even degree. According to the Traversability Rules, this graph has an Euler path. Applying Fleury's algorithm we find that [*f, e, d, c, h, g, a, b*] is an Euler path from *A* to *C* (there are others).

8. Every vertex has even degree so there is an Euler circuit (by the Traversability Rules). One possibility is [*a, b, c, d, e, f*] (there are others).

9. This graph has four vertices of odd degree (*A*, *D*, *E*, and *F*) so there is no Euler circuit (or path) by the Traversability Rules.

10. Vertices *A* and *D* have odd degree, while all other vertices have even degree. According to the Traversability Rules, this graph has an Euler path. Applying Fleury's algorithm we find that [*a, b, g, f, e, c, d*] is an Euler path from *A* to *D* (there are others).

11. By representing the streets that the mail carrier must cover by edges and each intersection as a vertex, we see that there are more than two vertices with odd degree. Thus, it is impossible to find an Euler a path or circuit; the mail carrier will have to retrace his steps at some point.

12. By representing each of the roads by an edge and each intersection as a vertex, we see that there are two vertices with odd degree (the intersection of Fair Oaks Blvd. at San Juan Ave. and the intersection of Sunset Ave. at San Juan Ave). Thus, according to the Traversability Rules there is an Euler path in the graph. It is possible for the employee to drive along each road once and only once – he must start at one of the intersections above and end at the other.

13. Edges *c* and *e* are bridges as a bridge is an edge in a graph that, when removed, creates a disconnected graph.

14. Edges *e* and *g* are bridges as a bridge is an edge in a graph that, when removed, creates a disconnected graph.

15. We start at vertex *A* and proceed to *C*, then *B*, then to *D* and finally back to *A* (our choices are determined by the Nearest-Neighbor Method). The length of this Hamilton circuit is 2 + 3 + 6 + 5 = 16.

16. In order we visit the vertices *A*, *B*, *E*, *C*, *D* and then back to *A* (as determined by the Nearest-Neighbor Method). The length of this Hamilton circuit is 1 + 3 + 3 + 7 + 9 = 23.

17. Using the Nearest-Neighbor Method, the pilot should fly to Salt Lake City, then Helena, on to Olympia and then return to Sacramento. The length of this flight is 650 + 483 + 629 + 693 = 2455 miles.

18. Using Kruskal's algorithm, the highway should consist of the three roads extending from Guadalajara. The total cost will be 8 + 12 + 13 = $33 million.

19. The three edges extending from vertex *A* determine the minimal spanning tree.

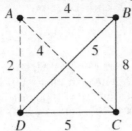

20. The edges with weights 1, 2, 3 and 4 determine the minimal spanning tree.

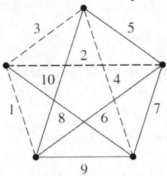

Appendix The Metric System

Section A.1 Metric Units of Measurement

1. a. 1000 (kilo means thousand)
    b. 0.001 (milli means one-thousandth)
    c. 100 (centi means one-hundredth)
    d. 1000 (kilo means thousand)

2. a. Liters
    b. Kilograms
    c. Millimeters
    d. Centimeters
    e. Grams

3. The height of a professional basketball play is (c) 200 cm.

4. The dimensions of the living room in an ordinary home are (a) 4 m by 5 m.

5. The diamter of an aspirin tablet is (a) 1 cm.

6. The length of the 100-yd dash is about (c) 100 m.

7. The weight of an average human male is (a) 70 kg.

8. The length of an ordinary lead pencil is (b) 19 cm.

9. a. 8 km = 8000 m (1 km = 1000 m)
    b. 4 m = 400 cm (1 m = 100 cm)
    c. 3409 cm = 34.09 m (1 cm = 0.01 m)
    d. 49.4 mm = 4.94 cm (1 mm = 0.1 cm)

10. a. 8413 mm = 8.413 m (1 mm = 0.001 m)
    b. 7.3 m = 7300 mm (1 m = 1000 mm)
    c. 319 mm = 0.319 m (1 mm = 0.001 m)
    d. 758 m = 0.758 km (1 m = 0.001 km)

11. The bed is 2.10 m. (1 cm = 0.01 m)

12. The diameter of a vitamin C tablet is 0.6 cm. (1 mm = 0.1 cm)

13. The race is 1500 m. (1 km = 1000 m)

14. The depth of a swimming pool is 160 cm. (1 m = 100 cm)

15. a. $300(52.5) = 15,750 \, \text{cm} = 157.5 \, \text{m}$
    b. $50(52.5) = 2625 \, \text{cm} = 26.25 \, \text{m}$
    c. $30(52.5) = 1575 \, \text{cm} = 15.75 \, \text{m}$

16. a. 6.3 kl = 6300 liters (1 kl = 1000 l)
    b. 72.3 ml = 0.0723 liters (1 ml = 0.001 l)
    c. 1.3 liters = 1300 ml (1 l = 1000 ml)
    d. 3479 ml = 0.003479 kl (1 ml = 0.000001 kl)

17. A meter is 100 cm $= 10 \cdot 10$ cm , so a cubic meter $= (10 \cdot 10)^3 \, \text{cm}^3 = 1000 (10^3 \, \text{cm}^3) = 1000$ liters. Note: $10^3 \, \text{cm}^3 = 1000 \, \text{cm}^3 = 1$ liter.

18. Less; 60 ml = 0.06 liter

19. 1000 ml = 1 liter, so 1 liter of sea water weights $1 \, 1 \cdot 3.5 \, \text{g/l} = 3.5 \, \text{g}$.

20. 1 liter = 1000 ml, so 1000 ml of hydrogen would weigh $1000 \, \text{ml} \cdot 0.0001 \, \text{g/ml} = 0.1 \, \text{g}$.

21. The volume is $50 \cdot 20 \cdot 10 = 10,000 \, \text{cm}^3 = 10$ liters.

22. 20 gal of gas is 20 gal $\cdot$ 3.8 l/gal = 76 liters.

23. Since 5/20 = 1/4, 1/4 of a liter or 250 ml are needed.

24. a. 10 kl = 10,000 liters
    b. $10,000 \, \text{l} \cdot \dfrac{26.4 \, \text{gal}}{100 \, \text{l}} = 2640 \, \text{gal}$

25. a. 14 kg = 14,000 g (1 kg = 1000 g)
    b. 4.8 kg = 4800 g (1 kg = 1000 g)
    c. 2.8 g = 0.0028 kg (1 g = 0.001 kg)
    d. 3.9 g = 3900 mg (1 g = 1000 mg)

26. a. 37 mg = 0.037 g (1 mg = 0.001 g)
    b. 49 mg = 0.000049 g (1 mg = 0.000001 g)
    c. 41 g = 0.041 kg (1 g = 0.001 kg)
    d. 3978g = 3.978 kg (1 g = 0.001 kg)

27. 1 liter = 1000 cm^3, so 1 liter weighs 1000 g or 1 kg.

28. The amount of milk in a quart carton is about (b) 1 liter.

29. The water needed to fill a 1-liter bottle weights (b) 1 kg. (See problem 27.)

30. The weight of a newborn baby is about
    (c) 3.5 kg.

31. $59°F = \dfrac{5}{9}(59-32) = \dfrac{5}{9}\cdot 27 = 15°C$

32. $113°F = \dfrac{5}{9}(113-32) = \dfrac{5}{9}\cdot 81 = 45°C$

33. $86°F = \dfrac{5}{9}(86-32) = \dfrac{5}{9}\cdot 54 = 30°C$

34. $-4°F = \dfrac{5}{9}(-4-32) = \dfrac{5}{9}\cdot(-36) = -20°C$

35. $-22°F = \dfrac{5}{9}(-22-32) = \dfrac{5}{9}\cdot(-54) = -30°C$

36. $0°F = \dfrac{5}{9}(0-32) = \dfrac{5}{9}\cdot(-32) \approx -18°C$

37. $10°C = \dfrac{9}{5}\cdot 10 + 32 = 18 + 32 = 50°F$

38. $25°C = \dfrac{9}{5}\cdot 25 + 32 = 45 + 32 = 77°F$

39. $-10°C = \dfrac{9}{5}\cdot(-10) + 32 = -18 + 32 = 14°F$

40. $-15°C = \dfrac{9}{5}\cdot(-15) + 32 = -27 + 32 = 5°F 5$

41. $500°F = \dfrac{5}{9}(500-32) = \dfrac{5}{9}\cdot 468 = 260°C$

42. $131°F = \dfrac{5}{9}(131-32) = \dfrac{5}{9}\cdot 99 = 55°C$

43. $41°C = \dfrac{9}{5}\cdot 41 + 32 = 73.8 + 32 = 105.8°F$

44. $70°C = \dfrac{9}{5}\cdot 70 + 32 = 126 + 32 = 158°F$

45. $98.6°F = \dfrac{5}{9}(98.6-32) = \dfrac{5}{9}\cdot 66.6 = 37°C$

46. $3410°C = \dfrac{9}{5}\cdot 3410 + 32 = 6138 + 32 = 6170°F$

47. a. $41°F = \dfrac{5}{9}(41-32) = \dfrac{5}{9}\cdot 9 = 5°C$

    b. $212°F = \dfrac{5}{9}(212-32) = \dfrac{5}{9}\cdot 180 = 100°C$

48. $-58°F = \dfrac{5}{9}(-58-32) = \dfrac{5}{9}\cdot(-90) = -50°C$

49. $-78°C = \dfrac{9}{5}\cdot(-78) + 32$
    $= -140.4 + 32 = -108.4°F$

50. Answers will vary.

51. $2.75(31) + 71.48 = 156.73$, so the female with a 31 cm long humerus was about 157 cm tall.

52. (i) Letter-sized paper sheet ≈ (d) 21.5×28 cm
    (ii) A newspaper ≈ (e) 35×56 cm
    (iii) A credit card ≈ (b) 54×86 mm
    (iv) A regular bank check ≈ (c) 70×150 mm
    (v) A postage stamp ≈ (a) 20×25 mm

53. (i) A person ≈ (d) 72 kg
    (ii) A book ≈ (c) 1 kg
    (iii) A small automobile ≈ (e) 1000 kg
    (iv) A common pin ≈ (a) 80 mg
    (v) An orange ≈ (b) 68 g

54. Let $C = mK + b$, then
    $$m = \dfrac{100-0}{373.15-273.15} = \dfrac{100}{100} = 1 \text{ and}$$
    $0 = 1 \cdot 273.15 + b$

    $b = -273.15$
    Thus the relationship between the Celsius and Kelvin scales is $C = K - 273.15$.

Section A.2 Convert If You Must

1. 8 in. $= 8(2.54) = 20.32$ cm

2. 5.2 in. $= 5.2(2.54) = 13.21$ cm
    (Both 5.2 and 2.54 are exact.)

3. $12 \text{ cm} = 12(0.394) = 4.73 \text{ in.}$

4. $25 \text{ cm} = 25(0.394) = 9.85 \text{ in.}$

5. $51 \text{ yd} = 51(0.914) = 46.61 \text{ m}$

6. $1.2 \text{ yd} = 1.2(0.914) = 1.10 \text{ m}$

7. $3.7 \text{ m} = 3.7(1.09) = 4.03 \text{ yd}$

8. $4.5 \text{ m} = 4.5(1.09) = 4.91 \text{ yd}$

9. $4 \text{ mi} = 4(1.61) = 6.44 \text{ km}$

10. $6.1 \text{ mi} = 6.1(1.61) = 9.82 \text{ km}$

11. $3.7 \text{ km} = 3.7(0.621) = 2.30 \text{ mi}$

12. $14 \text{ km} = 14(0.621) = 8.69 \text{ mi}$

13. $6 \text{ lb} = 6(0.454) = 2.72 \text{ kg}$

14. $8 \text{ lb} = 8(0.454) = 3.63 \text{ kg}$

15. $5 \text{ kg} = 5(2.20) = 11.00 \text{ lb}$

16. $1.2 \text{ kg} = 1.2(2.20) = 2.64 \text{ lb}$

17. $5 \text{ qt} = 5(0.946) = 4.73 \text{ liters}$

18. $6.1 \text{ qt} = 6.1(0.946) = 5.77 \text{ liters}$

19. $8.1 \text{ liters} = 8.1(1.06) = 8.59 \text{ qt}$

20. $11 \text{ liters} = 11(1.06) = 11.66 \text{ qt}$

21. $75 \text{ cm} = 75(0.394) \div 12 = 2.46 \text{ ft}$

22. $800 \text{ m} = 800 \cdot 100 \cdot 0.394 \div 12 = 2620 \text{ ft}$

23. $1 \text{ in}^3 = (2.54)^3 = 16.39 \text{ cm}^3$

24. $1 \text{ cm}^3 = \left(\dfrac{1}{2.54}\right)^3 = 0.06 \text{ in}^3$

25. $2 \text{ yd} = 2(36)(2.54) = 182.88 \text{ cm}$

26. $3 \text{ yd} = 3(36)(2.54) = 274.32 \text{ cm}$

27. $78 \text{ cm} = 78(0.394) \div 36 = 0.85 \text{ yd}$

28. $100 \text{ cm} = 100(0.394) \div 36 = 1.09 \text{ yd}$

29. $40 \text{ mph} = 40(1.61) = 64.4 \approx 64 \text{ km/hr}$

30. a. $22 \text{ mi} = 22(1.61) = 35 \text{ km}$

    b. $93 \text{ mi} = 93(1.61) = 150 \text{ km}$

31. $63 \text{ yd} = 63(0.914) = 57.6 \text{ m}$

32. $296 \text{ yd} = 296(0.914) = 271 \text{ m}$

33. $8848 \text{ m} = 8848(1.09)(3) = 28,900 \text{ ft}$

34. $24 \text{ in.} = 24(2.54) = 61.0 \text{ cm}$

35. $1234 \text{ lb} = 1234(0.454) = 560 \text{ kg}$

36. Vehicles can hold from $5 \text{ qt} = 5(0.946)$
    $= 4.73 \text{ liters to } 10 \text{ qt} = 10(0.946) = 9.46 \text{ liters.}$

37. $30 \text{ mi} = 30(1.61) = 48.3 \text{ km}$

38. $125 \text{ km/hr} = 125(0.621) = 77.6 \text{ mi/hr}$

39. $52 \text{ kg} = 52(2.20) = 114 \text{ lb}$

40. $12.7 \text{ liter} = 12.7(1.06) = 13.5 \text{ qt}$

41. $2(52.3 + 96.84) = 298.28 \approx 298 \text{ m}$
    $= 298(1.09) = 325 \text{ yd}$

42. $2(21.5 + 32.63) = 108.26 \approx 108 \text{ ft}$
    $= (108 \div 3)(0.914) = 33.0 \text{ m}$

43. $14 \text{ tons} = 14 \cdot 2000 \div 2200 = 12.7 \text{ metric tons}$

44. $15 \text{ tons} = 15 \cdot 2000 \div 2200 = 13.6 \text{ metric tons}$

45. $\dfrac{50(1.61)}{4(0.946)} = 21.3$ km/liter

57. $1234 \text{ lb} = 1234(0.454)(1000) \approx 560,000 \text{ g}$

46. Answers will vary. Important items are that the metric system is a simple decimal system so conversion simply requires moving the decimal appropriately. The U. S. customary system is a mixed up batch of units such as the inch, the foot, the yard, and the mile. This also applies to volume and weight.

47. $1900 \text{ m} = 1.9 \text{ km} = 1.9(0.621) = 1.18 \text{ mi}$

48. $320,000 \text{ kg} = 320,000(2.20) \div 2000$
$= 704,000 \div 2000 = 352 \text{ tons}$

49. $316 \text{ ft} = 3792 \text{ in.}$, so $316 \text{ ft } 5\dfrac{3}{4} \text{ in.} =$
3797.75 in., or
$3797.75(2.54) = 9646.285 \text{ cm} \approx 96.5 \text{ m}$

50. $16 \text{ liters} = 16(1.06) \div 4 = 4.24 \text{ gal}$

51. $39 \text{ in.} = 39(2.54) \approx 99.1$
$23 \text{ in.} = 23(2.54) \approx 58.4$
$33 \text{ in.} = 33(2.54) \approx 83.8$
To three significant digits, the measurements would be
99.1 cm–58.4 cm–83.8 cm.

52. $1 \text{ liter} = 1(1.06) \text{ qt} \cdot 32 \text{ oz/qt} = 33.92 \text{ oz}$,
so $\$42 \div 33.92 \text{ oz} = \$1.24 \text{ per oz.}$

53. $15 \text{ mi} = 15(1.61) \approx 24 \text{ km}$

54. $146 \text{ mi} = 146(1.61) \approx 235 \text{ km}$

55. $4 \text{ pt} = 4(0.5) = 2 \text{ qt}$ and $4.5 \text{ pt} =$
$4.5(0.5) = 2.25 \text{ qt}$, since 1 qt is about a liter, you should drink between 2 and 2.25 liters per day.

56. $9770 \text{ oz} =$
$9770 \div 16 \cdot 0.454 \cdot 1000 \approx 277,000 \text{ g}$

CPSIA information can be obtained
at www.ICGtesting.com
Printed in the USA
FFOW02n0920141013
2052FF